SILYLATION of ORGANIC COMPOUNDS

a
technique
for
gas-phase
analysis

SILYLATION OF ORGANIC COMPOUNDS

by Alan E. Pierce

PIERCE CHEMICAL COMPANY
ROCKFORD, ILLINOIS

To Barbara,
whose patience and understanding are
bound here as firmly as the very pages.

Preface

The rapid expansion of the field of gas chromatography has received great impetus in the last five years from the use of silylation, which is the substitution of the trimethylsilyl group, $-Si(CH_3)_3$, for active hydrogen in a compound. This convenient derivatization method has made possible the analysis by gas chromatography and mass spectrometry of many compounds heretofore not volatile or stable enough for these techniques. There is thus opened up a new area of gas-phase analysis, on the microgram and sub-microgram scale, particularly applicable to large molecules that occur in samples of natural origin. The method has been used with all types of hydroxy and amino compounds and has been applied most extensively to carbohydrates and steroids.

This book is intended to provide a review of the literature and a manual of procedure. The factors affecting the use of trimethylsilyl compounds in gas chromatography and mass spectrometry will be discussed, but a thorough description of these analytical techniques is beyond the scope of this book. Auxiliary information on the properties and chemistry of silylated organic compounds is included. The literature has been reviewed to July, 1968.

The helpful criticism of my associates at Pierce Chemical Company is gratefully acknowledged. Their experience in the preparation and use of silylating reagents has provided a valuable supplement to the literature findings.

Several chapters have been reviewed by investigators outstanding in their research areas. My deepest thanks to them for their review and suggestions, which have improved the factual accuracy, consistency of presentation, and interpretation in these sections. These investigators and the chapters reviewed are: Dr. Ronald Bentley, Carbohydrates; Dr. John D. Diekman, Mass Spectrometry; Dr. Evan C. Horning, Steroids; and Dr. Johann F. Klebe, Theoretical Aspects of Silylation.

I am indebted to Dr. Justine Simon Walhout for most of the review, organization and writing of the chapter on theoretical aspects, and for helpful criticism of other parts of the manuscript.

My thanks also to the following for contributing manuscripts in advance of publication: Robert A. Benkeser, Ronald Bentley, S. C. Brooks, W. J. Carnes, J. R. Chapman, J. R. Clamp, D. W. Clayton, John Diekman, Lawrence Fishbein, R. Fumagalli, Takeshi Hashizume, Johann F. Klebe, G. Kresze, Jacob Lehrfeld, James A. McCloskey, Charles R. Nony, John J. Pisano, Bhandaru Radhakrishnamurthy, Bengt Smith, Charles C. Sweeley, W. H. Tallent, R. M. Teeter, R. B. Watts, Robert West and R. D. Wood.

A.E.P.

Rockford, Illinois
July, 1968

Contents

Introduction

1. DEFINITION AND SCOPE

The term "silyl" in this review, as used in nearly all of the literature in this field, will mean the trimethylsilyl group, -Si(CH$_3$)$_3$, unless otherwise designated. The radical is derived from trimethylsilane and abbreviated, TMS:

$$CH_3-\underset{\underset{CH_3}{|}}{\overset{\overset{CH_3}{|}}{Si}}-$$

Trimethylsilyl (TMS)

$$CH_3-\underset{\underset{CH_3}{|}}{\overset{\overset{CH_3}{|}}{Si}}-H$$

Trimethylsilane

"Silylation", then, is the introduction of the silyl group into a molecule, usually in substitution for active hydrogen, occasionally in replacement of the metal component of a salt. The reagents that have been used for this purpose are derivatives of trimethylsilane, (CH$_3$)$_3$SiH. The more common ones, with their abbreviations which will be used in this book, are as follows:

$$CH_3-\underset{\underset{CH_3}{|}}{\overset{\overset{CH_3}{|}}{Si}}-Cl$$

Trimethylchlorosilane
(TMCS)

$$CH_3-\underset{\underset{CH_3}{|}}{\overset{\overset{CH_3}{|}}{Si}}-NH-\underset{\underset{CH_3}{|}}{\overset{\overset{CH_3}{|}}{Si}}-CH_3$$

Hexamethyldisilazane
(HMDS)

$$CH_3-\underset{\underset{CH_3}{|}}{\overset{\overset{CH_3}{|}}{Si}}-N(C_2H_5)_2$$

N-Trimethylsilyldiethylamine
(TMSDEA)

$$CH_3-\overset{\overset{O}{\|}}{C}\underset{NH-\underset{\underset{CH_3}{|}}{\overset{\overset{CH_3}{|}}{Si}}-CH_3}{}$$

N-Trimethylsilylacetamide

$$CH_3-C\begin{array}{l}O-Si(CH_3)_3 \\ \\ N-Si(CH_3)_3\end{array}$$

$$\begin{array}{c}N=CH \\ \\ HC=CH\end{array}\Big> N-Si\begin{array}{l}CH_3 \\ | \\ CH_3\end{array}CH_3$$

N,O-Bis(trimethylsilyl)acetamide
(BSA)

N-Trimethylsilylimidazole
(TSIM)

The following examples of silylation are illustrative:

$$C_2H_5OH + (CH_3)_3SiCl \rightarrow C_2H_5OSi(CH_3)_3 + HCl$$
TMCS

$$C_3H_7SNa + (CH_3)_3SiCl \rightarrow C_3H_7SSi(CH_3)_3 + NaCl$$
TMCS

$$C_7H_{15}COOH + (CH_3)_3SiN(C_2H_5)_2 \rightarrow$$
TMSDEA

$$C_7H_{15}COOSi(CH_3)_3 + (C_2H_5)_2NH$$

$$2(C_4H_9)_2NH + (CH_3)_3SiNHSi(CH_3)_3 \rightarrow 2(C_4H_9)_2NSi(CH_3)_3 + NH_3$$
HMDS

$$CH_3CHC\begin{array}{c}O \\ \\ \end{array}\quad + 2CH_3C\begin{array}{c}OSi(CH_3)_3 \\ \\ NSi(CH_3)_3\end{array} \rightarrow$$
$$\quad NH_2\ OH$$

BSA

$$CH_3CHC\begin{array}{c}O \\ \\ \end{array}\quad + 2CH_3C\begin{array}{c}O \\ \\ NHSi(CH_3)_3\end{array}$$
$$\quad NH\ \ OSi(CH_3)_3$$
$$\quad Si(CH_3)_3$$

Dimethylsilyl and chloromethyldimethylsilyl compounds will also be included in this review. Triethylsilyl compounds or other silyl derivatives higher than trimethyl have less of the advantages of trimethylsilyl compounds; hence are not included. In many cases where higher alkyl derivatives were made, the trimethylsilyl compounds were also prepared, so that the parent compounds are included in this work.

The replacement of active hydrogen by the silyl group reduces the polarity of the compound and decreases the possibilities of hydrogen bonding. Consequently, where there is marked intermolecular hydrogen bonding in the parent compound the silylated derivative is usually more volatile. Further, stability is enhanced upon silylation by reduction in the number of reactive sites with active hydrogen.

The advantages of volatility and stability imparted by silylation make the process a natural tool for gas-phase purification and analysis. The derivatives are simply and conveniently prepared. In many cases the reactants are mixed at room temperature and the reaction is complete in a few minutes.

The products generally can be distilled. They may be analysed, without isolation, by gas chromatography, mass spectrometry, or a combination of these techniques. Following distillation or gas chromatography the silyl compound can be readily hydrolysed to recover the original substance. Indeed, about the only disadvantage of silylation is the need for dry conditions and the high sensitivity of some of the products to moisture.

The greatest use of silylation has been for gas chromatography. Many hydroxy and amino compounds ordinarily regarded as nonvolatile or unstable at 200-300° have been successfully chromatographed after silylation. For instance, completely silylated derivatives of filipin, a macrolide antibiotic (276), and stachyose, a tetrasaccharide (764), whose molecular weights are 1676 and 1556, respectively, have been analysed by mass spectrometry and gas chromatography. The use of silylation has frequently increased the accuracy of gas chromatographic analysis by improving resolution and peak symmetry or by decreasing adsorption of the sample on the column.

Other applications of silylated compounds include thin layer chromatography (TLC) and organic synthesis. Methods for the preparation of peptides and nucleosides take advantage of the reactivity of silyl compounds. The trimethylsilyl group has been used also as a blocking or protective group. This application is especially useful for sensitive compounds as the silyl group can be removed under mild hydrolysis conditions.

The compounds silylated are tabulated according to functional group(s) available for silylation, whether silylated or not, entry being in the latest position possible. Hydroxy acids, for instance, with different functional groups capable of silylation, are listed under acids, which follow hydroxy compounds. Hydroxy esters, however, can be silylated only on the hydroxyl, and so are classed as hydroxy compounds. Carbohydrates and steroids are grouped by themselves because there are so many entries.

The literature has been searched for all silylated organic compounds prepared by reaction of simple silylating agents. This means the reaction of O-H, N-H and S-H compounds or their salts with trimethylchlorosilane (TMCS), hexamethyldisilazane (HMDS), silylamines, silylamides, or combinations of these reagents to prepare silyl ethers, esters or amines, as illustrated previously. Less direct or less convenient methods of preparation are not included; they are not as helpful to the analyst, and they do not generally permit the recovery of the parent compound.

In a given reference it was not always clear which group(s) are silylated or capable of silylation, and the original author was not always concerned with the structure of the silyl derivative prepared as long as it performed nicely on the gas chromatograph by giving a single, well defined peak corresponding to the parent compound. As an example, some compounds with the amide configuration, -CO-NH-, have been reported to yield O-silyl derivatives, others N-silyl, and still others did not react, perhaps because conditions were not strong enough.

2. HISTORICAL

The earliest example of silylation found was that of Sauer (675) in 1944, who silylated methanol and ethanol with trimethylchlorosilane (TMCS) and pyridine. Sauer and Hasek (676) also silylated methyl amine (taken in excess) with TMCS. Schuyten *et al.* (695) reported the silylation of cellulose with TMCS in pyridine in 1948. Other early workers used TMCS alone with alcohols (136) or with metal salts of acids (24, 64, 694). The first silyl ester preparation directly from an acid, however, was reported in 1952 by Etienne (215), who obtained silyl acetate from acetic acid and TMCS in pyridine. The pyridine or amine in these preparations functions as an acid acceptor, *e.g.,*

$$
CH_3C\!\!\underset{OH}{\overset{O}{\big\backslash}} \;+\; Me_3SiCl \;+\; C_5H_5N \;\rightarrow
$$

$$
CH_3C\!\!\underset{OSiMe_3}{\overset{O}{\big\backslash}} \;+\; C_5H_5NH^+\,Cl^-
$$

Mjörne (530) in 1950 was apparently the first to use hexamethyldisilazane (HMDS) for silylation, heating the reagent with an amine until ammonia evolution ceased. Speier (749) developed the use of this reagent, applying the method to alcohols and phenols. He also patented the use of a mixture of TMCS and HMDS, in which method the ammonia from the HMDS reaction neutralizes the hydrogen chloride from the TMCS reaction (752):

$$3ROH + Me_3SiNHSiMe_3 + Me_3SiCl \rightarrow 3ROSiMe_3 + NH_4Cl$$

Some advantages of silyl ethers for gas chromatography were noted in 1958 by Langer, Pantages and Wender (455), who used silicone and ester columns. The earliest use of silyl derivatives for mass spectrometry was described in 1957 by Sharkey, Friedel and Langer (712), who observed the fragmentation patterns of silyl ethers.

The first silylated sugar was reported in 1956 by Schwarz, Baronetsky and Schöller (697) and by Henglein (314), who obtained and distilled pentasilylglucose. The octakis(trimethylsilyl)sucrose derivative was also prepared and distilled (158). Early attempts at separation of silylated sugar derivatives by gas chromatography were made by Hedgley and Overend (305). However, it was not until 1963 that this field of investigation received real impetus. A simple technique for derivatization, by HMDS and TMCS in pyridine, and gas chromatography was developed and applied successfully to over a hundred sugar compounds by Sweeley, Bentley, Makita and Wells (764). This paper is a classic in its field, and has influenced the development of silylation procedures for other classes of compounds.

N-Silyl (74, 75) and silyl ester derivatives (309) of amino acids were at first separately prepared. Fully silylated amino acids were reported by Rühlman (640) in 1959, made from sodium amino acid salts and TMCS. He investigated the gas chromatography of these compounds in 1961 (644), at which time he also reported their synthesis by the use of N-tri-methylsilyldiethylamine.

$$H_2N-CHR-C\overset{\displaystyle O}{\underset{\displaystyle OH}{{<}}} \quad + 2Et_2NSiMe_3 \rightarrow$$

$$Me_3Si-NH-CHR-C\overset{\displaystyle O}{\underset{\displaystyle OSiMe_3}{{<}}} \quad + 2Et_2NH$$

The use of silyl derivatives to improve the gas chromatography of phenolic and hydroxy-substituted steroids was first reported by Luukkainen, VandenHeuvel, Haahti and Horning in 1961 (498). The method was particularly useful with epimers, estrogens and the principal urinary 17-ketosteroids (801). The gas chromatography of some of the larger or less stable steroids has been facilitated by the use of silyl derivatives, *e.g.*, for the analysis of bile acids (209, 210), cortisone compounds (155, 297), and cardenolides (515). The concurrent use of O-methylhydroxylamine, a reagent for keto groups, has extended the usefulness of silylation for keto steroids (218) and keto acids (347a).

Among other silylation reagents discovered are some very powerful silyl donors such as the silylamides. N-Trimethylsilylacetamide was reported by Pump and Wannagat in 1962. N,O-Bissilyl derivatives were first described in Giessler's thesis (272) and reported by Birkofer, Ritter and Giessler (80) in 1963. The use of N,O-bis(trimethylsilyl)acetamide (BSA), a very powerful donor, was developed by Klebe, Finkbeiner and White (422). Birkofer, Richter and Ritter (73) in 1960 described N-trimethylsilylimidazole (TSIM), which under some conditions is still more effective than BSA (Chambaz and Horning, 155). The selectivity of BSA and TSIM reagents has recently been demonstrated (155, 349, 515).

The possible development of other silyl donors and the refinement of gas chromatographic techniques bode well for continued progress in the application of silylation in gas-phase analysis, particularly of natural substances.

1

Silylation Methods

The large number of reagents and procedures available for silylation enhances its versatility and usefulness. The choice of reagent and procedure varies with the type of compound and the purpose, whether preparative or analytical. There are usually several methods which may be applied to any one compound.

1-1. CLASSIFICATION

The following chart summarizes the silylation procedures mentioned in this review. The method number may be combined with a letter or letters designating additional solvents and entered thus in the tables.

10. Trimethylchlorosilane-based methods
    11. Trimethylchlorosilane (TMCS) alone; HCl is boiled off
    12. Ammonia is passed in
    13. Pyridine as acid acceptor
    14. Triethylamine (TEA) as acid acceptor
    15. Sodium salt of starting compound
    16. Salt other than sodium; *e.g.* Li, Sr
    17. Formamide, pyridine, hexane
    18. Base other than pyridine or TEA as acid acceptor
    19. TEA, $ZnCl_2$ catalyst

20. Hexamethyldisilazane-based methods
    21. Hexamethyldisilazane (HMDS) alone; elimination of NH_3
    22. TMCS, 10% or less of HMDS taken, by volume
    23. TMCS, more than 10% of HMDS taken
    24. Acid catalyst (not TMCS)
    25. TMCS, pyridine
    26. TMCS, THF

30. Silylamine methods
    31. TMS-methylamine
    32. TMS-aniline
    33. TMS-diethylamine (TMSDEA)

34. TMS-diethylamine, acid catalyst
35. TMS-n(or t)-butylamine
36. TMS-imidazole (TSIM)
37. Miscellaneous silylamines

40. Silylamide methods

41. TMS-formamide
42. TMS-acetamide (MSA)
43. N,O-Bis(TMS)acetamide (BSA)
44. BSA-TMCS
45. N-TMS-N-methylacetamide
46. N,O-Bis(TMS)trifluoroacetamide (BSTFA)
47. TMS-diphenylurea
48. Miscellaneous silylamides

50. Miscellaneous methods

51. Hexamethyldisiloxane
52. Hexamethyldisilthiane
53. Alkylthiotrimethylsilane
54. TMS acetate

Solvents used:

a. Acetone
b. Benzene
c. Chloroform
d. Dimethylformamide (DMF)
e. Ether
f. Formamide
g. Dioxane
h. Hexane
j. Cyclohexane
k. Ethyl acetate

m. Methylene chloride
n. Acetonitrile
p. Petroleum ether
py. Pyridine
r. Carbon disulfide
s. Dimethylsulfoxide (DMSO)
t. Tetrahydrofuran (THF)
u. Toluene
x. Xylene
z. Miscellaneous

For the preparation in quantity of a silylated organic compound, one is governed by economy of reagents and convenience of procedure rather than speed of reaction. Recommended procedures would include TMCS with triethylamine (Method 14), HMDS, alone or catalyzed (Methods 21, 22, 24), or TMSDEA (Method 33).

However, the major application of silylation currently is to gas chromatography. Here the considerations for derivatization are speed, simplicity, convenience, freedom from side reactions, and reproducibility. The wide variety of substrates and column conditions encountered has stimulated the development of many reagents and procedures just to meet these requirements. Factors which apply to these conditions are briefly discussed in the following sections, 1-2 to 1-4. Further consideration of some of these elements as they apply to various chemical categories appears in later chapters.

1-2. REAGENT PURITY

The reagents and solvents should be pure and dry. They should be tested in advance in the particular gas chromatographic system to be used. As the quantities taken are in high ratio to the substrate minute impurities may produce extraneous peaks in the chromatogram.

Commercial TMCS has been purified by precipitation of any hydrogen chloride present with pyridine, distillation of the TMCS and storage with a little pyridine added (196). TMCS has been freed from dimethyldichlorosilane, if present, by careful hydrolysis (758). Water is sparingly added until rapid evolution of hydrogen chloride subsides, and the charge is distilled. TMCS reacts appreciably at 150° or higher with either a glass or stainless steel chromatograph injector to produce many afterpeaks, similar to those prominent in the higher boiling fractions of commercial TMCS (760).

Pyridine has been purified by refluxing over potassium hydroxide, followed by distilling (608) and storing over the same agent (608, 617). Distillation from barium oxide was also recommended (504, 617, 768). This process removed extraneous peaks found even in reagent grade pyridine (771). Treatment with molecular seive 5A was also effective (617). One impurity eluted before pyridine on DEGS (618).

France *et al.* (236) purified tetrahydrofuran for steroid silylation by refluxing it over potassium hydroxide for 24 hours, distilling, and passing it through a column of silica gel. The solvent was then stored in a desiccator in the dark and prepared weekly. Lau (456) found numerous artifacts in tetrahydrofuran after exposure to air and suggested that it not be used unless freshly distilled.

1-3. REACTION CONDITIONS FOR GC SAMPLES

The usual reaction vessel is a tube or vial fitted with a Teflon-lined screw cap. A serum bottle closed with a septum is excellent, especially where rigorous exclusion of atmospheric moisture is desired. Care must be exercised in selecting the septum, especially if the reaction mixture may be kept for some time. Contact of the reaction mixture with ordinary plastic is apt to produce extra peaks (42, 618). To avoid formation of by-products in the silylation of catecholamines it was recommended that the glass vessels used be surface-silanized with 5% dichlorodimethylsilane in toluene (148).

Anhydrous reaction conditions are usually recommended as the silylated derivatives are sensitive to water in varying degrees. A 10- to 50-fold equivalent ratio of silylating agent to functional group being silylated is ordinarily taken. This will effectively consume small amounts of water and help preserve the silyl derivatives if kept in the reaction charge. The hexa-methyldisiloxane (bp 100°) formed elutes early.

$$2Me_3SiCl + H_2O \rightarrow Me_3SiOSiMe_3 + 2HCl$$

$$Me_3SiNHSiMe_3 + H_2O \rightarrow Me_3SiOSiMe_3 + NH_3$$

It does not interfere on most chromatograms. Lau, in a study of steroid silylation, found small amounts of water damaging only if the reaction mixture was heated (456). If the excess of reagent is hydrolysed the silylation of the organic substrate will be poor in yield; hence the amount of water that can be tolerated is limited. Brobst and Lott (111) were able to accommodate 40 mg of water in a sugar sample of 70 mg by using a large excess of HMDS catalysed by trifluoroactic acid. Brittain *et al.* (110) found N-TMS-imidazole extremely effective in moderate excess in the silylation of sugar syrups.

Liquid silylating agents are easy to handle and measure, a decided advantage when protection from moisture of the air is desired. Liquid reagents also may serve as the reaction solvent. Other solvents used include carbon disulfide, dimethylformamide (DMF), dimethylsulfoxide (DMSO), dioxane, pyridine, and tetrahydrofuran (THF). For analytical work the solvent is chosen to hasten the reaction by dissolving the compound being silylated. When DMF is used in silylation with HMDS a by-product is obtained, which also results from refluxing DMF and HMDS (241). The reaction of catecholamines and HMDS in DMF or DMSO is 10 to 20 times faster than in pyridine (402). DMSO as a solvent for silylation with HMDS causes separation of the product as a second liquid phase, practically pure (168, 241). Hydrocarbons, HMDS, and TMCS are insoluble in DMSO (168).

Dioxane may be used to make DMSO miscible with HMDS (402). Dioxane is also considered as effective as pyridine in the silylation of phenolic acids with HMDS–TMCS (89). Carbon disulfide is a useful silylation solvent for high sensitivity gas chromatography studies on account of the low response of flame ionization detectors to it (630). It has the added advantage of dissolving ammonium chloride, forming clear solutions of residues from evaporation of HMDS–TMCS–steroid reactions. Such solutions are very stable when kept refrigerated (793).

Solvents also may affect yields. Rühlmann and Kaufmann (647) silylated glycine ethyl ester hydrochloride with TMCS in TEA in the cold: in ether the yield was 10%; in chloroform, 70%. In refluxing solvents, Fessenden and Crowe (224) treated piperidine for three hours with HMDS catalysed by ammonium sulfate. In ether, dioxane, toluene, decalin and in quinoline the separate yields increased successively from 0% to 61%.

paralleling increase in boiling points. One suspects here principally a temperature effect.

Pyridine is the solvent most used in silylation for gas chromatography. More than just a solvent, it has been regarded as a silylation catalyst. Some have postulated a pyridin—TMCS complex, $C_5H_5NSiMe_3^+$ Cl^-, as the active silyl donor (see section 4-2). The evidence is not convincing as any acid acceptor promotes silylation with TMCS. Gottfried (279) found that cortisol (4-pregnen-11β,17α,21-triol-3,20-dione) with HMDS—TMCS in chloroform was silylated only at the primary C-21 hydroxyl whereas in pyridine di- and trisilylated products were formed. Again, Dalgliesh et al. (182) in a kinetic study of the silylation of citric acid observed that the formation of the monoether—triester was complete in HMDS alone at 65° or in pyridine at room temperature, but much slower when alone. Also, in the silylation of sterols with HMDS—TMCS in pyridine and in tetrahydrofuran, Makita and Wells (504, 848) concluded that the approximately 20-fold faster reaction in pyridine proved it a catalyst. However, in the pyridine experiment they also used ten times as much TMCS, which is known to catalyse silylation with HMDS.

For some silylations reaction in pyridine is slower than in other solvents. Mason and Smith (513) found that silylation of n-octylamine with 100% excess HMDS—TMCS (2:1)[1] at reflux proceeded in 46% yield but in boiling pyridine there was almost no reaction. M. G. Horning et al. (350) observed that the reaction of the catecholamines with BSA—TMCS at 60° was much slower in pyridine than in acetonitrile. The reaction of catecholamines and HMDS in DMF at 80° is 10 to 20 times faster than in pyridine (148). Resin and fatty acids were silylated by HMDS—TMCS (1:1) faster in refluxing petroleum ether (30-80°) than in hot pyridine (896).

Pyridine may have other undesirable effects. It is believed to promote the formation of secondary products in the silylation of 3-ketosteroids, presumably by reaction with their enol forms (527). Enolization of humulones, caused by pyridine, resulted in multiple products on silylation, whereas in dimethylformamide a single product was obtained (183). Also, in hot pyridine anomerization of sugars may occur (7, 764).

Pyridine sometimes causes marked tailing on the chromatogram, as was observed with a highly loaded DEGS column (22). In some work, particularly with steroids, tailing was so objectionable that the solvent was removed by evaporating the reaction mixture under dry nitrogen. The residue was then taken up in hexane, chloroform or tetrahydrofuran for injection. Pyridine also has been removed by adding hexane (880) or chloroform (887) to the reaction mixture and extracting with water.

1. All reagent ratios in this review are measured by volume.

The silylation reaction mixture is often injected directly into the gas chromatograph. The mixture obtained using HMDS–TMCS reagents (Methods 22, 23, 25 or 26) contains ammonium chloride, usually as a fine precipitate. Some stated that it had no bad effect (764); others separated the salt by settling or centrifuging, sampling then from the clear super-natant. Tallent (770) found that ammonium chloride caused extraneous peaks with products containing epoxide rings. This decomposition was avoided by taking up the silyl compound in hexane and washing with water. The use of BSA avoids this difficulty more satisfactorily as no ammonium chloride is formed and no water wash is necessary. Formation of ammo-nium chloride was also avoided by using trifluoroacetic acid as a catalyst for HMDS (112).

1-4. COMPLETENESS OF SILYLATION FOR GC

Reaction at room temperature for a few minutes is often sufficient for complete silylation. In other cases, warming for 15 to 30 minutes, refluxing, or standing overnight is recommended. When the substrate is solid, not easily soluble in the reagent or solvent used, silylation is generally complete upon solution. Occasionally temperatures as high as 150° are required. For glycerol derivatives, Smith and Carlsson (739) observed that the tempera-ture required for complete reaction was proportional to the number of hydroxyl groups.

The progress of silylation can be followed by chromatographing samples taken at intervals and comparing results. Where both substrate and deriva-tive elute the disappearance of the former peak indicates complete reaction. Where there is more than one functional group reacting there will be peaks, probably with longer retention time, corresponding to partially silylated derivatives. These peaks will disappear when silylation is complete.

When hydroxyl groups are being silylated, IR can be used to identify unsilylated material in the product (482, 740). TLC has been used to determine product homogeneity.

1-5. REACTIVITY OF SILYL ACCEPTORS AND DONORS

The general order of decreasing ease of silylation of proton-active acceptor groups is: alcohols (primary, secondary, then tertiary), phenols, carboxylic acids, amines (primary, then secondary), and amides. Support-ing information is summarized in Table 1-1 and detailed in Table 1-2. It is based largely on experiments in which not all the acceptor groups or com-pounds are silylated. The results of experiments listed on Table 1-2 are keyed by letter in Table 1-1, where the numerals indicate the increasing

TABLE 1-1. REACTIVITY OF SILYL ACCEPTORS
Decreasing Ease of Silylation of Functional Groups

Silyl Acceptor	Group	A	B	C	D	E	F	G	H*	J	K	L	M	N	O	P	Q
Primary alcohols	OH	1	1	2	1	1	1	1	1								
Secondary alcohols	OH	1	2							1	1						
Tertiary alcohols	OH	2	2														
Phenols	OH								2			1	1				
Pyrimidines	OH									2							
Aliphatic acids	COOH			1	2	2	2	1	3	2	2	2		1	1		
Primary amines	NH$_2$			3	3	2	2	1						2		1	
Acid amides	CONH$_2$							2									1
N-TMS-amides	CONHSi(CH$_3$)$_3$																2
Secondary amines	NH																2
Indoles	NH												2		2		2

*Order of increasing ease of hydrolysis of O-TMS.

TABLE 1-2. COMPARISON OF SILYL ACCEPTORS

Exp.	Compound	Method	Reagent	Silylation; Yield	Ref.
A	1-Pentanol, 3-pentanol	21	HMDS	Reaction goes	241
	2-Methyl-2-butanol	21	HMDS	No reaction	
B	Methyl citrate, methyl mandelate	25	HMDS-TMCS-py	Slow reaction	182
C	Hexanoic acid	21	HMDS	97%	513
	1-Octanol	21	HMDS	45%	
	n-Octylamine	21	HMDS	14%	
D	1-Octanol	22	HMDS-cat. TMCS	97%	513
	Hexanoic acid	22	HMDS-cat. TMCS	92%	
	1-Octylamine	22	HMDS-cat. TMCS	56%	
E	3,4-Methylenedioxybenzyl alcohol	25	HMDS-TMCS-py	Instantly	894
	2-Amino-2-(3,4-MDO-phenyl)-propane	25	HMDS-TMCS-py	Slow	
	3,4-MDO-benzyl amine	25	HMDS-TMCS-py	Unsuccessful	
F	Ethanolamine	14	TMCS (<1 mole), TEA	Ether only	822
		12	TMCS (1 mole), NH_3	Ether only	39
G	Alcohols, amines, acids	37	N-TMS-amides	Complete	422
	Amides	37	N-TMS-amides	Incomplete	
H	Ease of hydrolysis: TMS esters>TMS phenol ethers>TMS alcohol ethers				124
J	Nucleosides	25	HMDS-TMCS-py	Sugar OH only	671
K	Strontium lactate	11	TMCS (1.5 moles)	Ether only	307
L	p-Hydroxyphenylethylamine	21	HMDS	Ether only	402
M	5-Hydroxy-N,N-dimethyltryptamine	44	BSA-TMCS	Ether, complete; N-TMS, partial	336
N	Amino acids	21	HMDS	Ester only	652
		11	TMCS	Ester only	325
O	Indole acids	22	HMDS-cat. TMCS	Ester only	347
		43	BSA	Ester and N-TMS	
P	Butylamine	22	HMDS-cat. TMCS	Reaction goes	452
	Secondary amines	22	HMDS-cat. TMCS	No reaction	
Q	Acetamide	14	TMCS (1 mole), TEA	Mono-TMS only	80
		14	TMCS (excess), TEA	Bis(TMS)	

TABLE 1-3. REACTIVITY OF SILYL DONORS

Silyl Donor*	A	B	C	D	E	F	G	H	J	K	L	M	N	O	P	Q	R
35 N-TMS-butylamine	1	1															
11 TMCS			1														
21 HMDS	2		2	1	1	1	1	1									
21py HMDS, pyridine				2					1								
13 TMCS, pyridine					1				2	1							
14 TMCS, triethylamine		2	3		1	2	2			1	1						
22 HMDS, TMCS catalyst					1	2	2			1	1						
23 HMDS-TMCS					2												
24 HMDS-ammonium sulfate						3											
25 HMDS-TMCS-py				3			1		3	2	2	1					
31 N-TMS-aniline													1				
37 N-TMS-piperidine								2					1				
33 N-TMS-diethylamine							3						1	1			
47 N-TMS-N,N'-diphenylurea								3									
42 N-TMS-acetamide													2		1		
43 N,O-Bis(TMS)-acetamide												2	2		2	1	1
34 N-TMS-DEA, catalyst														2			
44 BSA-TMCS																2	2
36 N-TMS-imidazole																	3

*In approximate order of increasing silyl donor strength.

TABLE 1-4. COMPARISON OF SILYL DONORS

Exp.	Compound	Method	Reagent	Temp.	Silylation; Yield	Ref.
A	Urea	35	TMS-Butylamine		N-TMS only	186
		21	HMDS		N,N'-bis(TMS)	832
B	Acetamide	35	TMS-Butylamine (1.3 moles)		Mono-TMS only	186
		14	TMS (excess),TEA		BSA	80
C	Acetamide	11b	TMCS, benzene		0%	272
		21	HMDS		80%	
		14	TMCS, TEA		83%	
D	Citric acid	21p	HMDS	65	Increasing rate of	182
		21p	HMDS, pyridine	25	reaction: 21→21p→25	
		25	HMDS, TMCS, py	25		
E	t-Pentyl alcohol	21,22	HMDS-TMCS		No reaction	452
		23p			50%	
F	Dibutylamine	21	HMDS		20%	224
		24	HMDS, $(NH_4)_2SO_4$		52%	
	3-Heptanol	21	HMDS, cat. TMCS		No reaction	452
		22	HMDS, cat. TMCS		Reaction	
	Bu, pentyl amines	21	HMDS		Very slow reaction	
		22	HMDS, cat. TMCS		Fast reaction	
	Piperidine	21	HMDS		16%	224
		22	HMDS, cat. TMCS		35%	
		24	HMDS, $(NH_4)_2SO_4$		55%	
G	Octylamine	21,25	HMDS, TMCS	Ref.	<4%	513
		22		Ref.	46%	
		33	TMSDEA		82%	
H	N,N'-Dimethylurea	21	HMDS	25	1 hr, 0%	413
		32	N-TMS-aniline	25	1 hr, 3%	
		37	N-TMS-piperidine	25	1 hr, 10%	
		47	N-TMS-N,N'-diphenylurea	25	1 min, 100%	
J	Methyl α-glucopyranoside	21py	HMDS, py	25	Slight reaction	764
		13	TMCS, py	25	50%	
		25	HMDS, TMCS, py	25	90%	

Table 1-4. Comparison of Silyl Donors (cont'd.)

Exp.	Compound	Method	Reagent	Temp.	Silylation; Yield	Ref.
J	Cholesterol	21pyt	HMDS, py, THF		<10%	798
		13t	TMCS, py, THF		>90%	
		25t	HMDS-TMCS-py		100%	
K	2,6-Di-t-butylphenol	22	HMDS, TMCS		0%	243
		13	TMCS, py		0%	
		25	HMDS, TMCS, py		Good yield	
L	6,11-Dihydroxynaphtha-cenequinone	22	HMDS, TMCS catalyst		0%	243
		25	HMDS, TMCS, py		Good yield	
M	Iodoamino acids	25	HMDS, TMCS, py	125	90', 69-97%	709
		43n	BSA, CH_3CN	150	30', 97-100%	
N			TMS-amides are generally stronger silylators than TMS-amines			69
O	Glycine	33	TMSDEA		Bis(TMS)	642
		34	TMSDEA, $(NH_4)_2SO_4$		Tris(TMS)	323
P		42	In silylation, BSA → N-TMS-acetamide			
		43				
Q	Dimethoxyphenylethylamine	43	BSA		Mono- + bis(TMS) amine	336
		44	BSA-TMCS		Bis(TMS) amine only	
R	Cortol	43	BSA		Tris(TMS) ether	155
		44	BSA-TMCS		Tetrakis(TMS) ether	
		36	N-TMS-imidazole		Pentakis(TMS) ether	

difficulty of silylation, as shown by selectivity of reaction or differences in yields or reaction rates. The result in experiment C of hexanoic acid and HMDS appears inconsistent; this is probably due to acid catalysis of the HMDS reaction by hexanoic acid.

Similarly, the reactivity of silylating reagents was found to increase generally in this order: HMDS, TMCS (with bases), HMDS–TMCS, N-silyl secondary amines (except imidazole), TMS-amides, acid-catalysed silyl amines and amides, TMS-imidazole. Supporting evidence is not as complete or conclusive as for silyl acceptors and the order given is only approximate. Variable results from one method may be caused by different operating temperatures, sometimes controlled by refluxing solvent. Data are summarized in Tables 1-3 and 1-4. The results of Table 1-4 experiments are keyed by letter in Table 1-3, where the numerals indicate the order of increasing reagent reactivity.

1-6. TRIMETHYLCHLOROSILANE-BASED PROCEDURES

Method 11. TMCS alone (without base). This method has been used with alcohols, phenols and a few acids. TMCS in excess is refluxed many hours with the compound. Hydrogen chloride is expelled, driving the reversible reaction to the right (452). Low boiling solvents should not be used. Excess reagent and solvent, if any, are stripped and the product is distilled.

$$ROH + Me_3SiCl \rightarrow ROSiMe_3 + HCl$$

Method 12. TMCS with ammonia. Ammonia gas is passed rapidly into a cold stirred mixture of TMCS and substrate until an excess persists. With ammonia (or any other acid acceptor) the reaction is rapid and practically complete when run cold.

$$ROH + Me_3SiCl + NH_3 \rightarrow ROSiMe_3 + NH_4Cl$$

Methods 13, 14, and 18. TMCS with bases. The use of a base other than ammonia as acid acceptor with TMCS as silyl donor is common in preparative work. Pyridine and triethylamine are frequently used bases. There seems to be no particular reason for choice—good results have been obtained with each. Or, if an amine is being silylated an excess may be taken as acid acceptor. TMCS is added slowly to a stirred solution of a hydroxy or amino compound in at least one mole of the base intended as acid acceptor. The reaction is rapid and often complete when heat evolution stops. Sometimes heat is then applied to complete the reaction (269). The charge is filtered from the base hydrochloride and distilled.

Methods 15 and 16. TMCS with salts. Metal salts of thiols, alcohols, carboxylic acids and amines yield silyl derivatives with TMCS. This is not the method of choice, except for thiols. For alcohols and acids simpler methods are usually available.

$$C_3H_7SNa + Me_3SiCl \rightarrow C_3H_7SSiMe_3 + NaCl$$

Method 17. TMCS with formamide. The use of TMCS with formamide, pyridine and hexane in the silylation of carbohydrates and acids was investigated chiefly by Henglein and co-workers (307, 309, 310, 314). The pyridine accepts the HCl as usual from the TMCS reaction, then catalyses its consumption by formamide.

$$C_5H_5N \cdot HCl + HCONH_2 \rightarrow C_5H_5N + NH_4Cl + CO$$

The final reaction charge is in two phases with the product cleanly in the hexane layer.

1-7. HEXAMETHYLDISILAZANE-BASED PROCEDURES

Method 21. HMDS alone, elimination of ammonia. Alcohols, phenols, amines and acids may be silylated by refluxing with excess HMDS to constant charge temperature, cessation of ammonia evolution or solution of starting material. The reaction has been particularly useful with aliphatic alcohols and phenols.

$$2ROH + Me_3SiNHSiMe_3 \rightarrow 2ROSiMe_3 + NH_3$$

Langer *et al.* (452) showed that the reaction is catalysed by acid and hindered by alkali. Freedman and Croitoru (239) studied the effect of dehydrating agents and oxides on the reaction. There was no effect except a sharp reduction in yield from a hindered phenol such as 2,6-xylenol in the presence of a basic oxide such as nickel oxide.

Methods 22 to 26. HMDS with acid catalyst. The addition of a small amount of acidic catalyst usually increases the rate or degree of silylation by HMDS. Theoretical aspects are discussed in Chapter 4. TMCS is most commonly used, although it is not a true catalyst, as will be shown. A catalytic quantity of TMCS is here regarded as 10% or less of the HMDS taken, by volume. Aside from small amounts of hydrogen chloride the TMCS may contain, it of course generates acid in its reaction as a silylator. Mason and Smith (513) and Fessenden and Crowe (224) have studied the effect of various catalysts. Ammonium salts and sodium bisulfate (Method 24) were very effective, better than TMCS (Methods 22, 23, 25,

26). Ammonium sulfate has been most used; good yields for primary and secondary amines are reported.

The generally used procedures for preparing silyl derivatives for gas chromatography employ HMDS, TMCS and either pyridine or tetrahydrofuran (THF). The volatility of all reagents is important—this precludes the use of salt catalysts. The solvent chosen, depending on solubility of the substance to be silylated, is usually THF or $CHCl_3$ for steroids, pyridine for carbohydrates and other substances.

The function of TMCS, regardless of the amount taken in HMDS–TMCS mixtures is invariably called catalytic because the mixture is a better silylator than HMDS alone. Dalgleish et al. (182) found that citric acid was completely silylated by HMDS in pyridine at room temperature, but far more rapidly when TMCS was added to the mixture. VandenHeuvel (798) silylated cholesterol in tetrahydrofuran and pyridine in 10% yield with HMDS alone; with 3:1 HMDS–TMCS conversion was quantitative. The "catalytic" effect of TMCS, however, is proportional to the amount taken. In the attempted silylation of t-pentyl alcohols with refluxing HMDS containing a drop of TMCS, Langer et al. (452) detected no product, but with an equimolar amount of TMCS the expected TMS ether was obtained in good yield. Mason and Smith (513) silylated amino acids in twice the calculated amount of refluxing reagent, either HMDS with $<1\%$ of TMCS or HMDS–TMCS (2:1). After one hour's reflux the yields from the latter runs were twice to three times the yields of the former. Again, in the silylation of 5β-androstan-3α,11β-diol-17-one with HMDS–TMCS, Chambaz and Horning (155) with a 50:1 reagent mixture silylated only at 3α; with 25:1, both 3α and 3α,11β TMS ethers were obtained; and with 10:1, only the 3α,11β-bis (TMS)-ether was obtained.

The most used method of silylation, Method 25, as developed by Sweeley et al. (764) employs as an optimum an HMDS–TMCS ratio of 2:1, with little change in results over the range 4:1 to 1:1. Pyridine is the solvent; the amount is not critical. The ratio of silyl donor to acceptor group is many-fold; consequently there is enough of either HMDS or TMCS to effect the silylation. Indeed, with TMCS alone 50% of the maximum yield was obtained. The optimum 2:1 ratio of HMDS–TMCS is a 6:5 mole ratio, not far from the 1:1 ratio suggested by Speier (752) and by Langer et al. (452) to satisfy the silylation reaction:

$$3ROH + Me_3SiNHSiMe_3 + Me_3SiCl \rightarrow 3ROSiMe_3 + NH_4Cl$$

Clearly, then, TMCS is not a catalyst for HMDS, as: (1) the effect is proportional to the amount taken; (2) it is an effective silyl donor alone; and (3) it is at least partially consumed; NH_4Cl is formed.

Further proof of the consumption of TMCS lies in the results of mixed silylation reported by VandenHeuvel (798) and Supina *et al.* (761). These investigators used mixed pairs of disilazane-chlorosilane reagents selected from trimethylsilyl, dimethylsilyl and chloromethyldimethylsilyl compounds, with and without pyridine. In all cases both products of silylation were obtained; *e.g.,* cholesterol added to a mixture of pyridine, tetramethyl-disilazane and TMCS (3:1) yielded a mixture of dimethylsilyl and tri-methylsilyl ethers. The silazane product predominated in this case (761), but from the same reaction diluted with tetrahydrofuran the major product came from the chlorosilane (798).

1-8. SILYLAMINE METHODS

Silylamines have been used for the silylation of alcohols, amines, amino acids, amides, and ureas.

$$ROH + R'NHSiMe_3 \rightarrow ROSiMe_3 + R'NH_2$$

The reaction is run hot and completed by expulsion of the amine, $R'NH_2$. The preparation is analogous to that using HMDS, in which ammonia is expelled. In silylation of amines progress of the reaction depends upon forcing the silylamine-amine exchange by distillation of the more volatile amine, $R'R''NH$.

$$RNH_2 + Me_3SiNR'R'' \rightarrow RNHSiMe_3 + R'R''NH$$

R = alkyl, aryl, hetercyclic, or acyl
R' = H or low alkyl
R'' = low alkyl or phenyl

The exchange reaction just given applies to ordinary basic amines and their silyl derivatives. The behavior of silyl derivatives of acidic amines differs. For instance, N-trimethylsilylimidazole (TSIM) readily reacts with hydroxyl groups,

$$ROH + \begin{matrix} N = CH \\ | \quad\quad \ \searrow \\ HC = CH \end{matrix} NSiMe_3 \rightarrow ROSiMe_3 + \begin{matrix} N = CH \\ | \quad\quad \ \searrow \\ HC = CH \end{matrix} NH$$

but not with basic amino groups as in catecholamines (350). It does how-ever silylate the indole nitrogen (336a). TSIM has only recently been used for silylation (155) and has not yet been fully investigated.

Method 31. N-Trimethylsilylmethylamine. This reagent which has been little used, was reported in reaction with C_4-C_{18} alcohols (186). Its low boiling point facilitates the preparation of low boiling derivatives.

Method 32. N-Trimethylsilylaniline. This silylamine has been prepared *in situ* from TMCS and aniline (2 moles), then used directly for the preparation of low boiling TMS ethers, which are distilled off in high yields (439).

Method 33. N-Trimethylsilyldiethylamine (TMSDEA). This reagent has been the most used of the silylamines. It has been extensively applied to amino acids by Rühlmann and co-workers (641, 642). All functional groups—amino, carboxylic, hydroxyl, and sulfhydryl—are silylated. When a moderate excess of TMSDEA is heated with the substrate, diethylamine distils. The amount distilled indicates the progress of the reaction.

Method 34. N-Trimethylsilyldiethylamine (TMSDEA) with acid catalyst. As with HMDS, yields with TMSDEA are improved by the addition of acid catalysts. In silylation of amino acids Mason and Smith (513) found trichloroacetic acid and silica-alumina catalyst (Houndry S-46) most effective, better than TMCS. With ammonium sulfate catalyst, Rühlmann *et al.* (323) were able to introduce three and four silyl groups into ethanolamine and ethylene diamine, respectively.

Method 35. Trimethylsilyl-n (or t)-butylamine. These reagents were used for silylation of amino acids, amides and ureas (186). In use and behavior they are similar to trimethylsilyldiethylamine.

Method 36. N-Trimethylsilylimidazole (TSIM). This appears to be one of the most rapid and powerful silylating agents reported for hydroxyl groups. It does not react with basic amino groups (336a). It silylates the hindered 11β-hydroxyl of steroids, where BSA alone or HMDS–TMCS do not react, and it is catalysed by TMCS (155). A mixture of TSIM, BSA, and TMCS (3:3:2) reacted with all five hydroxyl groups of 5β-pregnan-3α, $11\beta,17\alpha,20\alpha,21$-pentol (cortol), whereas BSA-TMCS alone does not react with the 17α-hydroxyl (155). TSIM also silylates sugars without anomerization, reacting completely even in the presence of water (110).

Method 37. Miscellaneous silyl amines used have not shown any particular advantages over those already described.

Silyl Donor	Acceptor	Ref.
N-Trimethylsilylpiperidine	N,N'-Dimethylurea	413
N-Trimethylsilylpyrrolidine	Alcohols	186
N-TMS-Amino acid TMS esters	Amino acids	645

1-9. SILYLAMIDE METHODS

The silylamides are good solvents and are often used alone. N-TMS-acetamide (Method 42) and N-TMS-diphenylurea (Method 47) are solids at room temperature; the other silylamides listed in Methods 41-47 are liquids. N-TMS-acetamide (mp 52-54°) has been used molten in the silylation of sugars (78). The acetamide formed was removed by filtration and the excess reagent and product were distilled.

N,O-Bis(trimethylsilyl)amides are among the most powerful silyl donors (422, 898). The structure of N,O-bis(trimethylsilyl)acetamide (BSA) is well substantiated and is discussed in section 4-4. The power of BSA as a silyl donor is increased by the addition of TMCS (Method 44) (336, 347). The bis(trimethylsilyl)trifluoroacetamide (BSTFA) (Method 46) has been used for amino acid silylation for GC (898). The reaction product, N-TMS-trifluoroacetamide, is eluted ahead of the more volatile amino acid TMS derivatives, where N-TMS-acetamide from BSA may interfere (422). Similarly, the use of BSTFA avoids interference of the reagent peaks with the peaks of lactic and pyruvic acid trimethylsilyl derivatives (347a).

Method 47. N-Trimethylsilyl-N,N'-diphenylurea. This reagent, m.p. 67-69°, is a very rapid silylator (413, 832). As the diphenylurea produced from reaction is insoluble, its precipitation effects silylation which might not otherwise proceed.

Method 48. Miscellaneous silyl amides are listed.

Silyl Donor	Acceptor	Ref.
N-TMS-succinimide	N-Methyl-N-hydroxy-methylformamide; α-phenyl-β-(methyl-amino)-ethanol; N-haloamides	192
N-TMS-Phthalimide	N-Haloamides	192
N,O-Bis(TMS)benzamide	N-Haloamides	68
N,N'-Diphenyl-N,N'-bis(TMS)urea	N-Methyl-DL-alanylglycine	417
N,N''-Diphenyl-N'-methyl-N,N''-bis(TMS)biuret	Sucrose	417

1-10. MISCELLANEOUS METHODS

Method 51. Hexamethyldisiloxane. Voronkov and Shabarova used excess hexamethyldisiloxane in the silylation of alcohols, with alkali catalyst (823), and in silylation of phenols, with acid catalyst, such as benzenesulfonic acid (824). Water was azeotropically removed during the reaction, the reagent acting as solvent. Yields averaged 50% and 80%, respectively.

$$2ROH + Me_3SiOSiMe_3 \rightarrow 2ROSiMe_3 + H_2O$$

Method 52. Hexamethyldisilthiane. Abel (3) prepared hexamethyldisilthiane from TMCS and sodium sulfide at 250°. This compound reacted with alcohols to give excellent yields of silyl ethers. The reagent also slowly silylated amines and carboxylic acids.

$$Me_3Si\text{-}S\text{-}SiMe_3 + 2ROH \rightarrow H_2S + 2ROSiMe_3$$

Method 53. Alkylthiotrimethylsilanes (2). These reagents were used for silylating alcohols and thiols.

$$Me_3SiSC_2H_5 + C_4H_9SH \rightarrow Me_3SiSC_4H_9 + C_2H_5SH.$$

1-11. EXPERIMENTAL PROCEDURES

Method 11p. 1,3-Bis(trimethylsiloxy)benzene (452). Resorcinol (11.0 g, 0.1 mole), 32.7 g (0.3 mole) TMCS, and 25 ml petroleum ether were refluxed 24 hr and distilled, yielding 19.4 g (76%), b 237-240°.

Method 12b. 4-Chlorobutoxytrimethylsilane (749). A mixture of 108.5 g (1.0 mole) 4-chloro-1-butanol, 108.5 g (1.0 mole) TMCS and one liter of benzene was stirred and chilled as ammonia was passed in rapidly. When the odor of ammonia persisted the mixture was filtered from ammonium chloride and the liquid was distilled. Yield, 145 g (80%). Pyridine or other amines used as acid acceptors showed no advantage over ammonia.

Method 13c. 2-Phenylethoxytrimethylsilane (269). One mole TMCS was added slowly to 2-phenylethanol (1 mole), pyridine (1 mole), and ether at 15°. Immediate pyridine hydrochloride pptn. corresponded to 85% reaction. The alcohol was completely consumed, however, by heating for 2 hr at 60°. The pyridine hydrochloride was filtered off and the filtrate was distilled.

Method 14. N-Trimethylsilylbenzamide (186). A mixture of 14.5 (0.1 mole) benzamide, 0.12 mole triethylamine and 200 ml benzene was treated with 0.1 mole TMCS, refluxed two hours and filtered hot. From the filtrate the product, mp 118-120°, was obtained by distillation, bp 142-143°/0.54mm, in 52% yield.

Method 17. Bis(trimethylsilyl) 2,3-bis(trimethylsiloxy)succinate (307). Tartaric acid (5 g, 0.033 mole), 9.9g (0.133 mole) pyridine, and 40 ml formamide were stirred together as a solution of 14.4 g (0.132 mole) TMCS in 80 ml hexane was added dropwise at room temperature. After 5 hr further at 45° the hexane layer was separated and distilled. Yield, 8.6 g (59%).

Method 21. 1-Trimethylsiloxyheptane (452). 1-Heptanol (29.2 g, 0.25 mole) was gradually heated to reflux with 24.9 g (0.15 mole) HMDS.

After 10 hr heating the reflux temperature had reached a maximum of 175°. The charge was fractionated, yielding 39 g (83%) product, bp 189-190°/740mm.

6,9-Bis(trimethylsilyl)hypoxanthine (551). Hypoxanthine (4.2 g) and 10 g HMDS were refluxed. The hypoxanthine slowly dissolved. After 12 hr reflux the charge was distilled, yielding 7.5 g, bp 113-117°/0.15 mm, mp 71-74°. C,H,N analysis was satisfactory.

Method 24. N-Trimethylsilyldibutylamine (224). Di-n-butylamine (32.3 g, 0.25 mole), 40.2 g (0.25 mole) HMDS, and 1.0 g ammonium sulfate were heated under reflux 15 hr and distilled. The fraction (26 g, 52%) boiling at 201-202° had a neutralization equivalent of 203 and silicon analysis, 13.9. Calcd. for $C_{11}H_{27}SiN$: 201 and 13.9, respectively. Another run, without ammonium sulfate, yielded 10 g (20%) of product.

Methods 25, 26, for GC. These are procedures of Sweeley et al. (764) and Luukkainen et al. (498), designed for the analysis of sugars and steroids, respectively, but suitable for other types of compounds.

Method No.	mg Sample	ml HMDS	ml TMCS	Solvent	Reaction
25	10	0.2	0.1	Pyridine 1 ml	Room temp 5', warm few min. at 75° if sample is not dissolved. Disregard slight NH₄Cl ppt.
26	10	0.2	0.02	THF 1 ml	Overnight at room temp., evaporate and take up residue in hexane or THF for injection.

The reactions can be conducted in serum bottles or small capped (caps are Teflon lined) vials and the reagents conveniently measured with syringes. Protection from moisture is advisable.

Method 33. N-Trimethylsilylamino acid trimethylsilyl esters (642, 646). The free amino acid is stirred with excess N-trimethylsilyldiethylamine in a bath at 120°. When no more diethylamine distills the remaining charge is fractionated. Yields 87-97%.

Method 34. N-Trimethylsilylacetamide (186). Trimethylsilyl-t-butylamine (19g) is heated with 7 g acetamide at 75° as 7 g t-butylamine distils. The residue is distilled, yielding 15g (96%), bp 185-186°, mp 52-54°.

Method 42. Tris(trimethylsilyl)pyridoxol (611). A solution of 20 mg pyridoxol hydrochloride in 10 ml dry pyridine, with 18 mg n-$C_{28}H_{38}$ as an internal standard was shaken with 560 mg N-trimethylsilylacetamide several minutes and allowed to stand. After 15 minutes the resulting solution was analysed by gas chromatography. Mass spectrometry showed that the fully silylated derivative, $C_{17}H_{35}NO_3Si_3$, was formed.

Method 43. Silylated amino acids for gas chromatography (422). Twenty-two amino acids were separately silylated in 10-50 mg quantities, using a slight excess of BSA in acetonitrile, heating in capped vials near the boiling point. Clear solutions were obtained in 10 to 30 min and gas chromatographic analysis showed sharp single peaks for all amino acid derivatives except arginine-TMS, which decomposed on the column.

2

Gas Chromatography

2-1. INTRODUCTION

This chapter will discuss various aspects of gas chromatography (GC), particularly as they affect silylated compounds. For a recent, fuller treatment of gas chromatography the reader is referred to the volume edited by Ettre and Zlatkis (216).

When compounds are silylated they become less polar, which makes them more likely subjects for analysis by gas chromatography. As a result of reduced polarity, the derivatives are often more volatile and stable and are adsorbed less on the column. The effect of small differences between parent compounds is increased so that compounds with overlapping peaks may show good resolution after silylation. Also, the shape of a peak may be improved. Thus, in Fig. 2-1 Vandenheuvel and Horning (808) showed that the silyl derivatives of estrone and estradiol are better separated, with much less tailing, than the parent compounds. The estriol-TMS peak is well shaped and much larger than the estriol peak (approximately same size of samples), which indicates that column loss has been reduced.

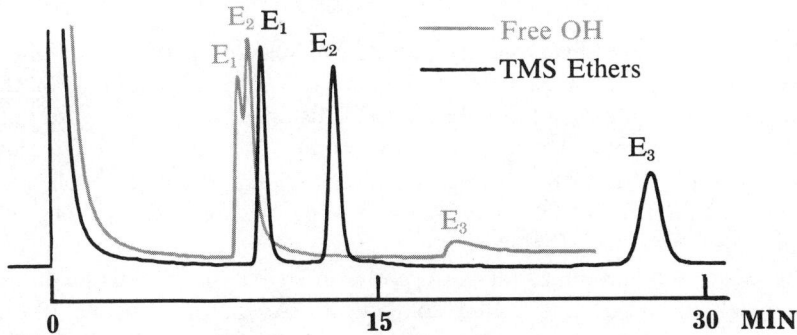

Fig. 2-1. GC analysis of a mixture of estrone (E_1), estradiol (E_2), and estriol (E_3) before (gray line) and after (solid line) formation of TMS ethers. Column conditions: 1% JXR on 100-120 mesh Gas-Chrom P; 6 ft x 4 mm glass U-tube; 210° C; 16 p.s.i. Used by permission of Plenum Publishing Corp., New York.

2-2. SUPPORT TREATMENT

For quantitative work diatomaceous earth supports must be thoroughly deactivated (342, 565). The adsorptive properties of the support are reduced by acid washing and silanizing. Silanizing is treatment with dichlorodimethylsilane or HMDS, which converts active sites (silanol groups) to less polar silyl ethers, and gives a surface which will hold a thin coating of stationary phase.

Any acid condition on the column is to be avoided. An SE-30 column previously used for analysis of trifluoroacetyl derivatives decomposed TMS derivatives (881). Presumably trifluoroacetic acid was bound or adsorbed on the column and the acidic condition caused the decomposition. Similar decomposition has been caused by the use of acid-stabilized DEGS as a stationary phase (880).

Silanizing the support increases the apparent polarity of a polyester stationary phase. Possibly on an unsilanized support there is orientation of polar polyester groups toward polar sites of the support. This exposes the less polar groups of the phase as the active surface. Silanizing results in a more random surface distribution of the polar groups of the stationary phases (808).

The affinity of active support sites for silyl groups results in loss of silyl groups from the derivative if the column has not been thoroughly silanized. N-TMS-amino acid TMS esters have been reported to emerge as amino acid TMS esters (336, 653).

2-3. STATIONARY PHASES

Just as with other substances, the polarity, or selectivity, of the stationary phase used affects the column performance of TMS compounds. For the identification of mixtures of closely related substances it is best to use both selective and nonselective phases (344, 764). Two peaks which elute together from a nonselective phase are often well separated by a selective, or polar, phase. The nonselective or nonpolar phase, however, is preferable with a sample mixture of wide volatility range.

The most used stationary phases reported for silyl compounds have also been widely used for unsilylated compounds. A complete listing of the phases mentioned in this review is given in the Glossary. The following classification is approximate as even the "nonselective" phases may have some selectivity, or polarity. Phenylmethyl silicones, for instance, are more polar than methyl silicones.

Nonselective	Selective
SE-30	NGS
SE-52	EGS
F-60	QF-1
JXR	XE-60
OV-1	OV-17

The choice of phase for TMS compounds is usually not critical but results from trial. Many investigators have obtained good results from different phases for the same TMS derivatives. The relative polarity can be more precisely determined by the method of Rohrschneider (620) and used as a basis for predicting retention time. The relative selectivity of certain phases for different polar groups in steroids has been recognized (see Chapter 11).

The generally accepted method of applying the stationary phase is the filtration technique described by Horning, Moscatelli and Sweeley (343). For TMS compounds of low molecular weight, column loading of 10-20% of stationary phase is common. For higher molecular weight compounds, such as some sterols and glycosides, an application of the order of 1-3% is preferred. Retention times are longer and operating temperatures higher with the heavier loading. In a programmed system emergence temperatures of n-alkanes were 20-40° lower on 1% F-60 than on 10% (182). However, the phase loading must not be too low or it will not properly cover the support. VandenHeuvel and Horning (808) found substantial loss of free testosterone (smaller loss of the silylated derivative) on 0.5% SE-30 in comparison with a 2% SE-30 column.

2-4. SAMPLE PREPARATION

Procedures for derivatization are described in Chapter 1. In many cases the reaction mixture (0.5-5.0 μl) was injected directly. Excess reagent and solvent usually eluted considerably ahead of TMS derivatives.

Pyridine, the most used silylation solvent, was considered objectionable in the chromatograph by many investigators. Sato and von Rudloff (674) claimed that it tends to overlap and distort peaks of short retention time. Wood et al. (880), working with monoglycerides, also found that tailing of pyridine interfered with early sample peaks. They therefore added water to the reacted sample and extracted the TMS ethers with hexane. Last traces of pyridine were removed by evaporating the hexane solution to dryness. Even when pyridine was not used the reagents and solvents used for steroid silylation were often removed by evaporation in a stream of nitrogen. The residue obtained was taken up in tetrahydrofuran, chloroform or hexane for injection.

2-5. COLUMN TEMPERATURE

The separation temperature is a most important variable in the determination of relative retention times. VandenHeuvel *et al.* showed the substantial effect of temperature change on relative retention time over a range of only 20° (803). Further, as oven temperatures may only approximate the column temperature, the use of a temperature-independent standard becomes more urgent. The MU value of a compound is such a standard, and is discussed in section 2-8. Linear programming of column temperature has broadened the range of compounds which may be determined in a single run. A series of 20 TMS sugars, from C_4 to C_{18}, were separated thus (764), programming at 2.3°/min. Wide ranges of urinary steroids or other metabolites have been separated in programmed runs, at a rate of 1° or 2°/min (182, 264).

Some programming was much faster than 2°/min, yet seemed to give satisfactory quantification as long as the necessary resolution was obtained. The elution temperature varies with the rate of temperature rise. Suchanec (758) programmed the TMS ethers of a mixture of pentaerythritol compounds on SE-30 beginning at 125°. For the tripentaerythritol derivative, programmed at 13°/min, elution occurred at 302° in 13′; at a rate of 4.6°/min the compound eluted at 285° in 35′. Jones and Schmeltz (381a) programmed a wide range TMS esters at 6°/min. Although retention times varied elution temperatures were reproducible to ± 2°.

2-6. DETECTOR RESPONSE

As ionization detection systems do not give uniform response to all organic compounds it is necessary to determine the ratio of peak area to sample for each component over the range studied. Fortunately, the response is linear for most TMS compounds. In some instances correction factors may be necessary.

A flame ionization detector, properly designed, allows quantitative results in the nanogram range. Some examples of this are described in later sections. The relation of structure to response of an argon ionization detector was discussed by Sweeley and Chang (765).

Failure to obtain consistent response may be due to operational losses. Byrne *et al.* (144) atributed yield losses on gas chromatography of silyl ethers to several possible causes: (1) evaporation of the more volatile TMS ethers during isolation; (2) overlapping of peaks of the more volatile TMS ethers with solvent peaks; and (3) nonemergence of the less volatile derivatives.

Horning and Gardiner (338) suggested that column losses be detected by analysing successively smaller samples containing the standard and the compound being investigated. The ratio of peak areas will change if loss is occurring.

2-7. RETENTION FACTORS

The effect of silylation on volatility of simple compounds is discussed in section 14-1. As expected, a decrease in boiling point caused by silylation also shortens retention time in gas chromatography. This was clearly shown by Nelson *et al.* (548) in their study of phenols using an SE-30 Column (Table 2-1).

Table 2-1. Silylation vs. Retention

	Column temp.	Retention time, min Phenol	TMS ether
o-Methoxyphenol (bp 205°)	108°	3.8	5.5
p-Methoxyphenol (bp 243°)	162	2.6	1.9
4-Allyl-2-methoxyphenol	112	13.0	14.2
4-Propenyl-2-methoxyphenol*	150	4.3, 6.1	5.0, 6.8
4-Hydroxy-3-methoxybenzaldehyde	148	5.8	5.4
n-Propylguaiacol	118	8.8	10.6
p-Hydroxybenzaldehyde	194	3.0	1.6
Syringaldehyde	180	3.7	1.8
Acetovanillone	135	4.0	4.4

cis and *trans* forms assumed

In the methoxyphenols, the *ortho* isomer has limited intramolecular hydrogen bonding and the silyl ether exhibits longer retention because of increased molecular weight. The *para* compound is highly associated through intermolecular hydrogen bonding and therefore shows a higher boiling point and greater retention, which is sharply reduced by silylation as the ether cannot form hydrogen bonds.

2-8. RETENTION DATA EVALUATION

Absolute retention times, given in minutes for a certain stationary phase and temperature, are poorly reproducible, and are shown in the tables of this review only for lack of more significant retention data. The ratio of the retention time of the sample to that of a standard *is* more significant as the standard is subject to the same variations in column conditions that affect the sample. This relative retention time is, however, strongly temperature-dependent (803, 860). A list of standards is given in the Glossary. The standard selected should elute near the sample but should not interfere with it. The usual standard is a hydrocarbon or a compound capable of silylation and related to the sample. The latter is added to the sample before silylation and it is assumed that the standard is completely and uniformly silylated each time. This assumption may be erroneous. For instance, Halpern *et al.* (289) found that inositol, which has been used as a standard (130), gave different peak areas for different reaction times because of its low solubility in pyridine, the silylation solvent. They therefore recommended the use of inert internal standards, such as hydrocarbons, which undergo no changes during the procedure.

Retention data become still more significant and reproducible when reported as methylene units (MU) (182, 802, 803, 804) or steroid numbers (SN) (290, 804, 806, 808), as described by Horning, Vanden-Heuvel and co-workers. The method is based on comparison of the retention times of the sample and two hydrocarbon standards, which elute before and after the sample, respectively. The number assigned to a standard is the number of carbon atoms in it. The value for the sample is calculated by interpolation of retention times. The method applies even to programmed runs, in which neither the emergence temperature nor retention time is sufficient for characterization of the sample (182). Allowance for the contribution of functional groups is additive and based upon experiment. The contribution of the trimethylsiloxy group in steroids varied with group location, configuration, and stationary phase used: 2.5-3.3 SN units on SE-30 (902.4); 2.1-3.4 on QF-1 and 1.3-3.1 on NGS (290). The MU and SN values vary with the column used but are not so temperature-dependent as relative retention data are. They are closely reproducible between laboratories and assist in identification of unknown compounds.

3

Mass Spectrometry

3-1. INTRODUCTION

For a comprehensive treatment of mass spectrometry of organic compounds the reader is referred to the recent book by Budzikiewiez, Djerassi and Williams (133). Briefly, mass spectrometry consists in measuring the mass/charge *(m/e)* ratio of ions produced by electron bombardment of a substance in high vacuum. Initially, the loss of an electron results in a molecular ion, M^+, which may fragment to smaller neutral particles and ions. The distribution and intensity of the ions are characteristic of the sample compound. The m/e measurement may be to the nearest mass unit, as in ordinary spectrometers, or to the fourth decimal place in high resolution instruments. The latter accuracy permits close decisions as to molecular formulas and isotopic composition.

Since the pioneering work of Sharkey, Friedel and Langer (712) in 1957, there has been increasing interest in the mass spectrometry of silylated organic compounds. As with gas chromatography, the increased volatility of these derivatives has made possible the analysis of many compounds not previously considered suitable. Molecular weight determination and the appearance of characteristic fragments from silyl derivatives have aided in the identification of the parent compound even in those cases where it could be analysed directly by mass spectrometry. In addition, deuterium labeling experiments have clarified the course and mechanism of fragmentation, especially as used by Diekman *et al.* (193, 194, 195) and McCloskey *et al.* (517).

The combination of gas chromatography and mass spectrometry (GC–MS) is an extremely powerful tool for identification. Samples of eluant from a gas chromatograph are used for mass spectrometry, or better, the gas chromatograph is coupled with the mass spectrometer as described by Ryhage (661), by Watson and Biemann (840), and by Leemans and McCloskey (461). With the combination instrument suspected overlap peaks from the chromatograph requiring as much as a minute to emerge may be detected by analysing every few seconds utilizing fast-scan modifications. Thus the chromatograph effluent can be continuously monitored, providing rapid, prompt analysis and positive correlation of sample and spectrum. The use of GC–MS with silyl compounds has been described (121, 211, 212, 213, 349, 581, 766, 781).

3-2. SAMPLE PREPARATION

Teeter (774) silylated carboxylic acids and amino acids with refluxing hexamethyldisilazane (HMDS) catalysed by ammonium chloride (Method 24, section 1-7). A 1-μl sample of the reaction mixture was used directly for mass spectral analysis. The excess HMDS present protected the TMS compounds. There was no interference in the spectrum as the molecular weights of the TMS esters were usually higher than that of HMDS. Apparently his interest was only in the determination of the molecular ions.

Some artifacts may appear if samples for direct injection are not carefully prepared or preserved. For instance, the molecular ion of acetamide, m/e 59, will appear if the amide is not completely removed following silylation with N-TMS-acetamide. Again, hydrolysis of silyl ethers exposed to air will produce trimethylsilanol, $(CH_3)_3SiOH$, for which the M–15 ion is b, m/e 75 (section 3-5), and hexamethyldisiloxane, $(CH_3)_3SiOSi(CH_3)_3$, for which the M–15 ion is e, m/e 147 (453) (section 3-5).

The gas chromatograph, of course, is most useful in sample preparation. With good resolution the sample is obtained pure and with coupled GC–MS it is protected from possible hydrolysis by atmospheric moisture.

3-3. MOLECULAR AND M – 15 IONS

Often in mass spectrometry determination of molecular weight (mass to charge ratio, or m/e, of the molecular ion) is all that is desired. Such determination is substantiated, of course, when both parent compound and silyl derivative can be analysed. Fischer-Tropsch alcohol–hydrocarbon mixtures show interfering mass spectra and normally must be separated for analysis. However, silylation of the mixture produces TMS ethers, which yield distinct mass spectra free from interference (453). Again, silylated N-chloroacetyldodecahydrolucensomycin shows a molecular ion whereas the free compound does not (265).

The molecular ions of most silylated compounds are weak or nonexistent. However, at about 10 ev ionizing energy instead of the usual 70 ev, fragmentation is less and the molecular ion therefore more intense (194, 711).

The M–15 peak, resulting from loss of methyl by the molecular ion, is prominent in most spectra and serves for determination of molecular weight. In TMS esters, for instance, the loss of methyl is so favored that the M–15 ion dominates the spectrum sometimes obscuring other structural informa-tion (774).

The inlet temperature of the coupled GC–MS is a factor in the relative molecular ion and M–15 ion intensities (159). When a probe at a tem-perature lower than that of the spectrometer inlet is used, higher molecular ion and lower M–15 intensities were obtained. Indeed, even a change in the inlet system has caused variation in the mass spectrum (193).

3-4. FRAGMENTATION, GENERAL

The trimethylsilyl group is not a consistent director of characteristic fragmentation (193, 194), and cleavage is sometimes much the same for silyl as for other derivatives. The fission of ordinary dialkyl ethers is similar to that of silyl ethers, for instance. The behavior of steroid 5-en-3-ol TMS ethers is exceptional, however, where the TMS group directs the fragmenta-tion in a characteristic manner, as will be described.

The fragments containing the TMS group, whether unbroken, cleaved or rearranged, are unique for silyl compounds, and of course aid in their identification. This identification is expedited by high resolution mass measurements and by the use of compounds labeled with heavy isotopes. Both O^{18} (781) and deuterium (193, 194, 390, 392, 517, 766) labeling has been used most helpfully.

In this chapter the bond fission notation described by Budzikiewiez et al. (133) will be used. At the site of fission, shown by a wavy line, the frag-ment retaining the charge will be indicated and odd-electron ions will be shown as $[R]^{+\cdot}$.

$$[CH_3CH_2CH_2-O-Si(CH_3)_2 \overbrace{}^{117} CH_3]^{+\cdot} \xrightarrow{-CH_3^\cdot}$$

$$CH_3CH_2CH_2-\overset{+}{O}=Si(CH_3)_2$$

$$m/e\ 117$$

3-5. FRAGMENTATION OF SILYL ETHERS

In mass spectra of silylated aliphatic monohydroxy compounds such as simple alcohols, diglycerides and hydroxy esters, the silicon-containing ions (a, b, c, d) are common.

$$(CH_3)_3Si^+ \qquad H\overset{+}{O}=Si(CH_3)_2 \qquad CH_2=\overset{+}{O}SiH(CH_3)_2$$

$$a,\ m/e\ 73 \qquad\qquad b,\ m/e\ 75 \qquad\qquad c,\ m/e\ 89$$

$$CH_2 = \overset{+}{O}Si(CH_3)_3 \qquad\qquad (CH_3)_2Si = \overset{+}{O}Si(CH_3)_3$$

$$d, m/e \ 103 \qquad\qquad\qquad e, m/e \ 147$$

The TMS ethers are like other ethers, subject to α-fission, which can occur at A, B, or C. Fission at A, produces the M − 15 ion and is greatly

$$\underset{R'}{\overset{B \qquad\qquad\qquad A}{R{\mid}CH-O-Si(CH_3)_2{\mid}CH_3}} \qquad\qquad R, R' = H \ or \ alkyl$$

C

preferred over loss of alkyl at B in straight chain compounds (R′ = H). When R′ is methyl cleavage at C will also produce the M − 15 ion. Using deuterated 2-butanol TMS ether Karabatsos et al. (391) showed that 21% of the M − 15 ions arise from methyl at C − 1, 79% from the TMS group. Diekman et al. (194) found with labeled 2-pentanol TMS ether, 20% from C − 1, 80% from TMS. The molecular ion of cholesterol TMS ether loses methyl from the TMS group; the parent ion which has lost the TMS group (as trimethylsilanol, MW = 90) now loses the angular methyl group at C-19 (193).

The M − 15 ion may be further cleaved at B (R′ = H), resulting in c, m/e 89, by hydrogen transfer mostly from β and γ positions and elimination of olefin. Diekman et al. (194) proved the course of this fission by deuterium labeling. If, however, fission occurs at the C−O bond, ion b, m/e 75, will be formed, by nonspecific hydrogen transfer and elimination of olefin. If fission occurs originally at B (R′ = H) the fragment d, m/e 103, is formed, which may eliminate formaldehyde to produce ion a, m/e 73. This also is like the behavior of dialkyl ethers (197).

Not all alcohols produced the four ion fragments (a-d) just described. Ion c, for instance, is always weak for secondary alcohols, and 2-pentanol TMS ether gives none at all (194). It was explained that formation of this ion would require fission at both B and C as well as hydrogen transfer, not a likely possibility. The relative abundance of fragment ions a and b differs for primary, primary branched and secondary alcohol TMS ethers. Further, ion c, m/e 89, is useful in determining the point of branching, as most derivatives with γ-branching show intense peaks at m/e 89 (712).

Benzyl alcohol TMS ether yielded the M − 15 ion which rearranged with loss of formaldehyde to $C_6H_5\overset{+}{Si}(CH_3)_2$ (194). Phenyl TMS ethers behaved like their aliphatic counterparts. TMS ethers of 2, 6-t-alkyl-phenols readily yielded molecular ions at low voltage (244). Various N-acylcatecholamine silyl ethers gave the same fragment ions as aliphatic alcohol TMS ethers. In addition, cleavage of the molecular ion at the α-carbon yielded a neutral fragment containing the N-acylamino moiety and a residual ion containing all TMS ether groups originally present (349). The behavior of TMS ether Schiff bases from catecholamines was analogous (148).

Polysilyl derivatives of polyols, such as glycols, carbohydrates, mono-glycerides, N-acetylsphingosine and pyridoxol, in addition to ions a to d, yield ions containing more than one silyl residue, such as e, m/e 147. This results from two silyl groups, either on adjacent carbon atoms as in TMS sugars, or brought near each other through expulsion of the central portion of the molecule as in TMS polymethylene glycols. After loss of methyl from one silyl group rearrangement occurs, by way of the intermediate postulated by McCloskey et al. (517), $(CH_3)_2Si\overset{+}{=}O-CH_2-OSi(CH_3)_3$, m/e 177, or through a cyclic oxonium ion such as p, as proposed by Diekman et al. (195) and Richter et al. (611). Ion e may further fragment (611).

$$Me_2Si\overset{+}{=}OSi(CH_3)_3 \rightarrow (CH_3)_3\overset{+}{Si} \xrightarrow{-C_2H_4} CH_3\overset{+}{SiH_2}$$

$$e,\ m/e\ 147 \qquad a,\ m/e\ 73 \qquad f,\ m/e\ 45$$

$$Me_3Si-\overset{+}{\underset{O}{O}}\overset{\diagup(CH_2)_n}{\diagdown}\underset{\underset{Me_2}{Si}}{O}$$

$$p$$
$$(n\ =\ 2\text{-}8)\quad Me_2$$

In addition to the ions already mentioned persilylated monosaccharides fragment in various ways, yielding ions such as g to k (162, 320, 581, 766).

$$(CH_3)_3SiOCH\overset{+}{=}OSi(CH_3)_3 \qquad [(CH_3)_3SiOCH=CHOSi(CH_3)_3]^+$$

$$g,\ m/e\ 191 \qquad\qquad h,\ m/e\ 204$$

$$(CH_3)_3SiOCH=CHCH\overset{+}{=}OSi(CH_3)_3$$

$$j,\ m/e\ 217$$

$$(CH_3)_3SiOCH=C[OSi(CH_3)_3]CH\overset{+}{=}OSi(CH_3)_3$$

$$k,\ m/e\ 305$$

Persilylated disaccharides (glycopyranosylaldoses), fragmented to pro-duce 2,3,4,6-tetra-O-TMS-D-glucopyranose with 1-linked silylated frag-ments of the aldose, original disaccharide linkage being maintained (162).

For polysilyl ethers in particular, numerous mass spectral ions result from cleavage of one or more neutral trimethylsilanol (Me_3SiOH, m/e 90) fragments yielding M − 90, M − 180, etc. peaks; also cleavage of a methyl group from these fragments, yielding M − 90 − 15, M − 180 − 15, etc. peaks (162, 276).

Of all the silyl compounds investigated by mass spectrometry, most work has been reported for hydroxy steroids. Fragmentation of their silyl ethers yields ions a and b, none of c or d, and the usual M − 15 (loss of methyl), M − 90 (loss of trimethylsilanol) and M − 15 − 90. Also, 20-hydroxypregnane TMS ethers suffer α-fission at C − 20 to yield ion m:

$$\underset{\displaystyle\text{20}}{\text{HC}}\overset{\displaystyle\text{CH}_3}{\underset{\displaystyle\big|}{\big|}}\text{—OSi(CH}_3)_3 \;\rightarrow\; \text{CH}_3\text{CH}=\overset{+}{\text{O}}\text{Si(CH}_3)_3$$

$$m, \; m/e \; 117$$

$$\longrightarrow \;\; (\text{CH}_3)_3\text{Si}\overset{+}{\text{O}}=\text{CH–CH}=\text{CH}_2 \;\text{ or}$$

$$n, \; m/e \; 129$$

$$[\text{M} - (\text{CH}_3)_3\text{SiOCH–CH}=\text{CH}_2]^+$$

$$\text{M} - 129$$

As mentioned before (section 3-4) a characteristic fragmentation directed by the silyl group is that which occurs with 5-en-3-ol steroid TMS ethers. The fragment produced may be charged or neutral, which results in peaks at m/e 129 and M − 129, both usually intense. The ratio of the intensities of m/e 129 to M − 129 substantially decreases with substitution at C-4; 4,4-dimethylsterols yield a much more intense peak for M − 129 than for m/e 129. Diekman and Djerassi (193) have shown conclusively by deuterium labeling that the fission produces a fragment containing carbon atoms 1,2 and 3 of ring A, with hydrogen transfer from C-2. Earlier work had postulated involvement of carbon atoms 2, 3 and 4 (211).

The formation of fragment n is characteristic of silylated 5-en-3-ol steroids. 3-Hydroxysteroids with unsaturation at C-4 or C-7 do not show this fission (121, 426). However, this ion is not entirely unique for sterols, as it also appears in the mass spectrum of 2,3,4-tris-(O-TMS)-D-glucosan (320), at 10% intensity. M − 129 ion is missing.

The mass spectrum of cholesterol TMS ether, particularly the m/e 129 intensity, was found by Diekman and Djerassi (193) to vary with the measuring conditions especially the instrument and inlet system used. A several-fold increase was observed in going from an Atlas CH-4 mass spectrometer with direct inlet system to a CEC 21-103C instrument with heated inlet system.

3-6. FRAGMENTATION OF SILYL ESTERS AND AMINES

Teeter (774) examined the behavior of aliphatic carboxylic acid TMS esters. A characteristic fragmentation of the molecular ion involved loss of methyl group followed by skeletal rearrangement with loss of carbon dioxide.

$$[R-COOSi(CH_3)_3]^{+\cdot} \xrightarrow{-CH_3^\cdot} RCO\overset{+}{O}=Si(CH_3)_2 \xrightarrow{-CO_2} R\overset{+}{Si}(CH_3)_2$$

$$M \qquad\qquad\qquad M-15 \qquad\qquad\qquad M-59$$

However, M. G. Horning et al. (347a) found that the TMS derivatives of α-keto acids produced M-117 fragments, assumed due to loss of COOSiMe$_3$.

TMS-benzylamine behaved analogously to TMS-benzyl alcohol (3-5), losing $CH_2=NH$ from its $M-15$ ion. In addition, the TMS amine was found subject to regular α-fission, yielding $CH_2=\overset{+}{N}HSi(CH_3)_2$, nitrogen analog of ion d.

The molecular ions of amino acid TMS esters characteristically lose ammonia and methyl (774).

$$[R-CH_2CH(NH_2)COOSi(CH_3)_3]^+ \xrightarrow[-CH_3]{-NH_3}$$

$$RCH=CHCO\overset{+}{O}=Si(CH_3)_2$$

$$M-32$$

However, for N-TMS-amino acid TMS esters the ion, $(CH_3)_3Si\overset{+}{N}H=CH-COOSi(CH_3)_3$, m/e 218, is common.

4

Theoretical Aspects of Trimethylsilylation

In collaboration with Justine Simon Walhout

Since trimethylsilylation is a fairly recent development, it is natural that practical methods and procedures outnumber studies of a theoretical nature. This chapter attempts to summarize the current understanding of the mechanism and other theoretical aspects of trimethylsilylation.

4-1. PROPERTIES OF THE TRIMETHYLSILYL GROUP

Size and Shape. Silicon has a covalent radius of 1.17 Å (116); the radius of carbon is 0.77 Å (572). The Si—C bond distance in the trimethylsilyl group varies with the element on the fourth silicon bond, however, being 1.89 Å in Me_3SiCl (118) and 1.93 Å in Me_4Si (117). The C—Si—C bond angles are approximately tetrahedral; hence the trimethylsilyl group has the same geometry as the t-butyl group but is larger. Silicon, therefore, has more room for the groups bonded to it, *i.e.,* there is less steric strain within the trimethylsilyl group than within the t-butyl group. The group itself, however, is large and exerts steric effects, even to the point of changing the relative stability of isomers (764). Seyferth *et al.* (707) have suggested that in Me_3Si compounds steric factors are always important and may in some cases make the study of electronic factors very difficult.

Bonding Power. Carbon is limited to four covalent bonds, but silicon has available $3d$ orbitals for additional bonding. Many compounds and ions are known where silicon is bonded penta- or hexacovalently, and some of these substances will be mentioned later in the chapter. Sommer, in his excellent book, *Stereochemistry, Mechanism and Silicon* (747, p 12ff), gives evidence indicating that a trimethylsilicon will not form such stable expanded octet substances, however, as such requires that silicon be made more positive by the presence of electronegative groups (as in $SiF_6^=$). This, however, does not preclude the possibility that the $3d$ orbitals are involved in the tetravalent bonding of silicon.

Bond Energies. The generalization is often made that silicon, in comparison with carbon, forms less stable bonds to carbon and hydrogen, but stronger bonds to nitrogen, sulfur, oxygen and chlorine. Actual values for bond energies vary with the method used in determining them. Hess *et al.* (319) calculated the following values for the dissociation of Me_3Si-Y from data from electron impact studies:

Y	Kcal./mole $\pm$ 10 Kcal.
H	88
CH_3	85
C_2H_5	83
$SiMe_3$	86
OMe	127
F	193
Cl	126
Br	86
$N(C_2H_5)_2$	131

Later values (47, 169) are lower than this—and disagree with each other, but the relative order seems correct. These data are important in considering fragmentation in mass spectrometry, but in considering heterolytic cleavage of bonds in solution other factors are important.

Electronegativity. Silicon is less electronegative than carbon. On Pauling's scale, silicon has an electronegativity of 1.8; carbon, of 2.5; nitrogen, 3.0; oxygen, 3.5; and hydrogen, 2.1. Thus silicon is more positive than any of these elements, to which it is commonly bonded, if you consider the dipole of the single covalent bond. The Me_3Si group has an electron pushing ($+I$) inductive effect on the group to which it is bonded.

Conjugative Ability. Examination of some of the available data reveals that the $+I$ effect is inadequate to explain the chemistry of the Me_3Si group. West and Baney (855) have made a study of the acidity and basicity of silanols compared to alcohol. Trimethylsilanol can be converted to its sodium salt with 12N sodium hydroxide:

$$Me_3SiOH + NaOH \rightarrow Me_3SiO^- Na^+ + H_2O$$

This shows that silanols are stronger acids than alcohols, but from inductive effects alone, they should be weaker. This can be explained by postulating that one of the unshared pairs of electrons on the oxygen is shared by the silicon through its *d* orbitals, a concept referred to hereafter as dative $d_\pi-p_\pi$ bonding (747) or simply $(p \rightarrow d)\pi$ bonds. West and Baney found that the silanols were, nevertheless, nearly as strong bases as the alcohols, and concluded that only one of the unshared pairs of oxygen was involved in $(p \rightarrow d)\pi$ bonding. Assuming a bent Si—O—H bond, which seems likely, the *p-d* interaction can be pictured in this way:

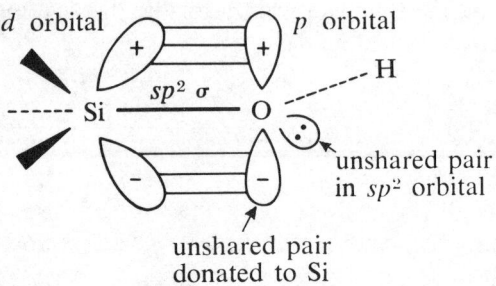

It is apparent that a nitrogen, sulfur, pi-bonded carbon, etc., could be substituted for the oxygen, and that silicon therefore should have an electron-taking resonance (-T) effect acting in opposite direction to its +I effect.

Other evidence has led Pitt more recently (589) to suggest that in the silanol itself $(p \rightarrow d)\pi$ bonding is not important, but that in the resulting *ion* it is very important. His conclusion is based on electronic spectral evidence, in which pi symmetry exists in excited states but not in the ground state of silicon bonded to nitrogen or oxygen. This theory would also explain why the basicity of the silanols is not less than that of alcohols.

Many different kinds of evidence support $(p \rightarrow d)\pi$ bonding (4, 5, 52, 53, 92, 170, 179, 280, 548, 589, 722, 757, 855). One of these, chosen to demonstrate the -T effect of the Me_3Si group, is the classical study of *m*- and *p*-Me_3Si-anilines, phenols, and benzoic acids by Benkeser and Krysiak (53). Their acidity constants reveal a definite conjugative effect of the Me_3Si group; *e.g.,* the pK_a of the conjugate acid of dimethylaniline in 50% ethanol at 20° is 4.35, the pK_a of the *m*-TMS derivative is 4.41; therefore *m*-Me_3Si-dimethylaniline is a slightly stronger base than dimethylaniline as expected from the +I effect. But the pK_a of the conjugate acid of *p*-Me_3Si-dimethylaniline is 3.98, and therefore *p*-Me_3Si-dimethylaniline is a weaker base. This can be explained if structures such as **1** are important:

$$(CH_3)_2 \overset{+}{N} = \!\!\!\!\bigcirc\!\!\!\! = \overset{-}{Si}(CH_3)_3$$

1   **2**

In a recent communication, Ebsworth (207) pointed out that the geometry of the molecule cannot be directly related to the presence or absence of $(p{\rightarrow}d)\pi$ bonding. Some of the earlier work did assume that the atom contributing the electrons would have to have them in a p orbital. Ebsworth suggested that an unshared pair in a sp^3 orbital can overlap with a d orbital enough for pi bonding if the orientation of the orbitals is just right. In the light of this, some of the evidence for silicon pi bonding should be reevaluated. However, such evidence as the two examples above is not affected.

Whether silicon *transmits* a conjugative effect remains controversial. Hogben *et al.* (330) found that pentafluoroaniline and its N-Me$_3$Si derivative have the same effect on the *p*-fluorine, in an NMR study. Yoder and Zuckerman (890a) found no evidence for transmission of conjugation by silicon in the system, **2**. Zuckerman (897) suggested that the two d orbitals of silicon involved in the bonding in **2** may have a node between them and be therefore nontransmitting. However, from a study of coupling constants for N^{15}-H in NMR, Me$_3$SiNHC$_6$H$_5$ seems more like aniline than like **3** or **4** (897).

3   4

In oxygen rather than nitrogen compounds, the effect *does* seem to be carried (92). Other work indicates that paired silicon atoms also transmit conjugative properties. Kumada (449) has shown that the Si—Si bond is an effective chromophore, indeed that there is a linear correlation between the absorption maxima of the disilanes, **5**, and the stilbenes, **6**.

5   6

Part of the controversy develops because some workers are dealing with ground state molecules only (NMR) while others are working with excited states (*e.g.,* UV). Reacting molecules, of course, are not in a ground state.

The apparent inability of silicon to transmit a conjugative effect at times may also be explained by a competitive interaction; that is, silicon may not be as effective in competing for an unshared pair of electrons as another acceptor, such as a benzene ring, or the involvement of one group with the d orbitals of silicon may prevent a second from doing likewise. (See Chvalovsky, 164, for a discussion of this.) This idea is also in accord with Jaffe's earlier conclusions from molecular orbital theory (375).

It is concluded, then, that the trimethylsilyl group can have a -T effect on its substituent through $(p{\rightarrow}d)\pi$ bonding, and this will be assumed in the rest of this chapter.

Bond Polarizability. The Si–Y bond always exceeds the C–Y bond in bond refraction (calculated from molar refractions) and is thus more polarizable (747, pp 27, 28). An attacking reagent can induce a charge separation in the Si–Y bond more easily than in the C–Y bond; therefore, bond energies are not as important in determining the reactivity of Si bonds. This may be due to d orbital participation in all silicon bonds. Eaborn (205) concludes that even methyl groups on silicon have more freedom of movement than on carbon, *i.e.,* they sweep out a larger cone in their rotation as shown by electron diffraction of gases or x-ray studies on crystals.

Free Existence. The trimethylsilyl anion presumably exists in alkali metal complexes such as Me_3SiK. However, such silanions form less readily than their carbon analogs and are of little concern here. The trimethylsilyl free radical, $Me_3Si^{\bullet}$, does not form readily. At 523-555° and 0.2-0.8 mm $Me_3Si\text{-}SiMe_3$ is less than 4% decomposed (47). (Interestingly, $Ph_3Si\text{-}SiPh_3$ is also thermally stable, unlike its carbon analog.)

The existence of the trimethylsiliconium ion is of more interest in silylation considerations. Sommer (747, p 30) reports the appearance potential of Me_3Si^+ in electron impact ionization as 250 ± 4 kcal/mole and reasons that siliconium ion formation relative to carbonium ion formation is favored in some cases. Yet evidence for the existence of Me_3Si^+ as an intermediate in reactions (corresponding to Me_3C^+ in reactions of t-butyl alcohol, for example) is scarce (97). In very polar solvents, some ionization seems to occur. Kreshkov *et al.* (437) found that Me_3SiCl in acetonitrile behaved as a weak electrolyte does in water solution. Sommer (747, p 84ff) also cites the racemization of an optically active silyl chloride in nitromethane–chloroform as evidence for the existence of siliconium ions. The possibility of siliconium ions in reaction mechanisms must, therefore, be considered.

IR Spectra. Fairly definite bands are characteristic of the trimethylsilyl group and are useful for identification. These bands are of course subject to shifts caused by interaction with the rest of the molecule. The symmetrical Si–CH_3 deformation band occurs at approximately 1250 cm^{-1}, and Si—CH_3, stretching bands at about 840 and 760 cm^{-1}. In phenols the 760 band is at 755 cm^{-1} (548) and in alkoxy compounds at 763 cm^{-1} (596). A characteristic Si—O band is found at 1090-1020 cm^{-1} (548), and a Si—N (hetero) band at 1170-1180 cm^{-1} (829). IR data are included in many of the papers referred to in this book. IR spectroscopy has been a valuable tool in the structural determination of many silyl derivatives.

Summary. In comparing the trimethylsilyl group with the t-butyl group we find: (1) the Me_3Si group is larger and is within itself less crowded but can exert a greater steric effect; (2) each group exerts a +I effect, but Me_3Si also can exert a —T effect because of the presence in silicon of unused outer orbitals that are not in the t-butyl group (this is a greater effect than hyperconjugation in t-butyl); (3) bonds formed by the Me_3Si are often thermodynamically stronger than corresponding Me_3C bonds, but they are much more polarizable and therefore more reactive; and (4) there seems to be less tendency for silanions, silyl free radicals, or siliconium ions to form than for carbanions, carbon free radicals, or carbonium ions as reaction intermediates, perhaps merely because other modes of reaction are more available to silicon than to carbon.

4-2. THE MECHANISM OF SILYLATION

Review of Proposals for $Me_3SiX + HY \rightarrow Me_3SiY + HX$ Reactions. Trimethylsilylation reactions are difficult to study kinetically. The reactions are rapid, and the reagents are decomposed by water, which limits conditions under which they can be studied. Nevertheless, some studies have ben made which suggest mechanisms for reactions involving the trimethylsilyl group.

Grubb (283) studied the rate of condensation of silanol in methanol to hexamethyldisiloxane,

$$2Me_3SiOH \rightarrow Me_3SiOSiMe_3 + H_2O,$$

a reaction which can be considered as the silylation of silanol. He found that Me_3SiOH also reacted with the solvent in a reversible reaction,

$$Me_3SiOH + MeOH \rightleftharpoons Me_3SiOMe + H_2O,$$

and he incorporated the study of this reaction into his rate data, as the Me_3SiOMe so formed reacted with silanol to give $Me_3SiOSiMe_3$ also. The reaction was catalyzed by acid or base, hydrochloric acid being 500 times as effective as potassium hydroxide. Grubb proposed a bimolecular rate determining step. For acid catalysis:

$$Me_3Si-OH \ + \ Me_3Si-\overset{+}{\underset{H}{O}}-CH_3 \ \leftrightarrows \ \left[Me_3Si-\overset{+}{\underset{H}{O}}---\overset{\overset{Me \ Me}{\diagdown \diagup}}{\underset{Me}{Si}}---\overset{H}{\underset{}{O}}-CH_3 \right] \ \leftrightarrows$$

$$Me_3Si-O-SiMe_3 \ + \ H^+ \ + \ CH_3OH$$

For base catalysis:

$$Me_3Si-O^- \ + \ Me_3Si-OCH_3 \ \leftrightarrows \ \left[Me_3Si-\overset{-}{O}---\overset{\overset{Me \ Me}{\diagdown \diagup}}{\underset{Me}{Si}}---OCH_3 \right] \ \leftrightarrows$$

$$Me_3Si-O-SiMe_3 \ + \ CH_3O^-$$

Langer *et al.* (452) postulated the same type of mechanism for the reactions of alcohols and amines with hexamethyldisilazane. They proposed as an intermediate,

$$R-X: \ \rightarrow \ \overset{\overset{Me \ Me}{\diagdown \diagup}}{\underset{H \quad Me}{Si}}----\overset{H}{\underset{H}{N}}\overset{+}{----}SiMe_3 \qquad (X = O \text{ or } NH)$$

Protonation of the reagent was assumed because the addition of a drop of TMCS catalyzed the reaction, and a pellet of potassium hydroxide retarded it. (Unlike silanol, alcohols and amines do not form salts with hydroxide. With phenols, as with silanols, hydroxide acts as a catalyst.)

Pump and Wannagat (598) proposed three mechanisms for the reaction of amides with hexamethyldisilazane, all of which involved nucleophilic attack on silicon by nitrogen. Ismail (367) found that the reaction of phenols with HMDS was catalyzed by 0.5 mole-% alkali. He proposed the following sequence:

$$2Me_3SiNHSiMe_3 \ + \ 2PhO^- \ \rightarrow \ 2Me_3SiNH^- \ + \ 2Me_3SiOPh$$

$$2Me_3SiNH^- \ + \ 2PhOH \ \rightarrow \ 2Me_3SiNH_2 \ + \ 2 \ PhO^-$$

$$2Me_3SiNH_2 \ \rightarrow \ (Me_3Si)_2NH \ + \ NH_3$$

When the silylating reagent is trimethylchlorosilane (TMCS), we find again a similarity in proposals regarding mechanism. Henglein and

Scheinost (314) silylated the hydroxyl group in glucose and pectins with TMCS in formamide, with varying amounts of pyridine. They interpreted their results as follows:

Others have postulated similar mechanisms. Birkofer *et al.* (70) proposed the same pyridine–TMCS complex in their study of the cleavage of N-carbobenzoxyamino acids by TMCS and pyridine. Prey and Kubadinow (596) and Horii *et al.* (334) also proposed the same sequence as Henglein and Scheinost, but in none of these cases is there evidence for the TMCS–pyridine complex that could not be explained by considering pyridine merely as a HCl acceptor or catalyst for the decomposition of formamide. Sweeley and Vance (767) raised a major objection to the proposed mechanism as pyridinium chloride alone did not catalyse the reaction of glucose and HMDS in pyridine. Giessler (27) postulates a similar inter-

mediate, $R_3Si–NEt_3^+ Cl^-$, when triethylamine is substituted for pyridine.

Klebe and Bush (420) studied the rate of silylation of alcohols by N-trimethylsilylacetanilides, and found the reaction to be first order in alcohol and in silylamide. The second order rate constant decreased when t-butyl alcohol was substituted for ethyl alcohol.

Several kinetic studies have been made of solvolysis reactions of tri-methylsilyl derivatives, and such evidence is pertinent as it involves silylation of solvent. McInnes (519) made a kinetic study of the preferential alcoholysis of the 6-TMS group in 2,3,4,6-tetra-O-trimethylsilyl-α-D-glucose (R'OTMS). The rate was second order depending on [R'OTMS] and [OR$^-$]. If a bulkier alcohol was used, the rate decreased. The mechanism was thought to be S_N2 or to involve a pentacovalent intermediate; thermodynamic values calculated indicated that the activated complex was highly polar. Similar studies have been made on Me_3SiOPh (18) and on menthoxytrimethylsilane (747, p 130). The solvolysis of both are second order and are catalyzed by acid or base. For Me_3SiOPh base catalysis is more effective, and for menthoxytrimethylsilane acid catalysis is better.

Thus, while conclusive evidence for a mechanism is lacking, the various authors do agree that (1) the rate determining step in trimethylsilylation reactions is bimolecular and (2) the transition state or intermediate involves nucleophilic substitution on silicon.

Relevant Mechanism Studies on Other Silyl Compounds. Swain *et al.* (762) studied the rate of hydrolysis of Ph_3SiF and Ph_3CF, and found sharp differences which, they concluded, meant that a siliconium ion did not form. They proposed a pentacovalent intermediate, **7**, as being consistent with his results. They used substituted phenyl compounds and showed that the charge on the silicon in the intermediate must be less positive than in the ground state (*e.g., p*-methyl substitution decreases the rate). In their 1953 review article comparing carbon and silicon, Gilman and Dunn (273) agreed with Swain, pointing out also that strain from three phenyl groups in the tetrahedral state is less in the silyl group than in the carbon system, therefore there is less need to gain planarity by ion formation. Rochow (619) also accpted Swain's work, but suggested that more detailed kinetic studies were needed. It should be noted here that Me_3SiX hydrolyzes more readily than Ph_3SiX, the reverse of the situation with carbon compounds. This is plausible if both go through a pentacovalent intermediate, whereas with carbon compounds the mechanism is different for each type.

$$\text{7} \qquad\qquad \text{8} \qquad\qquad \text{9}$$

Eaborn (205) reviews solvolysis data in compounds where the rate is sufficiently diminished by steric hindrance to be measurable, for example i-Pr_3SiCl and ROH at $0°$. This particular reaction is base-catalyzed and second order, and the following mechanism was proposed (Allen and Modena, 21):

$$BH + R'OSiR_3 + Cl^-$$

However, Eaborn reasoned that since (1) a bridgehead halide such as **8** does hydrolyze (unlike its carbon analog), (2) silicon has $3d$ orbitals available, and (3) steric hindrance to substitution is usually greater than expected, a "flank attack" could occur, as in **9**. He also felt that a transition state complex rather than an intermediate might be involved, making clear that such a pentacovalent intermediate should have a definite life and therefore would be detectable. Chipperfield and Prince (161) investigated this problem, which will be discussed later, and did not find evidence for a stable intermediate. They studied the hydrolysis rates of R_3SiCl in ether or acetone with the addition of aqueous acetone, measured by changes in conductivity due to the HCl produced. Their results confirmed conclusions of Swain *et al.* (762) that electrons supplied to silicon retard the reaction rate; therefore in the transition state the formation of the new bond is more important than breaking of the old.

With the synthesis and study of optically active silicon compounds, primarily by Sommer, verification of the above suggestions, based on kinetic data, could be made. Sommer has summarized much of this work in his book (747). The primary silyl compound used was α-naphthylphenyl-methylsilyl chloride, hereafter referred to as R_3Si^*Cl. Sommer has found that reactions of R_3Si^*X compounds are highly stereospecific, and he has assigned relative configuration to a great many compounds. The same stereochemistry revealed for R_3Si^*Cl has been found to apply also to RPhMeSiX where R = neopentyl, benzhydryl, or ethyl. Therefore one may with reasonable certainty apply it also to Me_3SiX chemistry.

Sommer found, *e.g.*, that inversion occurred in the following ether exchange:

$$(+)\text{-}R_3Si^*OMe + MeOH \xrightarrow[\text{base catalyst}]{\text{neutral, acid or}} (-)\text{-}R_3Si^*OMe + MeOH$$

Likewise with R_3Si^*Cl and a variety of reagents, HOE, (where E = H, K, Me, cyclo-C_6H_{11}, menthyl or t-Bu), in a variety of good to poor ionizing solvents (pentane, xylene, ether, chloroform, etc.) the reaction to form R_3Si^*OE and HCl proceeded rapidly and with predominate inversion. Therefore these silicon reactions seem to be proceeding exactly as the carbon S_N2 reaction (a Walden inversion). Sommer calls the silicon inversion reactions occurring with nucleophilic substitution S_N2-Si reactions. He does this because, in addition to the obvious similarities to S_N2 mechanism of carbon (inversion via trigonal bipyramid geometry, 'long bonds' to leaving and entering group, etc.), there are also important differences.

One difference is that S_N2-Si *can* proceed with retention of configuration. This happens with the bridgehead silyl halides referred to earlier. These compounds possess less internal strain than their carbon analogs and react rapidly, because of the availability of *d*-orbital participation. Transition states such as follows can be pictured, where the transition state may involve either tetragonal pyramidal or trigonal bipyramidal geometry. (Y is the entering group, the nucleophile.)

Another difference is participation by the $3d_{z^2}$ or $3d_{x^2-y^2}$ orbital to lower the free energy of the transition state—or at least the possibility of this participation. Still a third difference is that $3d$ orbital involvement affects the participation of substituent groups, making silicon quite electron-rich in the transition state compared with the ground state (*i.e.*, rho in the Hammett equation can be positive and larger for silicon than for carbon).

Sommer has also shown that, while S_N2-Si is by far the most common mechanism for silicon substitution, several other mechanisms can operate. These will be mentioned only briefly here; the evidence for them is detailed by Sommer (747). S_Ni-Si is a retention reaction involving a cyclic transition state such as shown here, where EY is the acceptor molecule:

This state occurs only in nonpolar solvents, and then only if X is a poor leaving group, *i.e.* not able to accommodate a negative charge well in the transition state. S_N2^*-Si involves a pentacovalent silicon intermediate where the rate determining step is the *breakdown* of the intermediate. This is rare, occurring primarily with fluorides. S_N2^{**}-Si involves again a pentacovalent intermediate, but with its *formation* being rate determining, and its breakdown rapid. This mechanism is extremely rare. A potentially more important mechanism is the S_N1-Si type. R_3Si*Cl did give racemization with Cl in extremely polar solvents, such as CH_3CN, CH_3NO_2 and $PhNO_2$, indicating ionization as the rate determining step. Sommer feels that there are intimate *or* solvent separated ion pairs, $(R_3Si*)^+----Cl^-$, rather than free ions.

Later work by Sommer *et al.* (748) on the silicon—nitrogen bond shows that reaction of R_3Si*Cl with amines (pyrrolidine, iso-butylamine) also gives inversion of configuration, as would be expected. The same result was obtained by Rühlmann *et al.* (648), where R_3Si*Cl reacted with $R'NH_2$ in pentane or ether with inversion ($R' = Me, Bu, C_6H_{11}, PhCH_2$). The hydrolysis or alcoholysis of the resulting silylamine, $R_3Si*NHR$; also occurred, with inversion (400, 648) if conditions allowed protonation, or with retention of configuration if protonation is not allowed.

Probable Mechanism of Trimethylsilylation. One can now apply the theory outlined above to the reaction,

$$HY + Me_3SiX \rightleftharpoons Me_3SiY + HX$$

Since the entering group, Y, is usually a stronger base than the leaving group, X, and since the solvent is usually one of moderate polarity, S_N2-Si is the usual mechanism of the reaction. The transition state of the reaction (in a neutral solution) would be

$$\overset{\displaystyle R\ R}{\underset{\displaystyle H\quad R}{\overset{\delta+}{Y}----\overset{\diagdown\diagup}{\underset{|}{Si}}----\overset{\delta-}{X}}}$$

However, in Sommer's words (747, p 126), there is "evidence for the existence of a wide range of polar mechanisms for organosilicon reactions." Therefore one must watch for the possibility of S_Ni-Si if X does not readily accommodate a negative charge and if the solvent is nonpolar, and for the possibility of S_N1-Si if the solvent is highly polar and the basicity of Y is approximately equal to that of X. Catalysis will also be very important, with acid or base catalysis being favored, depending on the exact nature of Y and X. This will be developed in section 4-3.

Transition State Versus an Intermediate. The above S_N2-Si mechanism has been shown as involving a transition state in which X and Y are breaking and forming bonds with Si, rather than involving an intermediate where X and Y are bound to Si by normal covalent bonds. It was mentioned in the first section that penta- and hexacovalently bonded silicon compounds are known. Among the pentacovalent compounds, which appear to have a trigonal bipyramid geometry such as is associated with dsp³ hybridization, **10**, are triptych-siloxazolidines (252), also known as sila-tranes (821), $[Ph_3Si(bipyridyl)]^+$ (173), **12** (251), and dimethylsilyl-amine pentamer (638). The hexacovalent substances appear to all be

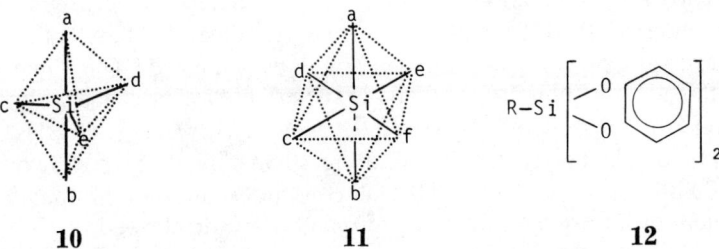

| **10** | **11** | **12** |

octahedral, with d²sp³ hybridization, **11**, and include SiF_6 (757), MeSiCl-(acetylacetonyl)₂ (524), and $SiF_4 \cdot 2NMe_3$ (205). This sort of data made the existence of an intermediate plausible in all silicon reactions. However, all attempts to detect one with R_3SiX have failed. Chipperfield and Prince (161), in experimental work referred to earlier in this section, examined the hydrolysis rates of i-Pr₃SiCl closely for formation of any intermediate and found the same rate at 4.5 milliseconds as at 20 seconds. Therefore any intermediate formation would have to have been extremely rapid. Sommer (747, pp 64, 73) concludes that a stable intermediate with five equivalent bonds to silicon does not exist for Me₃SiX but rather there is a transition state similar to that of carbon in S_N2 reactions. As more negative groups are bonded to silicon, the mechanism gradually changes to a stable intermediate formation, as shown in the following:

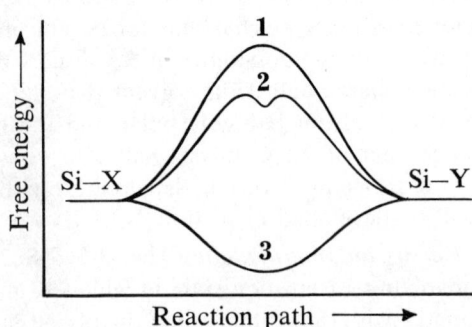

1. Transition state such as in S_N2-Si reactions.
2. Unstable intermediate such as in S_N2^*Si or S_N2^{**}-Si reactions.
3. Stable pentacovalent intermediate.

This agrees with Jaffe's conclusions (375) after molecular orbital studies, namely, that valence shell d-orbital involvement was important only if the central atom were positively charged, or if it had at least 10% contribution from a resonance form where it was positively charged. Sommer (747, p 185) does propose d_z^2 orbital participation in the transition state and feels this participation stabilizes the transition state, lowering the activation energy for silicon more than for carbon compounds, and explaining their ready reactivity.

4-3. STRUCTURE-ACTIVITY RELATIONSHIPS IN SILYLATION

Introduction. Most systematic studies of structure-reactivity effects in silicon substitution reactions have been made on the substituents of silicon, where steric effects play a large role. With Me₃Si- we have a constant factor here and, as we have seen, the fastest reaction rate. However, in the reaction postulated,

$$
HY: \ + \ \underset{\underset{Me}{\diagdown}}{\overset{\overset{Me}{\diagup}}{Me-Si-X}} \ \rightarrow \
\left[
\begin{array}{c}
Me \ Me \\
\overset{\delta+}{Y:} \ \diagdown \diagup \ \overset{\delta-}{X} \\
--- Si --- \\
| \quad | \\
H \quad Me
\end{array}
\right]
\ \rightarrow \ \underset{\underset{Me}{\diagdown}}{\overset{\overset{Me}{\diagup}}{Y-Si-Me}} \ + \ HX,
$$

several other factors should be considered: catalytic effects, the nature of X, the nature of Y, solvent effects, and equilibrium effects. A discussion of each of these effects should explain the difference in donor and acceptor abilities discussed in Chapter 1.

Catalytic Effects. Many examples of acid or base catalyzed silylations have already been given. In some cases a silylation was catalyzed by either, but better by one than by the other.

Base catalysis can function in the way postulated by Allen and Modena (21) and by Chipperfield and Prince (161), *i.e.* by aiding in the removal of the proton in the transition state.

$$
\begin{array}{cc}
& Me \ Me \\
& \diagdown \diagup \quad \delta- \\
& Y --- Si --- X \\
\delta+ & | \qquad | \\
B --- H & Me
\end{array}
$$

It also can function in *complete* removal of the proton from stronger acids, *e.g.* phenols and carboxylic acids (367). In this case the reaction proceeds as follows, with Y⁻ as the nucleophile and (2) as the rate determining step:

$$HY + B^- \rightarrow Y^- + HB \tag{1}$$

$$Y^- + Me_3Si-X \rightarrow \left[\begin{array}{c} \overset{Me}{\diagdown} \overset{Me}{\diagup} \\ \overset{\delta-}{Y} ---- \overset{|}{Si} ---- \overset{\delta-}{X} \\ | \\ Me \end{array} \right] \rightarrow Y-\overset{Me}{\underset{Me}{Si}}-Me + X^- \tag{2}$$

$$X^- + HB \rightarrow HX + B^- \tag{3}$$

Still a third possible mode of base catalysis is that postulated by Henglein and Scheinost (314), Birkofer *et al.* (70), Horii *et al.* (334), and Prey and Kubadinow (596), mentioned earlier, where the base (pyridine or triethylamine) first reacts by substitution with Me₃SiCl. This product then is itself substituted by HY. This would involve two Walden inversions, which suggests a way of testing the hypothesis. Wannagat and Schwarz (839) found however that no complex was formed (no heat evolution) from pyridine and Me₃SiCl. What appears to be base catalysis by pyridine may be a solvation of Me₃SiCl, merely weakening the Si–Cl bond for nucleophilic substitution. Or, the apparent catalysis of pyridine with Me₃SiCl may be due only to its effective removal of HCl, a product of the reaction.

In acid catalysis, protonation of the silyl donor occurs, weakening the Si–X bond. When Me₃SiNHSiMe₃ (HMDS) is the reagent protonation to Me₃SiN̂H₂SiMe₃ seems necessary for good donor ability (452). In general terms, acid catalysis can be expressed as follows:

$$Me_3SiX + H^+ \rightarrow Me_3Si\overset{+}{X}H \tag{1}$$

$$HY + Me_3Si\overset{+}{X}H \rightarrow \left[\begin{array}{c} \overset{Me}{\diagdown} \overset{Me}{\diagup} \\ \overset{\delta+}{Y} ---- \overset{|}{Si} ---- \overset{\delta+}{X}-H \\ | \quad\quad | \\ H \quad\quad Me \end{array} \right] \rightarrow \overset{+}{Y}-SiMe_3 + HX \tag{2}$$

$$\overset{+}{\underset{H}{Y}}-SiMe_3 \rightarrow H^+ + Y-SiMe_3 \tag{3}$$

The rate determining step would be (2). In the last step the proton could be removed by HY, functioning as a proton transfer agent; the reactive species of the acceptor is HY, however.

The Nature of X in the TMS Donor. The nature of the leaving group, X, is very important in several ways. The silylation reagents are characterized by what we might call good leaving groups. Factors that characterize a good leaving group are: low basicity, ability to stabilize a negative charge in the transition state, and little or no $p \rightarrow d$ bonding with the silicon.

X should be a weaker base than Y; formation of the transition state is reversible. Chloride is, of course, a very weak base. But in other silylators X does not seem so weak, *e.g.* HMDS or $RCONHSiMe_3$; hence it is apparent that the other factors are very important. Klebe and Bush (420) have studied the silylating ability of N-TMS-acetanilides and have found that N-TMS-*p*-nitroacetanilide is a better donor than the *p*-methyl compound, which indicates that less electron availability on the nitrogen likewise increases donor ability. However, N-methyl-N-TMS-acetamide is a better donor than N-TMS-acetanilide, which is presumed due to the conjugative donation of electrons from the benzene ring to the nitrogen. Sommer (747, p 147) also concludes that a decrease in pK_a of the conjugate acid of X, HX, will bring an increase in rate of reaction with a nucleophile. Thus, the trimethylsilyl amides make better silylating agents than do trimethylsilylamines.

The ability of X to accommodate a negative charge in the transition state is a very important factor in neutral or base catalyzed silylations. Sommer (747, pp 58-59) illustrates this with the difference in solvolysis between R_3Si^*OR' and R_3Si^*OCOR'. The two X groups, OR and OCOR, differ little in polarity or size, but the latter is far more reactive. In fact, under conditions where it gives a S_N2-Si inversion solvolysis, R_3SiOR' reacts only in a S_Ni-Si retention reaction. The difference can be seen in the ability of OCOR' to stabilize the developing negative charge in the transition state, thereby lowering its free energy of activation.

$$
\begin{array}{c}
\overset{R}{}\,\overset{R}{} \\
\overset{\delta+}{Y} - - - \overset{\backslash /}{\underset{|}{Si}} - - - \overset{\delta-}{OR'} \\
\overset{|}{H} \quad \overset{|}{R}
\end{array}
\qquad vs.
$$

$$
\begin{array}{c}
\overset{R\ R}{} \qquad O \\
\overset{\delta+}{Y} - - - \overset{\backslash /}{\underset{|}{Si}} - - - \overset{\delta-}{\underset{}{O}} \overset{||}{-} CR' \quad \longleftrightarrow \quad \overset{\delta+}{Y} - - - \overset{\backslash /}{\underset{|}{Si}} - - - O \overset{\delta-}{\overset{||}{=}} CR' \\
\overset{|}{H} \quad \overset{|}{R} \qquad\qquad\qquad\qquad \overset{|}{H} \quad \overset{|}{R}
\end{array}
$$

The same principle explains the superior donor ability of N-TMS-amides or ureas in comparison with TMS-amines, HMDS, or TMCS, *e.g.*

$$\overset{\delta+}{Y} - - - \overset{\overset{\displaystyle Me}{\diagdown}\overset{\displaystyle Me}{\diagup}}{\underset{\displaystyle Me}{Si}} - - - \overset{\delta-}{NHR'} \qquad vs.$$

$$\overset{\delta+}{Y} - - - \overset{\overset{\displaystyle Me}{\diagdown}\overset{\displaystyle Me}{\diagup}}{\underset{\displaystyle Me}{Si}} - - - \overset{\delta-}{NH} - \overset{\overset{\displaystyle O}{\|}}{C}R' \longleftrightarrow \overset{\delta+}{Y} - - - \overset{\overset{\displaystyle Me}{\diagdown}\overset{\displaystyle Me}{\diagup}}{\underset{\displaystyle Me}{Si}} - - - NH = \overset{\overset{\displaystyle \delta- }{\overset{\displaystyle O}{\|}}}{C}R'$$

It explains why N-TMS-imidazole is a good silylator, compared to other amines.

$$\overset{\delta+}{Y} - - - \overset{\overset{\displaystyle Me}{\diagdown}\overset{\displaystyle Me}{\diagup}}{\underset{\displaystyle Me}{Si}} - - - \overset{\delta-}{N} \longleftrightarrow \overset{\delta+}{Y} - - - \overset{\overset{\displaystyle Me}{\diagdown}\overset{\displaystyle Me}{\diagup}}{\underset{\displaystyle Me}{Si}} - - - N$$

In BSA, the negative charge can be distributed not only as in the mono-TMS-amides, but also to the silicon by $p \rightarrow d$ bonding (420). In acid catalysis, the leaving group is protonated and therefore leaves as a neutral molecule. Here its ability to be protonated may be important; *e.g.*, TMS-diethylamine is a better silylator than TMS-n-butylamine since diethylamine is a stronger base (pK_b, 2.90) than n-butylamine (pK_b, 3.39).

A decrease in $p \rightarrow d$ bonding of X to silicon should also increase the ease of silyl donation. At the conclusion of section 4-2 it was suggested that the d_{z^2} orbital of silicon might be involved in bonding in the transition state. The d_{xz} orbital is also available for unshared electron pairs on X to interact with:

d_{xz} orbital for $(p \rightarrow d)\pi$ bond

$d_{z^2}-p$ hybrid orbital for sigma bond

Such interaction would shorten and strengthen the Si—X bond. Therefore a decrease in this type of bonding should improve donor ability. Competition for the unshared electrons within X would be one way of doing this, so this effect would be indistinguishable from the negative charge stabilization discussed above. Competition for the d orbital of silicon would also accomplish a decrease in X—Si $p{\rightarrow}d$ bonding. Whether this could occur by solvation is unknown. Protonation of the X group effectively destroys $p{\rightarrow}d$ bonding also.

Klebe (419) has recently proposed another explanation for the good donor ability of silylamides. In the NMR of disiloxadiazines, reversible intramolecular rearrangements were found to occur at two temperature levels. One explanation of this is that one of the silicon atoms is coordinated to an amide oxygen by an expanded shell, the other silicon remaining tetrahedral. At the lower temperature the coordinated oxygen shifts, at the higher temperature the coordinated silicon converts to uncoordinated and vice versa. Klebe proposes the following displacement of amide from a silylamide by alcohol as an extension of his conclusions on the disiloxadiazines:

$$R^3OSiR_3 \ + \ R^2CONHR^1$$

This idea, while attractive, is as yet unsubstantiated, but it emphasizes the complexities that may be involved in the interaction of the silicon center and the leaving group.

In summary, and referring to Table 1-3, donor ability is improved for HMDS by acid catalysis, for TMCS by base catalysis [They thus may catalyse each other (452).], and for TMS amines and amides by acid catalysis. As an alkyl group is substituted by an aryl or acetyl group donor ability is enhanced by ability to stabilize a negative charge in the transition state and by decreased $p{\rightarrow}d$ interaction. In BSA these last two factors reach an optimum.

The Nature of Y in the TMS Acceptor. In considering the nature of HY, the molecule being silylated, it is apparent that the strength of Y as a nucleophile is very important. The order established experimentally in Table 1-1 shows that O—H compounds are, in general, more easily silylated than N—H compounds. Since amines are stronger bases than alcohols, this may seem contradictory; but O—H compounds will also be stronger acids than N—H compounds and loss of hydrogen is involved in the reaction as well as the nucleophilic character of Y. Several factors operate in making oxygen more effective: (1) oxygen has two pairs of unshared electrons available while nitrogen has only one, (2) the oxygen electrons are sterically more available as the atom is bonded to only one group other than hydrogen and nitrogen in secondary amines is bonded to two, and (3) the greater $p{\rightarrow}d$ bonding possibility at Si—O in comparison with Si—N can lower the energy of the former transition state. Ease of silylation decreases in order ROH $\rightarrow$ PhOH $\rightarrow$ RCOOH $\rightarrow$ PhCOOH because the oxygen electron pairs are increasingly used in conjugative effects within the molecule:

$$R—\overset{..}{\underset{..}{O}}—H, \qquad \overset{:O:}{\underset{\shortparallel}{RC}}—\overset{..}{\underset{..}{O}}—H \longleftrightarrow RC{=}\overset{+}{\underset{..}{O}}—H$$

It should be noted that basic catalysts will be very effective in promoting reactions of these acceptors, especially the phenols and acids.

Decreasing easy of silylation $RNH_2 \rightarrow RCONH_2 \rightarrow RCONHSiMe_3$ can also be explained similarly—increased use of the unshared nitrogen electrons within the molecule.

$$R—\overset{..}{N}H_2, \qquad \overset{:O:}{\underset{\shortparallel}{R—C}}—NH_2 \longleftrightarrow R—C{=}\overset{+}{N}H_2$$

$$\overset{:O:}{\underset{\shortparallel}{R—C}}—NH—SiMe_3 \longleftrightarrow R—C{=}\overset{+}{N}H—SiMe_3$$

$$\searrow \quad \overset{:O:}{\underset{\shortparallel}{R—C}}—\overset{+}{N}H{=}\overset{-}{Si}Me_3 \quad \nearrow$$

The differences in order of reactivity of alcohols and of amines cannot be explained by inductive effects. From inductive effects, secondary alcohols and amines should be better nucleophiles than primary, and tertiary alcohols still more so. This is not the case. As in carbon S_N2 reactions steric effects are important here, where the differences in basicity are not very great anyway, and the oxygen or nitrogen electrons are sterically shielded from ready access to the silicon atom. Steric effects are also observed with some molecules in other classes. Intramolecular hydrogen bonding, such as in salicylic acid, may also affect ease of silylation of groups.

Another factor is the effect of certain combinations of X and Y. For example, the expected order of reactivity may be changed. Mason and Smith (513) found that hexanoic acid alone reacted well with HMDS, while 1-octanol and 1-octylamine reacted in poor yield. One explanation is that hexanoic acid protonates the HMDS, but the alcohol and amine cannot. Hence hexanoic acid is both catalyst and silyl acceptor. This reasoning was verified, as when TMCS and HMDS were used together, the alcohol reacted as readily as the acid, and the amine yield improved also.

Another X-Y combination factor is in effect when HY is very weakly nucleophilic and the leaving group does not readily accommodate a negative charge. Here a S_Ni-Si mechanism may prevail. Pump and Wannagat (598, 832), for example, give evidence favoring the following transition state for the silylation of amides with HMDS (no other solvent was used):

$$
\begin{array}{c}
\text{H} \\
| \\
\text{R}'_3\text{Si—N—SiR}'_3 \\
\uparrow \quad \downarrow \\
| \\
\text{H}_2\text{N—C}^+\text{—R} \\
| \\
\text{O}^-
\end{array}
\quad \rightarrow \quad \text{R}'_3\text{SiNH}_2 \; + \; \text{RCONHSiR}'_3
$$

$$2\,\text{R}'_3\text{SiNH}_2 \rightarrow \text{R}'_3\text{SiNHSiR}'_3 \; + \; \text{NH}_3$$

If this mechanism is correct, it would explain why amides and TMCS do not react directly (*i.e.,* without base) (834). (Also if this mechanism is correct, it is not a true silylation as defined in the Introduction.)

A final factor to consider in the nature of HY is its solubility in the reaction medium. This has posed some problems, especially with amides, where highly polar solvents such as acetonitrile have had to be used at times (420).

Solvent Effects. A systematic study of solvent effects is lacking. As stated in Chapter 1, temperature factors have not always been separated from solvent effects. In general, the more polar solvents seem to favor faster reaction than nonpolar solvents. This is to be expected when the transition state involves separation of charge. For acid catalyzed reactions, $HY + TMS\overset{+}{X}H$, or for base catalyzed reactions, $Y^- + TMSX$, however, there would be less need of polar solvents, as far as stabilization of the transition state is concerned. However, they may still be necessary to dissolve the TMS acceptor, as pointed out above.

Although S_N1-Si reactions may occur in very polar solvents, it will be remembered, evidence that they do is lacking. However, with a good donor like BSA in a solvent like acetonitrile, this possibility should be considered. The evidence of Klebe and co-workers (420, 422) and Pump and Rochow (597) for rapid intramolecular $SiMe_3$ interchange also lends plausibility to this possibility. However, if a true S_N1-Si reaction were occurring, the nature of HY should have no effect on rate. Although BSA is a universally good donor, it does act at significantly different rates with various acceptors (350, 422). Klebe and Bush (420) state that there are pronounced solvent effects on equilibrium position and on rates in silyl transfer reactions. Kriegsmann (443) has shown that in a group of trialkyl and triaryl silanes the solvent has as great an influence on the IR stretching frequencies as do the silicon substituents. Clearly more work is needed on solvent effects.

Equilibrium Effects. The trimethylsilylation mechanism as proposed is reversible. This fact cannot be ignored, as very often the silylation conditions are set up to drive the reaction to completion in a way that overrides the structural differences just discussed. For example, from the work of Wannagat and co-workers referred to earlier (598, 832), the weak nucleophile, an amide, normally would seem an unlikely candidate for silylation by the unprotonated HMDS:

$$2RCONH_2 + 2Me_3SiNHSiMe_3 \leftrightarrows$$
$$2RCONHSiMe_3 + (Me_3Si)_2NH + NH_3$$

but by refluxing and driving the NH_3 from the reaction mixture silylation does occur, and in good yield.

Or, consider the silylation of alcohols with TMCS:

$$ROH + Me_3SiCl \leftrightarrows ROSiMe_3 + HCl$$

This reaction is not only reversible but there is a side reaction of olefin formation if R is secondary or tertiary. Therefore the prominent role of pyridine, triethylamine, and other bases in TMCS reactions may be only in removal of HCl, thus driving the reaction to the right, rather than in any true catalytic activity such as has been suggested by some authors and discussed earlier in this section.

As stated in section 1-3, a 10- to 50-fold ratio of silylating agent to functional group is commonly used, and this of course helps to drive the reaction to completion, which is important in analytical work. Consequently ease of removal of the second reaction product or its noninterference in analytical work, is an important factor in the choice of silylating reagent.

Another outcome of reversibility is that the time allowed for reaction may be significant in determining the structure of the product. That is, the kinetically determined product may not be the thermodynamically stable one. Klebe and Bush (420) studied such a situation in the alcoholysis of bis(trimethylsilyl)-N-phenyl-N'-methylurea. The reaction occurred rapidly to give one product, and slowly rearranged at 1/1000 the rate of alcoholysis to the thermally stable product:

$$
\underset{\underset{Ph \quad Me}{|\qquad\quad|}}{Me_3SiN-\overset{\overset{O}{\|}}{C}-NSiMe_3}
\quad\xrightarrow[\text{fast}]{ROH}\quad
\underset{\underset{Ph \quad Me}{|\quad\quad|}}{HN-\overset{\overset{O}{\|}}{C}-NSiMe_3}
\quad\xrightarrow{\text{slow}}\quad
\underset{\underset{Ph \quad Me}{|\qquad\quad|}}{Me_3SiN-\overset{\overset{O}{\|}}{C}-NH}
$$

Klebe's work on silyl tautomerism also makes it clear that many complicating factors exist in silylation, and that prediction of product is not always possible where positions do not differ markedly. (Note: Silyl rearrangements catalysed by strong base, e.g. West et al. (856), are beyond the scope of this discussion. They are described in section 14-7.)

In addition to concentration and time factors in silylation reactions, temperature effects have also been noted (643) and these effects were attributed to shifting of equilibria.

Examples of reactions where the equilibrium of the reaction has been studied include: silyl amino acid–amine (641), silylamine–amine (224), silylester–amine (643), silylamine–alcohol (272), silylalkoxide–alcohol (205, p 295ff), and silylamide–amide (420). Reactions of silylamides with alcohols, amines or acids (420) are substantially irreversible because the equilibrium lies so far to the right. Results of these equilibrium studies in general agree with the conclusions one would draw from the discussion of the nature of X and Y above.

Conclusion. The interplay of the various factors discussed in this section can be illustrated by two actual silylations: the one, poor; the other, excellent.

An example of a poor silylation is the following (224):

$$2 \underset{}{\bigcirc}\text{NH} + \text{Me}_3\text{Si}-\text{NH}-\text{SiMe}_3 \leftrightarrows 2 \underset{}{\bigcirc}\text{N}-\text{SiMe}_3 + \text{NH}_3$$

Conditions: 2:1 molar ratio of piperidine:HMDS; refluxed 3 hours.
Result: 16% yield of silylpiperidine.
Reasons for poor yield:

(1) No acid catalyst used to protonate the nitrogen of HMDS, therefore X is a poor leaving group.
(2) HY (piperidine) is a fairly weak nucleophile, comparable to HX; a greater difference would be desirable.
(3) No stabilization of negative charge is possible in the transition state, except in increased $p{\to}d$ bonding:

$$\underset{\text{H}}{\overset{}{\bigcirc}}\overset{\delta+}{\text{N}}{:}---\underset{\underset{\text{Me}}{|}}{\overset{\overset{\text{Me Me}}{\diagdown\diagup}}{\text{Si}}}---\overset{\delta-}{\text{NH}}-\text{SiMe}_3$$

Reasons for reacting at all:

(1) With no solvent, the bases act as their own polar solvent, stabilizing the separation of charge in the transition state somewhat.
(2) Ammonia is being removed, which drives the reaction to the right.
(3) Piperidine, the acceptor, although it is a secondary amine, has no steric hindrance since the alkyl N-substituent is held back from front shielding of the nitrogen.

In contrast, an excellent silylation is the following (513):

$$2\text{C}_8\text{H}_{17}\text{OH} + \text{Me}_3\text{Si}-\text{NH}-\text{SiMe}_3 \xrightarrow{\text{TMCS}} 2\text{C}_8\text{H}_{17}\text{OSiMe}_3 + \text{NH}_3$$

Conditions: 100% molar excess of HMDS (1.5 ml), 0.01 ml TMCS, re-fluxed one hour.
Result: 97% yield of 1-trimethylsiloxyoctane.
Reasons for good yield:

(1) Acid catalyst protonates HMDS, decreasing $p{\to}d$ bonding to silicon and making X less basic.
(2) Octanol is a good nucleophile; Y is a much stronger base than HX.
(3) The excess of reagent drives the reaction.
(4) The ammonia is removed by refluxing, driving the reaction further.
(5) The reagents provide a polar medium, although this is less needed with a catalyst.

It is evident, then, that many factors affect the ease of silylation and the yield. More investigation is needed where all factors but one are held constant to arrive at a complete understanding of silylation.

4-4. THE SPECIAL CASE OF N- *VERSUS* O-SILYLATION

Simple Amides. Of the tautomeric forms of an amide, $RCONH_2$ and $RC(OH) = NH$, the former predominates, although both N- and O-alkyl derivatives can be made. It would seem, therefore, that both N- and O-trimethylsilyl derivatives could be prepared. Birkofer and Ritter (77) observed that the O-silyl form would be favored by the greater thermal stability of the Si—O bond in comparison with the Si—N bond, but that the N-silyl form would be favored by the continued possibility of amide resonance in the derivative.

Giessler (272) attempted to synthesize N- and O-TMS amides and found that the product of silylation did not depend on the method used. For simple alkyl amides IR, NMR, and dipole moment data showed that the product is the N-TMS-amide, $RCONHSiMe_3$ (where R = Me, Et, n-Pr, Cl_3C, Ph). O-Silylation may, in fact, occur first, with rapid tautomeric shift to the thermodynamically stable N-TMS-amide. It would seem then, that the continuation of amide resonance in the product is the important factor. That the N-TMS-amide should be the more stable can be shown by the following resonance forms:

$$
\begin{array}{ccc}
\overset{\text{O}}{\underset{\|}{}} & \overset{\text{O}^-}{\underset{|}{}} & \overset{\text{O}^-}{\underset{|}{}} \\
\text{R–C–NH–Si–Me}_3 \longleftrightarrow & \text{R–}\overset{+}{\text{C}}\text{–NH–SiMe}_3 \longleftrightarrow & \text{R–C}=\overset{+}{\text{N}}\text{H–SiMe}_3 \\
\text{I} & \text{Ia} & \text{Ib}
\end{array}
$$

$$
\begin{array}{ccc}
\overset{\text{OSiMe}_3}{\underset{|}{}} & \overset{\text{OSiMe}_3}{\underset{|}{}} & \overset{+\,\text{OSiMe}_3}{\underset{\|}{}} \\
\text{R–C}=\text{NH} \longleftrightarrow & \text{R–}\overset{+}{\text{C}}\text{–}\overset{-}{\text{NH}} \longleftrightarrow & \text{R–C–}\overset{-}{\text{NH}} \\
\text{II} & \text{IIa} & \text{IIb}
\end{array}
$$

The Ia form is far more important than the IIa form, as oxygen is more electronegative than nitrogen; likewise the Ib form is more stable than the IIb form, as nitrogen can better accommodate the positive charge than oxygen.

This reasoning also holds for secondary amides, where Giessler also found N-silylation in RCONHR′ (R = Me, R′ = Me, Et, Ph). However, Giessler found one exception to this generalization: N-vinylpropionamide. Here, on the basis of dipole moment and IR data, the O-silyl derivative was identified. This is understandable, as now forms like IIa and IIb above are further stabilized by resonance involving the vinyl group. Hence the O-silyl form is more stable than the N-silyl form for this amide:

$$
\overset{\text{OSiMe}_3}{\underset{\text{EtC}-\overset{+}{\text{N}}-\text{CH}=\text{CH}_2}{|}} \longleftrightarrow \overset{\overset{+}{\text{OSiMe}_3}}{\underset{\text{EtC}-\overset{-}{\text{N}}-\text{CH}=\text{CH}_2}{\|}} \longleftrightarrow \overset{\overset{+}{\text{OSiMe}_3}}{\underset{\text{EtC}-\text{N}=\text{CH}-\overset{-}{\text{CH}}_2}{\|}}
$$

Giessler (272) stated that the O-silyl and N-silyl forms do not exist together. However, Klebe and Bush (420) from work on silyl acetanilides, concluded that in some cases they do exist in tautomeric equilibrium. Their evidence came from NMR studies of silyl acetanilides. Below 10°, two signals appear for the protons of the trimethylsilyl group, but above 10° these two signals merge to one, which becomes sharper as the temperature rises. The other possible interpretation of their data, that of geometric isomerism, they discard since a compound incapable of such isomerism gives the same type of NMR data. The theory is further supported by data from substituted acetanilides, where they show that with electron-withdrawing substituents on the phenyl group the O-silyl form is favored and with electron-donating substituents, the N-form. The equilibrium constants for the tautomerism, **13**, were calculated.

13   **14**

The stabilization of the O-silyl form again can be explained on the basis of resonance contributions of the phenyl group (like those of the vinyl group just discussed) e.g., **14**. This tautomerism may be facilitated by the expanded octet structures of silicon, **15**, as suggested by Klebe (419).

15

In summary, then, simple amides tend to give N-silylation. However, if the amide is N-substituted by a group capable of giving resonance stabilization to the O-substituted form (but not to the N-substituted form), either a mixture of isomers (silyl tautomers) or the O-silylated form exclusively may result from silylation.

Cyclic Amides and Imides. Cyclic amides and imides are silylated as simple amides to yield N-silyl or O-silyl derivatives or both. For instance, lactams, such as caprolactam, **16**, undergoes N-silylation (272). So does succinimide (272), where the presence of the second carbonyl group evidently does not lend sufficient stability to the O-silyl form.

16   17

On the other hand, 2-pyridone, **17**, forms exclusively the O-derivative. Since 2-pyridone predominates in the equilibrium mixture with its tautomer, 2-hydroxypyridine (558), it is clearly not the amount of the reactive form which is significant, but the thermodynamic stability of the silylated product. The development of heteroaromaticity seems to be a stabilizing factor with cyclic amides and imides (77). Other compounds that give exclusively O-silylation are shown in the following examples from Giessler (272): barbituric acid, **18**; tetrahydropyridazine-3,6-dione, **19**; and tetrahydroquinoxaline-2,3-dione, **20**.

18

19

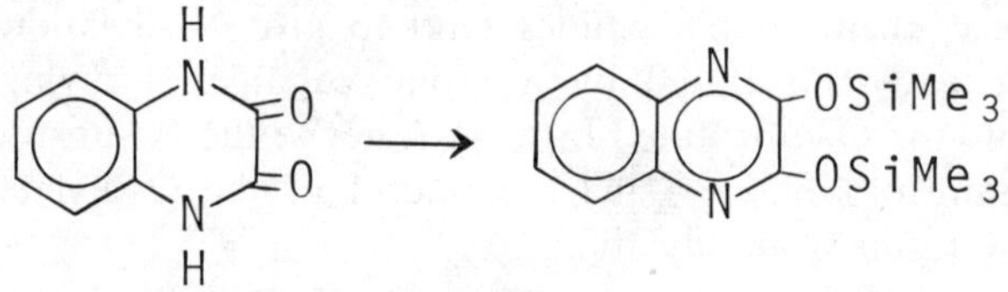

20

In each of the above cases heteroaromaticity is gained by O-silylation. The same can be true in a five-membered ring, 1-phenylpyrazolidine-3,5-dione, **21**.

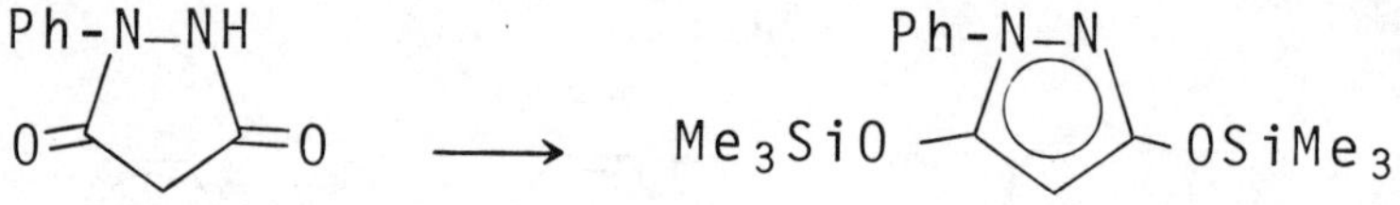

21

This is in contrast to the reaction of hydantoin, another 5-membered ring, where O-silylation would give rise to heteroaromaticity, but N-silylation occurs (272):

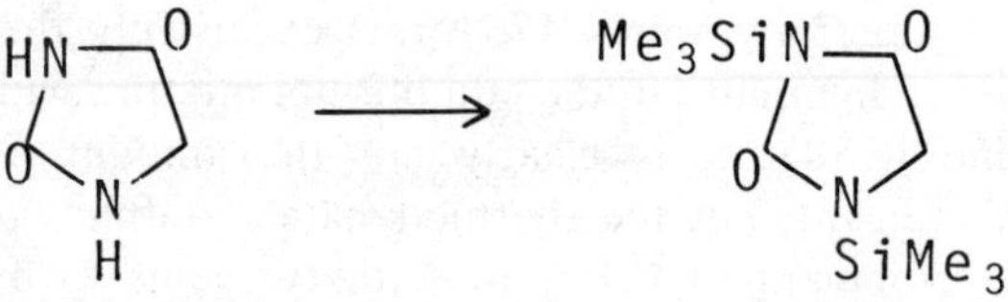

Both N- and O-silylation may occur in the same molecule; for example uric acid (272) and oxindole (422):

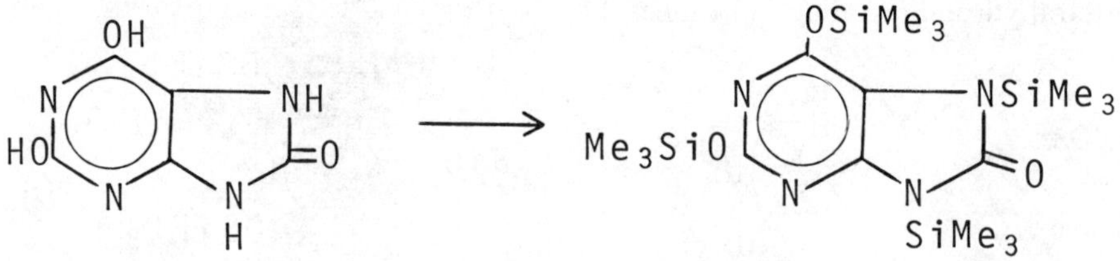

Uric acid

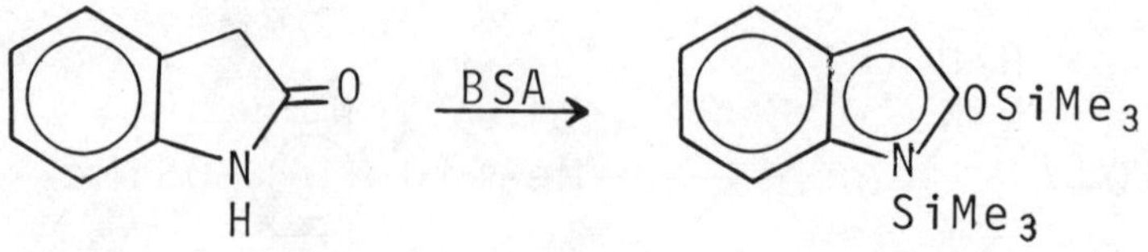

Oxindole

The latter example and that of 1-phenylpyrazolidine-3,5-dione, **21**, show how enolization can contribute to a stable heteroaromatic structure. The examples of hydantoin and uric acid indicate that in five-membered rings with two hetero nitrogen atoms aromaticity does not always result. Another example of work by Giessler that does not fit the general pattern is the reaction of thiazolidine-2,4-dione, **22**. Silylation gives, according to his IR data, the nonheteroaromatic system, **23**, rather than **24**.

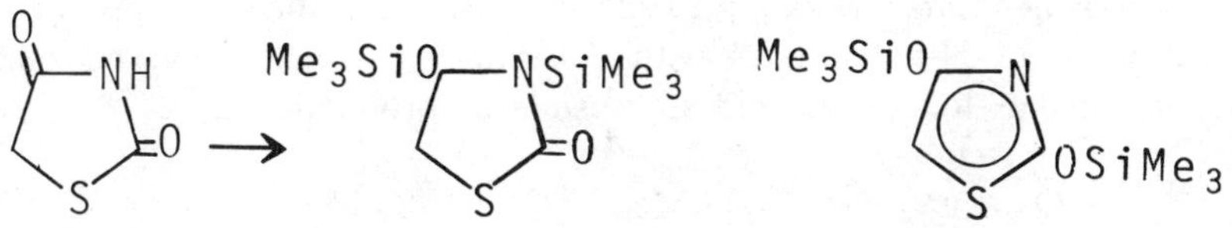

22   **23**   **24**

Some of these silylation products might, on further study, reveal the silyl tautomerism postulated by Klebe and Bush (420).

In two instances silylation produces tautomeric pairs of products: homodihydrocarbostyril, **25**, (420, 422); and 2,3-dihydroazepin-2-one, **26**, (Giessler, 272, as reinterpreted by Klebe and Bush, 420).

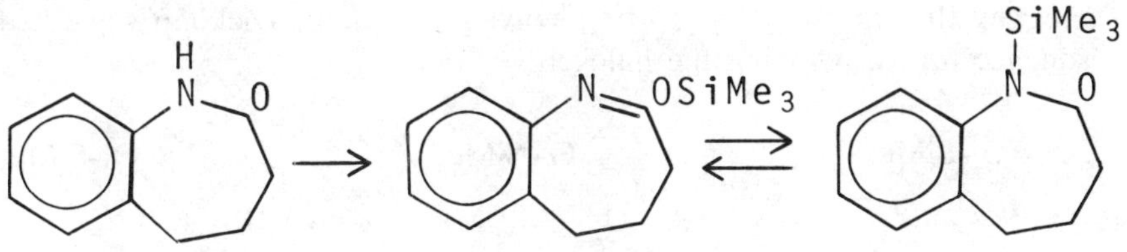

25

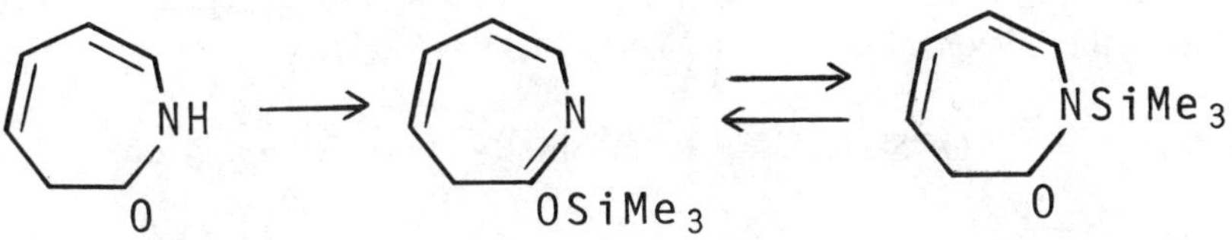

26

In the case of **25**, there is an analogy to the acetanilides which has been discussed. In **26** the O-silyl form has six pi electrons, which does not result in aromaticity in a seven membered ring. However, the three double bonds do afford a high degree of conjugation.

As with simple amides, then, cyclic amides and imides will give N-silylation unless there is significant resonance stabilization of the O-silyl form. If the resonance is heteroaromatic in character, O-silylation usually is exclusive. In some cases tautomerism exists (perhaps in many more as yet unstudied). In some compounds, both N-and O-silylation occur simultaneously because of structural differences in the molecule. In all cases it appears to be the thermodynamic stability of the product that determines the site of silylation.

N-Haloamides. Dickopp (192), also Birkofer and Dickopp (68), treated a group of N-haloamides with BSA or bis(trimethylsilyl)benzamide and obtained N-halo-iminoacid silyl esters as products.

$$(R = Me, Ph; X = Cl, Br; R' = Me, Ph)$$

N-trimethylsilylsuccinimide and N-trimethylsilylphthalimide were also used, with O-silylation resulting.

The halogen atoms therefore appear to stabilize the O-silyl form in the same way that the vinyl group or phenyl group does. Dickopp suggested resonance forms involving the halogen:

and others can be written. We arrive finally at a hybrid structure, **27**, which involves the silicon also.

syn-   anti-

27   **28**

In most of the previous cases of O-silylation of amides or imides, the ring structure permitted only one of two possible geometric isomers to exist. However, with the N-halo-iminoacid silyl esters syn- and anti- forms are possible, **28,** and Dickopp distinguished them by NMR. When R is methyl, the structure is anti; when R is phenyl, it is in the syn form. With R groups of intermediate size, a mixture of isomers, varying in proportion with temperature, is obtained.

The Structure of BSA. Bis(trimethylsilyl)acetamide has gained prominence as an excellent silylator. Its structure now is well established as N,O-bis(trimethylsilyl)acetamide, **29,** rather than the isomeric N,N-bis(trimethylsilyl)acetamide, **30.**

$$
CH_3-C
\begin{array}{c}
\nearrow OSiMe_3 \\
\searrow NSiMe_3
\end{array}
\qquad
CH_3-C
\begin{array}{c}
\nearrow O \\
\searrow N(SiMe_3)_2
\end{array}
\qquad
CH_3-C
\begin{array}{c}
\nearrow OEt \\
\searrow NSiMe_3
\end{array}
$$

29   **30**   **31**

However, problems in its structure determination were significant enough to warrant special consideration here. Several other bis(trimethylsilyl)-amides have also been synthesized (597), whose structure determination has paralleled that of BSA. The structure of bis(trimethylsilyl)trifluoroacetamide, however, was shown as the N,N-bis compound, analagous to **30** (898). No supporting evidence was given.

Krüger and Rochow (446) synthesized bis(TMS)benzamide. The IR spectrum of this molecule showed a band characteristic of the C—O—Si grouping (normally at 1010-1140 cm^{-1}), and lacked the 950-1000 cm^{-1} band that Si—N—Si should show. The NMR spectrum showed two close signals and the authors concluded it was the N,O-isomer, analagous to **29,** where the protons of the methyl groups of the N-silyl should give a slightly different signal than those of the methyl groups of the O-silyl. They discounted the possibility of geometric isomerism, as the relative area of the two peaks did not change with temperature. However, at higher temperature, *both* signals diminished and a new signal appeared, reversibly. This the authors interpreted at that time as a Chapman rearrangement of the N,N-bis(TMS)benzamide. (See Pump and Rochow, 597, for later conclusions.)

Giessler (272) considered the two possible structures for BSA, and found the IR spectrum like that of **31** and unlike that of the silylated secondary amides. The dipole moment of BSA, 1.27μ, also indicated an N,O-bis(TMS) structure. However, the NMR spectrum at room temperature gave only one SiMe$_3$ proton signal, instead of the expected two. Below

0° the signal split. Since the IR spectrum showed no change as low as -30°, isomerization was discarded by Giessler as a cause of the splitting. (A Chapman rearrangement such as postulated by Krüger and Rochow would show definite IR differences.) Giessler felt his evidence was inconclusive, but he favored the N,N-bis(TMS) structure, explaining the conflicting IR and dipole moment data by loss of amide resonance because of the unshared pair of electrons on the nitrogen being used by the two silicon atoms in ($p{\rightarrow}d$) bonding, **32**.

$$
\begin{array}{cc}
\underset{\textbf{32}}{
\begin{array}{c}
\text{O} \\
\parallel \\
\text{CH}_3\text{—C} \\
\diagdown \\
\text{N} \overset{\text{SiMe}_3}{\underset{\text{SiMe}_3}{}}
\end{array}
}
&
\underset{\textbf{33}}{
\begin{array}{c}
\text{O}^- \\
\diagup \\
\text{R—C} \\
\diagdown\!\!\diagdown \\
\overset{+}{\text{N}}(\text{SiMe}_3)_2
\end{array}
}
\end{array}
$$

However, he did not exclude the N,O-form, stating that the NMR of both SiMe$_3$ groups could fall together at higher temperature for some undetermined reason.

Pump and Rochow (597) later studied the NMR of six other bis(TMS) amides. A typical pattern for the SiMe$_3$ protons showed two sharp signals at lower temperature with a 1:1 intensity ratio; with rising temperature these two signals became lower and broader, finally fusing at a definite reproducible temperature to a single peak which became higher and sharper as the temperature rose. For BSA at -20° signals appear at 0.082 ppm and 0.162 ppm; and at 60°, one signal at 0.127 ppm, with a fusion temperature of 28°. This pattern is also typical of a hydrogen exchange.

Pump and Rochow propose three theories to explain this phenomenon: (1) N,O $\leftrightarrows$ N,N tautomerism; (2) N,N-bis-substitution with restricted rotation around the C—N bond resulting in geometric isomerism; and (3) intramolecular TMS group interchange between the N- and O- positions. Theory (1) they discard, since the IR spectrum does not change for selected compounds between 25° and 120°C (in agreement with Giessler's work and conclusions). Theory (2) is discarded because of IR data against the N,N form, and also because it is hard to see how the form, **33**, could be that important with the two silicon atoms also vying for the nitrogen electron pair. (The IR bands for C=O and C=N— overlap and are therefore useless in determining silyl positions.) Theory (3) is therefore favored. Here the exchange of trimethylsilyl groups between the nitrogen and oxygen is so rapid at higher temperatures that the instrument no longer differentiates the two positions—the two signals merge into one.

Klebe and co-workers (420, 422) accepted the conclusions of Pump and Rochow (597). Their observation of the same NMR phenomenon in a molecule incapable of two restricted rotational forms, trimethylsilyl-homodihydrocarbostyril, further dismisses theory (2) above. Their theory of acetanilide silyl tautomerism, discussed previously, emphasizes the mobility of the TMS group intramolecularly when two positions within the molecule do not differ greatly in stability.

The reactivity of BSA could, of course, be explained by either structure. The presence of the second TMS group competing for the unshared electrons of the nitrogen and oxygen weakens the bond of the first TMS group. The evidence, however, points to **29** as the structure, with the TMS groups oscillating between the two positions *within* the molecule.

5

Alcohols and Phenols

5-1. INTRODUCTION

This chapter includes alcohols, phenols and alicyclic hydroxy compounds. Esters of hydroxy fatty acids and phenolic acids and nonaromatic hydroxy compounds with tertiary nitrogen are also included. The divisions by table are for convenience only and do not indicate any significant class differences in preparation or properties of silyl derivatives.

Hydroxy compounds in general are the proton-active compounds most easily silylated and the products are relatively stable. Their stability is attested by the fact that the hydrolysis reaction, $2ArOSiMe_3 + H_2O \rightarrow 2ArOH + Me_3SiOSiMe_3$, can be reversed by azeotropic distillation of water (Method 51, section 1-10).

Most of the early work in silylation was done with alcohols, before the discovery of gas chromatography (GC), and hence more physical data have been reported for this class of compounds than for others, as the tables in this chapter will show. Many silyl ethers have been distilled and analysed for their elements. Most of the simple silyl monoethers have boiling points higher than those of the parent substances. In contrast, the silyl derivatives of the polyhydroxy compounds are far more volatile than the free compounds and many such substances have been analysed by GC for the first time through the use of silylation.

5-2. SILYLATION

The relative ease of silylation of alcoholic and phenolic hydroxyls has been documented in section 1-5. Steric considerations support the observed order of reactivity of alcohols: primary > secondary > tertiary. The tertiary alcohol group is not silylated by HMDS alone but in boiling dimethylformamide or dimethylsulfoxide the reaction proceeds (241). Higher charge temperature with the solvents may be a factor here. Tertiary hydroxyl groups in hop acids were not silylated by HMDS in DMF, apparently at room temperature (183). Also, HMDS with a catalytic amount of

TMCS did not silylate the tertiary aliphatic hydroxyl, whereas a mixture of equivalent weights of these reagents in petroleum ether produced the silyl ethers in good yield (452, 892). TMCS in pyridine was also effective (269). The presence of tertiary alcoholic groups in carotenoids was proved by their silylation with HMDS–TMCS in pyridine after attempted acetylation had failed (44, 45, 316, 317, 518). (Only primary and secondary hydroxyls can be acetylated.) Silylation of tertiary hydroxyls was demonstrated by spectrophotometric and paper chromatographic examination (316). The tertiary 6-hydroxyl of azafrin methyl ester, however, did not react (518).

Hindered aromatic hydroxyls are also encountered. Tri-t-alkylphenols were not silylated by HMDS–TMCS in pyridine but HMDS–TMCS in DMF reacted (244). The former reagent silylated 2,6-di-t-butylphenol, which indicates involvement of the *para* position. The p-hydroxyl group of the iodothyronines is not silylated even with BSA (709).

Henglein and Krämer (311) reported that TMCS silylates only one hydroxyl of pyrocatechol but *all three* of pyrogallol. Both pyrocatechol groups reacted with TMCS–formamide–pyridine. Similarly, TMCS alone silylates only positions 5, 7, 4' of catechin whereas all five hydroxyls react in formamide–pyridine (311).

Sprung (754) readily prepared 2-trimethylsiloxyethanol from excess ethylene glycol and TMCS, but the C_3-C_5 polymethylene glycols yielded mostly the bis(TMS) derivatives under similar conditions.

For bench scale preparative work, TMCS or HMDS is often used with the simpler compounds; TMCS–pyridine for polyhydroxy compounds. HMDS-based methods are commonly used for analytical samples. Due to the ease of silylation of the hydroxyl group, there is little need for the more potent silyl donors.

5-3. ALCOHOLS

Various derivatives of long chain alcohols have been compared for analysis by GC. Wood (877) estimated C_{14}-C_{20} saturated and unsaturated alcohols using 15% EGSS-X and 5% SE-30 columns, TMS and trifluoro-acetyl (TFA) derivatives. Best results were obtained with the polar EGSS-X phase with TFA derivatives, as the resolution of TMS ethers of saturated and unsaturated C_{16} and C_{18} alcohols was poor. VandenHeuvel, Gardiner and Horning (803) found that the selectivity order for silyl ethers of long chain alcohols is CNSi > F-60-Z > SE-52. Separation of the silyl ethers was excellent on all phases. Only on the relatively selective CNSi was the retention time of the silyl derivatives less than that of the alcohols. MU values for 10 kinds of derivatives and the free alcohols were compared.

Many types of glycol and aliphatic polyols have been silylated. The silyl derivatives of *cis*- and *trans*-cyclohexanediol have different boiling points (108). The derivatives of *cis-trans* pairs from cyclohexanediol, 1,2-indanediol and hydrobenzoin were separated by GC on OV columns. Indanediol and hydrobenzoin TMS ethers were also separated by TLC on silica gel; the cyclohexanediol derivatives were not visible under UV light. The mass spectra of 1,10-decanediol bis(TMS) ether and 1,10-decanediol-d_{18} bis(TMS) ether have been compared (517). The latter contained perdeuterated TMS groups, from BSA-d_{18}.

The molecular weight distribution of ethylene oxide condensates has been studied, through gas chromatographic analysis of the silyl ethers (149, 442, 785). Tornquist (785), using preparative GC, obtained polyethylene glycol bis(TMS) ethers of 5 to 10 ethoxy units, and recorded retention data for compounds up to 13 units. Di- and tri-pentaerythritols were incompletely silylated, as shown by IR, by TMCS in pyridine at the boil. Heating for five hours in a sealed tube at 150° was required for complete reaction (740). However, brief boiling with HMDS–TMCS in pyridine effected quantitative conversion and a precise GC analysis of commercial pentaerythritol using the silyl derivatives was developed (758). The components included condensed pentaerythritols up to 5 units, formal derivatives and pentaerythrose, and the silylated samples were analysed directly on SE-30.

Wood *et al.* (879) examined the TMS derivatives of methyl mono-, di-, tri-, and tetrahydroxystearates and found them suitable for estimation by GC. The diastereoisomers, however, were not satisfactorily resolved. Best results were obtained with a large bore capillary column coated with Apiezon L. Packed and capillary columns of DEGS were less satisfactory. Resolution of the diastereoisomers as their trifluoroacetates was later accomplished (878).

A thorough discussion and review on the silylation of *myo*-inositol and the estimation of its hexakis(TMS) ether by GC has been given by Roberts (617). The use of dimethylsulfoxide to dissolve the inositol and hasten the silylation by HMDS–TMCS–pyridine has been recommended (233). With a QF-1 column and a flame ionization detector quantification at the nanogram level has been achieved (460). Gas chromatography of TMS ethers of various inositols (460, 488, 850) and their O-methyl derivatives (612) is described.

The first use of TMS derivatives in mass spectrometry was described by Sharkey, Friedel and Langer (712) in 1957, primarily for analysis of alcohols in mixtures with hydrocarbons. A detailed analysis of the fragmentation patterns of silyl ethers of C_4 to C_{10} alcohols was presented. This application was extended to alcohol–water mixtures. There was no interference from hexamethyldisiloxane, which resulted from the silylation of water. Diekman *et al.* (194) further elucidated the modes of fragmentation of 1-pentanol and 2-pentanol TMS ethers through the use of deuterium labeling.

5-4. THIN LAYER CHROMATOGRAPHY

TMS ethers of alcohols and glycols have been separated by thin layer chromatography on silica gel. Brooks and Harrison (127) thus resolved a mixture containing TMS ethers of hydroxylated derivatives of cyclodiene insecticides. The lower polarity of the ethers allowed their clean separation from the hydroxy compounds. Adcock and Betts (8) studied monoterpene alcohol TMS ethers. Not all were successfully separated but some separations were most helpful. Geraniol and citronellol, for instance, cannot be resolved on ordinary silica gel plates, but their TMS ethers can be thus separated. Leibman and Ortiz (469) investigated the separation of glycol TMS ethers and found TLC and GC satisfactory for resolution of *cis-trans* pairs. For both procedures excess reagents were first removed after silylation. Direct spotting of reaction mixtures for TLC was unsatisfactory. Kelly and Jensen (406) determined the R_F values on paper for TMS ethers of bacterioruberin and of its mono-, bis-, and tris-anhydro derivatives.

5-5. GLYCERIDES

In the silylation of mono- and diglycerides the thermal isomerization of 2-monoglycerides to 1-isomers and of 1,2-diglycerides to 1,3-isomers, which occurs with the free compounds, was considered. Kresze *et al.* (440) was careful to silylate at room temperature. Wood *et al.* (880) silylated with HMDS–TMCS in pyridine for five minutes, added hexane and removed the excess reagents and solvent by washing and evaporation. They showed that isomerization does not occur in the silylation reaction (880). Watts and Dils (842) used HMDS–TMCS (2:1) in hexane–ether and found that 1-monoglycerides isomerize to 2-isomers if a large proportion of TMCS is used or if the derivatives stand with the reagent overnight.

Mono- and diglyceride TMS ethers are readily separated by GC. Wood *et al.* (880) quantitatively analysed isomeric pairs of 1- and 2-monoglycerides as well as monoglyceride mixtures, using packed and large bore capillary (0.03 in.) columns of DEGS polyester and Apiezon L. On SE-30 monoglyceride TMS ethers of C_8-C_{18} chain length were well separated but the 1- and 2-isomer pairs were not resolved. Also, although a mixture of TMS derivatives of 1-monostearin, 1-monoolein and 1-monolinolein was resolved on DEGS; mixtures of 1- and 2-isomers were not. This column did not distinguish unsaturation (771). Saturated and monounsaturated C_{14}-C_{18} monoglycerides and glyceryl ethers, however, were resolved on a JXR column (656). Polar columns were not effective.

Monoglyceride TMS ethers were separated from diglyceride TMS derivatives on 3% QF-1 (842) or 3% JXR (663) columns, but 1,2- and 1,3-isomers were not distinguished. Retention time within these groups is proportional to the total side chain carbon content (440, 842). With a JXR column it was possible to analyse commercial mixtures with recoveries of 96-101% (663).

Isomeric glyceride TMS ethers which could not be separated by GC could be identified in other ways. Enantiomorphic pairs of diglyceride TMS ethers were separated by TLC on silica gel impregnated with silver nitrate (533). NMR spectra show characteristic differences for isomeric compounds (440). And mass spectra of silyl derivatives distinguish between 1- and 2-monoglycerides (378) and between 1,2- and 1,3-diglycerides (159).

5-6. PHENOLS

The silylation of alkyl substituted monohydric phenols and the gas chromatography of silyl ethers have been investigated on a wide variety of silicone and polyester stationary phases on packed columns (9, 455, 533, 741). The use of capillary columns improved the separation of some derivatives and was applied to many alkylphenol TMS ethers (9, 238, 281, 434). The resolution of m- and p-cresol derivatives, poor on packed columns, was satisfactory on a capillary column coated with tri-2,4-xylenyl phosphate (9). The mass spectra of TMS derivatives of phenol, cresols (712), and coal hydrogenation products (713) have been described.

Methyl esters of phenolic acids have been made with diazomethane (182, 348, 797, 864). After a short reaction period, which may be limited to one minute to avoid methyl ether formation (182, 348), the solvents and excess reagent were evaporated and the residue silylated at room temperature with HMDS–TMCS in pyridine (182, 348), tetrahydrofuran (864), or ethyl acetate (797). Silylation was complete and single products were obtained, as observed on gas chromatography of the reaction mixtures. Silylation followed by diazomethane treatment yielded multiple products (863).

Many more complex phenols, mostly of natural origin, have been separated as silyl derivatives by GC. Hydroxy- and polyhydroxyanthraquinones were investigated by Furuya et al. (258) on SE-30 and retention times of parent compound and TMS ether compared for 26 samples. Retention time increased, for parent and derivative, with increasing number of hydroxyls.

Tocopherols have been identified and estimated as their TMS derivatives. Slover *et al.* (736) silylated with HMDS–TMCS in pyridine and separated the ethers on SE-30 or Apiezon L columns. They investigated all 14 possible methylated tocols and tocotrienols. The most serious interference, between β- and γ-tocopherols, was fairly well resolved on Apiezon L. Nair and co-workers (540, 541) silylated with BSA and analysed on a biphase column, SE-52/XE-60 (2:1). Although β- and γ-tocopherols were not separated, their oxidation products were well resolved and served as a basis for estimation.

The active principles of cannabis are phenolic and have been analysed as their TMS ethers on SE-30, SE-52, and Carbowax 20M (63, 167, 304). Separation was good and elution was always in the order: cannabidiol, tetrahydrocannabinol, cannabinol. Morphine, apomorphine and codeine may be determined by GC of their TMS ethers on an SE-30 column (114, 115, 510). The estimation of morphine in opium by this method gave results close to those obtained by official methods (510).

The silylation of flavonoids has yielded derivatives especially suitable for NMR study (826). They are formed under mild conditions and give products soluble in solvents appropriate for NMR. The absence of phenolic protons in the spectra has proved complete silylation (22, 826). NMR analysis of flavonoid glycosides from several plant sources permitted determination of the hydroxyl substitution pattern of the nucleus, position of glycosidation, and nature of the sugar group (500, 502). Furuya separated by GC the silyl derivatives of 22 flavonoids and related compounds (256). On SE-30 he found that retention time increased with the number of original hydroxyl groups in the side phenyl group. With anthocyanidins Al Shakir (22) observed the opposite. Flavonol derivatives had retention times greater than those of flavone ethers (256). Since flavanone derivatives usually showed a main peak followed by minor ones, chemical change on the column was suspected (256).

Catecholamines have been treated with HMDS and acetone or other ketones (148, 401, 402), which converted hydroxyl groups to silyl ethers and primary amino groups to Schiff bases. Secondary amino groups remained unchanged. The acetone Schiff bases were well separated on a 10% F-60 column, programmed to 180° (148).

The hydroxyl content of coal was determined by silylating a powdered sample with refluxing HMDS–TMCS in pyridine (245, 246). After removal of the solvent and excess reagents by vacuum distillation the reacted coal was washed with petroleum ether, dried and analysed for silicon. Asphaltene and vitrains were similarly assayed (246).

In the following tables the silylation of polyhydric compounds is considered complete (all hydroxy groups react) unless otherwise indicated.

TABLE 5-1. ALCOHOLS

Formula	Compound	Method	Yield %	B.P./mm; M.P.	n_D^t	Stat. Phase, Temp., Retention Data	Ref.
CH_4O	Methanol	12		b 56-57		ApL, TTP	592
		13e	46	b 56.5-56.7/747	1.3679^{20}		675
		18		b 55			388
		21		b 55.3-55.8/740	1.3675^{20}		452, 892
		32	91	b 57-58	1.3680^{20}		439
		53	76	b 57	1.3685^{20}		2
		21				Mass Spec.	453
		21				Mass Spec.	712
		52	97			Mass Spec.	819
$C_2H_4O_2$	Glycolaldehyde	25				SE-52, 125°, 0.044/gu EGS, 140°, 0.25/marp	764
C_2H_6O	Ethanol	11		b 74/736	1.3712^{25}		240
		12		b 75		ApL, TTP	592
		13x	44	b 74.9-75.0/745	1.3742^{20}		675
		21,31	90-95	b 74.5			50
		22		b 74.6/738	1.3742^{20}		452, 892
		32	93	b 75-76	1.3745^{20}		439
		52	92	b 75	1.3745^{20}		3
		21				Mass Spec.	453
		21				Mass Spec.	712
C_3H_4O	Propargyl alcohol	13e	47	b 110.8/757	1.4090^{20}		528
C_3H_6O	Allyl alcohol	11		b 98-99	1.3840^{20}		431
		11		b 32-33/23	1.4075^{25}		514
		21	61-86	b 100	1.3950^{24}		222

Table 5-1. Alcohols (cont'd.)

Formula	Compound	Method	Yield %	B.P./mm; M.P.	n_D^t	Stat. Phase, Temp., Retention Data	Ref.
C_3H_7ClO	3-Chloro-1-propanol	12		b 155/733	1.4160^{25}		749
		12b	76	b 155/733	1.4164^{25}		751
		13	56	b 53/17-20	1.4148^{28}		196
$C_3H_7NO_2$	N-Hydroxymethyl-N-methyl-formamide	48	99	b 87-87.2/10	1.4340^{20}		192
C_3H_8O	1-Propanol	12		b 100		ApL, TTP	592
		21	60	b 100.3-0.8/738	1.3838^{20}		452, 892
		21				DC-550, Flex PTC	454
		33	82				587
		53		b 99	1.3822^{20}		2
		21				Mass Spec.	453
		21				Mass Spec.	712
						Mass Spec.	389, 392
	1-Propanol-1,1-d_2	12				Mass Spec.	392
	2-Propanol	13		b 87		ApL, TTP	592
		33		b 85-86	1.3811^{25}		221
		53	81	b 87	1.3782^{20}		587
		52	78	b 88	1.3788^{20}		2
		21				Mass Spec.	3
						Mass Spec.	712
						Mass Spec.	389
$C_3H_8O_2$	2-Methoxyethanol	11		b 128	1.3952^{20}		136
		22				SE-30, 100°, 1.0'; Mass Spec.	195

Table 5-1. Alcohols (cont'd.)

Formula	Compound	Method	Yield %	B.P./mm; M.P.	n_D^t	Stat. Phase, Temp., Retention Data	Ref.
C_4H_7ClO	3-Chloro-2-butene-1-ol	11	51	b 164-165	1.4350^{20}		582
$C_4H_7Cl_3O$	2,2,2-Trichloro-t-butanol	11		b 95-98			90
C_4H_7NO	Acetone cyanohydrin	13b	95	b 145.5-147	1.4022^{20}		249
C_4H_8O	1-Butene-3-ol	21	91	b 107	1.3934^{27}		224
$C_4H_8O_2$	Vinyloxyethanol	13e		b 147/715	1.4139^{20}		721
$C_4H_8O_3$	Methyl lactate	25				F-60, 9.18 MU	182
C_4H_9ClO	4-Chloro-1-butanol	11	72	b 63-64/11	1.4252^{20}		22
		12b	80	b 81/24	1.4218^{25}		749
		21	79	b 79/24	1.4219^{25}		751
	4-Chloro-2-butanol	12b	56	b 59-60/21	1.4174^{25}		379
$C_4H_{10}O$	1-Butanol	11	76	b 123	1.3925^{20}		178
		11	>24	b 123.4-3.6/754	1.3925^{20}		675
		12		b 124		ApL, TTP	592
		14e	85	b 123-124	1.3930^{20}		272
		15	62	b 123.7-125/737	1.3924^{20}		452, 892
		22				DC-550, Pent, PTC	454
		31	93	b 122-125			186
		53	93	b 125	1.3934^{20}		2
		52	94	b 125	1.3930^{20}		3
		51	51	b 124	1.3926^{20}		823
		21				Mass Spec.	453
		21				Mass Spec.	712
	1-Butanol-2,2-d_2					Mass Spec.	391
	1-Butanol-3,3-d_2					Mass Spec.	391

Table 5-1. Alcohols (cont'd.)

Formula	Compound	Method	Yield %	B.P./$_{mm}$; M.P.	n_D^t	Stat. Phase, Temp., Retention Data	Ref.
$C_4H_{10}O$	2-Butanol					Mass Spec.	390, 391
		21				Mass Spec.	712
	2-Methyl-1-propanol	22		b 114.5-4.7/742	1.3881^{20}		452, 892
		21				DC-550, Flex, PTC	454
						Mass Spec.	390
		21				Mass Spec.	712
	2-Methyl-1-propanol-1,1-d_2					Mass Spec.	390
	t-Butanol	12		b 103			592
		13e	78	b 101/754	1.3913^{20}		269
		13		b 100/750	1.3881^{23}		858
		33					587
		53	79	b 105	1.3915^{20}		2
		52	58	b 105	1.3910^{20}		3
		21				Mass Spec.	390
		22				Mass Spec.	712
$C_4H_{10}O_2$	2-Ethoxy-1-ethanol	22				SE-30, 100°, 1.5' Mass Spec.	195
$C_4H_{11}NO$	2-Dimethylaminoethanol	11m					250
		22				SE-30, 95°, 1.5' Mass Spec.	195
$C_5H_5NO_4$	5-Nitrofurfuryl alcohol	13e	70	b 100/2	1.4998^{20}		494
$C_5H_6O_2$	Furfuryl alcohol	13		b 70-71/19	1.4447^{20}		493
$C_5H_8N_2O$	N-(β-Hydroxyethyl)-pyrazole	25				C-20M, 110°, 0.55', 0.90'	229

Table 5-1. Alcohols (cont'd.)

Formula	Compound	Method	Yield %	B.P./mm; M.P.	n_D^t	Stat. Phase, Temp., Retention Data	Ref.
$C_5H_9NO_2$	N-Hydroxymethyl-pyrrolidone	25				C-20M, 120°, 2.3'	895
$C_5H_{10}O$	1-Penten-3-ol	21	91	b 130	1.4047^{24}		222
$C_5H_{10}O_2$	Tetrahydrofurfuryl alcohol	13e	83	b 56.5-57/10	1.4319^{20}	TLC	595
		13b		b 172-173	1.4271^{20}		386
$C_5H_{10}O_3$	Ethyl lactate	17	76	b 65-66/14	1.4058^{20}		307
	Methyl β-hydroxybutyrate	25				10% F-60, 10.26 MU	182
						1% F-60, 10.24 MU	
	Methyl α-hydroxyiso-butyrate	25				10% F-60, 9.60 MU	182
$C_5H_{11}ClO$	5-Chloro-1-pentanol	21	95	b 96	1.4261^{25}		751
		21 12b	96	b 98/24	1.4268^{25}		749
	1-Chloro-3-pentanol	13	80	b 69-70/13	1.4283^{20}		286
$C_5H_{12}O$	1-Pentanol	13	49	b 145-149	1.4020^{20}		476
		15					452, 892
		21		b 148.9-9.4/739	1.4000^{20}		452
		22				Flex, DC-550, PTC	454
		22				SF-96, 85°, 3.0' Mass Spec.	194
		33					587
		51	51	b 145-147	1.4010^{20}		738
		21		b 149	1.4000^{20}		823
		21				Mass Spec.	453
		21				Mass Spec.	712

Table 5-1. Alcohols (cont'd.)

Formula	Compound	Method	Yield %	B.P./mm; M.P.	n_D^t	Stat. Phase, Temp., Retention Data	Ref.
$C_5H_{12}O$	1-Pentanol-5,5,5-d_3					Mass Spec.	194
	2-Pentanol	22				SF-96, 70°, 6.5'	194
						Mass Spec.	
		21				Mass Spec.	712
	2-Methyl-1-butanol	22	75			DC-550, PTC, Flex	454
		22		b 138.4-140/744	1.3980^{20}		452, 892
		21				Mass Spec.	712
	3-Methyl-1-butanol	13b	34	b 122-126/760	1.3940^{28}		481
		22		b 142/735	1.3976^{20}		452, 892
		33					587
		51	45	b 144/760	1.3977^{20}		823
		21				Mass Spec.	712
	2-Methyl-2-butanol	23	50	b 129.6-130/743	1.3980^{20}		452, 892
		21s				Ap	241
		21				Mass Spec.	712
	3-Methyl-2-butanol	21				Mass Spec.	712
	2,2-Dimethyl-1-propanol	13e		b 121-122	1.3934^{20}		270
		23		b 122.5-2.7/734	1.3907^{20}		452, 892
	1-Pentanol	21				Mass Spec.	712
		13b	37	b 145-147/760	1.4020^{22}		481
$C_5H_{12}O_2$	4-Methoxy-1-butanol	22				SE-30, 110°, 2.5'	195
						Mass Spec.	

Table 5-1. Alcohols (cont'd.)

Formula	Compound	Method	Yield %	B.P./mm; M.P.	n_D^t	Stat. Phase, Temp., Retention Data	Ref.
$C_5H_{12}O_2$	2-Propyloxyethanol	22				SE-30, 50°, 7.1'; Mass Spec.	195
$C_6H_6O_3$	5-Hydroxymethylfurfural	13				polyester	144
		13				HTC, 124°	262
	2-Furylhydroxymethyl ketone	13				HTC, 124°	262
$C_6H_{10}O$	Sorbic alcohol						441
$C_6H_{10}O_2$	3,4-Dihydro-α-pyran-2-methanol	13b	44	b 98-99/37	1.4386^{32}		483
$C_6H_{10}O_3$	Mevalonolactone	25				10% F-60, 13.62 MU; 1% F-60, 13.62 MU	182
	2-Hydroxyethyl methacrylate	25				C-20M	229
$C_6H_{10}O_5$	Dimethyl D(-)-malate	25				10% F-60, 12.72 MU; 1% F-60, 12.88 MU	182
$C_6H_{12}O$	1-Hexen-3-ol	21	63	b 151	1.4101^{24}		222
	Cyclohexanol	13	84	b 53/10	1.4315^{20}		596
		13		b 169-170	1.4289^{25}		221
		51	24	b 170	1.4318^{20}		823
$C_6H_{12}O_2$	Tetrahydropyran-2-methanol	13e	85	b 66/10	1.4442^{20}	TLC	595
$C_6H_{12}O_3$	Diethyleneglycol vinyl ether	13e		b 85/11	1.4260^{20}		721
	Methyl α-hydroxyiso-valerate	25				10% F-60, 10.58 MU; 1% F-60, 10.50 MU	182
$C_6H_{13}ClO$	1-Chloro-3-hexanol	13		b 80-81/13	1.4312^{20}		286
$C_6H_{13}NO_2$	N-(2-Hydroxyethyl)-morpholine	25				C-20M	229

Table 5-1. Alcohols (cont'd.)

Formula	Compound	Method	Yield %	B.P./mm; M.P.	n_D^t	Stat. Phase, Temp., Retention Data	Ref.
$C_6H_{14}O$	1-Hexanol	15		b 170.5-0.7/741	1.4058^{20}		452, 892
		21				DC-550, PTC	454
		33					587
		51	48	b 171	1.4056^{20}	Mass Spec.	823
		21				Mass Spec.	453
		21				Mass Spec.	712
	2-Ethyl-1-butanol	22		b 157.4-8.4/741	1.4062^{20}		452, 892
		21				Mass Spec.	712
	2-Methyl-1-pentanol	21					454
		22		b 159.3-60.2/749	1.4042^{20}		452, 892
		23p	59	b 158.2-60.2/749	1.4042^{20}		452, 892
		21				Mass Spec.	453
		21				Mass Spec.	712
	3-Methyl-1-pentanol	22		b 163/733	1.4061^{20}		452, 892
		21				Mass Spec.	712
		21				Mass Spec.	453
	2-Hexanol	15		b 154-155/741	1.4020^{20}		452, 892
		51	42	b 156	1.4022^{20}	Mass Spec.	823
		21				Mass Spec.	712
$C_6H_{14}O_2$	5-Methoxy-1-pentanol	22				SE-30, 110°, 3.6' Mass Spec.	195

Table 5-1. Alcohols (cont'd.)

Formula	Compound	Method	Yield %	B.P./mm; M.P.	n_D^t	Stat. Phase, Temp., Retention Data	Ref.
$C_6H_{14}O_3$	Carbitol	22				SE-30, 135°, 2.0' Mass Spec.	195
C_7H_7ClO	p-Chlorobenzyl alcohol	22				SF-96, 200°, 2.9' Mass Spec.	194
C_7H_7FO	p-Fluorobenzyl alcohol	22				SF-96, 190°, 3.4' Mass Spec.	194
$C_7H_7NO_3$	p-Nitrobenzyl alcohol	22				SF-96, 240°, 4.2' Mass Spec.	194
C_7H_8O	Benzyl alcohol	13	84	b 92/19	1.4773^{20}		269
		22				SF-96, 125°, 2.6' Mass Spec.	194
$C_7H_{10}ClNO$	Hydroxyethylpyridinium chloride	42		b 81/11			78
		11py					375
$C_7H_{10}O$	2-Methyl-3-hexyn-5-en-2-ol	14	75	b 35/6	1.4403^{20}		363
$C_7H_{10}O_2$	1-(2-Furyl)-1-propanol	13e	68	b 85-87/25	1.4428^{20}		494
$C_7H_{14}O_2$	2-Methoxycyclohexanol	13	80	b 75/10	1.4363^{20}		596
$C_7H_{14}O_3$	Methyl α-hydroxycaproate	25				10% F-60, 11.48 MU 1% F-60, 11.52 MU	182
$C_7H_{16}O$	1-Heptanol	21	83	b 188.9-9.9/740	1.4108^{20}		452, 892
		21				DC-550, PTC	454
		33					587
		51	49	b 190	1.4107^{20}		823
		21				Mass Spec.	453
		21				Mass Spec.	712
	3-Ethyl-3-pentanol	21s		b 170-171			241

Table 5-1. Alcohols (cont'd.)

Formula	Compound	Method	Yield %	B.P./mm; M.P.	n_D^t	Stat. Phase, Temp., Retention Data	Ref.
$C_7H_{16}O$	3-Heptanol	11		b 178			892
		22		b 176.1-6.2/740	1.4098^{20}		452, 892
$C_7H_{16}O_2$	2-Pentyloxyethanol	21				Mass Spec.	712
		22				SE-30, 85°, 12.0'; Mass Spec.	195
$C_8H_8O_3$	Piperonyl alcohol	25				C-20M, 160°, 0.45/pip	894
$C_8H_9ClO_2$	2-(o-Chlorophenoxy) ethanol	12b,12u		b 158/26	1.4948^{25}		749, 750
	2-(p-Chlorophenoxy) ethanol	12,12u		b 166/29	1.4927^{25}		749, 750
$C_8H_{10}O$	1-Phenylethanol	22				10% + 1%. F-60, 12.22 MU	182
		22	85	b 91/14	1.4702^{20}		269
		25				C-20M	229
	2-Phenylethanol	13	85	b 102/18	1.4739^{20}	F-60	269
		25				SF-96; Mass Spec.	182
$C_8H_{10}OS$	2-Hydroxyethyl phenyl thioether	22				SE-30, 212°, 1.6'; Mass Spec.	194
$C_8H_{10}O_2$	p-Methoxybenzyl alcohol	25				SF-96, 205°, 7.2'; Mass Spec.	195
	2-Phenoxy-1-ethanol	22				SE-30, 176°, 1.6'; Mass Spec.	194
$C_8H_{11}NO$	2-Phenylaminoethanol	22				SE-30, 180°, 3.0'; Mass Spec.	195

Table 5-1. Alcohols (cont'd.)

Formula	Compound	Method	Yield %	B.P./mm; M.P.	n_D^t	Stat. Phase, Temp., Retention Data	Ref.
$C_8H_{12}O_2$	1-(2-Furyl)butanol	13	52	b 75-76/10	1.4481^{20}		494
$C_8H_{14}O$	2-Cycloocten-1-ol	25				PPG, GE-96, 100→150°	786, 787
	3-Cycloocten-1-ol	25				PPG, GE-96, 100→150°	786, 787
	4-Cycloocten-1-ol	25				PPG, GE-96, 100→150°	786, 787
	2-Vinylcyclohexanol	25				PPG, GE-96	786
$C_8H_{14}O_5$	Dimethyl β-hydroxy-β-methylglutarate	25				10% F-60, 13.94 MU / 1% F-60, 14.12 MU	182
$C_8H_{15}BrO$	trans-2-Bromocyclooctanol	25				PPG, GE-96	786
$C_8H_{15}ClO$	trans-2-Chlorocyclooctanol	25				PPG, GE-96	786
$C_8H_{16}O_2$	2-Ethoxycyclohexanol	13	88	b 83/10	1.4336^{20}		596
$C_8H_{16}O_3$	2,6-Dimethoxycyclohexanol	13	88	b 104/10	1.4387^{20}		596
$C_8H_{16}O_4$	Triethyleneglycol vinyl ether	13e		b 80/2	1.4343^{20}		721
$C_8H_{18}O$	1-Octanol	11	90	b 205-206	1.4149^{20}		892
		21		b 211.2-2.2/749	1.4149^{20}		452, 892
		21	45				513
		24	49				
		22	97				
		23	93				
		25	92				
		33	93				
		33					587
		51	50	b 211	1.4151^{20}		823
		21				Mass Spec.	453

Table 5-1. Alcohols (cont'd.)

Formula	Compound	Method	Yield %	B.P./mm; M.P.	n_D^t	Stat. Phase, Temp., Retention Data	Ref.
$C_8H_{18}O$	1-Octanol	21				Mass Spec.	712
	2-Ethyl-1-hexanol	22		b 194.6/735	1.4148^{20}		452, 892
	2-Octanol	21				Mass Spec.	712
		51	44	b 190-191	1.4140^{20}		823
$C_8H_{18}O_2$	2-Cyclohexyloxyethanol	22				SE-30, 110°, 14.0'; Mass Spec.	195
$C_9H_6O_3$	3-Hydroxycoumarin	25				SE-30, 180°, 5.5'	257
	4-Hydroxycoumarin	25				SE-30, 180°, 9.0'	257
$C_9H_7NO_3$	N-Hydroxymethyl-phthalimide	25				C-20M, 190°, 1.4'	895
$C_9H_{10}O$	Cinnamyl alcohol	23	79	b 128/15	1.5105^{20}		269
$C_9H_{10}O_3$	Methyl mandelate	25				10% F-60, 14.10 MU; 1% F-60, 14.20 MU	182
$C_9H_{11}ClO_2$	1-p-Chlorophenoxy-2-propanol	13u					750
$C_9H_{12}O$	3-Phenyl-1-propanol	13	88	b 118/19	1.4744^{20}		269
		22				SF-96, 145°, 2.8'; Mass Spec.	194
	1-Phenyl-2-propanol	13	79	b 102/18	1.4690^{20}		269
	2-Phenyl-2-propanol	22				SF-96, 175°, 5.9'; Mass Spec.	194
$C_9H_{12}O_2$	3-Phenoxy-1-propanol	22				SE-30, 200°, 3.7'; Mass Spec.	195
$C_9H_{13}NO$	p-Dimethylaminobenzyl alcohol	22				SF-96; Mass Spec.	194
$C_9H_{14}O_7$	Trimethyl citrate	25				F-60	348

Table 5-1. Alcohols (cont'd.)

Formula	Compound	Method	Yield %	B.P./mm; M.P.	n_D^t	Stat. Phase, Temp., Retention Data	Ref.
$C_9H_{14}O_7$	Trimethyl citrate	25				10% F-60, 15.60 MU 1% F-60, 15.66 MU	182
	Trimethyl isocitrate	25				F-60	348
		25				10% F-60, 16.00 MU 1% F-60, 16.12 MU	182
$C_9H_{18}O_3$	Methyl 5-hydroxyoctanoate	25				ApL, 230°, 16.50' Mass Spec.	885
$C_9H_{20}O$	1-Nonanol	13	47	b 227.5-9.5/727	1.4190^{20}		892
		22	68	b 228.1-8.9/734	1.4190^{20}		452, 892
		33					587
		51	44	b 230	1.4191^{20}		823
		21c				ApN, 160°, 1.24/gcl	169
		21				Mass Spec.	453
		21				Mass Spec.	712
	4-Methyl-2-propyl-2-pentanol	21s		b 174-176			241
$C_{10}H_8O_4$	4-Hydroxy-7-methoxy coumarin	25				SE-30, 180°, 23.3'	257
$C_{10}H_{10}O$	Phenylpropynylcarbinol	21			1.5006^{20}		708
$C_{10}H_{12}O$	cis-1-Phenyl-2-buten-1-ol	16e	61	b 60-63/0.1	1.4890^{25}	DC-710	708
	trans-1-Phenyl-2-buten-1-ol	16e	59	b 54-57/0.1	1.4869^{25}	DC-710	708
	trans-1-Phenyl-2-buten-3-ol	16e	85	b 70-73/0.1	1.5014^{25}	DC-710	708
$C_{10}H_{12}O_3$	Methyl phenyllactate	25				10% F-60, 14.80 MU 1% F-60, 14.78 MU	182

Table 5-1. Alcohols (cont'd.)

Formula	Compound	Method	Yield %	B.P./mm; M.P.	n_D^t	Stat. Phase, Temp., Retention Data	Ref.
$C_{10}H_{12}O_4$	Methyl p-methoxymandelate	25				10% F-60, 16.58 MU 1% F-60, 16.62 MU	182
$C_{10}H_{14}O$	2-Phenylbutan-2-ol	11	<85	b 174.5/100	1.4228^{20}		452, 892
		13	72	b 108/16	1.4805^{20}		269
		15	16	b 244-245/735			452, 892
		51	46	b 104/5	1.4227^{20}		823
$C_{10}H_{14}O_2$	2-Phenoxymethyl-2-propanol	22				SE-30, 140°, 3.5' Mass Spec.	195
	4-Phenoxy-1-butanol	22				SE-30, 190°, 2.4' Mass Spec.	195
$C_{10}H_{16}O$	Carveol	25h				TLC	8
$C_{10}H_{18}O$	Dihydrocarveol	25h				TLC	8
	Fenchol (Fenchyl alcohol)	25h				TLC	8
		24py,25				TLC	122
	Geraniol	13b	60	b 94-96/4.5	1.4515^{20}		480
		25h				TLC	8
	Linallol	25h				TLC	8
	α-Terpineol	25h				TLC	8
	Terpineol	25				SE-30, 140°	450
$C_{10}H_{20}O$	Citronellol	13b	52	b 90-91/4.5	1.4459^{20}		480
		25h				TLC	8
	Menthol	13b	69	b 70-71/4.5	1.4450^{24}		480
		25h				TLC	8
$C_{10}H_{22}O$	1-Decanol	13p	85	b 240-244	$1.4228-1.4232^{20}$		452, 892

Table 5-1. Alcohols (cont'd.)

Formula	Compound	Method	Yield %	B.P./mm; M.P.	n_D^t	Stat. Phase, Temp., Retention Data	Ref.
$C_{10}H_{22}O$	1-Decanol	15	16	b 244-245/735	1.4341^{20}		823
		51	46	b 104/5	1.4227^{20}	Mass Spec.	453
		21				Mass Spec.	712
$C_{11}H_{10}O_2$	α-(2-Furyl)-benzyl alcohol	13	32	b 117-119/5	1.5200^{20}		494
$C_{11}H_{14}O_5$	Methyl vanilmandelate	25				SE-30, 185°, 1.21/mhip; QF-1, 170°, 0.80/mhip; XE-60, 173°, 0.81/mhip; EGA, 195°, 0.86/mhip	864
$C_{11}H_{15}NO_3$	α4,3-O-Isopropylidene-pyridoxol	25				10% F-60, 18.18 MU; 1% F-60, 18.38 MU	182
$C_{11}H_{16}O_2$	5-Phenoxy-1-pentanol	25				SE-30, 115°, 6.9'	436
		22				SE-30, 160°, 4.8'; Mass Spec.	195
$C_{11}H_{22}O_3$	Methyl 4-hydroxydecanoate	25				ApL, 230°, 18.04'; Mass Spec.	885
	Methyl 5-hydroxydecanoate	25				ApL, 230°, 18.78'; Mass Spec.	885
$C_{11}H_{24}O$	1-Undecanol	22		b 258-261/733, 190.6-1.6/102	1.4258^{20}		452, 892
$C_{12}H_{10}Cl_6O$	6-Hydroxy-6,7-dihydro-aldrin	23				SE-30, 100→300°	149
		21				Mass Spec.	453
		22py				TLC	127
$C_{12}H_{18}O_2$	6-Phenoxy-1-hexanol	22				SE-30, 165°, 4.9'; Mass Spec.	195

Table 5-1. Alcohols (cont'd.)

Formula	Compound	Method	Yield %	B.P./mm; M.P.	n_D^t	Stat. Phase, Temp., Retention Data	Ref.
$C_{12}H_{24}O$	Cyclododecanol	21k				CNSi, 175°, 0.22/eic; SE-52, 189°, 0.24/eic; F-60-Z, 190°, 0.23/eic	803
$C_{12}H_{24}O_3$	Methyl 4-hydroxy-undecanoate	25				ApL; Mass Spec.	885
	Methyl 5-hydroxy-undecanoate	25				ApL; Mass Spec.	885
$C_{12}H_{26}O$	1-Dodecanol	22		b 198.5-200.6/100, 271-273/742	1.4269^{25}, 1.4289^{20}		452, 892
		21k				CNSi, 175°, 0.16/eic; SE-52, 189°, 0.17/eic; F-60-Z, 190°, 0.17/eic	803
		23				SE-30, 100→300°	149
		25				ApL, 120°, 0.19/hdlt	761
$C_{13}H_9ClO_2S$	cis-2-Chlorothioxanthen-9-ol 10-oxide	25	80	m 170.5-171.5		TLC, NMR, IR	775
	trans-2-Chlorothio-xanthen-9-ol 10-oxide	25	74	m 151-152		TLC, NMR, IR	775
$C_{13}H_{10}OS$	Thioxanthen-9-ol	24	13	m 82-84		NMR, IR	775
$C_{13}H_{10}O_2S$	cis-Thioxanthen-9-ol 10-oxide	25	66	m 119-120.6		TLC, NMR, IR	775
	trans-Thioxanthen-9-ol 10-oxide	25	80	m 99-101		TLC, NMR, IR	775
$C_{13}H_{10}O_3S$	Thioxanthen-9-ol 10,10-dioxide	25	85	m 122-124		TLC, NMR, IR	775
$C_{13}H_{12}O$	Benzhydrol	13	89	b 111/0.6	1.5290^{20}		269
		13x	81	b 124-124.5/2	1.5265^{20}		119
		16e	64	b 92-95/0.2	1.5272^{20}		708

Table 5-1. Alcohols (cont'd.)

Formula	Compound	Method	Yield %	B.P./mm; M.P.	n_D^t	Stat. Phase, Temp., Retention Data	Ref.
$C_{13}H_{12}O$	Benzhydrol	22				SF-96, 250°, 4.2'; Mass Spec.	194
$C_{13}H_{20}O_2$	7-Phenoxy-1-heptanol	22				SE-30, 173°, 5.3'; Mass Spec.	195
$C_{13}H_{26}O_3$	Methyl 3-hydroxy-dodecanoate	25				SE-30, 200°, 11.5'	888
	Methyl 5-hydroxy-dodecanoate	15				ApL, 230°, 21.78'; Mass Spec.	885
$C_{13}H_{28}O$	1-Tridecanol	23				SE-30, 100→300°	149
$C_{13}H_{28}O_2$	Undecyloxyethanol	23				SE-30, 100→300°	149
$C_{14}H_{14}O$	1,2-Diphenylethanol	13		b 90/0.005	1.5198^{20}	SE-30, 100→300°	269
$C_{14}H_{30}O$	1-Tetradecanol	23				SE-30, 100→300°	149
		25				ApL, 120°, 0.44/hdlt	761
		21k				SE-52, 189°, 0.40/eic; F-60-Z, 190°, 0.39/eic; CNSi, 178°, 0.39/eic	803
		23				SE-30, 190°; EGSS, 130°	877
$C_{14}H_{30}O_2$	Dodecyloxyethanol	23				SE-30, 100→300°	149
$C_{15}H_{16}O$	1,3-Diphenylpropan-2-ol	23	70	b 99/0.02 m 35	1.5281^{20}		269
$C_{15}H_{26}O$	Cedrol	24py,25				TLC	122
	Nerolidol	22				SE-30, 100°; Mass Spec.	43
	(+)δ-Nerolidol				1.4807^{20}	Mass Spec.	152
$C_{15}H_{30}O_3$	2-(1-Hydroxy)-propyl laurate	25				SE-52/QF-1, 280°	866
	1-(2-Hydroxy)-propyl laurate	25				SE-52/QF-1, 280°	866

Table 5-1. Alcohols (cont'd.)

Formula	Compound	Method	Yield %	B.P./mm; M.P.	n_D^t	Stat. Phase, Temp., Retention Data	Ref.
$C_{15}H_{30}O_3$	Methyl 3-hydroxymyristate	25				SE-30, 200°, 24'	888
	Methyl 5-hydroxymyristate	25				ApL, 230°, 26.50' Mass Spec.	885
$C_{15}H_{32}O$	1-Pentadecanol	23				SE-30, 100→300°	149
$C_{15}H_{32}O_2$	Tridecyloxyethanol	23				SE-30, 100→300°	149
$C_{15}H_{32}O_3$	$CH_3(CH_2)_{10}$-$O(C_2H_4O)_2H$	23				SE-30, 100→300°	149
$C_{16}H_{32}O$	Palmitoleyl alcohol	25				SE-30, 190° EGSS, 130°	877
$C_{16}H_{32}O_3$	3-Hydroxybutyl laurate	25				SE-52/QF-1, 280°	866
	4-Hydroxybutyl laurate	25				SE-52/QF-1, 280°	866
	3-(Hydroxymethyl)-propyl laurate	25				SE-52/QF-1, 280°	866
	Methyl 5-hydroxy-pentadecanoate	25				ApL, 230°, 27.88' Mass Spec.	885
$C_{16}H_{32}O_4$	Diethyleneglycol mono-laurate	25				SE-52, 100→300°, 0.833, 0.920/gyp	759
$C_{16}H_{34}O$	1-Hexadecanol	23				SE-30, 100→300°	149
		25				ApL, 120°, 10.4'	761
		25				SE-30, 190° EGSS, 130°	877
		21k				SE-52, 189°, 0.86/eic F-60-Z, 190°, 0.87/eic CNSi, 175°, 0.92/eic	803
$C_{16}H_{34}O_2$	Tetradecyloxyethanol	23				SE-30, 100→300°	149
$C_{16}H_{34}O_3$	$CH_3(CH_2)_{11}O(C_2H_4O)_2H$	23				SE-30, 100→300°	149
$C_{17}H_{21}NO_4$	Scopolamine	43				OV-17, 140→300°	336

Table 5-1. Alcohols (cont'd.)

Formula	Compound	Method	Yield %	B.P./mm; M.P.	n_D^t	Stat. Phase, Temp., Retention Data	Ref.
$C_{17}H_{23}NO_3$	Atropine	43				OV-17, 140→300°	336
$C_{17}H_{28}O_2$	Nonylphenyloxyethanol	13				SE-30, 150→345°	442
$C_{17}H_{34}O_3$	Methyl 5-hydroxypalmitate	25				ApL, 240°, 30.65'; Mass Spec.	885
	Methyl 16-hydroxypalmitate	25				SE-52, 250°	106
		21				SE-30, 195° Mass Spec.	214
$C_{17}H_{36}O$	1-Heptadecanol	23				SE-30, 100→300°	149
$C_{17}H_{36}O_2$	Pentadecyloxyethanol	23				SE-30, 100→300°	149
$C_{17}H_{36}O_3$	$CH_3(CH_2)_{12}O(C_2H_4O)_2H$	23				SE-30, 100→300°	149
$C_{17}H_{36}O_4$	$CH_3(CH_2)_{10}O(C_2H_4O)_3H$	23				SE-30, 100→300°	149
$C_{18}H_{21}NO_3$	Codeine	25				SE-30, 225°	510
$C_{18}H_{32}O$	Linolenyl alcohol	25				SE-30, 190° EGSS-X, 130°	877
$C_{18}H_{34}O$	Linoleyl alcohol	25				SE-30, 190° EGSS-X, 130°	877
$C_{18}H_{36}O$	Oleyl alcohol	25				SE-30, 190° EGSS-X, 130°	877
$C_{18}H_{36}O_3$	2-(5-Hydroxy)-hexyl laurate	25				SE-52/QF-1, 280°	866
	Methyl 5-hydroxyhepta-decanoate	25				ApL, 240°, 35.52'	885
$C_{18}H_{38}O$	Stearyl alcohol	13b	55	b 189-191/3	1.44000^{20}		34
		25				SE-30, 190° EGSS-X, 130°	877
		23				SE-30, 100→300°	149
		25				ApL, 120°, 2.28/hdlt	761

Table 5-1. Alcohols (cont'd.)

Formula	Compound	Method	Yield %	B.P./mm; M.P.	n_D^t	Stat. Phase, Temp., Retention Data	Ref.
$C_{18}H_{38}O$	Stearyl alcohol	23p				SE-30, 200°, 1.19/mst PPE, 200°, 0.58/mst DEGS, 200°, 0.35/mst	896
$C_{18}H_{38}O_2$	Hexadecyloxyethanol	23				SE-30, 100→300°	149
$C_{19}H_{34}O_3$	Methyl 18-hydroxyoctadeca-9,12-dienoate	21				SE-30, 195° Mass Spec.	214
$C_{19}H_{36}O_3$	Methyl 18-hydroxyocta-dec-9-enoate	21				SE-30, 195° Mass Spec.	214
	Methyl ricinolate	25				ApL, 250°, 20.3' ApL, 245°, 13.5' DEGS, 220°, 2.0' Carb, 210°, 1.8' FFAP, 220°, 4.3'	237
						DEGS, 208°	879
$C_{19}H_{38}O_3$	Methyl 5-hydroxystearate	25				ApL, 240°, 38.37' Mass Spec.	885
	Methyl 9-hydroxystearate	25				Carb, 200°	237
						DEGS, 215°	879
	Methyl 12-hydroxystearate	25				ApL, 250°, 22.1' ApL, 245°, 14.6' DEGS, 220°, 2.0' Carb, 210°, 1.8' FFAP, 220°, 4.3'	237
$C_{19}H_{40}O_5$	$CH_3(CH_2)_{10}O(C_2H_4O)_4H$	23				SE-30, 100→300°	149
$C_{20}H_{24}O_5$	Gibberellin A5 methyl ester	25				SE-30, 160→250° Mass Spec.	503
		25				QF-1, 179°, 2.2/chn SE-33, 187°, 0.35/chn	154

Table 5-1. Alcohols (cont'd.)

Formula	Compound	Method	Yield %	B.P./mm; M.P.	n_D^t	Stat. Phase, Temp., Retention Data	Ref.
$C_{20}H_{24}O_5$	Gibberellin A_7 methyl ester	25				QF-1, 179°, 2.5/chn SE-33, 187°, 0.41/chn	154
$C_{20}H_{26}O_5$	Gibberellin A_4 methyl ester	25				SE-30, 160→250° Mass Spec.	503
		25				QF-1, 179°, 2.2/chn SE-33, 187°, 0.38/chn	154
$C_{20}H_{26}O_6$	Gibberellin A_6 methyl ester	25				QF-1, 179°, 3.75/chn SE-33, 187°, 0.49/chn	154
		25				SE-30, 160→250° Mass Spec.	503
$C_{20}H_{28}O_5$	Gibberellin A_{10} methyl ester	25				QF-1, 179°, 3.1/chn SE-33, 187°, 0.46/chn	154
$C_{20}H_{30}O$	Dehydroabietyl alcohol	23p				SE-30, 200°, 1.82/mst PPE, 200°, 2.45/mst DEGS, 200°, 2.16/mst	896
	Vitamin A	22py				BDS, 200°	828
		43				OV-1, 239°pr OV-17, 226°pr	347
	Abietyl alcohol	42				QF-1, 160°; Mass Spec.	813
$C_{20}H_{32}O$		23p				SE-30, 200°, 2.02/mst PPE, 200°, 2.31/mst DEGS, 200°, 1.82/mst	896
	Isopimaryl alcohol	23p				SE-30, 200°, 1.58/mst PPE, 200°, 1.53/mst DEGS, 200°, 1.34/mst	896

Table 5-1. Alcohols (cont'd.)

Formula	Compound	Method	Yield %	B.P./mm; M.P.	n_D^t	Stat. Phase, Temp., Retention Data	Ref.
$C_{20}H_{32}O$	Palustryl alcohol	23p				SE-30, 200°, 1.74/mst; PPE, 200°, 1.65/mst; DEGS, 200°, 1.28/mst	896
	Pimaryl alcohol	23p				SE-30, 200°, 1.50/mst; PPE, 200°, 1.23/mst; DEGS, 200°, 1.03/mst	896
$C_{20}H_{40}O_2$	2-Hydroxyethyl oleyl ether	13				SE-30, 150→345°	442
	Ethylene glycol mono-stearate	25				SE-52, 100→300°, 0.898, 0.983/gyP	759
$C_{20}H_{40}O_3$	Methyl 5-hydroxy-nonadecanoate	25				ApL, 230°, 42.43'; Mass Spec.	885
$C_{20}H_{42}O$	Arachidyl alcohol	25				SE-30, 190°; EGSS-X, 130°	877
$C_{20}H_{42}O_3$	$CH_3(CH_2)_{15}O(C_2H_4O)_2H$	23				SE-30, 100→300°	149
$C_{20}H_{42}O_4$	$CH_3(CH_2)_{13}O(C_2H_4O)_3H$	23				SE-30, 100→300°	149
$C_{20}H_{42}O_5$	$CH_3(CH_2)_{11}O(C_2H_4O)_4H$	23				SE-30, 100→300°	149
$C_{21}H_{28}O_6$	Gibberellin (Bamboo) methyl ester	25				QF-1, 179°, 1.9/chn; SE-33, 187°, 0.55/chn	154
$C_{21}H_{28}O_7$	Gibberellin A_{13} methyl ester	25				QF-1, 179°, 1.2/chn; SE-33, 187°, 0.52/chn	154
		25				SE-30, 160→250°; Mass Spec.	503
$C_{21}H_{30}O_5$	Gibberellin A_{14} methyl ester	25				QF-1, 179°, 0.88/chn; SE-33, 187°, 0.37/chn	154

Table 5-1. Alcohols (cont'd.)

Formula	Compound	Method	Yield %	B.P./mm; M.P.	n_D^t	Stat. Phase, Temp., Retention Data	Ref.
$C_{21}H_{44}O_4$	$CH_3(CH_2)_{14}O(C_2H_4O)_3H$	23				SE-30, 100→300°	149
$C_{22}H_{42}O_4$	Diethylene glycol monooleate	25				SE-52, 100→300°, 0.866, 1.098/gyp	759
$C_{22}H_{44}O_4$	Diethylene glycol monostearate	25				SE-52, 100→300°, 0.774, 0.849/gyp	759
$C_{23}H_{42}ClNO$	18-Hydroxyoctadecyl pyridinium chloride	23					375
$C_{29}H_{48}O_4$	Ubichromenol	42				UCW-98, 250°	859
$C_{29}H_{50}O_3$	α-Tocopherolquinone	42					543
$C_{29}H_{50}O_4$	Ubichromanol	42				UCW-98, 250°	859
$C_{40}H_{52}O_3$	1',2'-Dihydro-4,2'-diketo-1'-hydroxytorulene	25					316
$C_{40}H_{54}O_2$	2'-Dehydroplectani-axanthine	25					44, 45
$C_{40}H_{58}O$	5-Hydroxy-5,6-dihydro-β-carotene	25					317
	Rhodopin	25	95				518
$C_{42}H_{58}O_3$	Plectaniaxanthine mono-acetate	25					45
$C_{45}H_{74}O$	Solanesol	26				SE-30, 300°, 8.9'	844
$C_{50}H_{76}O$	Tris-anhydro-bacterio-ruberin	25				Mass Spec.	406

TABLE 5-2. ALIPHATIC AND ALICYCLIC POLYOLS

Formula	Compound	Silyl-ation	Method (Yield %)	B.P./mm; M.P.	n_D^t	Stat. Phase, Temp., Retention Data	Ref.
$C_2H_3Cl_3O_2$	Chloral hydrate	T_2	13(50%)	b 232-234/759, 69-70/1.8 m 2.0	1.4468^{20}		313
$C_2H_6O_2$	Ethylene glycol	T_1	14(76%)	b 151-152	1.4117^{20}		754
		T_2	14(65%) 11(90%)	b 165-166	1.4034^{20}		754
		T_2	22(75%)	b 170-172/734	1.4031^{20}		452, 892
		T_2	22			SE-30, 125°, 1.3' Mass Spec.	195
		T_2				SKT-V, SKT	811
		T_2	23b	b 65/20	1.4052^{20}	SiO, 100→300°, 0.11/hdcn	785
		T_2	41,45			SE-30, 175→300°	69
			13			SE-30, 160°pr	442
$C_3H_6O_3$	1,3-Dihydroxyacetone	T_2	13			HTC, 125° DDS, 125° EGS, 175°	261
$C_3H_8O_2$	1,2-Propanediol		25			SE-52, 125°, 0.57/ag	764
		T_2	22	b 172-172.7	1.4031^{20}		892
		T_2	13(90%)	b 97/58	1.4031^{20}		754
		T_2	25	b 53/7	1.4035^{20}	SKT-V, SKT	811
		T_2	41,45			SE-30, 105°pr	91
		T_2	25			SE-30	69
			25			SE-30, 65→180°, 2.0'	734
			21			Mass Spec.	712

Table 5-2. Aliphatic and Alicyclic Polyols (cont'd.)

Formula	Compound	Silyl-ation	Method (Yield %)	B.P./mm; M.P.	n_D^t	Stat. Phase, Temp., Retention Data	Ref.
$C_3H_8O_2$	1,3-Propanediol	T_1	13	b 81.5-82/23	1.4178^{20}		754
		T_2	13(90%)	b 69/11	1.4066^{20}		754
		T_2	25			ApL, 120°, 0.49/btd	761
		T_2	22			SE-30, 125°, 1.8'; Mass Spec.	195
		T_2		b 57-58/8	1.4111^{20}	SKT-V, SKT	811
		T_2	41,45			SE-30	69
$C_3H_9O_6P$	1-Glycerophosphate dimethyl ester	T_2	25			EGS, 158°, 14.8'	847
	2-Glycerophosphate dimethyl ester	T_2	25			EGS, 158°, 12.3'	847
$C_4H_8O_4$	Dimeric glycol-aldehyde	T_2	13			HTC, 125°; DDS, 125°; EGS, 175°	261
$C_4H_{10}O_2$	1,2-Butanediol	T_2		b 74/21	1.4103^{20}	SKT-V, SKT	811
	1,3-Butanediol	T_2		b 68-70/10	1.4100^{20}	SKT-V, SKT	811
			25			SE-30, 65→180°, 3.0'	734
	1,4-Butanediol	T_1	11	b 203			433
		T_2	11		1.4130^{15}		433
		T_2	13(76%)	b 91-94/16	1.4123^{20}		754
		T_2	25			ApL, 120°, 15.8'	761
		T_2	22			SE-30, 145°, 1.9'; Mass Spec.	195
	meso-2,3-Butanediol	T_2		b 67/20	1.4081^{20}	SKT-V, SKT	811
$C_4H_{10}O_3$	1,2,3-Butantriol	T_3		b 120-122/6.5	1.4134^{20}	SKT-V, SKT	811
		T_3	41,45			SE-30	69

Table 5-2. Aliphatic and Alicyclic Polyols (cont'd.)

Formula	Compound	Silyl-ation	Method (Yield %)	B.P./mm; M.P.	n_D^t	Stat. Phase, Temp., Retention Data	Ref.
$C_4H_{10}O_3$	1,2,4-Butanetriol	T_3		b 111-113/12	1.4160^{20}	SKT-V, SKT	811
	Diethyleneglycol		25			SE-52, 100→300°	759
		T_2	22			SE-30, 115°, 1.4' Mass Spec.	195
			13			SE-30, 187°pr	442
			25			SE-30, 65→180°, 5.0'	734
		T_2	23b			SiO, 100→300°, 0.41/hdcn	785
$C_4H_{11}NO_2$	Diethanolamine		25			SE-52, 100→300°	759
$C_4H_{16}B_{10}O_2$	1,2-Bis(hydroxymethyl)carborane	T_2	11u(90%)	b 140-146/0.05			696
$C_5H_{10}O_4$	Pentaerythrose	T_3	25			SE-30, 125→326°	758
$C_5H_{12}O_2$	Neopentylglycol	T_2	13(90%)	b 126-128/21	1.4185^{20}		754
		T_2	25			ApL, 120°, 0.57/btd	761
		T_2	13u(54%)	b 186	1.4117^{34}		484
	1,5-Pentanediol	T_2	25			ApL, 120°, 1.89/btd	761
		T_2	22			SE-30, 145°, 3.0' Mass Spec.	195
		T_2		b 91-92/7	1.4173^{20}	SKT-V, SKT	811
$C_5H_{12}O_3$	1,1,1-Tris(hydroxymethyl)ethane	T_3	13(90%)	b 122-123/16	1.4155^{20}		754
$C_5H_{12}O_4$	Pentaerythritol	T_4	13(90%)	b 128-129/5	1.4179^{20}		754
		T_4	25			SE-30, 125→326°	758
		T_4	13,23	b 150/17		SE-30, 125→275°	740
$C_6H_8O_6$	Dimethyl dihydroxymaleate	T_2	25			10% F-60, 15.26 MU / 1% F-60, 15.20 MU	182

Table 5-2. Aliphatic and Alicyclic Polyols (cont'd.)

Formula	Compound	Silyl-ation	Method (Yield %)	B.P./mm; M.P.	n_D^t	Stat. Phase, Temp., Retention Data	Ref.
$C_6H_{10}O_6$	Bis(2-hydroxyethyl) oxalate	T_2	13(50%)	b 130/1	1.4310^{20}		754
	myo-Inosose-2	T_5	25	m 98			488
			25			DEGS, 70→220°, 1.05/gu	618
			25			SE-30, 175°, 1.02/gu; EGS, 150°, 1.58/gu	850
			25			DEGS, 70→220°	617
			25			SE-30, 70→350°, 10.5'; DEGS, 70→220°, 9.7'	536
	Dimethyl tartarate	T_2	25			10% F-60, 14.74 MU; 1% F-60, 14.82 MU	182
$C_6H_{12}O_2$	cis-1,2-Cyclo-hexanediol	T_2	13e(87%)	b 72/0.5	1.4338^{22}	OV-1/OV-17, 80°, 8.6'; TLC	108
			25				469
	trans-1,2-Cyclo-hexanediol	T_2	13e(78%)	b 84-86/0.3	1.4328^{22}	OV-1/OV-17, 80°, 9.6'; TLC	108
			25				469
	1,2-Cyclohexanediol	T_2	13(84%)	b 94/10	1.4320^{20}		596
	1,4-Cyclohexanediol	T_2	13(84%)	m 53-54			596
$C_6H_{12}O_4$	Pentaerythritol monoformal	T_2	25			SE-30, 125→326°	758
$C_6H_{12}O_6$	1,3-Dihydroxy-acetone dimer	T_4	13			HTC, DDS, 125°; EGS, 175°	261
	Glyceraldehyde dimer	T_4	13			HTC, DDS, 125°; EGS, 175°	261

Table 5-2. Aliphatic and Alicyclic Polyols (cont'd.)

Formula	Compound	Silyl-ation	Method (Yield %)	B.P./mm; M.P.	n_D^t	Stat. Phase, Temp., Retention Data	Ref.
$C_6H_{12}O_6$	Inositol		25			SE-30, 160°, 1.85/srbl	761
			25			SE-30, 210°pr	827
						DC-430, 160°, 5.21/vana, 190°, 1.67/gall, 240°, 0.10/cat	672
		T_6	25			SE-30, 175°, 1.38/gu; EGS, 150°, 1.10/gu	850
		T_6	21d,22d			SE-30, UCW-98, 148→290°	867
		T_6	25d			SE-52, 120→250°	550
	(+)-Inositol		25			EGS, 150°, 1.13/gu	764
	(-)-Inositol		25			SE-30, 145°	232
	epi-Inositol	T_6	25			SE-30, 175°, 1.74/gu; EGS, 150°, 1.82/gu	850
	muco-Inositol	T_6	25			SE-30, 175°, 1.18/gu; EGS, 150°, 0.91/gu	850
	myo-Inositol		25			EGS, 150°, 2.56/gu	764
			25s			SE-30, 145°	233
			25			SE-30, 185°	851
			25			EGS, 158°	846
			25			DEGS, 70→220°, 1.13/gu	618
		T_6	13	m 117-118		ApL, 180°	221
		T_6	25			SE-30, 190°	845
		T_6	25			SE-30, 175°, 2.32/gu; EGS, 150°, 2.35/gu	850
		T_6	25			SE-30, 70→350°, 11.5'; DEGS, 70→220°, 10.6'	617

Table 5-2. Aliphatic and Alicyclic Polyols (cont'd.)

Formula	Compound	Silyl-ation	Method (Yield %)	B.P./mm; M.P.	n_D^t	Stat. Phase, Temp., Retention Data	Ref.
$C_6H_{12}O_6$	myo-Inositol	T_6	25	m 118–119		JXR, 140→210°, 1.36/miss, 1.08/sin, 1.00/min	488
		T_6	25			10% F-60, 21.42 MU; 1% F-60, 21.46 MU	182
	neo-Inositol	T_6	25			SE-30, 175°, 1.10/gu; EGS, 150°, 1.51/gu	850
	scyllo-Inositol	T_6	25			DEGS, 70→220°, 1.08/gu	618
		T_6	25			SE-30, 175°, 1.83/gu; EGS, 150°, 1.67/gu	850
		T_6	25			JXR, 140→210°, 1.24/miss, 1.00/sin, 0.093/min	488
$C_6H_{13}NO_5$	Methoxyethyl N,N-dimethylcarbamate	T_2	25			C-20M, 190°, 0.25'	895
$C_6H_{14}O_2$	1,6-Hexanediol	T_2	13	b 126–127/21	1.4185^{20}	SKT-V, SKT	754
		T_2				SKT-V, SKT	811
		T_2	22	b 95–97/8		SE-30, 160°, 1.8'; Mass Spec.	195
		T_2	25k			SE-52, 189°, 0.07/eic; F-60-Z, 190°, 0.07/eic; CNSi, 175°, 0.07/eic	803
$C_6H_{14}O_3$	1,1,1-Tris(hydroxy-methyl)propane	T_3	13 (90%)	b 124–126/10	1.4201^{20}	SE-30, 220°pr	754
	Triethyleneglycol	T_2	13			SiO, 100→300°, 0.83/hdcn	442
		T_2	23b				785
		T_2	25			SE-30, 65–180°, 8.0'	734

Table 5-2. Aliphatic and Alicyclic Polyols (con't'd.)

Formula	Compound	Silyl-ation	Method (Yield %)	B.P./mm; M.P.	n_D^t	Stat. Phase, Temp.., Retention Data	Ref.
$C_6H_{15}N_3O_6$	Tris(2-hydroxyethyl) cyanurate	T_3	13(90%)	b 180-181/0.3	1.4618^{20}		754
$C_7H_{10}O_5$	Quinide	T_3	21py				260
$C_7H_{12}O_6$	2-O,C-Methylene-myo-inositol	T_5	25			DEGS, 70→220°	617
			25			SE-30, 70→350°, 11.2'; DEGS, 70→220°, 10.3'	536
$C_7H_{14}O_3$	3-Methoxy-1,2-cyclo-hexanediol	T_2	13(87%)	b 119/10	1.4368^{20}		596
$C_7H_{14}O_4$	Methyl β,6-dihydroxy-β-methylvalerate	T_2	25			10% F-60, 14.66 MU; 1% F-60, 14.68 MU	182
$C_7H_{14}O_6$	Bornesitol	T_5	25			JXR, 140→210°, 1.15/miss, 0.93/sin, 0.86/min	488
	Ononitol	T_5	25			JXR, 140→210°, 1.08/miss, 0.87/sin, 0.80/min	488
	Pinitol	T_5	25			SE-30, 190°	612
		T_5	25			JXR, 140→210°, 0.86/miss, 0.69/sin, 0.64/min	488
		T_5	25			XF-1105, 122°, 0.74/gu; OS-138, 160°, 0.49/gu; BDS, 142°, 0.60/gu; XF-1112, 150°, 0.76/gu	62
	Quebrachitol	T_5	25			SE-52, C-20M, ApL, 140→230°	756
		T_5	25			JXR, 140→210°, 0.77/miss, 0.62/sin, 0.58/min	488

Table 5-2. Aliphatic and Alicyclic Polyols (cont'd.)

Formula	Compound	Silyl-ation	Method (Yield %)	B.P./mm; M.P.	n_D^t	Stat. Phase, Temp., Retention Data	Ref.
$C_7H_{14}O_6$	Sequoyitol		25			SE-30, 190°	612
						DC-430, 160°, 2.82/vana	672
$C_7H_{14}O_7$	2-O-Hydroxymethyl-myo-inositol	T_6	25			DEGS, 70→220°	617
$C_7H_{16}O_2$	1,7-Heptanediol	T_2	22			SE-30, 155°, 2.7', Mass Spec.	195
$C_8H_{10}O_2$	1,4-Bis(hydroxymethyl)benzene	T_2	13u(63%)	b 273	1.4736^{26}		484
	Phenylethyleneglycol		25			OV-1/OV-17, 130°, 3.6'	469
$C_8H_{12}O_5$	Methyl shikimate		25			10% F-60, 18.00 MU 1% F-60, 18.20 MU	182
$C_8H_{12}O_6$	Bis(β-hydroxyethyl)maleate	T_2	13(38%)	b 148-150/0.6	1.4460^{20}		754
$C_8H_{14}O_6$	Diethyl tartrate	T_2	13f(77%)	b 125-126/3	1.4292^{20}		307
	Methyl quinate	T_2	25				182
$C_8H_{16}O_2$	cis-1,2-Cyclooctanediol	T_2	25			10% F-60, 18.22 MU 1% F-60, 18.40 MU	787
	trans-1,2-Cyclooctanediol	T_2	25			GE-96, PPG, 100→150°	786, 787
	trans-1,4-Cyclooctanediol	T_1	25			GE-96, PPG	786
	trans-1,4-Cyclohexanedimethanol	T_2	13b(70%)	b 141-142/17	1.4342^{29}		484
	trans-2,2,4,4-Tetramethylcyclobutane-1,3-diol	T_2	13bh(50%)	m 69-70			477

Table 5-2. Aliphatic and Alicyclic Polyols (cont'd.)

Formula	Compound	Silyl-ation	Method (Yield %)	B.P./mm; M.P.	n_D^t	Stat. Phase, Temp.•, Retention Data	Ref.
$C_8H_{18}O_2$	1,8-Octanediol	T_2	22			SE-30, 155°, 4.2'; Mass Spec.	195
	2,2,4-Trimethyl-pentane-1,3-diol	T_2	13u(62%)	b 224	1.4278^{20}		484
$C_8H_{18}O_5$	Tetraethylene glycol	T_2	13			SE-30, 252°pr	442
		T_2	23b			SiO, 100→300°, 1.21/hdcn	785
$C_9H_{10}O_2$	cis-1,2-Dihydroxy-indane		25			SE-30, 65→180°, 10.5'	734
		T_2	25			OV-1/OV-17, 120°, 14.6'; TLC	469
	trans-1,2-Dihydroxy-indane		25			OV-1/OV-17, 120°, 15.8'; TLC	469
$C_9H_{20}O_2$	1,9-Nonanediol	T_2	25k			SE-52, 189°, 0.24/eic; F-60-Z, 190°, 0.23/eic; CNSi, 175°, 0.23/eic	803
$C_9H_{20}O_7$	Triglycerol		25			JXR, 120→325°	662
$C_{10}H_{14}O_4$	3,4-Dimethoxy-phenylglycol	T_2	25			10% F-60, 18.24 MU; 1% F-60, 18.38 MU	182
$C_{10}H_{20}O_2$	Terpin (hydrate)	T_2	25			SE-30, 140°	450
$C_{10}H_{20}O_6$	1,3,4,5-O-Tetra-methyl-myo-inositol	T_2	25			NGS, 128°, 6.8'; 137°, 5.3'; 142°, 3.3'	459
	1,4,5,6-O-Tetra-methyl-myo-inositol	T_2	25			NGS, 142°, 3.8'	459
$C_{10}H_{20}O_8$	Dipentaerythrose hemiacetal	T_6	25			SE-30, 125→326°	758

Table 5-2. Aliphatic and Alicyclic Polyols (cont'd.)

Formula	Compound	Silyl-ation	Method (Yield %)	B.P./mm; M.P.	n_D^t	Stat. Phase, Temp., Retention Data	Ref.
$C_{10}H_{22}O_2$	1,10-Decanediol	T_2	43			OV-17; Mass Spec.	517
$C_{10}H_{22}O_6$	Pentaethylene glycol	T_2	13			SE-30, 276°pr	442
		T_2	23b			SiO₂, 100→300°, 1.53/hdcn	785
$C_{10}H_{22}O_7$	Dipentaerythritol	T_6	13,23	b 205/10		SE-30, 125→275°	740
		T_6	25			SE-30, 125→326°	758
$C_{11}H_{14}O_3$	1-Allyloxy-2,4-di-methylolbenzene	T_2	13	b 115-116/0.04	1.4832^{20}		138
$C_{11}H_{22}O_6$	1,2,3,4,5-O-Penta-methyl-myo-inositol	T_1	25			NGS, 137°, 6.4'	459
	1,2,3,4,6-O-Penta-methyl-myo-inositol	T_1	25			NGS, 137°, 7.7'	459
	1,2,4,5,6-O-Penta-methyl-myo-inositol	T_1	25			NGS, 128°, 8.4'; 137°, 5.6'; 142°, 4.9'	459
	1,3,4,5,6-O-Penta-methyl-myo-inositol	T_1	25			NGS, 137°, 3.6'	459
$C_{11}H_{24}O_8$	Bispentaerythritol monoformal	T_6	25			SE-30, 125→326°	758
$C_{12}H_{10}Cl_6O_2$	trans-6,7-Dihydroxy-6,7-dihydro-aldrin	T_2	25e			SE-52, 193°; TLC	127, 492
$C_{12}H_{14}O_6$	Bis(β-hydroxyethyl) phthalate	T_2	13 (50%)	b 156-162/0.5	1.4770^{20}		754
	Bis(β-hydroxyethyl) terephthalate	T_2	13 (37%)	b 170-174/0.3	1.4812^{20}		754
$C_{12}H_{16}O_4$	1-Allyloxy-2,4,6-tri-methylolbenzene	T_3	13	b 143-146/0.04	1.4708^{20}		138

Table 5-2. Aliphatic and Alicyclic Polyols (cont'd.)

Formula	Compound	Silylation	Method (Yield %)	B.P./mm; M.P.	n_D^t	Stat. Phase, Temp., Retention Data	Ref.
$C_{12}H_{26}O_7$	Hexaethylene glycol	T_2	13			SE-30, 296°pr	442
		T_2	23b			SiO, 100→300°, 1.82/hdcn	785
$C_{14}H_{14}O_2$	Hydrobenzoin		25			OV-17, 130°, 18.0' TLC	469
	Isohydrobenzoin		25			OV-17, 130°, 19.0' TLC	469
$C_{14}H_{30}O_8$	Heptaethylene glycol	T_2	13			SE-30, 160→275°	442
		T_2	23b			SiO, 100→300°, 2.09/hdcn	785
$C_{15}H_{26}O$	(+)δ-Nerolidol				1.4807^{20}	Mass Spec.	152
$C_{15}H_{28}O_2$	Caparrapidol	T_2	22			SE-30, 100°; Mass Spec.	43
		T_2				Mass Spec.	152
						Mass Spec.	120
$C_{15}H_{30}O_3$	Caparrapitriol	T_3	22			SE-30, 100°; Mass Spec.	43
		T_3				Mass Spec.	152
						Mass Spec.	120
$C_{15}H_{32}O_{10}$	Tripentaerythritol	T_8	25			SE-30, 125→326°	758
		T_8	13,23			SE-30	740
$C_{16}H_{32}O_4$	2,4-Dihydroxybutyl laurate	T_2	25h			SE-52, QF-1, 280°	866
	3,4-Dihydroxybutyl laurate	T_2	25h			SE-52, QF-1, 280°	866
	2-(1,4-Dihydroxy)-butyl laurate	T_2	25h			SE-52, QF-1, 280°	866
$C_{16}H_{33}NO_3$	Lauric acid diethanol amide	T_2	25			SE-52, 100→300°	759

Table 5-2. Aliphatic and Alicyclic Polyols (con't'd.)

Formula	Compound	Silyl-ation	Method (Yield %)	B.P./mm; M.P.	n_D^t	Stat. Phase, Temp.., Retention Data	Ref.
$C_{16}H_{34}O_9$	Octaethylene glycol	T_2	13			SE-30, 333°pr	182
		T_2	23b			SiO, 100→300°, 2.33/hdch	785
$C_{16}H_{34}O_{11}$	Pentaerythritoldi-pentaerythritol monoformal	T_8	25			SE-30, 125→326°	758
$C_{17}H_{34}O_4$	Methyl 10,16-di-hydroxypalmitate		25			SE-52, 250°	106
		T_2	21			SE-30, 214° Mass Spec.	214
$C_{17}H_{34}O_5$	Methyl 9,10,16-tri-hydroxypalmitate		25			SE-52, 250°	106
$C_{17}H_{36}O_{12}$	Trispentaerythritol diformal	T_8	25			SE-30, 125→326°	758
$C_{18}H_{36}O_4$	2,6-Dihydroxyhexyl laurate	T_2	25h			SE-52, QF-1, 280°	866
	5,6-Dihydroxyhexyl laurate	T_2	25h			SE-52, 280°	866
	2-(1,6-Dihydroxy)-hexyl laurate	T_2	25h			SE-52, 280°	866
$C_{18}H_{38}O_{10}$	Nonaethylene glycol	T_2	13			SE-30, 350°pr	442
		T_2	23b			SiO, 100→300°, 2.57/hdcn	785
$C_{19}H_{36}O_6$	Methyl 8,9-dihydroxy-heptadecane-1,17-dioate	T_2	21			SE-30, 214° Mass Spec.	214
$C_{19}H_{38}O_4$	Methyl threo-9,10-dihydroxystearate	T_2	25			DEGS, ApL	879

Table 5-2. Aliphatic and Alicyclic Polyols (cont'd.)

Formula	Compound	Silylation	Method (Yield %)	B.P./mm; M.P.	n_D^t	Stat. Phase, Temp., Retention Data	Ref.
$C_{19}H_{38}O_5$	Methyl threo-9,10,12-trihydroxystearate	T_3	25			ApL, 240° 20% DEGS, 215° 10% DEGS, 208°	879
	Methyl 9,10,18-tri-hydroxystearate	T_3	21			SE-30, 214° Mass Spec.	214
	Methyl erythro-9,10,-18-trihydroxystearate	T_3	21			SE-30, 214° Mass Spec.	214
	Methyl threo-9,10,-18-trihydroxystearate	T_3	21			SE-30, 214° Mass Spec.	214
$C_{19}H_{38}O_6$	Methyl erythro-9,10-erythro-12,13-tetra-hydroxystearate	T_4	25			ApL, 240° 20% DEGS, 215° 10% DEGS, 208°	879
	Methyl 9,10,12,13-tetrahydroxystearate	T_4	21			SE-30, 214° Mass Spec.	214
$C_{19}H_{38}O_7$	Methyl 9,10,12,13,18-pentahydroxystearate	T_5	21			SE-30, 214° Mass Spec.	214
$C_{20}H_{24}O_6$	Gibberellin A_3 methyl ester		25			QF-1, 179°, 3.75/chn SE-33, 187°, 0.79/chn	154
$C_{20}H_{26}O_6$	Gibberellin A_1 methyl ester		25			QF-1, 179°, 3.20/chn SE-33, 187°, 0.72/chn	154
			25			SE-30, 160→250° Mass Spec.	503

Table 5-2. Aliphatic and Alicyclic Polyols (cont'd.)

Formula	Compound	Silyl- ation	Method (Yield %)	B.P./mm; M.P.	n_D^t	Stat. Phase, Temp., Retention Data	Ref.
$C_{20}H_{26}O_7$	Gibberellin A_8 methyl ester		25			QF-1, 179°, 4.00/chn; SE-33, 187°, 1.26/chn	154
						SE-30, 160→250° Mass Spec.	503
$C_{20}H_{28}O_6$	Gibberellin A_2 methyl ester		25			QF-1, 179°, 4.53/chn; SE-33, 187°, 0.35/chn	154
$C_{20}H_{30,32,34}O_5$	Prostaglandin E		43			SE-30	347
$C_{20}H_{38}O_6$	Methyl 9,10-di-hydroxyoctadecane-1,18-dioate	T_2	21			SE-30, 214°; Mass Spec.	214
$C_{20}H_{42}O_{11}$	Decaethylene glycol	T_2	13			SE-30, 365°pr	442
		T_2	23b			SiO, 100→300°, 2.76/hdcn	785
$C_{20}H_{42}O_{13}$	Tetrapentaerythritol	T_{10}	25			SE-30, 125→326°	758
$C_{21}H_{30}O_6$	Gibberellin (Lupinus-I)		25			QF-1, 179°, 1.35/chn; SE-33, 187°, 0.57/chn	154
$C_{21}H_{38}O_5$	Prostaglandin $F_{1\alpha}$ or $F_{2\alpha}$ methyl ester	T_3	26h			HiEff, 190°	141, 142
$C_{21}H_{44}O_{14}$	Bis(dipentaerythritol) monoformal	T_{10}	25			SE-30, 125→326°	758
$C_{22}H_{46}O_2$	1,22-Docosanediol	T_2	43			OV-17; Mass Spec.	517
$C_{22}H_{46}O_{12}$	Undecaethylene glycol	T_2	13			SE-30, 375°pr	442
		T_2	23b			SiO, 100→300°, 2.95/hdcn	785

Table 5-2. Aliphatic and Alicyclic Polyols (cont'd.)

Formula	Compound	Silyl-ation	Method (Yield %)	B.P./mm; M.P.	n_D^t	Stat. Phase, Temp., Retention Data	Ref.
$C_{24}H_{50}O_{13}$	Dodecaethylene glycol	T_2	13			SE-30, 375°pr	442
		T_2	23b			SiO, 100→300°, 3.12/hdcn	785
$C_{25}H_{36}O_4$	Colupulone	T_3	23d,25			Mass Spec.	183
$C_{25}H_{52}O_{16}$	Pentapentaerythritol	T_{12}	25			SE-30, 125→326°	758
$C_{26}H_{54}O_{14}$	Tridecaethylene glycol	T_2	13			SE-30, 375°pr	442
$C_{28}H_{40}O_4$	Azafrin methyl ester	T_1	25			Mass Spec.	518
$C_{29}H_{50}O_4$	Dihydro-cis-phytylubiquinone	T_2	42			ApN, 250°; Mass Spec.	859
	Dihydro-trans-phytylubiquinone	T_2	42			ApN, 250°, 40.6' Mass Spec.	859
$C_{31}H_{48}O_2$	cis-Dihydrovitamin K_1	T_2	42			ApL, 275° UCW-98, 250° Mass Spec.	859
	trans-Dihydro-vitamin K_1	T_2	42			ApL, 275° UCW-98, 250°, 30.2' Mass Spec.	859
$C_{33}H_{55}N_5O_{19}$	Penta-N-acetyl-paromomycin	T_8	25			Mass Spec.	188
$C_{35}H_{58}O_{11}$	Filipin	T_9	25			Mass Spec.	276
$C_{35}H_{58}O_{12}$	Lagosin	T_{10}	25			Mass Spec.	276
$C_{35}H_{68}O_{11}$	Decahydrofilipin	T_9	25			Mass Spec.	276
$C_{35}H_{68}O_{12}$	Decahydrolagosin	T_{10}	25			Mass Spec.	276
$C_{36}H_{50}O_2$	trans-Dihydro-vitamin K_2	T_2	42py			UCW-98, 280°, 52.9' Mass Spec.	859

Table 5-2. Aliphatic and Alicyclic Polyols (cont'd.)

Formula	Compound	Silyl- ation	Method (Yield %)	B.P./mm; M.P.	n_D^t	Stat. Phase, Temp.., Retention Data	Ref.
$C_{36}H_{51}NO_{14}$	N-Acetylpimaricin methyl ester	T_5	25			Mass Spec.	277
$C_{36}H_{53}NO_{13}$	Lucensomycin	T_5	25			Mass Spec.	265
$C_{37}H_{67}NO_{13}$	Erythromycin	T_2	23b				752
$C_{40}H_{52}O_4$	1,1'-Dihydroxy-2,2'-diketo-1,1'2,2'-tetrahydro-3,3'4,4'-tetradehydrolycopene	T_2	25				44
$C_{40}H_{54}O_2$	Isozeaxanthin	T_2	25			Mass Spec.	518
$C_{40}H_{60}O_2$	1,2,1',2'-Tetrahydro-1,1'-dihydroxyly-copene	T_2	25			Mass Spec.	518
$C_{43}H_{54}INO_{15}$	N-Acetylpimaricin p-iodophenacyl ester	T_5	25			Mass Spec.	277
$C_{44}H_{60}O_6$	1,2,1',2'-Tetrahydro-3,4,3',4'-dehydro-1,1'-dihydroxy-2,2'-diacetyllycopene	T_2	25				44
$C_{50}H_{72}O_2$	Bis(anhydro)bacterio-ruberin	$T_{1,2}$	25			Mass Spec.	406
$C_{50}H_{74}O_3$	Anhydrobacterio-ruberin	T_{1-3}	25			Mass Spec.	406
$C_{50}H_{76}O_4$	Bacterioruberin	T_{1-4}	25			Mass Spec.	406
$C_{56}H_{82}O_2$	trans-Dihydro-vitamin K_2	T_2	42			UCW-98, 280° Mass Spec.	859

TABLE 5-3. GLYCEROL ESTERS AND ETHERS

Formula	Compound	Method (Yield %)	B.P./mm; M.P.	Stationary Phase, Col. Temp., Retention Data	Ref.
$C_6H_{12}O_4$	Diglycerol (cyclic)	25		JXR, 120→325°	662
$C_6H_{14}O_5$	Diglycerol (linear)	25		JXR, 120→325°	662
		13		ApM, 205°	739
$C_9H_{18}O_4$	1-Monocaproin	13(95%)	b 105-107/0.01	SE-30, 221°pr	440
$C_{11}H_{22}O_4$	1-Monocaprylin	13(95%)	b 125-128/0.01	SE-30, 242°pr	440
$C_{13}H_{26}O_4$	1-Monocaprin	13(95%)	b 135-140/0.01	SE-30, 263°pr	440
		25		ApL, 180→240°; SE-30, 127→190°	880
	2-Monocaprin	25		Mass Spec.	378
		25		ApL, 180→240°; SE-30, 127→190°	880
		25		Mass Spec.	378
$C_{15}H_{28}O_5$	1,2-Dicaproin	13(72%)	b 116/0.07	SE-30, 259.5°pr	440
		13		SE-30, 216°pr	442
	1,3-Dicaproin	13(60%)	b 109/0.01	SE-30, 262°pr	440
		13		SE-30, 220°pr	442
$C_{15}H_{30}O_4$	1-Monolaurin	13(90%)	b 140-144/0.01	SE-30, 281°pr	440
		25		SE-52/QF-1, 280°	866
		25		ApL, 180→240°; SE-30, 127→190°	880
		25		Mass Spec.	378
	2-Monolaurin	13(90%)	b 140/0.01	SE-30, 277.5°pr	440
		25		ApL, 180→240°; SE-30, 127→190°	880
		25		Mass Spec.	378

Table 5-3. Glycerol Esters and Ethers (cont'd.)

Formula	Compound	Method (Yield %)	B.P./mm; M.P.	Stationary Phase, Col. Temp., Retention Data	Ref.
$C_{15}H_{32}O_3$	Glyceryl lauryl ether	25		SE-30, 230° / XE-60, 200° / EGS, 215°	881
$C_{17}H_{32}O_5$	1-Capro-3-caprylin	13		SE-30, 279°pr	440
$C_{17}H_{34}O_4$	1-Monomyristin	13(90%)	b 152-155/0.01	SE-30, 297.5°pr	440
		25		JXR, 125→325°	663
		25		ApL, 180→240° / SE-30, 127→190°	880
		25		Mass Spec.	378
	2-Monomyristin	25		ApL, 180→240° / SE-30, 127→190°	880
		25		Mass Spec.	378
	1- or 2-Monomyristin	25		SE-52, 100→300°	759
		25		ApL, 240°, 0.65/cal / JXR, 225°, 0.73/cal / DEGS, 200°, 1.00/cal / XE-60, 185°, 1.23/cal	656
$C_{17}H_{36}O_3$	Glyceryl myristyl ether	25		SE-30, 230° / XE-60, 200° / EGS, 215°	881
		25		ApL, 240°, 0.50/cal / JXR, 225°, 0.53/cal / XE-60, 185°, 0.50/cal / DEGS, 200°, 0.50/cal	656
$C_{19}H_{36}O_5$	1-Capro-3-caprin	13(80%)	b 130/0.01	SE-30, 294°pr	440
	1,2-Dicaprylin	13(71%)	b 145/0.01		440
	1,3-Dicaprylin	13		SE-30, 246°pr	442
		13(70%)	b 130/0.01	SE-30, 294.5°pr	440
		13		SE-30, 250°pr	442

Table 5-3. Glycerol Esters and Ethers (cont'd.)

Formula	Compound	Method (Yield %)	B.P./mm; M.P.	Stationary Phase, Col. Temp., Retention Data	Ref.
$C_{19}H_{38}O_3$	Glyceryl hexadec-9-enyl ether	25		ApL, 240°, 0.92/cal JXR, 225°, 0.94/cal	656
$C_{19}H_{38}O_4$	1-Monopalmitin	13(90%)	b 160/0.01	SE-30, 312°pr	440
		25		JXR, 125→325°	663
		25		SE-52, 100→300°	759
		25		SE-30, 127→190° ApL, 180→240° EGS, 215°	880
		25		Mass Spec.	378
	2-Monopalmitin	25		SE-52, 100→300°	759
		25		SE-30, 127→190° ApL, 180→240° EGS, 215°	880
	Monopalmitin	25		Mass Spec.	378
		25		SE-30, 110→400°	771
		25		ApL, 240°, 1.36/cal JXR, 225°, 1.35/cal XE-60, 185°, 2.43/cal DEGS, 200°, 2.07/cal	656
$C_{19}H_{40}O_3$	Chimyl alcohol	43py		OV-1, 110→400°	770
		25		EGS, QF-1, 185→205°	94
		25		SE-30, 230° XE-60, 200° EGS, 215°	881
		25		ApL, 240°, 7.75' JXR, 225°, 9.5' XE-60, 185°, 4.25' DEGS, 200°, 6.5'	656
$C_{21}H_{36}O_4$	1-(or 2)-Monolinolenin	25		Mass Spec.	378

Table 5-3. Glycerol Esters and Ethers (cont'd.)

Formula	Compound	B.P./mm; M.P.	Method (Yield %)	Stationary Phase, Col. Temp., Retention Data	Ref.
$C_{21}H_{38}O_4$	1- or 2-Monolinolein		25	DEGS, 215°	880
			25	Mass Spec.	378
$C_{21}H_{38}O_5$	Monodimorphecolin		22py,43py	OV-1, 110→400°	770
	Monovernolin		22py,43py	OV-1, 110→400°	770
$C_{21}H_{40}O_3$	Glyceryl linoleyl ether		25	SE-30, 110→400°	771
			25	SE-30, 230° ; XE-60, 200° ; EGS, 215°	881
			25	EGS, 150°	882
$C_{21}H_{40}O_4$	1-Monoolein	b 165-170/0.01	13(80%)	SE-30, 326°pr	440
			25	JXR, 125→325°	663
			25	DEGS, 215°	880
			25	Mass Spec.	378
	2-Monoolein		25	DEGS, 215°	880
			25	Mass Spec.	378
	Monoolein		25	SE-30, 110→400°	771
			25	ApL, 240°, 2.31/cal; JXR, 225°, 2.34/cal; XE-60, 185°, 4.70/cal; DEGS, 200°, 4.38/cal	656
$C_{21}H_{40}O_5$	Monoricinolin		25	SE-30, 110→400°	771
$C_{21}H_{42}O_3$	Glyceryl oleyl ether		25	SE-30, 230°; XE-60, 200°; EGS, 215°	881
			25	ApL, 240°, 1.80/cal; JXR, 225°, 1.70/cal; XE-60, 185°, 1.94/cal; DEGS, 200°, 2.10/cal	656

Table 5-3. Glycerol Esters and Ethers (cont'd.)

Formula	Compound	Method (Yield %)	B.P./mm; M.P.	Stationary Phase, Col. Temp., Retention Data	Ref.
$C_{21}H_{42}O_3$	Glyceryl oleyl ether	25		EGS, 150° / SE-30, 285°	882
$C_{21}H_{42}O_4$	1-Monostearin	13(80%)	b 165/0.01	SE-30, 325°pr	440
		25		JXR, 125→325°	663
		25		ApL, 180→240° / SE-30, 127→190° / EGS, 215°	880
		25		Mass Spec.	378
	2-Monostearin	25		ApL, 180→240° / SE-30, 127→190° / EGS, 215°	880
		25		Mass Spec.	378
	Monostearin	22py,43py		OV-1, 110→400°	770
		25		ApL, 240°, 2.64/cal / JXR, 225°, 2.57/cal / XE-60, 185°, 4.70/cal / DEGS, 200°, 4.13/cal	656
		25		SE-52, 100→300°, 1.077/gyp	759
		25		SE-30, 110→400°	771
$C_{21}H_{44}O_3$	Batyl alcohol	25		EGS, QF-1, 185→205°	94
		25		SE-30, 230° / XE-60, 200° / EGS, 215°	881
		25		ApL, 240°, 2.02/cal / JXR, 225°, 1.88/cal / XE-60, 185°, 1.95/cal / DEGS, 200°, 2.05/cal	656
		25	m <20	EGS, 150°	882
$C_{22}H_{44}O_6$	Diglycerol monopalmitate	25		JXR, 120→325°	662

Table 5-3. Glycerol Esters and Ethers (cont'd.)

Formula	Compound	Method (Yield %)	B.P./mm; M.P.	Stationary Phase, Col. Temp., Retention Data	Ref.
$C_{23}H_{44}O_5$	1,2-Dicaprin	13(65%)	b 164/0.01	SE-30, 322.5°pr	440
	1,3-Dicaprin	13		SE-30, 271°pr	442
		13(70%)	b 155/0.01	SE-30, 323°pr	440
		13		SE-30, 275°pr	442
	3-Lauro-1-caprylin	13(75%)	b 160/0.01	SE-30, 323°pr	440
	Monolesquerolin	25		SE-30, 110→400°	771
$C_{23}H_{46}O_4$	1-(or 2)-Monoarachidin	25		Mass Spec.	378
$C_{24}H_{46}O_6$	Diglycerol monooleate	25		JXR, 120→325°	662
$C_{24}H_{48}O_6$	Diglycerol monostearate	25		JXR, 120→325°	662
		25		SE-52, 100→300°, 0.264, 0.622/gyp	759
$C_{25}H_{48}O_5$	3-Lauro-1-caprin	13(70%)	b 172/0.01	SE-30, 337°pr	440
$C_{25}H_{50}O_8$	Triglycerol monopalmitate	25		JXR, 120→329°	662
$C_{27}H_{52}O_5$	1,2-Dilaurin	13(74%)	b 201-202/0.02	SE-30, 348.5°pr	440
		13		SE-30, 297°pr	442
	1,3-Dilaurin	13(65%)	b 195/0.01	SE-30, 348°pr	440
		13		SE-30, 300°pr	442
$C_{27}H_{52}O_8$	Triglycerol monooleate	25		JXR, 120→325°	662
$C_{27}H_{54}O_8$	Triglycerol monostearate	25		JXR, 120→325°	662
		25		SE-52, 100→300°, 0.247, 0.446, 0.608/gyp	759
$C_{31}H_{60}O_5$	Dimyristin	25		JXR, 125→325°	663
$C_{33}H_{64}O_5$	Myristopalmitin	25		JXR, 125→325°	663
$C_{35}H_{68}O_5$	1,2-Dipalmitin	25		XE-60, 255→; Mass Spec.	159
		25		TLC	533

Table 5-3. Glycerol Esters and Ethers (cont'd.)

Formula	Compound	Method (Yield %)	B.P./mm; M.P.	Stationary Phase, Col. Temp., Retention Data	Ref.
$C_{35}H_{68}O_5$	1,3-Dipalmitin	25		XE-60, 255°→; Mass Spec.	159
	Dipalmitin	25		JXR, 125→325°	662, 663
		25		SE-30, 110→400°	771
		25		SE-52, 100→300°, 2.269/gyp	759
		43py		OV-1, 110→400°	770
$C_{37}H_{70}O_5$	Palmitolein	25		JXR, 125→325°	663
$C_{37}H_{72}O_5$	2-Palmito-1-stearin	25		XE-60, 255°→; Mass Spec.	159
	Palmito stearin	25		SE-52, 100→300°, 1.928/gyp	759
	2-Stearo-1-palmitin	25		XE-60, 255°→; Mass Spec.	159
$C_{38}H_{74}O_7$	Diglycerol dipalmitin	25		JXR, 120→325°	662
$C_{39}H_{72}O_5$	Diolein	25		JXR, 120→325°	662, 663
		25		TLC	533
$C_{39}H_{74}O_5$	Oleostearin	25		JXR, 125→325°	663
$C_{39}H_{76}O_5$	1,2-Distearin	25		XE-60, 255°→; Mass Spec.	159
	Distearin	25		JXR, 125→325°	662, 663
		25		SE-52, 100→300°, 1.659/gyp	759
		25		SE-30, 100→400°	771
		43py		OV-1, 110→400°	770
$C_{40}H_{78}O_7$	Diglycerol monopalmitate monostearate	25		JXR, 125→325°	662
$C_{42}H_{78}O_7$	Diglycerol dioleate	25		JXR, 120→325°	662
$C_{42}H_{82}O_7$	Diglycerol distearate	25		JXR, 120→325°	662
$C_{45}H_{85}O_9$	Triglycerol dioleate	25		JXR, 120→325°	662
$C_{45}H_{89}O_9$	Triglycerol distearate	25		JXR, 120→325°	662

TABLE 5-4. MONOHYDRIC PHENOLS

Formula	Compound	Method	Yield %	B.P./mm; M.P.	n_D^t	Stat. Phase, Temp., Retention Data	Ref.
$C_6H_5Cl_3O$	2,4,5-Trichlorophenol	21	87	b 74–78/0.2	1.5248^{20}		367, 368
	2,4,6-Trichlorophenol	11	84	b 110/2	1.5252^{20}		171
		11u	70	b 147/20	1.5231^{25}		658
		21	89	b 75–79/0.15	1.5253^{20}		367, 368
$C_6H_4Cl_2O$	2,4-Dichlorophenol	11		b 132/24	1.5070^{25}		749
	2,6-Dichlorophenol	11	85	b 115/15	1.5116^{20}		171
C_6H_5BrO	p-Bromophenol	11	90	b 126/25	1.5123^{25}		749
		11		b 98–98.5/7	1.5145^{20}		278
		13	72	b 122/20			549
		13	76–85				248
		13b		b 113/14			247
C_6H_5ClO	o-Chlorophenol	11		b 212/742, 106/23	1.4910^{25}		749
	m-Chlorophenol	11	85–95				171
		11	85–95				171
		11	88	b 45/2	1.4950^{20}		53
	p-Chlorophenol	11	85–95				171
		11	90	b 101/14	1.4923^{25}		749
		51	59	b 214/758	1.4930^{20}		824
C_6H_5IO	o-Iodophenol	11		b 134/25	1.5441^{25}		749
$C_6H_5NO_3$	o-Nitrophenol	12b	30	b 115/3	1.5076^{20}		429
		21	90	b 84/1.0	1.5090^{20}		367, 368

Table 5-4. Monohydric Phenols (cont'd.)

Formula	Compound	Method (Yield %)	B.P./mm; M.P.	n_D^t	Stationary Phase, Col. Temp., Retention Data	Ref.
$C_6H_5NO_3$	p-Nitrophenol	21(90%)	b 95-96/0.75	1.5293^{20}		367, 368
C_6H_6O	Phenol	11	b 174-187			109
		11(84%)	b 180	1.4772^{25}		658
		11	b 81/23, 182.5/736	1.4753^{25}		749
		11	b 68-69/13, 145/20	1.4787^{20}, 1.4883^{20}		18
		51(72%)	b 178/760	1.4800^{20}		824
		25			ApL, 120°, 11.2'	761
		11p,21	b 181.9-2.4/747	1.4782^{20}	DC-550, 125°	452, 455
		13,24			MS-550, 100°, 0.108/indl	281
		24			TXP, 116°, 9.1'	9
		24			DOSb, TXP, 125°, 8.4'	238, 239
		25			10% F-60, 10.48 MU; 1% F-60, 10.40 MU	182
		26			TCP, 80°	566
		25			DC-430, 100-260°, 4.6'	303
		21			Mass Spec.	712
$C_7H_6O_2$	o-Hydroxybenzaldehyde	11	b 142/25	1.5079^{25}		749
		11(6%)	b 82/0.7	1.5103^{20}, 1.5084^{25}		429
	p-Hydroxybenzaldehyde	11(70%)	b 83-84/3	1.5198^{20}		876
		11b(22%)	b 102-103/0.7-3.7	1.5180^{21}	SE-30, 194°, 3.0'	429
		21py				548

Table 5-4. Monohydric Phenols (cont'd.)

Formula	Compound	Method (Yield %)	B.P./mm.; M.P.	n_D^t	Stationary Phase, Col. Temp., Retention Data	Ref.
$C_7H_6O_2$	p-Hydroxybenzaldehyde	25			SE-52, 160°, 0.46/van	674
		25			30% DC-430, 160°,0.91/van 190°, 0.23/vana 5% DC-430, 160°, 0.23/vana	672
$C_7H_6O_3$	3,4-Methylenedioxy phenol	13(78%)	b 124-125/14.5	1.4999[25]		59
		25			C-20M, 160°, 0.27,3.9/pip 200°, 2.7/pip	894
C_7H_7ClO	4-Chloro-3-methyl- phenol	11	b 125/23	1.4963[25]		749
C_7H_8O	o-Cresol	11,13	b 193	1.4812[20]		311
		21(85%)	b 106-108/10-11			368
		51(88%)	b 192, 77/12	1.4830[20]		824
		25			ApL, 120°, 1.74/pol	761
		23			ApL, 170°, 1.55/pol	741
		24			MS-550, 92°, 1.58/pol 100°, 0.164/indl	281
		24			DOSb, TXP, 125°, 11.6'	238, 239
		24			TXP, 116°, 1.37/pol	9
		25			DOP, 135°; SE-30, 100°	48
		21			DC-550, 125°, 1.59/pol DBTCP, 125°, 1.68/pol	455
		26			TCP, 80°, 1.58/pol	566
		21			Mass Spec.	712
	m-Cresol	11,13	b 198.5	1.4796[20]		311
		51(88%)	b 113/50	1.4791[20]		824

Table 5-4. Monohydric Phenols (cont'd.)

Formula	Compound	Method (Yield %)	B.P./mm; M.P.	n_D^t	Stationary Phase, Col. Temp., Retention Data	Ref.
C_7H_8O	m-Cresol	25			ApL, 120°, 1.78/pol	761
		23			ApL, 170°, 1.55/pol	741
		25			DOP, 135°; SE-30, 100	48
		25			DC-430, 100→260°,1.41/pol	303
		21			DC-550, 125°, 1.71/pol; DBTCP, 125°, 1.75/pol	455
		24			MS-550, 92°, 1.63/pol; 100°, 0.177/indl	281
		24			DOSb, TXP, 125°, 12.2'	238, 239
		24			TXP, 116°, 1.44/pol	9
		26			TCP, 80°, 1.76/pol	566
		21			Mass Spec.	712
		21			Mass Spec.	713
	p-Cresol	11,13	b 199	1.4738[20]		311
		51(42%)	b 59/1	1.4790[20]		824
		25			ApL, 120°, 1.98/pol	761
		23			ApL, 170°, 1.70/pol	741
		25			DOP, 135°; SE-30, 100°	48
		21			DC-550, 125°, 1.84/pol; DBTCP, 125°, 1.89/pol	455
		25			10% F-60, 11.46 MU; 1% F-60, 11.42 MU	182
		26			TCP, 80°, 1.95/pol	566
		24			DOSb, TXP, 125°, 13.4'	238, 239
		24			TXP, 116°, 1.58/pol	9

Table 5-4. Monohydric Phenols (cont'd.)

Formula	Compound	Method (Yield %)	B.P./mm; M.P.	n_D^t	Stationary Phase, Col. Temp., Retention Data	Ref.
C_7H_8O	p-Cresol	24			MS-550, 92°, 1.75/pol 100°, 0.190/indl	281
		21c			ApN, 160.4°, 0.72/gcl	164
		21			Mass Spec.	712
$C_7H_8O_2$	o-Hydroxybenzyl alcohol	13b(80%)	b 109-111/12-14			512
		25			DC-430, 100→260°, 2.11/pol	303
	p-Hydroxybenzyl alcohol	13	b 90-140/15			511
		25			DC-430, 100→260°, 2.44/pol	303
	o-Methoxyphenol	11	b 217	1.4855^{20}		311
		21			DC-550, 125°, 3.23/pol DBTCP, 125°, 3.48/pol	455
		21c			ApN, 160°; PPE, 160°	166
		21py			SE-30, 108°, 5.5'	548
		24			MS-550, 100°	281
		25			DC-430, 100→260°, 1.71/pol	303
	p-Methoxyphenol	21py			SE-30, 162°, 1.9'	548
$C_8H_6O_3$	Homogentisic acid lactone	14			SE-52, 170°, 5.5/naph	89
		25			10% F-60, 17.46 MU 1% F-60, 17.66 MU	182
$C_8H_8O_2$	o-Hydroxyacetophenone	12b(41%)	b 96-96.5/1.3	1.5036^{20}		429
$C_8H_8O_3$	Methyl o-hydroxy-benzoate	11	b 142/25	1.4911^{25}		749
		12b(43%)	b 122/10	1.4943^{20}		429
		25			10% F-60, 14.00 MU 1% F-60, 14.08 MU	182

Table 5-4. Monohydric Phenols (cont'd.)

Formula	Compound	Method (Yield %)	B.P./mm; M.P.	n_D^t	Stationary Phase, Col. Temp., Retention Data	Ref.
$C_8H_8O_3$	Methyl o-hydroxy-benzoate	25			F-60, 100→250°	348
	Methyl m-hydroxy-benzoate	25			10% F-60, 14.48 MU 1% F-60, 14.50 MU	182
	Methyl p-hydroxy-benzoate	25			SE-30, 110°, 1.8/pol	451
		25			10% F-60, 14.90 MU 1% F-60, 14.94 MU	182
		25			92→200°: SE-30, XE-60, QF-1	199
	Vanillin	21py			SE-30, 148°, 5.4'	548
		25			SE-52, 160°, 6.5' 192°, 0.48/van	674
		25			30% DC-430, 160°,1.87/van 190°,0.41/vana 5% DC-430, 160°,0.29/vana	672
		25			DC-430, 100→260°, 2.57/pol	303
$C_8H_{10}O$	o-Ethylphenol	21			DC-550, 125°, 2.36/pol DBTCP, 125°, 2.34/pol	455
		23			XF-1150, 150°, 2.1/pol	741
		24			TXP, 125°, 15.0'	238
		24			MS-550, 92°, 2.25/pol 100°, 0.242/indl	281
		24			TXP, 116°, 1.78/pol	9
	m-Ethylphenol	24			TXP, 116°, 2.11/pol	9
		24			MS-550, 92°, 2.54/pol 100°, 0.289/indl	281
		24			TXP, 125°, 17.6'	238

Table 5–4. Monohydric Phenols (cont'd.)

Formula	Compound	Method (Yield %)	B.P./mm; M.P.	n_D^t	Stationary Phase, Col. Temp., Retention Data	Ref.
$C_8H_{10}O$	m-Ethylphenol	23			XF-1150, 150°, 2.35/pol	741
		21			DC-550, 125°, 2.80/pol DBTCP, 125°, 2.81/pol	455
	p-Ethylphenol	21			Mass Spec.	713
		21			DC-550, 125°, 3.05/pol DBTCP, 125°, 3.10/pol	455
		24			TXP, 125°, 20.3'	238
		24			MS-550, 92°, 2.73/pol 100°, 0.319/indl	281
		24			TXP, 116°, 2.43/pol	9
	2,3-Xylenol	13b(75%)	b 210-212	1.4891[21]		326
		21			DC-550, 125°, 3.3/pol DBTCP, 125°, 3.75/pol	455
		23			XF-1150, 150°, 3.0/pol	741
		24			MS-550, 92°, 2.97/pol 100°, 0.344/indl	281
		24			TXP, 125°, 21.5'	238
		24			TXP, 116°, 2.59/pol	9
	2,4-Xylenol	13bh(73%)	b 209-210	1.4819[21]		479
		21			DC-550, 125°, 2.77/pol DBTCP, 125°, 3.01/pol	455
		23			XF-1150, 150°, 2.6/pol	741
		24			TXP, 116°, 2.25/pol	9
		24			DOSb, TXP, 125°, 18.8'	238, 239
		24			MS-550, 92°, 2.62/pol 100°, 0.289/indl	281
		26			TCP, 80°, 3.05/pol	566

Table 5-4. Monohydric Phenols (cont'd.)

Formula	Compound	Method (Yield %)	B.P./mm; M.P.	n_D^t	Stationary Phase, Col. Temp., Retention Data	Ref.
$C_8H_{10}O$	2,5-Xylenol	13b(65%)	b 205-207			326
		13b	b 207	1.4792^{34}		476
		13bh(65%)	b 207	1.4792^{34}		478
		21			DC-550, 125°, 2.48/pol; DBTCP, 125°, 2.69/pol	455
		23			XF-1150, 150°, 2.25/pol	741
		24			MS-550, 92°, 2.42/pol; 100°, 0.257/indl	281
		24			DOSb, TXP, 125°, 16.1'	238, 239
		24			TXP, 116°, 1.91/pol	9
		26			TCP, 80°, 2.49/pol	566
	2,6-Xylenol	13b(56%)	b 212	1.4833^{23}		326
		21			DC-550, 125°, 3.06/pol; DBTCP, 125°, 3.55/pol	455
		23			XF-1150, 150°, 3.0/pol	741
		24			TXP, 116°, 2.48/pol	9
		24			DOSb, TXP, 125°, 20.8'	238, 239
		24			MS-550, 92°, 2.80/pol; 100°, 0.319/indl	281
		25			DC-430, 100→260°	303
		26			TCP, 80°, 3.30/pol	566
		43b				418
	3,4-Xylenol	13b(58%)	b 213-215	1.4860^{22}		326
		21			DC-550, 125°, 3.61/pol; DBTCP, 125°, 3.89/pol	455

Table 5-4. Monohydric Phenols (cont'd.)

Formula	Compound	Method (Yield %)	B.P./mm; M.P.	n_D^t	Stationary Phase, Col. Temp., Retention Data	Ref.
$C_8H_{10}O$	3,4-Xylenol	23			XF-1150, 150°, 3.0/pol	741
		24			MS-550, 92°, 3.08/pol	281
					100°, 0.376/indl	
		24			TXP, 125°, 23.7'	238
		24			TXP, 116°, 2.84/pol	9
	3,5-Xylenol	13n(47%)	b 207-208	1.4775^{22}		326
		21			DC-550, 125°, 2.86/pol	455
					DBTCP, 125°, 2.85/pol	
		23			XF-1150, 150°, 2.4/pol	741
		24			TXP, 116°, 2.21/pol	9
		24			TXP, 125°, 18.2'	238
		24			MS-550, 92°, 2.57/pol	281
					100°, 0.289/indl	
$C_8H_{10}O_2$	2-(p-Hydroxyphenyl)-ethanol	25			F-60, 250°	348
	2-Methoxy-4-methyl-phenol	21c			ApN, 160°, 1.62/gcl	166
					PPE, 160°, 1.60/gcl	
$C_8H_{10}O_3$	2,4-Di(hydroxymethyl)-phenol	13	b 115-125/0.05		DC-430, 2.34/pol	511
	2,6-Dimethoxyphenol	25				303
$C_8H_{11}NO_3S$	N,N-Dimethyl-4-hydroxybenzene-sulfonamide				ApN, 190°	571
$C_9H_6O_3$	7-Hydroxycoumarin (Umbelliferone)	25			SE-30, 180°, 8.9'	257
	8-Hydroxycoumarin	14			SE-52, 150°, 1.67/naph	89
					170°, 8.1/naph	
$C_9H_6O_4$	4,7-Dihydroxycoumarin	25			SE-30, 180°, 34.5'	257

Table 5-4. Monohydric Phenols (cont'd.)

Formula	Compound	Method (Yield %)	B.P./mm; M.P.	n_D^t	Stationary Phase, Col. Temp., Retention Data	Ref.
C_9H_8O	4-Indenol	21			Lan, 145°; PPG, 151°	242
	5-Indenol	21			Lan, 145°; PPG, 151°	242
	6-Indenol	21			Lan, 145°; PPG, 151°	242
	7-Indenol	21			Lan, 145°; PPG, 151°	242
$C_9H_{10}O$	2-Allylphenol	12p(74%) 13p(50%)	b 86-87/4	1.4890^{20}		37
	4-Indanol	21	b 86-88/5		MS-550, 100°, 0.831/indl	242
		24				281
	5-Indanol	21	b 97-99/6-7		MS-550, 100°, 23.2'	242
		24			Mass Spec.	281
		21			SE-30, 135°, 4.4'	713
$C_9H_{10}O_3$	Acetovanillone	21py				548
	Ethyl p-hydroxy-benzoate	21(84%)	b 110/1.3	1.4995^{20}		368
	Methyl o-hydroxy-phenylacetate	25			10% F-60, 14.74 MU 1% F-60, 14.74 MU	182
		25			F-60, 14.72 MU	348
	Methyl m-hydroxy-phenylacetate	25			10% F-60, 15.08 MU 1% F-60, 15.18 MU	182
		25			F-60, 15.10 MU	348
	Methyl p-hydroxy-phenylacetate	25			10% F-60, 15.42 MU 1% F-60, 15.58 MU	182
		25			F-60, 0.80/mpam, 15.43 MU	348
		23k			NGS, 170°, 0.33/mdpa F-60-Z, 150°, 0.50/mdpa	797

Table 5-4. Monohydric Phenols (cont'd.)

Formula	Compound	Method (Yield %)	B.P./mm; M.P.	n_D^t	Stationary Phase, Col. Temp., Retention Data	Ref.
$C_9H_{10}O_4$	Methyl p-hydroxy-mandelate	25			F-60, 100-250°	348
		25			10% F-60, 17.52 MU 1% F-60, 17.66 MU	182
	Methyl 4-hydroxy-3-methoxybenzoate	25			10% F-60, 16.50 MU 1% F-60, 16.52 MU	182
	Syringaldehyde	21py			SE-30, 162°, 3.3'	548
		25			SE-52, 160°, 2.12/van	674
$C_9H_{12}O$	2-Ethyl-3-methyl-phenol	24			MS-550, 100°, 0.445/indl	281
	3-Ethyl-2-methyl-phenol	24			MS-550, 100°, 0.541/indl	281
	3-Ethyl-4-methyl-phenol	24			MS-550, 100°, 0.583/indl	281
	3-Ethyl-5-methyl-phenol	21			Mass Spec.	713
	4-Ethyl-2-methyl-phenol	24			MS-550, 100°, 0.483/indl	281
	4-Ethyl-3-methyl-phenol	24			MS-550, 100°, 0.603/indl	281
	5-Ethyl-2-methyl-phenol	24			MS-550, 100°, 0.415/indl	281
	5-Ethyl-3-methyl-phenol	24			MS-550, 100°, 0.470/indl	281
	6-Ethyl-2-methyl-phenol	23			ApL, 170°, 3.4/pol	741
	6-Ethyl-2-methyl-phenol	24			MS-550, 100°, 0.456/indl	281
	6-Ethyl-3-methyl-phenol	24			MS-550, 100°, 0.381/indl	281

Table 5-4. Monohydric Phenols (cont'd.)

Formula	Compound	Method (Yield %)	B.P./mm; M.P.	n_D^t	Stationary Phase, Col. Temp., Retention Data	Ref.
$C_9H_{12}O$	2-Isopropylphenol	23			ApL, 170°	741
		24			MS-550, 100°, 0.314/indl	281
	3-Isopropylphenol	24			MS-550, 100°, 0.386/indl	281
	4-Isopropylphenol	23			ApL, 170°, 3.45/pol	741
		24			MS-550, 100°, 0.438/indl	281
	2-n-Propylphenol	24			MS-550, 100°, 0.386/indl	281
	3-n-Propylphenol	24			MS-550, 100°, 0.479/indl	281
	4-n-Propylphenol	24			MS-550, 100°, 0.550/indl	281
	2,3,4-Trimethylphenol	24			MS-550, 100°, 0.762/indl	281
	2,3,5-Trimethylphenol	23			ApL, 170°, 4.2/pol	741
		24			MS-550, 100°, 0.550/indl	281
	2,3,6-Trimethylphenol	24			MS-550, 100°, 0.645/indl	281
		24			TXP, 125°, 39.0'	238
	2,4,5-Trimethylphenol	23			ApL, 170°, 4.35/pol	741
		24			MS-550, 100°, 0.550/indl	281
	2,4,6-Trimethylphenol	23			ApL, 170°, 5.0/pol	741
		21f				244
		24			MS-550, 100°, 0.554/indl	281
		24			TXP, 125°, 34.8'	238
		21			DC-550, 125°, 5.33/pol; DBTCP, 125°, 6.07/pol	455
	3,4,5-Trimethylphenol	23			ApL, 170°, 5.5/pol	741
		24			MS-550, 100°, 0.762/indl	281
$C_9H_{12}O_2$	4-Ethyl-2-methoxy phenol	21c			ApN, 160°, 2.36/gcl; PPE, 160°, 2.16/gcl	166

Table 5-4. Monohydric Phenols (cont'd.)

Formula	Compound	Method (Yield %)	B.P./mm; M.P.	n_D^t	Stationary Phase, Col. Temp., Retention Data	Ref.
$C_9H_{12}O_4$	4-Hydroxy-3-methoxy-phenylethylene glycol	43			F-60, 184°pr	347
		25			10% F-60, 18.68 MU	182
					1% F-60, 18.80 MU	
	2,4,6-Trimethylol-phenol	13	b 135-145/0.04			511
		15py	b 120-125/0.03			137
	2,4,6-Tris(hydroxy-methyl)phenol (sodium salt)	13	b 120-125/0.03	1.4621^{20}		138
$C_{10}H_6Cl_2O$	5,8-Dichloro-1-naphthol	13 (57%)	b 174.8-7.5/4	1.5885^{20}		225
$C_{10}H_8O$	1-Naphthol	11	b 271-272/742	1.5590^{20}		452
		13(67%)	b 98-102.3/2	1.5596^{20}		225
		25			SE-30, 130°, 1.4/ippc; QF-1, 130°, 1.0/ippc; C-20M, 170°, 0.40/ippc	228
	2-Naphthol	24			MS-550, 100°, 2.38/indl	281
		21			Mass Spec.	713
		13(71%)	b 98.2-101/8	1.5592^{20}		225
		24			MS-550, 100°, 2.70/indl	281
$C_{10}H_8O_4$	Scopoletin	21d,25			UCW-98, 148→290°, 2.88/cina	867
	6-Hydroxy-7-methoxy coumarin	25			SE-30, 180°, 17.9'	257
$C_{10}H_{10}O_3$	Methyl o-hydroxy-cinnamate	25			SE-30, 180°, 17.7	257
		25			10% F-60, 16.70 MU	182
					1% F-60, 16.82 MU	

Table 5-4. Monohydric Phenols (cont'd.)

Formula	Compound	Method (Yield %)	B.P./mm; M.P.	n_D^t	Stationary Phase, Col. Temp., Retention Data	Ref.
$C_{10}H_{10}O_3$	Methyl p-hydroxy-cinnamate	25			10% F-60, 17.82 MU 1% F-60, 17.88 MU	182
$C_9H_{10}O_4$	Methyl p-hydroxy-phenylpyruvate	25			10% F-60, 19.16 MU 1% F-60, 19.34 MU	182
$C_{10}H_{12}O$	2-Allyl-6-methyl-phenol	23			ApL, 170°, 5.55/pol	741
	1-Methyl-4-indanol	24			MS-550, 100°, 1.01/indl	281
	1-Methyl-5-indanol	24			MS-550, 100°, 1.22/indl	281
	2-Methyl-4-indanol	24			MS-550, 100°, 0.960/indl	281
	4-Methyl-5-indanol	24			MS-550, 100°, 1.69/indl	281
	5-Methyl-4-indanol	24			MS-550, 100°, 1.48/indl	281
	6-Methyl-4-indanol	24			MS-550, 100°, 1.28/indl	281
	6-Methyl-5-indanol	24			MS-550, 100°, 1.45/indl	281
	7-Methyl-4-indanol	24			MS-550, 100°, 1.55/indl	281
	7-Methyl-5-indanol	24			MS-550, 100°, 1.77/indl	281
$C_{10}H_{12}O_2$	Eugenol	21py			SE-30, 112°, 14.2'	548
	Isoeugenol	21py			SE-30, 150°, 5.0', 6.8'	548
$C_{10}H_{12}O_3$	Coniferyl alcohol	25			SE-52, 192°, 1.93/vana 242°, 0.32/pin	674
	Propyl p-hydroxy-benzoate	25			SE-30, 5.0/pol	451
		25			SE-52	197
$C_{10}H_{12}O_4$	Methyl 3-hydroxy-4-methoxyphenylacetate	23k			NGS, 170°, 0.69/mdpa F-60-Z, 150°, 1.03/mdpa	797

Table 5-4. Monohydric Phenols (cont'd.)

Formula	Compound	Method (Yield %)	B.P./mm; M.P.	n_D^t	Stationary Phase, Col. Temp., Retention Data	Ref.
$C_{10}H_{12}O_4$	Methyl 4-hydroxy-3-methoxyphenylacetate	23k			NGS, 170°, 0.69/mdpa F-60-Z, 150°, 1.05/mdpa	797
		25			10% F-60, 16.90 MU 1% F-60, 17.04 MU	182
		25			F-60	348
$C_{10}H_{12}O_5$	Methyl 4-hydroxy-3-methoxymandelate	25			10% F-60, 18.64 MU 1% F-60, 18.76 MU	182
		25			F-60, 100→250°, 0.67/mpam, 18.66 MU	348
		25			SE-30, 185°, 1.07/mhip XE-60, 173°, 0.95/mhip QF-1, 170°, 0.79/mhip EGA, 195°, 1.41/mhip	864
$C_{10}H_{14}O$	4-n-Butylphenol	24			MS-550, 100°, 0.955/indl	281
	4-sec-Butylphenol	24			MS-550, 100°, 0.693/indl	281
	4-t-Butylphenol	23			ApL, 170°, 4.7/pol	741
	2,4-Diethylphenol	24			MS-550, 100°, 0.661/indl	281
	3,5-Diethylphenol	24			MS-550, 100°, 0.726/indl	281
	2-Isopropyl-5-methylphenol	24			MS-550, 100°, 0.521/indl	281
	3-Isopropyl-5-methylphenol	24			MS-550, 100°, 0.600/indl	281
	4-Methyl-2-propylphenol	24			MS-550, 100°, 0.613/indl	281
	2-Methyl-6-propylphenol	23			ApL, 170°, 5.45/pol	741
	2,3,4,5-Tetramethylphenol	24			MS-550, 100°, 1.40/indl	281

Table 5-4. Monohydric Phenols (cont'd.)

Formula	Compound	Method (Yield %)	B.P./mm; M.P.	n_D^t	Stationary Phase, Col. Temp., Retention Data	Ref.
$C_{10}H_{14}O$	2,3,4,5-Tetramethyl-phenol	23			ApL, 170°, 9.7/pol	741
$C_{10}H_{14}O_2$	n-Propylguaiacol	21py			SE-30, 118°, 10.6'	548
	4-n-Propylguaiacol	21c			PPE, 160°, 3.23/gc1	166
$C_{10}H_{16}OSi$	3-Methyl-4-TMS-phenol	15	b 148/24	1.4892^{25}		749
$C_{11}H_{10}O_5$	5,7-Dimethoxy-6-hydroxy coumarin	25			SE-30, 180°, 25.5'	257
$C_{11}H_{12}O_4$	Methyl 4-hydroxy-3-methoxycinnamate	25			10% F-60, 19.44 MU 1% F-60, 19.60 MU	182
$C_{11}H_{14}O_3$	Butyl p-hydroxy-benzoate	25			BDS, 190°, 8.6/pol	451
$C_{11}H_{14}O_4$	Methyl 4-hydroxy-3-methoxyphenylpropionate	25			10% F-60, 17.80 MU 1% F-60, 17.86 MU	182
$C_{11}H_{16}O$	4-t-Pentylphenol	23			ApL, 170°, 7.9/pol	741
	2-t-Butyl-4-methyl-phenol	23			ApL, 170°, 5.9/pol	741
	2-t-Butyl-5-methyl-phenol	23			ApL, 170°, 5.45/pol	741
	4-t-Butyl-2-methyl-phenol	23			ApL, 170°, 5.9/pol	741
	Pentamethylphenol	24			MS-550, 100°, 3.09/indl	281
$C_{12}H_9ClO$	2-Phenyl-4-chloro-phenol	11	b 151/6	1.5562^{25}		749
	2-Phenyl-6-chloro-phenol	11	b 195/25	1.5582^{25}		749
$C_{12}H_{10}O$	5-Acenaphthenol	21			Mass Spec.	713

Table 5-4. Monohydric Phenols (cont'd.)

Formula	Compound	Method (Yield %)	B.P./mm; M.P.	n_D^t	Stationary Phase, Col. Temp., Retention Data	Ref.
$C_{12}H_{10}O$	2-Hydroxydiphenyl	11	b 164/21	1.5455^{25}		749
		21(90%)	b 103-3.5/1.0	1.5493^{20}		367, 368
		24			MS-550, 100°, 3.22/indl	281
	3-Hydroxydiphenyl	21			Mass Spec.	713
	4-Hydroxydiphenyl	13b(92%)				512
		21(70%)	b 138.5-40/0.95	1.5590^{20}		367, 368
		32(90%)	b 100-103/0.2	1.5588^{20}		143
$C_{12}H_{14}O$	2,6-Diallylphenol	23			ApL, 170°, 9.85/pol	741
$C_{12}H_{14}O_5$	Methyl 3,5-dimethoxy-4-hydroxycinnamate	25			10% F-60, 21.08 MU 1% F-60, 21.12 MU	182
$C_{12}H_{18}O$	2,4-Diisopropylphenol	23			ApL, 170°, 5.9/pol	741
	2,6-Diisopropylphenol	23			ApL, 170°, 5.3/pol	741
$C_{13}H_{20}O$	2-Methyl-4-t-hexyl-phenol	21(72%)	b 92.5/0.35	1.4878^{20}		367, 368
		23			ApL, 170°, 15.5/pol	741
$C_{14}H_8O_3$	1-Hydroxyanthra-quinone	25			SE-30, 240°, 2.3'	258
	2-Hydroxyanthra-quinone	25			SE-30, 240°, 2.8'	258
$C_{14}H_{10}O$	Phenanthrol	21			Mass Spec.	713
$C_{14}H_{12}O$	2-Hydroxystilbene	25			SE-52, 174°	727
	4-Hydroxystilbene	25			SE-52, 183°, 2.06'	727
$C_{14}H_{12}Cl_2O$	2(p-Chloro-α-methyl-benzyl)-4-chlorophenol	23		1.5510^{25}		752

Table 5-4. Monohydric Phenols (cont'd.)

Formula	Compound	Method (Yield %)	B.P./mm; M.P.	n_D^t	Stationary Phase, Col. Temp., Retention Data	Ref.
$C_{14}H_{13}BrO_2$	4-(4-Bromophenoxy)-2,6-dimethylphenol	43b	b 120/0.03			861
$C_{14}H_{14}O$	1-(p-Hydroxyphenyl)-1-phenylethane	21(95%)	b 113/0.25	1.5355^{20}		367, 368
$C_{14}H_{22}O$	2,4-Di-t-butylphenol	23			XF-1150, ApL, 10.8/pol	741
	2,6-Di-t-butylphenol	25	m 109-110			243
		43n 14(10%)	m 106-108			422
$C_{15}H_{10}O_4$	3-Hydroxy-1-methoxy-anthraquinone	25			SE-30, 240°, 5.8'	258
$C_{15}H_{14}O_2$	3-Hydroxy-5-methoxy-stilbene	25			SE-52, 192°, 7.30/vana 242°, 7.1'	674
	4-Hydroxy-3-methoxy-stilbene	25			SE-52, 174°	727
$C_{15}H_{18}OSi$	2-Hydroxy-3-TMS-diphenyl	11	b 200/24 m 62.9, 71.6			749
	2-Hydroxy-5-TMS-diphenyl	11	b 195/21	1.5329^{25}		749
$C_{15}H_{24}O$	2,6-Di-t-butyl-4-methylphenol	21d	m 122.8-124		Mass Spec.	244
	4-Nonylphenol	21(86%)	b 96-99/0.15	1.4863^{20}		367, 368
$C_{16}H_{10}O$	1-Pyrenol	21			Mass Spec.	713
$C_{16}H_{18}O_2$	Xylenoldimer, 4-(2,6-dimethylphenoxy)-2,6-dimethylphenol	23				172

Table 5-4. Monohydric Phenols (cont'd.)

Formula	Compound	Method (Yield %)	B.P./mm; M.P.	n_D^t	Stationary Phase, Col. Temp., Retention Data	Ref.
$C_{17}H_{19}NO_3$	Morphine	21t			SE-30, 200°	114
		21py			SE-30, 183°	115
		25			SE-30, 207°	510
		43				336
$C_{18}H_{12}O$	Chrysenol	21			Mass Spec.	713
$C_{18}H_{14}O$	2,6-Diphenylphenol	42	m 108-109			418
		43c	m 107-108			422
$C_{18}H_{14}O_3$	3-(3'-Phenoxyphenoxy)-phenol	43b				422
$C_{18}H_{24}O_3$	Methyl podocarpate	23p	m 80-82		SE-30, 200°, 2.16/mst; ApN, 200°, 2.36/mst; QF-1, 200°, 2.85/mst; PPE, 200°, 4.17/mst; DEGS, 200°, 6.97/mst	896
$C_{18}H_{30}O$	2,4,6-Tri-t-butyl-phenol	23d	m 85-87.5			244
$C_{20}H_{17}BrO_3$	4-Bromo-phenoxy-2',-6'-dimethyl-4'-hydroxy-diphenyl ether	43b	b 120/0.03			861
$C_{21}H_{26}O_2$	Cannabinol	22py			SE-30, 170°, 1.97/cbdl	63
		25			SE-30/SE-52, 240°, 1.74/cbdl	167
		25			C-20M, 180°, 2.96/anth	304
$C_{21}H_{30}O_2$	Tetrahydrocannabiniol	22py			SE-30, 170°, 4.15/eic, 1.44/cbdl	63
		25			SE-30/SE-52, 240°, 1.35, 1.44, 1.63/cbdl	167

Table 5-4. Monohydric Phenols (cont'd.)

Formula	Compound	Method (Yield %)	B.P./mm; M.P.	n_D^t	Stationary Phase, Col. Temp., Retention Data	Ref.
$C_{21}H_{30}O_2$	Tetrahydrocanna-biniol	25			C-20M, 180°, 1.63/anth	304
$C_{21}H_{36}O$	2,4,6-Tri-t-pentyl-phenol	23d	m 24.5-25.5		Mass Spec.	244
$C_{22}H_{21}BrO_3$	4-[4-(4-Bromophenoxy)-2,6-dimethylphenoxy]-2,6-dimethylphenol	43b	b 150/0.03			861
$C_{24}H_{26}O_3$	4-Bromophenoxy-2,2'-6,6'-tetramethyl-4'-hydroxydiphenyl ether	43b	b 150/0.03			861
	3,3',5,5'-Tetramethyl-4-hydroxy-4'-[3,5-dimethyl-4-(hydroxy)phenoxy]biphenyl	43b	b 190/0.01			861
	Xylenol trimer	23				172
$C_{26}H_{38}O_2$	Tocotrienol	25			SE-30, 235°, 1.35/octs ApL, 235°, 1.60/octs	736
$C_{26}H_{44}O_2$	Tocol	43h,43			SE-52/XE-60, 220°, 0.80/tocl	541
$C_{27}H_{40}O_2$	5-Methyl tocotrienol	25			SE-30, 235°, 1.21/octs ApL, 235°, 1.02/octs	736
	7-Methyltocotrienol	25			SE-30, 235°, 2.12/octs ApL, 235°, 1.91/octs	736
	8-Methyltocotrienol	25			SE-30, 235°, 1.85/octs ApL, 235°, 1.63/octs	736
					SE-30, 235°, 1.71/octs ApL, 235°, 1.38/octs	736
$C_{27}H_{46}O_2$	5-Methyltocol	25			SE-30, 235°, 1.60-1.62/octs ApL, 235°, 1.42-1.44/octs	736
		43			SE-52/XE-60, 220°, 1.07/tocl	540

Table 5-4. Monohydric Phenols (cont'd.)

Formula	Compound	Method (Yield %)	B.P./mm; M.P.	n_D^t	Stationary Phase, Col. Temp., Retention Data	Ref.
$C_{27}H_{46}O_2$	7-Methyltocol	43			SE-52/XE-60, 220°, 0.91/tocl	540
	8-Methyltocol (δ)	25			SE-30, ApL	736
		25			SE-30, 250°, 0.50/toca	365
		25			SE-30, 235°, 1.29/octs; ApL, 235°, 1.03-1.05/octs	736
		43			SE-52/XE-60, 220°, 0.83/tocl	540
		43h,43			SE-52/XE-60, 220°	541
$C_{28}H_{42}O_2$	5,7-Dimethyltoco-trienol	25			SE-30, 235°, 2.72/octs; ApL, 235°, 2.67/octs	736
	5,8-Dimethyltoco-trienol	25			SE-30, 235°, 2.15-2.19/octs; ApL, 235°, 1.80-1.82/octs	736
	7,8-Dimethyltoco-trienol	25			SE-30, 235°, 2.26/octs; ApL, 235°, 1.90/octs	736
$C_{28}H_{48}O_2$	5,7-Dimethyltocol	43h,43			SE-52/XE-60, 220°, 1.42/tocl	541
	5,8-Dimethyltocol (β)	25			SE-30, ApL	736
		43h,43			SE-52/XE-60, 220°, 1.08/tocl	541
		25			SE-30, 235°,1.65-1.66/octs; ApL, 235°, 1.37-1.38/octs	736
	7,8-Dimethyltocol (γ)	25			SE-30, 250°, 0.65/toca	365
		25			SE-30, 235°, 1.70-1.74/octs; ApL, 235°, 1.42-1.43/octs	736
		43h,43			SE-52/XE-60, 220°, 1.11/tocl	541

Table 5-4. Monohydric Phenols (cont'd.)

Formula	Compound	Method (Yield %)	B.P./mm; M.P.	n_D^t	Stationary Phase, Col. Temp., Retention Data	Ref.
$C_{29}H_{44}O_2$	5,7,8-Trimethyl-tocotrienol	25			SE-30, 235°, 3.22-3.24/octs ApL, 235°, 3.08-3.12/octs	736
$C_{29}H_{50}O_2$	5,7,8-Trimethyl-tocol (α)	25			SE-30, 250°, 0.89/toca	365
					SE-30, 235°, 2.42-2.49/octs ApL, 235°, 2.31-2.34/octs	736
		43h,43			SE-52/XE-60, 220°	541
		43			SE-52, XE-60, 220°, 1.66/tocl	540
		43			OV-17, 241°pr	347
$C_{33}H_{34}O_4$	Xylenol tetramer	23				172

TABLE 5-5. POLYHYDRIC PHENOLS

Formula	Compound	Method	Yield %	B.P./mm; M.P.	n_D^t	Stat. Phase, Temp., Retention Data	Ref.
$C_6H_5ClO_2$	2,4-Dihydroxychloro-benzene	11		b 153/25	1.4818^{25}		749
$C_6H_6O_2$	Hydroquinone ($\rightarrow T_1$)	11e		b 249			374
		11		b 239, 107-110/4 m 48			1
		11e		b 252			374
		11g	60	m 48.9-49.3			361
		13		m 52			311
		13b		b 237-239 m 42-46			484
		21	89	b 246.5/738			30
		22	80	b 102-103/2			472
		51	28	b 246; m 46			824
		23				SE-52, 150°, 170°	89
	Pyrocatechol ($\rightarrow T_1$)	11		b 214	1.4941^{20}		311
	($\rightarrow T_1$)	11e		b 226			374
	($\rightarrow T_1$)	51	87	b 218/756, 97/2	1.4870^{20}		824
		11e		b 220			374
		11e,13		b 220			601
		17		b 235	1.4685^{20}		311
		22	90	b 89-90/2.5	1.4690^{20}		472
		21				SiO, 187°	820
		23				SE-52, 150°, 2.26/naph	89
		24				MS-550, 100°, 0.494/indl	281

Table 5-5. Polyhydric Phenols (cont'd.)

Formula	Compound	Method	Yield %	B.P./mm; M.P.	n_D^t	Stat. Phase, Temp., Retention Data	Ref.
$C_6H_6O_2$	Pyrocatechol	21c				ApN, 160°, 1.39/gcl	166
						PPE, 160°, 0.89/gcl	374
	Resorcinol (→T₁)	11e		b 244			601
	(→T₁)	15e		b 244			1
		11		b 235-236/92	1.4755^{20}		374
		11e		b 239			452
		11p	76	b 237-240/740, 154-155/100	1.4760^{20}, 1.4748^{20}		311
		11,17		b 243	1.4739^{20}		601
		15e		b 239			30
		21	91	b 238.5/738			472
		22	88	b 97-98/2	1.4719^{20}		824
		51	59	b 238/776, 116/7	1.4743^{20}		
		23				SE-52, 150°, 2.92/naph	89
		25				DC-430, 2.04/pol	303
		24				MS-550, 100°, 0.740/indl	281
		21c				ApN, 160°, 1.86/gcl	166
		21d,22d				UCW, 148-290°	867
		21				Mass Spec.	713
$C_6H_6O_3$	Phloroglucinol	11,13	55	b 280-281	1.4668^{20}		311
		51	60	b 144/4	1.4679^{20}		824
		22s,25				0.05% SE-52, 87°, 6.2'; 3% SE-52, 125°, 9.75'	22
	Pyrogallol	25				JXR, 175°, 0.200/gu	761
		11	85	b 267-269	1.4677^{20}		311

Table 5-5. Polyhydric Phenols (cont'd.)

Formula	Compound	Method	Yield %	B.P./mm; M.P.	n_D^t	Stat. Phase, Temp., Retention Data	Ref.
$C_7H_6O_3$	Protocatechuic aldehyde	25				QF-1, 140°	230
		25				DC-430	673
		21				SiO, 195°	820
$C_7H_8O_2$	3-Methylcatechol	24				MS-550, 100°, 0.826/indl	281
	4-Methylcatechol	24				MS-550, 100°, 0.768/indl	281
		21c				PPE, 160°, 2.0/gcl; ApN, 160°, 1.27/gcl	166
	2-Methylresorcinol	24				MS-550, 100°, 1.16/indl	281
		21				Mass Spec.	713
	4-Methylresorcinol	24				MS-550, 100°, 1.08/indl	281
	5-Methylresorcinol	24				MS-550, 100°, 1.10/indl	281
		23				SE-52, 150°, 2.50/naph	89
		21c				ApN, 160°, 2.56/gcl	166
$C_7H_8O_5$	Methyl gallate	11,13			1.4799^{20}		311
$C_7H_{14}O_6$	Sequoyitol	25		b 309/312		DC-430, 160°, 2.82/vana	673
$C_8H_8O_4$	Methyl 2,3-dihydroxy-benzoate	25				10% F-60, 16.68 MU; 1% F-60, 16.60 MU	182
	Methyl 2,4-dihydroxy-benzoate	25				10% F-60, 17.28 MU; 1% F-60, 17.44 MU	182
	Methyl 2,5-dihydroxy-benzoate	25				10% F-60, 17.16 MU; 1% F-60, 17.22 MU	182
		25				F-60, 100→235°	348

Table 5-5. Polyhydric Phenols (cont'd.)

Formula	Compound	Method	Yield %	B.P./mm; M.P.	n_D^t	Stat. Phase, Temp., Retention Data	Ref.
$C_8H_8O_4$	Methyl 2,6-dihydroxy-benzoate	25				10% F-60, 16.50 MU / 1% F-60, 16.44 MU	182
	Methyl 3,4-dihydroxy-benzoate	25				10% F-60, 17.30 MU / 1% F-60, 17.40 MU	182
	Methyl 3,5-dihydroxy-benzoate	25				10% F-60, 17.48 MU / 1% F-60, 17.56 MU	182
	4-Ethylcatechol	21c				ApN, 160°, 2.82/gcl / PPE, 160°, 1.74/gcl	166
$C_8H_{10}O_4$	3,4-Dihydroxyphenyl-ethylene glycol	43				F-60, 188°pr	347
	3,4-Dihydroxyphenyl-glycol	25				10% F-60, 19.18 MU / 1% F-60, 19.36 MU	182
$C_9H_6O_4$	Daphnetin (7,8-Dihydroxycoumarin)	25				SE-30, 180°, 15.5'	257
	Esculetin (6,7-Dihydroxycoumarin)	25				SE-30, 180°, 23.4'	257
		25,21d				UCW-98, 148→290°, 3.08/cina	867
$C_9H_8O_2$	Indenediol	21				NMR	500
							713
$C_9H_{10}O_4$	Methyl 2,5-dihydroxy-phenylacetate	25				10% F-60, 17.74 MU / 1% F-60, 17.80 MU	182
	Methyl 3,4-dihydroxy-phenylacetate	25				10% F-60, 17.56 MU / 1% F-60, 17.60 MU	182
		25				F-60, 100→250°	348

Table 5-5. Polyhydric Phenols (cont'd.)

Formula	Compound	Method	Yield %	B.P./mm; M.P.	n_D^t	Stat. Phase, Temp., Retention Data	Ref.
$C_9H_{10}O_5$	Methyl 3,4-dihydroxy-mandelate	25				10% F-60, 19.16 MU 1% F-60, 19.30 MU	182
$C_9H_{12}O_2$	4-n-Propylcatechol	25				F-60, 100→250°	348
		21c				PPE, 160°, 2.48/gcl	166
$C_{10}H_8O_2$	1,5-Dihydroxy-naphthalene	13		m 87			225
		21	71	b 140-141/0.5 m 85			367, 368
	1,6-Dihydroxy-naphthalene	13	81	b 167.2-169/5	1.5330^{20}		225
	2,3-Dihydroxy-naphthalene	13	30	b 153.8-156/5 m 60-61			225
	2,7-Dihydroxy-naphthalene	13	22	m 51-53			225
		21	70	b 132-136/0.55 m 53			367, 368
	Naphthalenediols	21				Mass Spec.	713
$C_{10}H_8O_5$	Fraxetin (7,8-dihydroxy-6-methoxycoumarin)	25				SE-30, 180°, 29.0'	257
$C_{10}H_{10}O_4$	Methyl 3,4-dihydroxy-cinnamate	25				10% F-60, 20.12 MU 1% F-60, 20.18 MU	182
$C_{10}H_{12}O_4$	Methyl 3,4-dihydroxy-phenylpropionate	25				10% F-60, 18.48 MU 1% F-60, 18.52 MU	182
$C_{12}H_{10}O_2$	2,2'-Dihydroxydiphenyl	13b		b 164/7	1.5256^{20}		363
		21	90	b 116.5-8/0.55	1.5178^{20}		367

Table 5-5. Polyhydric Phenols (cont'd.)

Formula	Compound	Method	Yield %	B.P./mm; M.P.	n_D^t	Stat. Phase, Temp., Retention Data	Ref.
$C_{12}H_{10}O_2$	4,4'-Dihydroxydiphenyl	21	70	b 166-167/0.8 m 63-64			367
$C_{13}H_{12}O_2$	4,4'-Dihydroxydiphenyl-methane	13b					512
$C_{14}H_6O_8$	Ellagic acid	21py		m 197-198			548
$C_{14}H_8O_4$	Alizarin	25				SE-30, 240°, 4.5'	258
	Anthrarufin	25				SE-30, 240°, 4.1'	258
	Chrysazin	25				SE-30, 240°, 4.3'	258
	1,4-Dihydroxy-anthraquinone	22		m 92-99			243
	1,5-Dihydroxy-anthraquinone	22		m 138-142			243
	1,8-Dihydroxy-anthraquinone	22		m 98.8-101			243
	Histazarin	25				SE-30, 240°, 5.2'	258
	Purpuroxanthin	25				SE-30, 240°, 4.3'	258
	Quinizarin	25				SE-30, 240°, 3.7'	258
$C_{14}H_8O_5$	Anthragallol	25				SE-30, 240°, 6.4'	258
	Purpurin	25				SE-30, 240°, 6.4'	258
	1,2,4-Trihydroxy-anthraquinone	22		m 81-86.5			243
$C_{14}H_{10}O_9$	m-Digallic acid	25				DC-430, XE-60	673
$C_{14}H_{12}O_2$	Pinosylvin	25				SE-52, 242°, 1.10/pin	674
	4,4'-Dihydroxystilbene	25				SE-52, 183°, 8.52'	727
$C_{14}H_{22}O_2$	2,5-Di-t-butylhydro-quinone	11	40	m 129.1-130.1			361

Table 5-5. Polyhydric Phenols (cont'd.)

Formula	Compound	Method	Yield %	B.P./mm; M.P.	n_D^t	Stat. Phase, Temp., Retention Data	Ref.
$C_{15}H_8O_6$	Rhein	25				SE-30, 240°, 14.0'	258
$C_{15}H_{10}O_4$	Chrysophanol	25				SE-30, 240°, 5.4'	258
$C_{15}H_{10}O_5$	Aloe-emodin	25				SE-30, 240°, 11.4'	258
	Emodin	25				SE-30, 240°, 10.7'	258
	Islandicin	25				SE-30, 240°, 8.2'	258
$C_{15}H_{10}O_6$	Catenarin	25				SE-30, 240°, 14.3'	258
$C_{15}H_{12}O_4$	Isoliquiritigenin	25				SE-30, 240°, 6.3'	256
$C_{15}H_{16}O_2$	4,4'-Isopropylidene-diphenol	11	65-70	b 179-180/1.5	1.5178^{20}		1
		11		b 177-181/1.5			769
$C_{16}H_{12}O_5$	Physcion	25				SE-30, 240°, 9.2'	258
$C_{16}H_{16}O_4$	1-Methyl-3,7,8-tri-hydroxy-6-isopropyl-dibenzofuran	21					825
$C_{16}H_{18}O_4$	2-Methyl-4,6-dihydroxy-3'-isopropyl-4',5'-biphenyl	21				NMR	825
$C_{17}H_{16}O_5$	2',4'-Dihydroxy-3,4-dimethoxychalcone	25				NMR	500
$C_{17}H_{16}NO_2$	Apomorphine	21t				SE-30, 200°	114
$C_{18}H_{10}O_4$	6,11-Dihydroxynaph-thacenequinone	25		m 203-211			243
$C_{21}H_{22}O_5$	Xanthohumol	22s,25				0.05% SE-52, 200°, 7.0'; 3% SE-52, 18.0'	22
$C_{21}H_{30}O_2$	Cannabidiol	25				SE-30, SE-52	167
		25				C-20M, 180°, 0.43/anth	304
		22py				SE-30, 170°, 2.88/eic	63

Table 5-5. Polyhydric Phenols (cont'd.)

Formula	Compound	Method	Yield %	B.P./mm; M.P.	n_D^t	Stat. Phase, Temp., Retention Data	Ref.
$C_{21}H_{32}O$	Cannabigerol	25				SE-30, SE-52, 240°, 1.54/cbd1	167
$C_{23}H_{24}O_3$	Bisphenol A 3,5-dimethyl-4-hydroxy-phenyl ether	43b		b 212/0.01			861
$C_{24}H_{43}NO_2$	6-(N,N-Dimethylamino)-methyl-3-pentadecyl-catechol	22py	76	b 237–243		IR	140
$C_{26}H_{47}NO_2$	6-(N,N-Dimethylamino)-methyl-4,5-dimethyl-3-pentadecylcatechol	22py	62	b 205–214		IR	140
$C_{30}H_{30}O_8$	Gossypol	43r				JXR	602

TABLE 5-6. ANTHOCYANIDINS AND FLAVONOIDS

Formula	Compound	Method	B.P./mm; M.P., Stationary Phase	Temp.	Retention Data	Ref.
$C_{15}H_{10}O_4$	Daidzein	25	SE-30	240	6.8'	256
$C_{15}H_{10}O_5$	Apigenin	21py	NMR			826
		25	NMR			500
$C_{15}H_{10}O_6$	Baicalein	25	SE-30	240	5.6'	256
	Fisetin	25	SE-30	240	11.5'	256
	Kaempferol	25	SE-30	240	10.6'	256
		25	NMR			500
		25	SE-30	270 / 285 / 300	4.7' / 1.1' / 0.75'	569
	Luteolin	25	SE-30	240	15.3'	256
		25	NMR			500, 501
	[→T₃(7,3',4')]					
$C_{15}H_{10}O_7$	Orobol	25	NMR			500
	Morin	25	NMR			500, 501
	Quercetin	25	SE-30	240	7.9'	256
		25	SE-30	240	15.0'	256
		23s,25	0.05% SE-52	255 pr		405
			3% SE-52	250 pr		
		21py	NMR			826
		25	NMR			500
		22s,25	SE-30	250	3.769/arbn	22
			SE-52	260	3.348/arbn	
	Robinetin	25	SE-30	240	14.4'	256
		25	NMR			500

Table 5-6. Anthocyanidins and Flavonoids (cont'd.)

Formula	Compound	Method	B.P.;mm; M.P., Stationary Phase	Temp.	Retention Data	Ref.
$C_{15}H_{10}O_8$	Myricetin	25	SE-30	240	18.9'	256
		25	NMR			500
	Quercetagetin	25	SE-30	240	21.2'	256
$C_{15}H_{11}ClO_4$	Apigeninidin chloride	23s,25	SE-30, SE-52	250 pr	6.0'	405
		22s,25	SE-30	250	10.0'	22
			SE-52	250		
$C_{15}H_{11}ClO_5$	Pelargonidin chloride	23s,25	SE-30	250 pr		405
			0.05% SE-52	210 pr		
			3% SE-52	250		
		22s,25	SE-30	250	0.140/malv	22
			0.5% SE-52	210	0.261, 0.435/malv	
			3% SE-52	250	0.316/malv	
$C_{15}H_{11}ClO_6$	Cyanidin chloride	23s,25	SE-30	250 pr		405
			0.05% SE-52,	250 pr		
			3% SE-52			
		22s,25	SE-30	250	1.437/malv	22
			0.05% SE-52	210	1.347/malv	
			3% SE-52	250	1.60/malv	
$C_{15}H_{11}ClO_7$	Delphinidin chloride	23s,25	SE-30	250 pr		405
			0.05% SE-52	210 pr		
			3% SE-52	250 pr		
		22s,25	SE-30	250	0.781/malv	22
			0.05% SE-52	210	0.774/malv	
			3% SE-52	250	1.366/malv	
$C_{15}H_{12}O_3$	6-Hydroxyflavanone	25	NMR			500
$C_{15}H_{12}O_4$	Liquiritigenin	25	SE-30	240	4.0'	256
$C_{15}H_{12}O_5$	Naringenin	25	SE-30	240	6.7'	256
		25	NMR			500

Table 5-6. Anthocyanidins and Flavonoids (cont'd.)

Formula	Compound	Method	B.P./mm, M.P., Stationary Phase	Temp.	Retention Data	Ref.
$C_{15}H_{12}O_5$	Naringenin	21py	NMR			826
	Pinobanksin	25,26d	UCW-98	148→290		867
		25	SE-52	242	2.42/pin	674
$C_{15}H_{12}O_6$	Dihydrofisetin	25	NMR			500
	Dihydrokaempferol	25	NMR			500
	Eriodictyol	25	SE-30	240	7.9'	256
	Fustin	25	SE-30	240	7.0'	256
$C_{15}H_{12}O_7$	Dihydroquercetin	21py	NMR			826
		25	NMR			500
	Dihydrorobinetin	21py	NMR			826
		25	NMR			500
$C_{15}H_{14}O_6$	Catechin [→T₃(5,7,4')]	11	m 92°			311
		17	m 99-100°; NMR			311
		21py	SE-52	255 pr		826
		23s,25	30% DC-430	240	10.2/gall	405
		25	5% DC-430	240	6.3'	672
		25	XE-60	240		673
		25				274
		22s,25	SE-30	250	2.076/arbn	22
			SE-52	260	1.488/arbn	
	Epicatechin	25	DC-430	240		274
		25	XE-60	240		673
	Gleditsin	25	SE-30	240	6.4'	256

Table 5-6. Anthocyanidins and Flavonoids (cont'd.)

Formula	Compound	Method	B.P./mm; M.P., Stationary Phase	Temp.	Retention Data	Ref.
$C_{15}H_{14}O_7$	Epigallocatechin	25	XE-60	240		673
		25				274
$C_{16}H_{12}O_4$	Formononetin	25	SE-30	240	5.2'	256
	Tectochrysin	25	NMR			500
$C_{16}H_{12}O_5$	Biochanin A	25	NMR			500
	Genistein 5-methyl ether	25	NMR			500
	Wogonin	25	SE-30		4.4'	256
$C_{16}H_{12}O_7$	Isorhamnetin	25	NMR			500
		25	SE-30	240	11.5'	256
		25	NMR			627
	Rhamnetin	25	NMR			500
		23s,25	SE-30, SE-52	250 pr		405
		22s,25	SE-30	250	4.615/arbn	22
			SE-52	260	3.488/arbn	
	Tamarixetin	25	NMR			627
$C_{16}H_{13}ClO_3$	5-Deoxyapigenidin chloride 4'-methyl ether	22s,25	SE-30	250	0.583/apgn	22
			SE-52	250	0.52/apgn	
	7-Hydroxy-4'-methoxy-flavylium chloride	25	SE-30	240 pr	7.0'	405
			SE-52	250 pr	14.2'	
$C_{16}H_{13}ClO_4$	Apigenidin chloride 4'-methyl ether	23s,25	SE-30, SE-52	250 pr		405
		22s,25	SE-30	250	0.80/apgn	22
			SE-52	250	0.83/apgn	
$C_{16}H_{13}ClO_6$	Peonidin chloride	23s,25	SE-52	pr		405

Table 5-6. Anthocyanidins and Flavonoids (cont'd.)

Formula	Compound	Method	B.P./mm; M.P.; Stationary Phase	Temp.	Retention Data	Ref.
$C_{16}H_{13}ClO_6$	Peonidin chloride	22s,25	SE-30 0.05% SE-52 3% SE-52	250 210 250	0.710/malv 0.913/malv 0.916/malv	22
$C_{16}H_{13}ClO_7$	Petunidin chloride	23s,25	SE-30 0.05% SE-52 3% SE-52	250 pr 210 pr 250 pr		405
		22s,25	SE-30 0.05% SE-52 3% SE-52	250 210 250	1.078/malv 0.835/malv 0.583/malv	22
$C_{16}H_{14}O_5$	Sakuranetin	25	NMR			500
$C_{16}H_{14}O_6$	Hesperetin	25	SE-30	240	4.3'	256
	Homoeriodictyol	25	NMR			500, 501
$C_{17}H_{14}O_6$	5,7-Dihydroxy-3',4'-dimethoxyflavone	25	NMR			500
	Irisolidone	25	NMR			500
$C_{17}H_{15}ClO_4$	5-Deoxy-3-methoxy apigenidin chloride methyl ether	22s,25	SE-30 SE-52	250 250	4.20/apgn 6.00/apgn	22
	7-Hydroxy-3',4'-dimethoxy-flavylium chloride	25	SE-52	pr	9.8'	405
$C_{17}H_{15}ClO_5$	5,7-Dihydroxy-3',4'-di-methoxyflavylium chloride	23s,25	SE-52	250 pr		405
	3-Methoxy apigenidin chloride-4'-methyl ether	22s,25	SE-30 SE-52	250 250	1.083/apgn 1.16/apgn	22
$C_{17}H_{15}ClO_7$	Malvidin chloride	23s,25	SE-30 0.05% SE-52 3% SE-52	250 pr 210 pr 250 pr		405

Table 5-6. Anthocyanidins and Flavonoids (cont'd.)

Formula	Compound	Method	B.P./mm; M.P.; Stationary Phase	Temp.	Retention Data	Ref.
$C_{17}H_{15}ClO_7$	Malvidin chloride	22s,25	SE-30 0.05% SE-52 3% SE-52	250 210 250	12.8' 23.0' 12.0'	22
$C_{18}H_{16}O_7$	Penduletin	25	NMR			500
$C_{18}H_{16}O_8$	Irigenin	25	NMR			500
$C_{20}H_{20}O_7$	Nor-icaritin	25	SE-30	240	22.4'	256
$C_{22}H_{18}O_{10}$	Epicatechin gallate	25				274
$C_{22}H_{18}O_{11}$	Epigallocatechin gallate	25				274

6

Carboxylic Acids

6-1. INTRODUCTION

That the same reagent will esterify acids and form ethers with alcohols is surprising, if not unique. Yet either HMDS or TMCS is capable of silylating both alcohols and carboxylic acids, and in good yields. The carboxyl group is silylated less readily than the hydroxyl group (section 1-5). The usual procedures found for preparative work employ TMCS, with or without base. Analytical samples have generally been silylated by using a HMDS-based formula (Methods 21-25). BSA has been used with some phenolic acids (347). Silyl esters are stable in the presence of excess reagent (182) but alone are quickly decomposed by moisture, and have been likened in this reactivity to acid chlorides or anhydrides (307).

6-2. ALIPHATIC ACIDS

Lower aliphatic acid salts were readily converted to silyl esters by heating them with TMCS in an inert diluent (24, 25, 27, 28, 694). Dibasic acids were silylated directly with TMCS. Mason and Smith (513) silylated hexanoic acid in high yields by HMDS with any one of several acid catalysts. Since hexanoic acid may be considered as its own catalyst, and HMDS alone gave a 97% yield, it is difficult to draw conclusions from the small yield differences observed (see Table 6-1). Jones and Schmeltz (381a) separated 18 C_1-C_{10} aliphatic and hydroxyaliphatic acid TMS esters on a single gas chromatogram, using a 20% SE-30 column programmed from 70°.

Krebs cycle hydroxy acids have been silylated with HMDS–TMCS in pyridine (335). All carboxyl and hydroxyl groups quickly react. If BSA is used for silylation of aliphatic hydroxy acids it may be necessary to add 10-20% as much of TMCS for complete reaction. The tertiary hydroxyl group of mevalonic acid, for instance, required this addition of catalyst to give a single derivative rather than two compounds (347).

In the silylation of α-keto acids with HMDS–TMCS in pyridine multiple products, including the TMS ester–TMS enol ether were obtained (182, 335). However, if hydroxylamine was added first, TMS oxime derivatives of the keto acids were formed, which were stable on GC analysis and gave single peaks (335). Similarly, the methoxime–TMS esters were prepared (347a), from treatment of the keto acid with O-methylhydroxylamine hydrochloride in pyridine, followed by BSTFA. These derivatives were superior for quantitative work whereas oximes or enol TMS ethers were unsatisfactory.

Tallent and Kleiman (770) used BSA to silylate lipid hydrolysates for analysis by GC. The reaction solution could be injected directly. The silyl esters of the fatty acids gave sharp, well separated peaks, which eluted ahead of glyceride TMS ethers.

6-3. AROMATIC ACIDS

In working with benzenecarboxylic acids containing up to six carboxyl groups, Kaufman *et al.* (399) obtained only partial silylation using BSA or HMDS–TMCS–pyridine. For complete reaction it was necessary to reflux the acids in toluene with equal volumes of HMDS and TMCS until solution was complete. Separation of 10 silyl esters by GC on 3% Apiezon L or on 3% SE-52 was excellent.

The silylation of phenolic acids has been studied by several groups (89, 153, 182, 334, 347, 395). The acids were silylated by HMDS–TMCS in pyridine, dioxane or dimethylformamide, or by BSA (347). Carboxyl groups were converted to TMS esters and hydroxyl groups to TMS ethers. Reaction was usually complete in 15 minutes at room temperature and the resulting mixture was injected directly into the gas chromatograph. Columns used were SE-30, SE-52, XE-60 and F-60, with good separation on each. Ester columns were not suitable. MU values on F-60 were determined for urinary phenolic acid TMS derivatives (182).

Williams (863) silylated all six isomeric dihydroxybenzoic acids with HMDS–TMCS in pyridine or in tetrahydrofuran, then treated the products with diazomethane in the hope of obtaining methyl ester–TMS diethers. Multiple products resulted in every case, explained by cleavage of the TMS ether linkage. It would seem that the TMS ester link should have been more easily cleaved than the ether, as carboxyl groups are silylated less easily than hydroxyls.

Silylation of o-hydroxybenzoic acids did not give uniform results. Blakely (89) observed that most phenolic acid derivatives were usually formed in 2-3 minutes, but longer reaction time was needed for complete silylation of o-hydroxy compounds. From 2,3-dihydroxybenzoic acid he obtained two peaks, of about the same size, whose ratio did not change with variation of reaction conditions. Gentisic acid (2,5-dihydroxybenzoic acid) also gave two products, one of which was phenolic (395).

For salicylic acid both mono- and di-TMS derivatives have been reported (137, 163, 525, 631) with good elemental analyses but not with good agreement in boiling points among the investigators. Choby and Neuworth (163) concluded that the mono-TMS product was the ester, TMS salicylate, on the basis of its IR spectrum, which was more like that of methyl salicylate rather than o-methoxybenzoic acid.

Teeter (774) showed that simple silyl aliphatic carboxylates and benzoates in the mass spectrometer lose methyl then undergo decarboxylation to the M − 59 ion, $R–CH_2–\overset{+}{S}i(CH_3)_2$.

TABLE 6-1. CARBOXYLIC ACIDS

Formula	Compound	Method	Yield %	B.P./mm; M.P.	n_D^t	Stat. Phase, Temp., Retention Data	Ref.
CH_2O_2	Formic acid	13e	65	b 86.5			281
		25				SE-30, 88°pr	381a
$C_2HF_3O_2$	Trifluoroacetic acid	16		b 89.5–89.8/750	1.3380^{20}		16
$C_2H_2O_4$	Oxalic acid	11b		b 77.5–79/0.5 m 55.7			692
		25				10% F-60, 11.54 MU 1% F-60, 11.70 MU	182
		25				SE-30, 160°pr, 2.5'	381a
$C_2H_3BrO_2$	α-Bromoacetic acid	14b	65	b 62.5/16			86
$C_2H_3ClO_2$	Chloroacetic acid	16b		b 159/760, 70–71/30	1.4231^{20}		24
		17	53	b 57–58/14	1.4192^{20}		307
		21b	87	b 160	1.4246^{20}		73
$C_2H_4O_2$	Acetic acid	13e	76	b 103; m −32			215
		14					791
		21	84	b 102.5–103/738			30
		33	81	b 105	1.3880^{20}		643
		15		b 102–103	1.3890^{20}		31
		15					64
		15e	64	b 30–31/35			694
		25				SE-30, 96°pr	381a
$C_3H_4O_2$	Acrylic acid	15b		b 53–54/62	1.4112^{20}		28
$C_3H_4O_4$	Malonic acid	13e	73	b 97	1.4152^{20}		688
		22r				QF-1, 125°	630
		25				SE-30, 172°pr, 3.6'	381a
$C_3H_5BrO_2$	α-Bromopropionic acid	14b	77	b 63/12	1.4375^{20}		86

Table 6-1. Carboxylic Acids (cont'd.)

Formula	Compound	Method	Yield %	B.P./mm; M.P.	n_D^t	Stat. Phase, Temp., Retention Data	Ref.
$C_3H_5BrO_2$	β-Bromopropionic acid	14b	66	b 85.7/13			77, 86
$C_3H_6O_2$	Propionic acid	21	81	b 122.3/738			30
		52	85	b 122	1.3939^{20}		3
		53	90		1.3941^{20}		
		16b	80	b 144	1.4005^{20}		24
		15b	41	b 122-123	1.3931^{20}		27
$C_4HF_7O_2$	Heptafluorobutyric acid	24				Mass Spec.	774
$C_4H_4O_4$	Fumaric acid	11					693
		13fu	46	b 124/15; m 63-64			307
		14	72	m 63			315
		21b	95	b 123/14; m 64			85
		22r				QF-1, 125°	630
		25				SE-52, 90→170°	335
		25				SE-30, 194°pr, 6.4'	381a
		25				10% F-60, 13.62 MU / 1% F-60, 13.62 MU	182
	Maleic acid	24				Mass Spec.	774
		11					693
		14	68	b 101-102/3	1.4317^{25}		315
		22r				QF-1, 125°	630
		25				SE-30, 187°pr, 5.5'	381a
$C_4H_6O_2$	Crotonic acid	24				Mass Spec.	774
		33	91	b 47/9	1.4246^{20}		643
	Methacrylic acid	15b,15p		b 51-51.5/20	1.4131^{20}		28
	trans-Crotonic acid	25				SE-30, 128°pr	381a

Table 6-1. Carboxylic Acids (cont'd.)

Formula	Compound	Method	Yield %	B.P./mm; M.P.	n_D^t	Stat. Phase, Temp., Retention Data	Ref.
$C_4H_6O_3$	Acetoacetic acid	14u	87	b 32/0.01	1.4270^{22}		688
$C_4H_6O_4$	Succinic acid	11		b 172.5/10.5	1.4450^{20}		29
		25				SE-52, 90→170°	335
		25				10% F-60, 13.22 MU 1% F-60, 13.16 MU	182
		25				SE-30, 187°pr, 5.5'	381a
		24				Mass Spec.	774
$C_4H_7BrO_2$	α-Bromobutyric acid	14b	60	b 73.5/11	1.4400^{20}		86
	β-Bromobutyric acid	14b	56	b 80.5/10	1.4432^{20}		86
	γ-Bromobutyric acid	14b	75	b 92.5/11	1.4488^{20}		86
	α-Bromoisobutyric acid	14b	80	b 60/11	1.4349^{20}		86
$C_4H_8O_2$	Butyric acid	25				10% F-60, 260°, 8.52 MU	182
		25				SE-30, 119°pr	381a
	Isobutyric acid	15p	47	b 43.5-44/20	1.3950^{20}		27
		25				SE-30, 112°pr	381a
$C_5H_4O_3$	Furoic acid	25				SE-30, 2.7'	381a
$C_5H_6O_4$	Citraconic acid	25				SE-30, 194°pr, 6.4'	381a
$C_5H_6O_5$	α-Ketoglutaric acid (→T_3)	21py				10% F-60, 16.36 MU 1% F-60, 16.54 MU	182
$C_5H_8O_2$	trans-2-Methyl-2-butenoic acid	25				F-60, 10.18 MU	182
$C_5H_8O_4$	Glutaric acid	25				10% F-60, 14.20 MU 1% F-60, 14.28 MU	182
	Monoethyl malonate	14u	69	b 48/0.01	1.4140^{20}		688
$C_5H_9BrO_2$	γ-Bromovaleric acid	14b	62	b 97-98/11			86
$C_5H_{10}O_2$	Isovaleric acid	11		b 92.5-93.5/10	1.4258^{20}		29

Table 6-1. Carboxylic Acids (cont'd.)

Formula	Compound	Method	Yield %	B.P./mm; M.P.	n_D^t	Stat. Phase, Temp., Retention Data	Ref.
$C_5H_{10}O_2$	Isovaleric acid	25				SE-30, 128°pr	381a
	3-Methylbutyric acid	25				F-60, 9.39 MU	182
	Valeric acid	25				F-60, 9.87 MU	182
$C_6H_5NO_2$	Isonicotinic acid	25				SE-30, 134°pr	381a
	Nicotinic acid	25				SE-30, 187°pr, 5.5'	381a
						10% F-60, 12.96 MU	182
						1% F-60, 13.52 MU	
		25				SE-30, 187°pr, 5.5'	381a
		43				OV-17, 150°pr	347
	Picolinic acid	11		b 91/2			699
		25				10% F-60, 13.30 MU	182
						1% F-60, 13.58 MU	
$C_6H_6O_6$	cis-Aconitic acid	25				10% F-60, 17.82 MU	182
						1% F-60, 18.00 MU	
	trans-Aconitic acid	25				SE-52, 90→170°	335
		25				10% F-60, 17.80 MU	182
						1% F-60, 18.00 MU	
$C_6H_{10}O_3$	α-Ketoisocaproic acid	21py				10% F-60, 100→250	182
						1% F-60, 100→250	
$C_6H_{10}O_4$	Adipic acid	11	28	b 153-154/24.5	1.4275²⁰		29
		21	81	b 134.5-5.5/12			30
		25				SE-30, 222°pr	381a
		25				10% F-60, 15.20 MU	182
						1% F-60, 15.22 MU	
	Monoethyl methylmalonate	14u	80	b 64/0.01	1.4128²⁰		688
$C_6H_{12}O_2$	Ethylbutyric acid	25				SE-30, 137°pr	381a
	Hexanoic acid	25				10% F-60, 10.82 MU	182
		-				1% F-60, 10.82 MU	

Table 6-1. Carboxylic Acids (cont'd.)

Formula	Compound	Method	Yield %	B.P./mm; M.P.	n_D^t	Stat. Phase, Temp., Retention Data	Ref.
$C_6H_{12}O_2$	Hexanoic acid	25				SE-30, 149°pr, 2.1'	381a
		21	97			DC-200, 110°	513
		24	101				
		22	92				
		23	90				
		25	89				
		33	92				
	β-Methylvaleric acid	25				SE-30, 142°pr	381a
$C_7H_5NO_4$	p-Nitrobenzoic acid	24				Mass Spec.	774
	Quinolinic acid	25				10% F-60, 17.94 MU 1% F-60, 18.00 MU	182
$C_7H_6O_2$	Benzoic acid	16		b 221			24
		33	86	b 56/0.7	1.4860^{20}		643
		52	83	b 221	1.4860^{20}		3
		53	83	b 220	1.4858^{20}		
		25				SE-30, 180°, 0.29/gent ApL, 185°, 0.41/gent	395
		23				SE-30, 3% SE-52; 10% SE-52, 150°, 1.16/naph, 170°, 1.07/naph	89
		25				SE-52, 165°, 0.18/phba 190°, 0.22/phba	153
		25				SE-52, 120°, 0.22/moba 140°, 0.15/phba	334
		23u				SE-52, ApL, 90→260°	399
		25				10% F-60, 12.42 MU 1% F-60, 12.44 MU	182

Table 6-1. Carboxylic Acids (cont'd.)

Formula	Compound	Method	Yield %	B.P./mm; M.P.	n_D^t	Stat. Phase, Temp., Retention Data	Ref.
$C_7H_6O_2$	Benzoic acid	25				NGS, 1.70/pol	303
		22r				QF-1, 125°	630
		25				SE-30, 175°, 4.5'	381a
		24				Mass Spec.	774
$C_7H_{12}O_4$	Pimelic acid	25				10% F-60, 16.20 MU 1% F-60, 15.30 MU	182
$C_7H_{14}O_2$	Heptanoic acid	25				SE-30, 165°pr	381a
$C_8H_6Cl_2O_3$	3,6-Dichloro-o-anisic acid	25				SE-30, 140°, 2.4'	606
$C_8H_6O_4$	3,4-Methylenedioxo-benzoic acid	13				C-20M, 200°, 2.7/pip QF-1, 130°, 1.2/pip	894
		25				QF-1, 140°	230
	Isophthalic acid	11					693
		14	84	m 58			315
		23u				ApL, SE-52, 90→260°	399
		22r				QF-1, 125°	630
	Phthalic acid	11					693
		25				SE-52, 140°, 1.40/phba 160°, 1.33/phba	334
		23u				SE-52, ApL, 90→260°	399
	Terephthalic acid	11					693
		13fu	70	b 174/16; m 71			307
		14	82	b 72-74/10⁻⁴ m 76.5-77			315
		23u				SE-52, ApL, 90→260°	399
		24				Mass Spec.	774

Table 6-1. Carboxylic Acids (cont'd.)

Formula	Compound	Method	Yield %	B.P./mm; M.P.	n_D^t	Stat. Phase, Temp., Retention Data	Ref.
$C_8H_8O_2$	Phenylacetic acid	23				SE-52, 150°, 1.5/naph 170°, 1.38/naph	89
		25				SE-52, 120°, 0.29/moba 140°, 0.19/moba	334
		25				SE-30, 187°pr, 5.5'	381a
		25				10% F-60, 13.00 MU 1% F-60, 12.98 MU	182
		25				DC-430, 1.85/pol NGS	303
	m-Toluic acid	23u				SE-52, ApL, 90→260°	399
		22r				QF-1, 125°	630
$C_8H_8O_3$	p-Methoxybenzoic acid	25				SE-52, 165°, 0.65/phba 190°, 0.71/phba	153
		25				SE-52, 120°, 140°, 0.57/phba	334
$C_8H_{14}O_2S_2$	Lipoic acid	43				OV-17, 208°pr	347
$C_8H_{14}O_4$	Suberic acid	25				10% F-60, 17.16 MU 1% F-60, 17.28 MU	182
$C_8H_{16}O_2$	Octanoic acid	25				10% F-60, 12.74 MU 1% F-60, 12.84 MU	182
		25				SE-30, 180°pr	381a
		24				Mass Spec.	774

Table 6-1. Carboxylic Acids (cont'd.)

Formula	Compound	Method	Yield %	Stationary Phase	Temp.	Phys. Constants, Retention Data	Ref.
$C_9H_6O_6$	Hemimellitic acid	23u		SE-52, ApL	90→260		399
	Trimellitic acid	23u		SE-52, ApL	90→260		399
	Trimesic acid	23u		SE-52, ApL	90→260		399
$C_9H_8O_2$	Cinnamic acid	33	92			b 102/1, n$^{20}_D$ 1.5310	643
		25		SE-30	180	0.66/gent	395
				ApL	185	0.82/gent	
		23		SE-52	150	5.32/naph	89
					170	4.12/naph	
		25		SE-52	165	0.72/phba	153
					190	0.78/phba	
		25		SE-52	120	1.14/moba	334
					140	0.65/phba	
		25		10% F-60		15.38 MU	182
				1% F-60		15.30 MU	
		21d,25		UCW-98	148→290	4.41'	867
		21		SiO	168		820
$C_9H_8O_3$	o-Coumaric acid	21d,25		UCW-98	148→290	2.25/cina	867
	m-Coumaric acid	21d,25		UCW-98	148→290	2.47/cina	867
	p-Coumaric acid	21d,25		UCW-98	148→290	2.61/cina	867
	Phenylpyruvic acid	25		SE-52	140	1.51/phba	334
					160	1.44/phba	
	(→T₂)	25		10% F-60		17.16 MU	182
				1% F-60		17.12 MU	
$C_9H_8O_4$	Acetylsalicylic acid	25r		QF-1	125		630
		22r		QF-1	125	5.4'	631

Table 6-1. Carboxylic Acids (cont'd.)

Formula	Compound	Method	Yield %	Stationary Phase	Temp.	Phys. Constants, Retention Data	Ref.
$C_9H_8O_4$	3,4-Methylenedioxo-phenylacetic acid	13		C-20M / QF-1	200 / 130	3.9/pip / 1.7/pip	894
	Methyl terephthalate	24		Mass Spec.			774
$C_9H_{10}O_2$	Phenylpropanoic acid	23		SE-52	150 / 170	2.82/naph / 2.25/naph	89
		25		10% F-60 / 1% F-60		14.14 MU / 14.16 MU	182
$C_9H_{10}O_3$	m-Methoxyphenylacetic acid	25		10% F-60 / 1% F-60		15.20 MU / 15.16 MU	182
$C_9H_{10}O_4$	3,4-Dimethoxybenzoic acid	25		SE-52	165 / 190	1.54/phba / 1.46/phba	153
		25		10% F-60 / 1% F-60		17.18 MU / 17.30 MU	182
		25		SE-52	140 / 160	1.55/phba / 1.42/phba	334
		25		SE-30 / ApL	180 / 185	1.06/gent / 0.95/gent	395
$C_9H_{16}O_4$	Azelaic acid	11				b 180-181/23 / n_D^{20} 1.4310	29
		25		10% F-60 / 1% F-60		18.14 MU / 18.28 MU	182
$C_{10}H_6O_8$	Mellophanic acid	23u		ApL, SE-52	90→260		399
	Prehnitic acid	23u		ApL, SE-52	90→260		399
	Pyromellitic acid	23u		ApL, SE-52	90→260		399
$C_{10}H_8O_4$	3,4-Methylenedioxo-cinnamic acid	13		C-20M / QF-1	200 / 130	9.9/pip / 5.5/pip	888

Table 6-1. Carboxylic Acids (cont'd.)

Formula	Compound	Method	Yield %	Stationary Phase	Temp.	Phys. Constants, Retention Data	Ref.
$C_{10}H_{12}O_2$	Mesitoic acid	24		Mass Spec.			774
$C_9H_{12}O_4$	3,4-Dimethoxyphenyl-acetic acid	25		10% F-60 1% F-60		17.26 MU 17.40 MU	182
$C_{10}H_{16}N_2O_3S$	Biotin	43		OV-17	250 pr		347
$C_{10}H_{18}O_4$	Sebacic acid	17	50	SE-30 Mass Spec.	225	n_D^{20} 1.4342	307 461
$C_{10}H_{20}O_2$	Capric acid	24,25		SE-30 ApL	130 160		132
		25		10% F-60 1% F-60		14.66 MU 14.76 MU	182
		24		Mass Spec.			774
$C_{11}H_6O_{10}$	Pentacarboxylic acid	23u		ApL, SE-52	90→260		399
$C_{11}H_{11}Cl_2NO_3S$	3,4-Dichlorophenyl-mercapturic acid	25		F-60		23.42 MU	182
$C_{11}H_{12}ClNO_3S$	3-Chlorophenylmercapturic acid	25		10% F-60 1% F-60		22.24 MU 22.10 MU	182
$C_{11}H_{12}O_4$	2,3-Dimethoxycinnamic acid	23		SE-52	170	19.5/naph	89
	2,5-Dimethoxycinnamic acid	23		SE-52	170	30.7/naph	89
	3,4-Dimethoxycinnamic acid	23		SE-52	170	35.0/naph	89
		25		10% F-60 1% F-60		20.28 MU 20.40 MU	182

Table 6-1. Carboxylic Acids (cont'd.)

Formula	Compound	Method	Yield %	Stationary Phase	Temp.	Phys. Constants, Retention Data	Ref.
$C_{11}H_{14}O_4$	2,3-Dimethoxyphenyl-propionic acid	23		SE-52	170	21.6/naph	89
	2,5-Dimethoxyphenyl-propionic acid	23		SE-52	170	12.7/naph	89
$C_{11}H_{22}O_2$	Undecanoic acid	24,25		SE-30 ApL	130 160		132
$C_{12}H_6O_{12}$	Mellitic acid	23u		ApL, SE-52	90→260		399
$C_{12}H_{24}O_2$	Lauric acid	25		SE-52	100→300		759
		25		10% F-60 1% F-60		16.60 MU 16.60 MU	182
$C_{13}H_{26}O_2$	Tridecanoic acid	25		10% F-60 1% F-60		17.58 MU 17.58 MU	182
$C_{14}H_{28}O_2$	Myristic acid	33	85			b 147-148/2.3 n_D^{20} 1.4349	643
		22,43		OV-1			770
		25		10% F-60 1% F-60		18.56 MU 18.60 MU	182
$C_{15}H_{30}O_2$	Pentadecanoic acid	25		10% F-60 1% F-60		19.60 MU 19.64 MU	182
$C_{16}H_{32}O_2$	Palmitic acid	25		10% F-60 1% F-60		20.56 MU 20.60 MU	182
		22,43		OV-1			770
$C_{17}H_{34}O_2$	Heptadecanoic acid	25		10% F-60 1% F-60		21.52 MU 21.54 MU	182
$C_{18}H_{24}O_3$	Podocarpic acid methyl ether	23p		SE-30 ApN QF-1 PPE	200 200 200 200	2.42/mst 3.01/mst 3.05/mst 4.84/mst	896

Table 6-1. Carboxylic Acids (cont'd.)

Formula	Compound	Method	Yield %	Stationary Phase	Temp.	Phys. Constants, Retention Data	Ref.
$C_{18}H_{30}O_2$	α-Eleostearic acid	22,43		OV-1			770
$C_{18}H_{32}O_3$	Vernolic acid	22,43		OV-1			770
$C_{18}H_{34}O_2$	Oleic acid	23p		SE-30	200	1.44/mst	896
				ApN	200	1.33/mst	
				QF-1	200	1.19/mst	
				PPE	200	1.12/mst	
$C_{18}H_{36}O_2$	Stearic acid	25		SE-52	192	6.32/vana	674
					242	0.82/pin	
		25		10% F-60		22.54 MU	182
				1% F-60		22.58 MU	
		22,43		OV-1			770
		23p		SE-30	200	1.61/mst	896
				ApN	200	1.49/mst	
				QF-1	200	1.24/mst	
				PPE	200	1.13/mst	
		24		Mass Spec.			774
$C_{19}H_{38}O_2$	Nonadecanoic acid	25		10% F-60		23.56 MU	182
				1% F-60		23.54 MU	
$C_{20}H_{28}O_2$	Dehydroabietic acid	23p		SE-30	200	2.32/mst	896
				ApN	200	2.81/mst	
				QF-1	200	2.30/mst	
				PPE	200	4.08/mst	
$C_{20}H_{30}O_2$	Abietic acid	23p		SE-30	200	2.57/mst	896
				ApN	200	3.31/mst	
				QF-1	200	2.55/mst	
				PPE	200	4.05/mst	
$C_{20}H_{30}O_2$	Isopimaric acid	23p		SE-30	200	2.07/mst	896
				ApN	200	2.41/mst	
				QF-1	200	2.00/mst	
				PPE	200	2.61/mst	

Table 6-1. Carboxylic Acids (cont'd.)

Formula	Compound	Method	Yield %	Stationary Phase	Temp.	Phys. Constants, Retention Data	Ref.
$C_{20}H_{30}O_2$	Palustric acid	23p		SE-30	200	2.07/mst	896
				ApN	200	2.46/mst	
				QF-1	200	2.06/mst	
				PPE	200	2.84/mst	
	Pimaric acid	23p		SE-30	200	1.98/mst	896
				ApN	200	2.07/mst	
				QF-1	200	1.85/mst	
				PPE	200	2.12/mst	
$C_{20}H_{40}O_2$	Eicosanoic acid	25		10% F-60		24.50 MU	182
				1% F-60		24.54 MU	
$C_{22}H_{44}O_2$	Docasanoic acid	25		10% F-60		26.46 MU	182
				1% F-60		26.52 MU	
$C_{24}H_{48}O_2$	Tetracosanoic acid	25		10% F-60		27.21 MU	182
				1% F-60		27.28 MU	

TABLE 6-2. HYDROXY CARBOXYLIC ACIDS

Formula	Compound	Silylation	Method (Yield %)	Stat. Phase	Temp.	Phys. Constants, Retention Data	Ref.
$C_3H_6O_3$	Lactic acid	$T_1(OH)$	16(43%)				307
			25	SE-52	90→170		335
		T_2	25	10% F-60		10.70 MU	182
		T_2		1% F-60		10.88 MU	
$C_4H_4O_6$	Dihydroxymaleic acid	T_4	25	10% F-60		15.26 MU	182
				1% F-60		15.20 MU	
$C_4H_6O_5$	Malic acid	T_3	23,25	SE-30	130		132
				ApL	160		
		T_3	25	SE-52	90→170		335
		T_3	22r	QF-1	125		630
		T_3	24	Mass Spec.			774
	D(-)-Malic acid	T_3	25	10% F-60		15.26 MU	182
				1% F-60		15.34 MU	
$C_4H_6O_6$	Tartaric acid	T_4	17(59%)			b 132-135°/2.5 n_D^{20} 1.4295	307
		T_4	25	ApL	160		132
				SE-30	130		
	(+)-Tartaric acid	T_4	22r	QF-1	125		630
		T_4	25	10% F-60		16.84 MU	182
				1% F-60		17.00 MU	
$C_4H_8O_3$	α-Hydroxyisobutyric acid	T_2	25	10% F-60		10.78 MU	182
				1% F-60		10.72 MU	
	β-Hydroxybutyric acid	T_2	25	10% F-60		11.74 MU	182
				1% F-60		11.78 MU	
		T_2	43	OV-1	120 pr		347

Table 6-2. Hydroxy Carboxylic Acids (cont'd.)

Formula	Compound	Silyl-ation	Method (Yield %)	Stat. Phase	Temp.	Phys. Constants, Retention Data	Ref.
$C_5H_{10}O_3$	α-Hydroxyisovaleric acid	T_2	25	10% F-60 / 1% F-60		11.80 MU / 11.92 MU	182
$C_6H_8O_7$	Citric acid	T_4	25	ApL / SE-30	160 / 130		132
		T_4	25	SE-52	90→170		335
		T_4	25	10% F-60 / 1% F-60 / Mass Spec.		18.70 MU / 18.76 MU	182
		T_4	43	F-60 / OV-1	178 pr / 204 pr		347
		T_4	22r	QF-1	125		630
	Isocitric acid	T_4	25	10% F-60 / 1% F-60		18.80 MU / 18.92 MU	182
$C_6H_{10}O_5$	β-Hydroxy-β-methyl-glutaric acid	T_3	25	10% F-60 / 1% F-60		16.30 MU / 16.32 MU	182
		T_3	43	OV-1	178 pr		347
$C_6H_{12}O_3$	α-Hydroxycaproic acid	T_2	25	10% F-60 / 1% F-60		12.58 MU / 12.72 MU	182
$C_6H_{12}O_4$	β,δ-Dihydroxy-β-methylvaleric acid	T_3	25	10% F-60 / 1% F-60		15.86 MU / 16.00 MU	182
	Mevalonic acid	T_3	44	OV-1	172 pr		347
$C_7H_4Cl_2O_3$	3,6-Dichlorosalicylic acid		25	SE-30	140	3.5'	606
$C_7H_4Cl_2O_4$	3,6-Dichloro-2,5-dihydroxybenzoic acid		25	SE-30	140 / 165	7.20' / 6.4'	606

Table 6-2. Hydroxy Carboxylic Acids (cont'd.)

Formula	Compound	Silyl-ation	Method (Yield %)	Stat. Phase	Temp.	Phys. Constants, Retention Data	Ref.
$C_7H_6O_3$	o-Hydroxybenzoic acid	T_1(OH)	13			b 62°/1; n_D^{20} 1.4788	137
		T_1(COOH)	21(80%)			b 89.5°/2	163
		T_1	25	DC-430	110→260	1.93/pol	303
		T_1(COOH)	11b(95%)			b 106°/1.5	525
		T_2	13			b 77.5°/1.1 n_D^{20} 1.4788	137
		T_2	21(97%)			b 106°/2, 95°/0.5	163
		T_2	43c				422
			22r	QF-1	125	1.5'	631
			25	SE-30 / ApL	180 / 185	0.46/gent / 0.56/gent	395
			25	SE-52	165 / 190	0.61/phba / 0.69/phba	153
		T_2	23	SE-52	150 / 170	4.60/naph / 3.50/naph	89
		T_2	25	10% F-60 / 1% F-60	100→250	15.14 MU / 15.04 MU	182
		T_2	25	DC-430	110→260	2.65/pol	303
		T_2	22r	QF-1	125		630
		T_2	21	SiO	166		820
	m-Hydroxybenzoic acid	T_2	23	SE-52	150 / 170	6.10/naph / 4.38/naph	89
			25	SE-52	165 / 190	0.76/phba / 0.85/phba	153

Table 6-2. Hydroxy Carboxylic Acids (cont'd.)

Formula	Compound	Silylation	Method (Yield %)	Stat. Phase	Temp.	Phys. Constants, Retention Data	Ref.
$C_7H_6O_3$	m-Hydroxybenzoic acid	T_2	25	10% F-60	100→250	15.72 MU	182
				1% F-60		15.72 MU	
		T_2	22r	QF-1	125		630
	p-Hydroxybenzoic acid	T_2	13			b 82°/0.85 n_D^{20} 1.4838	137, 138
		T_2	21py	SE-30	180	1.8'	548
		T_2	23	SE-52	150	8.10/naph	89
					170	5.62/naph	
			25	SE-52	165	6.6'	153
					190	2.3'	
		T_2	25	SE-52	120	1.91/moba	334
					140	1.00/phba	
					160		
			23s,25	SE-52	105	4.2'	405
			22s,25	3% SE-52	125	8.5'	334
		T_2		0.05% SE-52	130	4.2'	
				DEGS	160	18.0'	
		T_2	25	10% F-60	100→250	16.34 MU	182
				1% F-60		16.34 MU	
		T_2	22r	QF-1	125		630
		T_2	25	NGS	110→260	2.96/pol	303
			21	SiO	176		820
			24	Mass Spec.			774
$C_7H_6O_4$	2,3-Dihydroxybenzoic acid	T_2	23	SE-52	150	9.2, 14.2/naph	89
					170	7.1, 11.4/naph	
		T_2 (OH,COOH)	25				395

Table 6-2. Hydroxy Carboxylic Acids (cont'd.)

Formula	Compound	Silyl-ation	Method (Yield %)	Stat. Phase	Temp.	Phys. Constants, Retention Data	Ref.
$C_7H_6O_4$	2,3-Dihydroxy-benzoic acid	T_3	25	SE-30 / ApL	180 / 185	1.26/gent / 0.97/gent	395
		T_3	25	10% F-60 / 1% F-60	100→250	17.58 MU / 17.58 MU	182
	2,4-Dihydroxy-benzoic acid	T_3	23	SE-52	150 / 170	21.0/naph / 13.1/naph	89
		T_3	25	SE-52	165 / 190	2.32/phba / 2.07/phba	153
		T_3	25	10% F-60 / 1% F-60	100→250	18.38 MU / 18.42 MU	182
	2,5-Dihydroxy-benzoic acid	T_2 (OH,COOH)	25				395
		T_2	25	SE-30 / ApL	180 / 185	3.5' / 4.1'	395
			25	SE-52	165 / 190	1.96/phba / 1.78/phba	153
		T_3	23	SE-52	150 / 170	17.5/naph / 11.1/naph	89
		T_3	25	10% F-60 / 1% F-60	100→250	18.00 MU / 18.08 MU	182
		T_3	22r	QF-1	125		630
			21	SiO	191		820
	2,6-Dihydroxy-benzoic acid		25	SE-52	165 / 190	1.90/phba / 1.75/phba	153
		T_3	23	SE-52	150 / 170	16.0/naph / 10.4/naph	89

Table 6-2. Hydroxy Carboxylic Acids (cont'd.)

Formula	Compound	Silyl-ation	Method (Yield %)	Stat. Phase	Temp.	Phys. Constants, Retention Data	Ref.
$C_7H_6O_4$	2,6-Dihydroxy-benzoic acid	T_3	25	10% F-60 1% F-60	100→250	18.00 MU 17.88 MU	182
	3,4-Dihydroxy-benzoic acid		25				673
		T_3	25	SE-30 ApL	180 185	1.28/gent 1.41/gent	395
		T_3	23	SE-52	150 170	21.2/naph 13.5/naph	89
			25	SE-52	165 190	2.41/phba 2.14/phba	153
			25	SE-52	140 160	2.80/phba 2.42/phba	334
		T_3	22s,25	SE-52 DEGS	130 160	3.34/phba 1.028/phba	22
			23s,25	SE-52 QF-1	105 105	14.0' 9.9'	405
			25	QF-1	140		230
		T_3	25	10% F-60 1% F-60	100→250	18.44 MU 18.50 MU	182
			25	DEGS	70→220	1.33/gu	618
	3,5-Dihydroxy-benzoic acid	T_3	25	ApL SE-30	185 180	1.30/gent 2.08/gent	395
			25	SE-52	165 190	2.40/phba 2.07/phba	153
		T_3	23	SE-52	150 170	22.9/naph 13.4/naph	89
		T_3	25	10% F-60 1% F-60	100→250	18.48 MU 18.62 MU	182

Table 6-2. Hydroxy Carboxylic Acids (cont'd.)

Formula	Compound	Silylation	Method (Yield %)	Stat. Phase	Temp.	Phys. Constants, Retention Data	Ref.
$C_7H_6O_4$	3,6-Dihydroxy-benzoic acid	T_3	21d,22d	SE-30	148→290		867
$C_7H_6O_5$	3,4,5-Trihydroxy-benzoic acid					b 325°; n_D^{20} 1.4715	311
		T_4	13	SE-30	180	1.20/gent	395
		T_4	25	ApL	185	1.90/gent	
		T_4	21py	SE-30	192	4.6'	548
		T_4	25	SE-52	165	4.57/phba	153
					190	3.58/phba	
			25	SE-52	160	4.80/phba	334
			22s,25	3% SE-52	120	7.7/phba	22
				0.05% SE-52	130		
				DEGS	160	1.055/phba	
$C_7H_8O_5$	5-Dehydroshikimic acid	T_3	23a	SE-30	160	2.2'	723
				QF-1	150	4.9'	
				XE-60	170	6.9'	
$C_7H_{10}O_5$	Shikimic	T_4	23	SE-30	160	2.2'	723
				QF-1	150	2.1'	
				XE-60	170	2.7'	
		T_4	25	10% F-60		18.58 MU	182
				1% F-60		18.80 MU	
			25	DEGS	70→220	0.99/gu	618
$C_7H_{10}O_6$	5-Dehydroquinic acid	T_4	21d,25	UCW-98	148→290	2.40/cina	867
		T_4	23a	SE-30	160	2.1'	723
				QF-1	150	2.7'	
				XE-60	170	4.6'	
$C_7H_{12}O_6$	Quinic acid	T_4	13				260
			25	DEGS	70→220	0.94/gu	618

Table 6-2. Hydroxy Carboxylic Acids (cont'd.)

Formula	Compound	Silylation	Method (Yield %)	Stat. Phase	Temp.	Phys. Constants, Retention Data	Ref.
$C_7H_{12}O_6$	Quinic acid		21d,25	UCW-98	148–290	2.63/cina	867
		T_5	23a	SE-30 / QF-1 / XE-60	160 / 150 / 170	3.0' / 1.8' / 2.1'	723
		T_5	25	10% F-60 / 1% F-60		19.10 MU / 19.28 MU	182
$C_8H_6Cl_2O_4$	3,6-Dichloro-5-hydroxy-2-methoxy benzoic acid	T_5	21py				260
			25	SE-30	165	4.1'	606
$C_8H_6O_5$	4-Hydroxyisophthalic acid	T_3	13			b 148–150°/1, n_D^{20} 1.4801	137, 138
$C_8H_8O_3$	o-Hydroxyphenyl-acetic acid			SE-52	150,170		89
		T_2	25	10% F-60 / 1% F-60	100→250	15.74 MU / 15.72 MU	182
	m-Hydroxyphenyl-acetic acid			SE-52	150,170		89
		T_2	25	10% F-60 / 1% F-60	100→250	16.18 MU / 16.24 MU	182
	p-Hydroxyphenyl-acetic acid	T_2	25	10% F-60 / 1% F-60	100→250	16.48 MU / 16.50 MU	182
		T_2		SE-52	150,170		89
	Mandelic acid	T_2	43py	F-60	156 pr		347
		T_2	11b			b 100°/1.5	524
		T_2	23	SE-52	170	2.9/naph	89
		T_2	25	SE-52	120 / 140	0.84/moba, 0.48/phba	334

Table 6-2. Hydroxy Carboxylic Acids (cont'd.)

Formula	Compound	Silyl-ation	Method (Yield %)	Stat. Phase	Temp.	Phys. Constants, Retention Data	Ref.
$C_8H_8O_3$	Mandelic acid	T_2	25	10% F-60	100→250	14.86 MU	182
				1% F-60		14.80 MU	
		T_2	22r	QF-1	125		630
$C_8H_8O_4$	2,5-Dihydroxy-phenylacetic acid	T_3	23	SE-52	170	14.7/naph	89
		T_3	25	10% F-60	100→250	18.66 MU	182
				1% F-60		18.70 MU	
	3,4-Dihydroxy-phenylacetic acid	T_3	23	SE-52	170	14.1/naph	89
		T_3	25	10% F-60	100→250	18.48 MU	182
				1% F-60		18.44 MU	
	p-Hydroxymandelic acid	T_3	25	10% F-60	100→250	18.08 MU	182
				1% F-60		18.26 MU	
		T_3	43	F-60	174 pr		347
	4-Hydroxy-3-methoxy-benzoic acid (vanil-lic acid)	T_2	25	SE-30	180	1.57/gent	395
				ApL	185	1.15/gent	
			25	SE-52	165	1.85/phba	153
					190	1.71/phba	
			25	SE-52	140	2.03/phba	334
					160	1.85/phba	
			25	SE-52	160	2.78/van	674
					192	5.7'	
					242	0.19/pin	
		T_2	22s,25	3% SE-52	125	12.75'	22
				0.05% SE-52	130	2.97/phba	
				DEGS	160	1.041/phba	
			23s,25	SE-52	105	12.5'	405
				QF-1	105	8.4'	

Table 6-2. Hydroxy Carboxylic Acids (cont'd.)

Formula	Compound	Silylation	Method (Yield %)	Stat. Phase	Temp.	Phys. Constants, Retention Data	Ref.
$C_8H_8O_4$	4-Hydroxy-3-methoxy-benzoic acid (vanillic acid)	T_2	25	10% F-60	100→250	17.72 MU	182
				1% F-60		17.72 MU	
		T_2	25	NGS	100→260	3.41/pol	303
			25	DC-430			673
			21	SiO	187		820
			21d,25	UCW-98	148→290	3.04/cina	867
$C_8H_8O_5$	3,4-Dihydroxy-mandelic acid	T_4	25	10% F-60	100→250	19.70 MU	182
				1% F-60		19.86 MU	
$C_9H_8O_3$	o-Hydroxycinnamic acid	T_2	25	SE-30	180	1.94/gent	395
				ApL	185	1.60/gent	
		T_2	23	SE-52	150	19.7/naph	89
					170	13.3/naph	
		T_2	25	SE-52	165	2.25/phba	153
					190	2.05/phba	
		T_2	25	10% F-60	100→250	18.14 MU	182
				1% F-60		18.18 MU	
	m-Hydroxycinnamic acid	T_2	25	SE-30	180	2.26/gent	395
				ApL	185	2.50/gent	
		T_2	23	SE-52	150	27.0/naph	89
					170	17.7/naph	
		T_2	25	SE-52	165	2.91/phba	153
					190	2.50/phba	
	p-Hydroxycinnamic acid	T_2	25	SE-30	180	2.23/gent	395
				ApL	185	2.95/gent	

Table 6-2. Hydroxy Carboxylic Acids (cont'd.)

Formula	Compound	Silyl-ation	Method (Yield %)	Stat. Phase	Temp.	Phys. Constants, Retention Data	Ref.
C$_9$H$_8$O$_3$	p-Hydroxycinnamic acid	T$_2$	23	SE-52	150 170	37.0/naph 23.6/naph	89
			25	SE-52	165 190	3.85/phba 3.32/phba	153
			25	SE-52	192 242	2.02/vana 0.34/pin	674
		T$_2$	22s,25	3% SE-52 0.05% SE-52 DEGS	150 130 160	8.0' 3.26/phba 1.055/phba	22
		T$_2$	25	10% F-60 1% F-60	100→250	19.40 MU 19.40 MU	182
		T$_2$	25	NGS	110→260	4.03/pol	303
			21	SiO	204		820
C$_9$H$_8$O$_4$	2,3-Dihydroxy-cinnamic acid	T$_3$	23	SE-52	170	37.2/naph	89
	3,4-Dihydroxy-cinnamic acid	T$_3$	25	SE-30 ApL	180 185		395
			25	SE-52	165 190	10.50/phba 7.01/phba	153
		T$_3$	23	SE-52	170	56.5/naph	89
			25	SE-52	192 242	4.42/vana 0.68/pin	674
		T$_3$	25	10% F-60 1% F-60	100→250	21.56 MU 21.64 MU	182
		T$_3$	25	DC-430, NGS	100→260	4.60/pol	303
			25	UCW-98	148→290	3.22/cina	867
			21	SiO	223		820

Table 6-2. Hydroxy Carboxylic Acids (cont'd.)

Formula	Compound	Silylation	Method (Yield %)	Stat. Phase	Temp.	Phys. Constants, Retention Data	Ref.
$C_9H_8O_4$	p-Hydroxyphenyl-pyruvic acid		21py	10% F-60 1% F-60		20.74 MU 20.82 MU	182
$C_9H_{10}O_3$	o-Hydroxyphenyl-propionic acid	T_2	23	SE-52	150 170	10.7/naph 7.50/naph	89
	m-Hydroxyphenyl-propionic acid	T_2	23	SE-52	150 170	13.4/naph 9.25/naph	89
	p-Hydroxyphenyl-propionic acid	T_2	23	SE-52	150 170	15.9/naph 10.6/naph	89
	α-Phenylhydracrylic acid	T_2	25	SE-30 ApL	180 185	0.77/gent 0.70/gent	395
	Phenyllactic acid		23 25	SE-52 10% F-60 1% F-60	170	α 3.5, β 5.3/naph 16.00 MU 16.00 MU	89 182
$C_9H_{10}O_4$	2,3-Dihydroxyphenyl-propionic acid	T_3	23	SE-52	170	21.6/naph	89
	2,5-Dihydroxyphenyl-propionic acid	T_3	23	SE-52	170	23.5/naph	89
	3,4-Dihydroxyphenyl-propionic acid	T_3	25	10% F-60 1% F-60	100→250	19.62 MU 19.66 MU	182
	4-Hydroxy-3-methoxy-phenylacetic acid	T_2	25	10% F-60 1% F-60	100→250	17.82 MU 17.90 MU	182
	p-Hydroxyphenyl-lactic acid	**T_2**	43py	F-60	170 pr		347
		T_3	23	SE-52	170	21.2/naph	89

CARBOXYLIC ACIDS

Table 6-2. Hydroxy Carboxylic Acids (cont'd.)

Formula	Compound	Silyl-ation	Method (Yield %)	Stat. Phase	Temp.	Phys. Constants, Retention Data	Ref.
$C_9H_{10}O_4$	p-Methoxymandelic acid		25	10% F-60		17.24 MU	182
				1% F-60		17.32 MU	
$C_9H_{10}O_5$	3,5-Dimethoxy-4-hydroxybenzoic acid	T_2	25	SE-30	180	2.63/gent	395
				ApL	185	2.00/gent	
			25	SE-52	165	3.32/phba	153
					190	2.82/phba	
			22s,25	3% SE-52	120	17.0'	22
				0.05% SE-52	130	4.55/phba	
				DEGS	160	1.041/phba	
			23s,25	SE-52	105	32.5'	405
				QF-1	105	17.5'	
		T_2	25	DC-430	160	2.00/vana	672
					190	0.83/gall	
		T_2	25	DC-430, NGS	100→260	3.90/pol	303
			21	SiO	200		820
	4-Hydroxy-3-methoxy-mandelic acid	T_3	43	F-60	185 pr		347
		T_3	25	10% F-60	100→250	19.16 MU	182
				1% F-60		19.36 MU	
$C_{10}H_7NO_3$	Kynurenic acid	T_2	43	OV-1		20.37 MU	347
$C_{10}H_7NO_4$	Xanthurenic acid	T_3	43	OV-1		22.51 MU	347
				OV-17		24.24 MU	
$C_{10}H_{10}O_4$	3-Hydroxy-4-methoxy-cinnamic acid		25	SE-52	165	7.55/phba	153
					190	5.46/phba	
			21d,25	UCW-98	148→290	3.02/cina	867
	4-Hydroxy-3-methoxy-cinnamic acid	T_2	25	SE-30	180		395
				ApL	185		

Table 6-2. Hydroxy Carboxylic Acids (cont'd.)

Formula	Compound	Silyl-ation	Method (Yield %)	Stat. Phase	Temp.	Phys. Constants, Retention Data	Ref.
$C_{10}H_{10}O_4$	4-Hydroxy-3-methoxy-cinnamic acid		25	SE-52	165, 190	7.80/phba, 5.85/phba	153
		T_2	23	SE-52	170	44.0/naph	89
		T_2	25	SE-52	192, 242	3.59/vana, 0.53/pin	674
		T_2	25	10% F-60, 1% F-60	100→250	20.98 MU, 21.02 MU	182
		T_2	25	DC-430, NGS	110→260	4.51/pol	303
		T_2	21d,25	UCW-98	148→290	3.04/cina	867
$C_{11}H_{12}O_5$	2,4-Dimethoxy-3-hydroxycinnamic acid		25	SE-52	165, 190	16.37/phba, 10.42/phba	153
	3,5-Dimethoxy-4-hydroxycinnamic acid	T_2	25	10% F-60, 1% F-60	100→250	22.50 MU, 22.56 MU	182
$C_{16}H_{18}O_9$	Chlorogenic acid		22s,25	SE-52, DEGS	130, 160	4.91/phba, 1.041/phba	22
		T_6	43	OV-1, OV-17		31.92 MU, 32.21 MU	347
		T_6	25	UCW-98	148→290	5.03/cina	347
$C_{16}H_{18}O_9$	4-O-Caffeoylquinic acid	T_6	21d,25	UCW-98	148→290	5.22/cina	867
	5-O-Caffeoylquinic acid	T_6	21d,25	UCW-98	148→290	5.31/cina	867
$C_{17}H_{20}O_9$	3-O-Feruloylquinic acid	T_5	21d,25	UCW-98	148→290	4.98/cina	867
	4-O-Feruloylquinic acid	T_5	21d,25	UCW-98	148→290	5.06/cina	867

Table 6-2. Hydroxy Carboxylic Acids (cont'd.)

Formula	Compound	Silyl-ation	Method (Yield %)	Stat. Phase	Temp.	Phys. Constants; Retention Data	Ref.
$C_{17}H_{20}O_9$	5-O-Feruloylquinic acid	T_5	21d,25	UCW-98	148→290	5.17/cina	867
$C_{17}H_{22}O_3$	Podocarpic acid	T_2	23p	SE-30 ApN QF-1 PPE	200 200 200 200	3.15/mst 3.16/mst 2.95/mst 3.71/mst	896
$C_{18}H_{32}O_3$	Dimorphecolic acid	T_2	22,43	OV-1			770
$C_{22}H_{30}O_4$	Cannabidiolcarb-oxylic acid	T_6	25	SE-30/52	240	2.33/cbdl	167
$C_{35}H_{49}NO_{14}$	N-Acetylpimaricin	T_6	25	Mass Spec.			277
$C_{35}H_{61}NO_{14}$	N-Acetyldodeca-hydropimaricin	T_7	25	Mass Spec.			277
$C_{38}H_{54}ClNO_{14}$	N-Chloroacetyl-lucensomycin	T_6	25	Mass Spec.			265
$C_{38}H_{67}NO_{14}$	N-Acetyldodeca-hydrolucensomycin	T_7	25	Mass Spec.			265

7

Amines and Hydroxyamines

The amino group is more difficult to silylate than alcohol or carboxyl groups, as shown in Chapter 1. From a mixture of hexanoic acid, 1-octanol, and 1-octylamine, under varied silylation conditions, the lowest yield by far was obtained from the amine (513). A possible explanation of this has been given (section 4-3). However, the difference in silylation capability appears not to be great as even HMDS alone, one of the weakest silyl donors, can silylate primary and many secondary amines.

7-1. AMINES

The silyl derivatives of most of the simple amines have been prepared and isolated by using TMCS and a base. Occasionally the base used was an excess of the amine to be silylated; more often pyridine or triethylamine was chosen. For analysis by GC, HMDS-based preparative methods were generally employed. The effect of various catalysts upon the reaction of HMDS with piperidine (224) and with 1-octylamine (513) has been studied. The substitution of two TMS groups in an amino group in one step has been accomplished in a few cases using acid-catalysed silyl donors: BSA–TMCS (336); N-methyl-N-TMS-acetamide with TMCS (66), and N-TMS-diethylamine with ammonium sulfate (323). Otherwise, a second TMS group may be introduced by lithiation of an amino or N-TMS compound and treatment with TMCS (139, 835).

Wannagat and co-workers studied the silylation of hydrazines with TMCS. 1-Methylhydrazine in ether yielded 1-methyl-2-TMS- or 1-methyl-1,2-bis(TMS)-hydrazine depending on the proportion of TMCS taken, and 1,1-dimethylhydrazine was silylated only once, in the 2-position (328, 836). However, at low temperature without solvent two TMS groups could be introduced into 1,1- or 1,2-dimethylhydrazines (831). The same results could be accomplished in better yield by lithiation with lithium phenyl, followed by treatment with TMCS (836, 838).

Cyclic amines, such as pyrrole or piperidine, were silylated using HMDS-based formulas, both for preparative work or for gas chromatography. However, the cyclic nitrogen of indoles usually required stronger reagents, such as BSA or BSA-TMCS.

7-2. CATECHOLAMINES

Sen and McGeer (701) silylated various catecholamines, or their hydrochlorides, with HMDS in pyridine at 95°. On analysis by GC, using different phases, they found no separation of epinephrine-TMS and norepinephrine-TMS or of metanephrine-TMS and normetanephrine-TMS. They assumed complete silylation of phenolic, alcoholic, and amino groups since phenylethylamine was found to form a new derivative under the silylation conditions used. Capella and Horning (148) also silylated phenylethylamine with HMDS and identified the product as the N-TMS derivative by GC–MS. Lindstedt (475) silylated phenolic amines, including catecholamines, with HMDS in dimethylformamide, and obtained good separation on a biphase column, 0.5% QF-1/0.05% EGS. Capella and Horning (148) showed by GC–MS that primary but not secondary amino groups of catecholamines were silylated by HMDS in dimethylformamide. Kawai and Tamura (402) used HMDS in dimethylsulfoxide and found the latter to be a superior solvent for this silylation. Like dimethylformamide, it greatly accelerated the silylation compared with pyridine, and it had no tendency to condense with primary amines as did dimethylformamide. Dioxane in amount equal to the dimethylsulfoxide was used to make the latter miscible with HMDS. Both groups of investigators (148, 401, 402) treated the silylation reaction mixture with a ketone, which converted the silylated primary amines to Schiff bases. These were chromatographed then as silyl ethers. Secondary amino groups were not affected by either the silylation or the ketone treatment.

M. G. Horning et al. (350) found that BSA or BSA–TMCS silylated catecholamine primary amino groups twice, secondary groups slowly or not at all. To obtain single products they treated the catecholamine with TMS-imidazole (TSIM) in acetonitrile, which silylated the hydroxyl groups. (N-Silylation did not occur even on heating at 60° for 48 hours.) BSA–TMCS was then added, which converted all primary amines to bis(TMS) derivatives and did not affect the secondary amines. Programmed separation of eight such derivatives on 5% OV-1 was excellent.

More recently M. G. Horning et al. (349) studied the silylation of catecholamine hydroxyls with TSIM, followed by N-acylation using N-acetyl- or N-heptafluorobutyrylimidazole. On GC of the reaction mixtures (flame ionization detector) the acetyl derivatives showed longer retention and trailed slightly on SE-30, OV-1, and OV-17. Electron capture detection remains to be studied.

7-3. SPHINGOSINES

The silylation of sphingosines and the analysis of the derivatives by gas chromatography and by mass spectrometry have been studied intensively. Practically all work reported involved silylation with HMDS—TMCS in pyridine. This method silylated only the hydroxyl groups of the free bases, as shown by mass spectra. The sphingosine hydrochlorides did not react under these conditions (266). BSA however silylated all hydroxyl and amino groups of the free compounds (763).

Gas chromatography with a SE-30 column separated sphingosine and dihydrosphingosine TMS derivatives (266). Sphingosine bases were not well separated according to differences in unsaturation on either SE-30 or XE-60 columns. The silyl derivative of N-acetylsphingosine can also be determined by GC. Its retention time is twice that of the TMS derivative of the free base (266).

Several mass spectral studies have been reported (267, 396, 397, 781). Deuterium (267) and O^{18} (781) labeling have been used. Mass spectra from TMS derivatives of N-acetylsphingosines are more useful than the data from the TMS ethers of the free bases (763).

Amines unsubstituted by free hydroxyl or carboxyl groups are listed in Tables 7-1 and 7-2. All hydroxyamino parent compounds are listed in Tables 7-3 and 7-4 regardless of proof of silylation of the amino group. There is doubt in many cases that the amino group was silylated; in other cases both O-silyl and O-silyl—N-silyl derivatives have been identified.

TABLE 7-1. AMINES

Formula	Compound	Silylation	Method (Yield %)	B.P./mm; M.P.	n_D^t	Stat. Phase, Temp., Retention Data	Ref.
CH_5N	Methylamine	T_1	11	b 71	1.3899^{20}		376
			18(55%)	b 70-70.6/747	1.3897^{20}		676
			18e(38%)	b 71	1.3905^{20}		676
		T_1	41,45			SE-30, 175→300°	69
		T_2	45(90%)	b 148	1.4222^{20}		66
CH_6N_2	Methylhydrazine	T_1	18b,18e	b 96-97	1.3820^{19}		836
		T_2 (1,2)	18b,18e	b 73-75/40			836
		T_2 (1,2)	18e(57%)	b 159-160	1.4209^{24}		856
		$T_1(2)$	18e	m -80; b 51/92	1.4153^{20}	ApL, 90°	328
		T_2 (1,2)	18p(67%)	m -(68-72); b 66/29	1.4241^{20}	ApL, 90°	328
C_2H_7N	Dimethylamine	T_1	11	b 85	1.3958^{20}		376
		T_1	18e	b 84	1.3950^{25}		584
		T_1	18x(23%)	b 85-86			530
	Ethylamine	T_1	41,45			SE-30, 175→300°	69
		T_1	11	b 40.6-41/124	1.3930^{20}		169
		T_1		b 90-91			376
			18e(25%)	b 90.1-90.8	1.3912^{20}		676
		T_1	41,45			SE-30, 175→300°	69
		T_2	45(95%)	b 60/20	1.4282^{20}		66
C_2H_7NO	N-Methylmethoxylamine	T_1	11	b 98/734			831
$C_2H_8N_2$	1,1-Dimethylhydrazine	T_1	11	b 100/721			831
		T_1	18b,18e	b 100	1.4018^{22}		836

Table 7-1. Amines (cont'd.)

Formula	Compound	Silylation	Method (Yield %)	B.P./mm; M.P.	n_D^t	Stat. Phase, Temp., Retention Data	Ref.
$C_2H_8N_2$	1,1-Dimethylhydrazine	T_1	18e(88%)	b 100	1.4030^{20}		833
		T_2	11	b 63/13			831
	1,2-Dimethylhydrazine	T_1	11	b 109			831
		T_2	11	b 61/13			
		T_1	18e(88%)	b 61-63/260			836
		T_2	18e	b 77/380			
				68-69/280			
		T_1	16(64%)	b 109	1.4045^{20}		833
				m -(62-66)			
		T_2	16h(62%)	b 61/13	1.4275^{20}		
	Ethylenediamine	T_2 (N,N')	18b(30%)	b 80.5/15	1.4274^{20}		312
		T_2 (N,N')	22(70%)	b 70/8	1.4256^{20}		857
		T_3	34(20%)	b 145-146/12			323
		T_4	34(69%)	m 49-50			
C_3H_7N	Allylamine	T_1	24	b 109.5/731	1.4127^{25}		753
C_3H_9N	Propylamine	T_1	41,45	b 43.2-43.4/70			170
		T_1				SE-30, 175→300°	69
		T_2	45(95%)	b 67/12	1.4310^{20}		66
	Isopropylamine	T_1	11	b 102-103	1.3944^{20}		376
		T_1	33(95%)	b 40-40.3/88			170
							323
		T_1	45(85%)	b 101	1.3933^{20}		57
$C_3H_{10}N_2$	N-Methylethylene-diamine	T_2	22(60%)				857
	Trimethylenediamine	T_2	21(95%)	b 90/12	1.4303^{20}		72

Table 7-1. Amines (cont'd.)

Formula	Compound	Silylation	Method (Yield %)	B.P./mm; M.P.	n_D^t	Stat. Phase, Temp., Retention Data	Ref.
C_4H_9NO	2-Aminoethyl vinyl ether	T_1	35	b 49-53/12			185
$C_4H_{11}N$	Butylamine	T_1	18e(36%)	b 130-135/750			473
		T_1	14e(18%)	b 66.2/59	1.4103^{25}		272
		T_1	14e	b 46/29	1.4103^{20}		641
		T_1	21	b 132-136.6	1.4060^{25}		586
		T_1	22(43%)	b 134-135/754	1.4094^{20}		452
		T_1	33(90%)				323
		T_1	52(13%)	b 135	1.4097^{20}		3
			53(58%)	b 134	1.4100^{20}		
	sec-Butylamine	T_2	45(88%)	b 86/12	1.4341^{20}		66
		T_1	18(30%)	b 124	1.4060^{20}		6
			24(31%)	b 124	1.4069^{20}		
	t-Butylamine	T_1	45(90%)	b 127	1.4047^{20}		66
		T_1	11	b 121-123	1.4055^{20}		376
		T_1	18	b 120-121	1.4054^{25}		586
		T_1	18b	b 118-119	1.4060^{25}		186
		T_1	33(79%)				323
	Isobutylamine	T_1	45(82%)	b 120	1.4048^{20}		66
		T_1	18	b 128	1.4073^{20}		6
		T_1		b 55.3-55.9/49			170
		T_2	45(83%)	b 83/12	1.4349^{20}		66
	Diethylamine	T_1	11	b 126	1.4101^{20}		376
		T_1	18p(33%)				452, 892
		T_1	18e(28%)				676
			51(12%)	b 126.1-6.4/750	1.4112^{20}		

Table 7-1. Amines (cont'd.)

Formula	Compound	Silylation	Method (Yield %)	B.P./mm; M.P.	n_D^t	Stat. Phase, Temp., Retention Data	Ref.
$C_4H_{11}N$	Diethylamine	T_1	18	b 126-127	1.4062^{25}		586
		T_1	18e(76%)	b 31/47	1.4110^{25}		584
		T_1	14e	b 33/26	1.4112^{20}		641
			41,45			SE-30, 175→300°	69
			18b	b 125-127	1.4105^{25}		186
$C_4H_{12}N_2$	1,1-Diethylhydrazine	T_1	11	b 144-145.4	1.4195^{20}		705
	N,N'-Dimethylethylene-diamine	T_2	14b	b 184-185/2.6	1.5294^{20}		415
	Tetramethylenediamine	T_2 (N,N')	18b(26%)	b 87-88/4	1.4346^{20}		312
		T_2 (N,N')	21(89%)	b 107/13	1.4324^{20}		72
$C_4H_{14}N_2Si$	1-Methyl-2-TMS-hydrazine	T_1 (2)	16e	m -70±2; b 58/17	1.4320^{20}	ApL, 90°	328
$C_5H_{11}NO$	N-Methylaminoethyl vinyl ether	T_1	35	b 56-58/12	1.4341^{20}		185
$C_5H_{13}N$	Isopentylamine	T_2	46(84%)	b 95/12	$1.4145-1.4155^{20}$		66
	Pentylamine	T_1	22(51%)	b 160.3-2.4/737			452, 892
	sec-Pentylamine	T_2	46(91%)	b 100/12	1.4357^{20}		66
		T_1	46(89%)	b 141	1.4106^{20}		66
$C_5H_{15}NSi$	N-TMS-ethylamine	T_1	13(13%)	b 164	1.4289^{20}		6
C_6H_7N	Aniline	T_1	18(46%)	b 206, 98-99/19			23
		T_1	14b	b 92-93/12			186
		T_1	14e	b 62/1.6	1.5213^{20}		641
		T_1-	21 (42,29%)	b 93/18, 96-98/24			530

Table 7-1. Amines (cont'd.)

Formula	Compound	Silylation	Method (Yield %)	B.P./mm; M.P.	n_D^t	Stat. Phase, Temp., Retention Data	Ref.
C_6H_7N	Aniline	T_1	43c		1.5222^{20}		418
		T_1	52(85%)	b 208			3
			53(71%)	b 207			
$C_6H_8N_2$	o-Phenylenediamine	T_2	16(90%)				835
		T_2 (N,N')	14u(97%)	b 137/14; m 33			72
	m-Phenylenediamine	T_2 (N,N')	14u	b 130/3.5	$1.5266^{20.5}$		93, 414
	p-Phenylenediamine	T_2 (N,N')	14u	m 103-105			93, 414
	1-Phenylhydrazine	T_1 (2)	16e	b 83-86	1.5201^{24}		856
		T_1 (2)	18b	b 72-74/0.5, 115-116/12	1.5409^{19}		836
		T_1 (2)	24(89%)	b 111-115/15	1.5229^{24}		224
			21(12%)				
$C_6H_{13}N$	Cyclohexylamine	T_1	14e	b 47/3	1.4453^{20}		641
		T_1	34(95%)				323
$C_6H_{13}NO$	2-Aminoisobutyl vinyl ether	T_1	14b(66%)	b 77/24, 68/15			185
$C_6H_{15}N$	Dipropylamine	T_1	18e	b 76-78/35	1.4209^{25}		584
	Diisopropylamine	T_1	18	b 157	1.4241^{20}		6
		T_1	24(35%)	b 163-164	1.4218^{25}		224
$C_6H_{16}N_2$	Hexamethylenediamine	T_2 (N,N')	18b(35%)	b 80-81/0.01	1.4383^{20}		312
C_7H_9N	Benzylamine	T_1	14b	b 95-96/15	1.4918^{25}		186
		T_1	21(52%)	b 98-99/22			530
		T_1	22			SF-96, 130°, 3.6' Mass Spec.	194

Table 7-1. Amines (cont'd.)

Formula	Compound	Silylation	Method (Yield %)	B.P./mm; M.P.	n_D^t	Stat. Phase, Temp., Retention Data	Ref.
C_7H_9N	p-Toluidine	T_1	22py,42			SE-30	231
$C_7H_{17}N$	Heptylamine	T_1	21(32%)	b 92-93/26			530
$C_7H_{19}NSi$	N-TMS-tert-butylamine	T_1	16e(15%)	m 56-57			139
$C_8H_9NO_2$	Methyl o-aminobenzoate	T_1	25			10% F-60, 15.12 MU 1% F-60, 15.04 MU	182
	Methyl p-aminobenzoate	T_1	25			10% F-60, 17.00 MU 1% F-60, 17.04 MU	182
$C_8H_{11}N$	1-Phenylethylamine	T_1	22			SF-96, 140°, 1.4' Mass Spec.	194
	N-Methylbenzylamine	T_1	43n(27%)			SF-96, 130°, 7.2' Mass Spec.	194
	2-Phenylethylamine	T_1	21			F-60-Z	336
		T_1	21py				701
		T_1	21(43%)	b 107/20			530
		T_1	22			SF-96, 135°, 3.0' Mass Spec.	194
	(ASB)	T_1	21d			F-60, 100→200°, 13.20 MU	148
$C_8H_{11}NO$	2-Phenoxyethylamine	T_1	43			SE-30, 145°, 3.7' Mass Spec.	195
$C_8H_{12}N_2$	N-Ethyl-N'-phenyl-hydrazine	T_1	16	b 113/10	1.5152^{20}		837
	N-Phenylethylene-diamine	T_1	16e	b 74-75/1	1.5178^{22}		857
		T_1	43			SE-30, 165°, 5.1' Mass Spec.	195
$C_8H_{19}N$	Dibutylamine	T_1	18e	b 90/49	1.4757^{25}		584

Table 7-1. Amines (cont'd.)

Formula	Compound	Silyl-ation	Method (Yield %)	B.P./mm; M.P.	n_D^t	Stat. Phase, Temp., Retention Data	Ref.
$C_8H_{19}N$	Dibutylamine	T_1	24(52%) 21(20%) 18(44%)	b 201-202	1.4762^{25}		224
		T_1	52(49%) 53(68%)	b 200	1.4291^{20}		3
	Di(2-butyl)amine	T_1	18	b 195	1.4385^{20}		6
	Diisobutylamine	T_1	24(46%)	b 190-192	1.4181^{25}		224
	Octylamine	T_1	21(<4%) 24(<4%) 22(56%) 23(46%) 25(<3%) 33(82%)			DC-200, 113-114°, 10.6'	513
	1,1,3,3-Tetramethyl-butylamine	T_1	14b	b 190-195			186
$C_8H_{24}N_2Si_2$	1,2-Bis(TMS)ethylene-diamine	T_1	16e(81%)	b 103-104/8	1.4420^{25}		857
$C_9H_{13}N$	Amphetamine	T_1	22			SF-96, 140°, 2.5' Mass Spec.	194
		T_1	41,45			SE-30, 175→300°	69
	N-Ethylbenzylamine	T_1	43n(22%)			SF-96, 132°, 5.9' Mass Spec.	194
$C_9H_{13}NO$	2-(4-Methoxyphenyl)-ethylamine (ASB)		21d			F-60, 15.60 MU	148
$C_9H_{15}NSi$	N-TMS-aniline	T_1	16t	b 72/2.6	1.4840^{20}		417
		T_1	16(80%)				421
$C_9H_{16}N_2Si$	1-TMS-2-phenylhydrazine	T_1	18j				856
$C_9H_{26}N_2Si_2$	N,N'-Bis(TMS)-N-methyl-ethylenediamine	T_1	16e(85%)	b 114-115/8	1.4466^{25}		857

Table 7-1. Amines (cont'd.)

Formula	Compound	Silyl-ation	Method (Yield %)	B.P./mm; M.P.	n_D^t	Stat. Phase, Temp., Retention Data	Ref.
$C_{10}H_{13}NO_2$	3,4-Methylenedioxo-phenylisopropylamine	T_1	25			C-20M, 160°, 0.45/pip; QF-1, 100°, 1.1/pip	894
$C_{10}H_{15}N$	2-Methylamino-1-phenylpropane	T_1	41,45			SE-30, 175→300°	69
$C_{10}H_{15}NO_2$	3,4-Dimethoxyphenyl-ethylamine	T_1	43			OV-17, 140→300°	336
		T_2	44			OV-17, 140→300°	
		T_1	44n,44py			OV-1, 16.93 MU; OV-17, 19.10 MU	350
		T_2	44n,44py			OV-1, 19.78 MU; OV-17, 21.35 MU	
	2-(3,4-Dimethoxyphenyl)-ethylamine (ASB)		21d			F-60, 17.40 MU	148
$C_{11}H_{20}N_2Si$	N-TMS-N'-phenylethylene-diamine	T_1 (N')	16e(85%)	b 104-107/1, 79-80/0.1	1.4950^{22}		857
$C_{12}H_{11}N$	Diphenylamine	T_1	16(83%)				835
$C_{12}H_{12}N_2$	4,4'-Diaminodiphenyl	T_2 (N,N')	14b				416
	N,N-Diphenylhydrazine	T_1	16(73%)	b 135-138/1, m 57-60			838
	Hydrazobenzene	T_1	16	b 138/1; m 55			837

Table 7-1. Amines (cont'd.)

Formula	Compound	Silyl-ation	Method (Yield %)	B.P./mm; M.P.	n_D^t	Stat. Phase, Temp., Retention Data	Ref.
$C_{12}H_{12}N_2O$	4,4'-Diaminodiphenyl ether	T_2 (N,N')	14b	b 196-197/1.4 m 72-73			93
		T_2 (N,N')	14b	b 196-197/1.4 m 72-73			414
$C_{12}H_{25}NO$	1,1,5-Trimethyl-7-vinyloxyheptylamine	T_1	33				185
$C_{13}H_{14}N_2$	4,4'-Diaminodiphenyl-methane	T_2 (N,N')	14b	m 52-54			93, 414

TABLE 7-2. CYCLIC AMINES

Formula	Compound	Silylation	Method (Yield %)	B.P./mm; M.P.	n_D^t	Stat. Phase, Temp., Retention Data	Ref.
CH_2N_4	Tetrazole	T_1	14b(70%)	b 66/0.1 m 28-30			85
CH_4N_5	5-Aminotetrazole	T_2	21(60%)	b 105/0.2 m 69-70			83, 85
$C_2H_3N_3$	1,2,4-Triazole	T_1	21(81%)	b 74/12	1.4604^{20}		73
C_2H_5N	Ethylene imine	T_1	14z(44%)	b 88-96	1.4082^{20}		679
		T_1	11e(60%)	b 95-96	1.4756^{20}		370
$C_3H_4N_2$	Imidazole	T_1	24(85%)	b 91/12			73, 77
		T_1	24				224
	Pyrazole	T_1	21(72%)	b 153	1.4599^{20}		73, 77
C_4H_5N	Pyrrole	T_1	16u(71%)	b 63/30	1.4679^{20}		73
		T_1	16(38%)				223
		T_1	24				224
		T_1	24(51%)			C-20M, 160°, 2.10'	223
C_4H_7NO	Pyrrolidone	T_1	14b(80%)	b 77-81/6			186
C_4H_9N	Pyrrolidine	T_1	14b(65%)	b 142	1.4333^{20}		73, 77
		T_1	21(42%)				224
C_4H_9NO	Morpholine	T_1	24(61%)	b 139-140	1.4297^{20}		
		T_1	18e	b 160	1.4407^{25}		584
$C_4H_{10}N_2$	Piperazine	T_2	14(34%)	b 210-216			101
$C_5H_8N_2$	3,5-Dimethyl-pyrazole	T_1	21(59%)	b 73/12	1.4708^{20}		73
		T_1	24				224
$C_5H_{11}N$	Piperidine	T_1	18e	b 156	1.4398^{25}		584

Table 7-2. Cyclic Amines (cont'd.)

Formula	Compound	Silyl-ation	Method (Yield %)	B.P./mm; M.P.	n_D^t	Stat. Phase, Temp., Retention Data	Ref.
$C_5H_{11}N$	Piperidine	T_1	14b(72%) 21(42%)	b 161	1.4423^{20}		73
		T_1	21(16-23%) 22(35%) 24g(35-61%)				224
$C_5H_{12}N_2$	2-Methylpiperazine	T_2	14e	b 106/11	1.4516^{20}		415
$C_6H_5N_3$	Benzotriazole	T_1	21				101
$C_6H_6N_4$	5-Aminoimidazo-[b]-pyridine (sulfate)	T_2	21(72%)	b 150-152/2			829
$C_6H_{14}N_2$	cis-2,5-Dimethyl-piperazine	T_2	14b	b 112/11	1.4563^{20}		415
	trans-2,5-Dimethyl-piperazine	T_2	14b	b 112/11	1.4522^{20}		415
$C_7H_5N_3O_2$	5-Nitrobenzimidazole	T_1	21g(83%)	b 180-181/1.5 m 142-145			829
$C_7H_6N_2$	Benzimidazole	T_1	21(89%)	b 112/0.3 m 66-67			73
		T_1	24				224
	Indazole	T_1	21(79%)	b 132/18	1.5446^{20}		73
		T_1	24				224
$C_7H_6N_4$	5-Phenyltetrazole	$T_1(2)$	21(88%)	b 104-106/0.05 m 25-27			85
$C_7H_6N_4O_3$	6-Nitro-4-methoxy-benzotriazole	T_1	21g(81%)	b 170-172/2 m 114-116			829
$C_7H_7N_3$	5-Aminobenzimidazole	T_2	21g(68%)	b 177-178/1.5			829
$C_8H_7N_3O_3$	6-Nitro-4-methoxy-benzimidazole	T_1	14g(78%)	b 202-204/1.5 m 182-185			829
$C_8H_9N_3O$	6-Amino-4-methoxy-benzimidazole	T_2	14g(73%)	b 186-189/2			829

TABLE 7-3. HYDROXYAMINES

Formula	Compound	Silylation	Method (Yield %)	Stat. Phase	Temp.	Retention Data, Physical Constants	Ref.
C_2H_7NO	Ethanolamine	$T_1(O)$	14 (50%)			b 134-135°; n_D^{20} 1.4165	822
		$T_1(O)$	12e (53%) 21 (80%)			b 134-135°; n_D^{20} 1.4165	39
			25				895
			25	DEGS	70→220	0.35/gu	618
		T_3	34 (60%)			b 101°/12; n_D^{20} 1.4360	323
$C_2H_8N_2O$	2-Hydroxyethyl-hydrazine		22py	10% C-20M 4% C-20M	220 110	0.30' 2.15'	229
$C_4H_{12}N_2O_2$	N,N'-Bis(2-hydroxy-ethyl)hydrazine		22py	C-20M	110	2.20'	229
$C_6H_4N_4O_3$	6-Nitro-4-hydroxy-benzotriazole	T_2	21 (76%)			b 162-166°/2	829
$C_6H_5N_3O$	5-Hydroxyimidazo-[b]pyridine	T_2	21 (79%)			b 132-134°/2	829
$C_6H_{14}N_2O$	1-Piperazineethanol	T_1	22	10% C-20M 4% C-20M	220 110	1.55' 4.25'	229
$C_6H_{14}N_2O_4$	Streptamine		25	DEGS	70→220		618
$C_7H_5N_3O_3$	6-Nitro-4-hydroxy-benzimidazole	T_2	21 (82%)			b 183-184°/3; m 104-106°	829
$C_7H_6N_2O$	5-Hydroxybenzimida-zole	T_2	21g (74%)			b 152-153°/3	829
$C_7H_7N_3O$	6-Amino-4-hydroxy-benzimidazole (sulfate)	T_3	21 (78%)			b 180-182°/3	829
$C_8H_9NO_3$	Methyl 3-hydroxy-2-aminobenzoate	$T_1(O)$	25	10% F-60 1% F-60		16.32 MU 16.24 MU	182

Table 7-3. Hydroxyamines (cont'd.)

Formula	Compound	Silyl-ation	Method (Yield %)	Stat. Phase	Temp.	Retention Data, Physical Constants	Ref.
$C_8H_{11}NO$	p-Hydroxyphenyl-ethylamine	$T_1(O)$	36n	OV-1	130→	14.56 MU	350
				OV-17	130→	16.37 MU	
		$T_1(O)$	36n	SE-30	130→	18.26 MU (Ac der.)	349
				OV-1	130→	18.35 MU (Ac der.)	
				OV-17	130→	21.58 MU (Ac der.)	
				SE-30	130→	16.39 MU (HFB der.)	
				OV-17	130→	17.59 MU (HFB der.)	
				Mass Spec.			
		$T_1(O)$	21d	QF-1/EGS	115-125		475
			21sg	DC-1107	170	0.27/epin	402
			41,45	SE-30	175→300		69
		$T_2(N,O)$	44n	OV-1	130→	16.32 MU	350
				OV-17	130→	17.14 MU	
		$T_3(N,O)$	36-44n	OV-1	130→	19.27 MU	350
				OV-17	130→	19.55 MU	
	2-Hydroxy-2-phenyl-ethylamine (ASB)	$T_1(O)$	21d	F-60	100→200	16.50 MU	148
	(ASB)		21d	F-60	100→200	14.90 MU	148
	2-Phenylamino-ethanol	T_1	22	SE-30	176	1.6'; Mass Spec.	195
$C_8H_{11}NO_2$	3,4-Dihydroxyphenyl-ethylamine	$T_2(O,O)$	21d	QF-1/EGS	115-125		475
			21pya	SE-30	180		401
			21py	SE-30	200	1.24/moty	701
					220	1.20/moty	
		$T_2(O,O)$	36n	OV-1	130→	16.81 MU	350
				OV-17	130→	18.30 MU	

Table 7-3. Hydroxyamines (cont'd.)

Formula	Compound	Silyl-ation	Method (Yield %)	Stat. Phase	Temp.	Retention Data, Physical Constants	Ref.
$C_8H_{11}NO_2$	3,4-Dihydroxyphenyl-ethylamine	$T_2(O,O)$	36n	SE-30	130→	20.35 MU (Ac der.)	349
				OV-1	130→	20.40 MU (Ac der.)	
				OV-17	130→	23.19 MU (Ac der.)	
				SE-30	130→	18.33 MU (HFB der.)	
				OV-17	130→	19.09 MU (HFB der.)	
				Mass Spec.			
		$T_2(O,O)$	21sg	DC-1107	170	0.60/epin	402
			41,45	SE-30	175→300		69
		$T_3(N,O,O)$	44n	OV-1	130→	18.32 MU	350
				OV-17	130→	18.82 MU	
		$T_4(N,N,O,O)$	36-44n	OV-1	130→	21.04 MU	350
				OV-17	130→	21.05 MU	
	(ASB)	$T_2(O,O)$	21d	F-60	100→200	18.60 MU	148
	p-Hydroxyphenyl-ethanolamine	$T_2(O,O)$	36n	OV-1	130→	16.69 MU	350
				OV-17	130→	17.90 MU	
		$T_2(O,O)$	36n	SE-30	130→	19.77 MU (Ac der.)	349
				OV-1	130→	19.80 MU (Ac der.)	
				OV-17	130→	22.00 MU (Ac der.)	
				SE-30	130→	17.92 MU (HFB der.)	
				OV-17	130→	18.13 MU (HFB der.)	
				Mass Spec.			
			21d	QF-1/EGS	115-125		475
		$T_3(N,O,O)$	44n	OV-1	130→	17.83 MU	350
				OV-17	130→	17.95 MU	
		$T_4(N,N,O,O)$	36-44n	OV-1	130→	20.53 MU	350
				OV-17	130→	20.36 MU	
	(ASB)	$T_2(O,O)$	21d	F-60	100→200	18.20 MU	148
$C_8H_{11}NO_3$	Norepinephrine	$T_2(O,O)$	21py	SE-30	200	2.04/moty	701
					220	1.84/moty	

Table 7-3. Hydroxyamines (cont'd.)

Formula	Compound	Silyl-ation	Method (Yield %)	Stat. Phase	Temp.	Retention Data, Physical Constants	Ref.
$C_8H_{11}NO_3$	Norepinephrine		21d	QF-1/EGS	115-125		475
			21t	SE-30	179	12.4'	113
		$T_3(O,O,O)$	21pya	SE-30	180		401
		$T_3(O,O,O)$	36n	SE-30	130→	21.43 MU (Ac der.)	349
				OV-1	130→	21.45 MU (Ac der.)	
				OV-17	130→	23.25 MU (Ac der.)	
				SE-30	130→	19.47 MU (HFB der.)	
				OV-17	130→	19.27 MU (HFB der.)	
				Mass Spec.			
		$T_3(O,O,O)$	36n	OV-1	130→	18.54 MU	350
				OV-17	130→	19.42 MU	
		$T_3(O,O,O)$	21sg	DC-1107	170	1.00/epin	402
			41,45	SE-30	175→300		69
		T_4 (N,O,O,O)	44n	OV-1	130→	19.41 MU	350
				OV-17	130→	19.45 MU	
		T_5 (N,N,O,O,O)	43,44	OV-17	140		336
		T_5 (N,N,O,O,O)	36-44n	OV-1	130→	21.99 MU	350
				OV-17	130→	21.55 MU	
		(ASB) $T_3(O,O,O)$	21d	F-60	100→200	20.00 MU	148
$C_9H_{12}N_2O_4$	1-(p-Nitrophenyl)-2-amino-1,3-pro-panediol		25	SE-30	110→260		714
$C_9H_{13}NO$	Norephedrine	$T_1(O)$	48h(71%)	SE-30	175→300	b 113-114°/10; n_D^{20} 1.4833	192
			41,45	SE-30	175→300		69
	(ASB)	$T_1(O)$	21d	F-60	100→200	14.50 MU	148
$C_9H_{13}NO_2$	3-Methoxy-4-hydroxy-phenylethylamine		21py	SE-30	200	1.6'	701
					220	1.0'	

Table 7-3. Hydroxyamines (cont'd.)

Formula	Compound	Silyl-ation	Method (Yield %)	Stat. Phase	Temp.	Retention Data, Physical Constants	Ref.
$C_9H_{13}NO_2$	3-Methoxy-4-hydroxy-phenylethylamine (ASB)	$T_1(O)$	21d	F-60	100→200	18.00 MU	148
	Oxedrine	$T_2(O,O)$	21d	QF-1/EGS	115-125		475
	1-Phenyl-2-amino-1,3-propanediol		25	SE-30	110→260		714
	Phenylephrine (ASB)	$T_2(O,O)$	21d	F-60	100→200	16.70 MU	148
$C_9H_{13}NO_3$	Epinephrine		21,43	OV-1	140		336
			21pya	SE-30	180		401
			21py	SE-30	200	2.04/moty	701
				SE-30	220	1.84/moty	
			21t	SE-30	179	13.4'	113
		$T_3(O,O,O)$	36n	SE-30	130→	21.82 MU (Ac der.)	349
				OV-1	130→	21.86 MU (Ac der.)	
				OV-17	130→	23.46 MU (Ac der.)	
				SE-30	130→	19.95 MU (HFB der.)	
				OV-17	130→	19.85 MU (HFB der.)	
				Mass Spec.			
		$T_3(O,O,O)$	36n	OV-1	130→	18.59 MU	350
				OV-17	130→	19.32 MU	
		$T_3(O,O,O)$	21sg	DC-1107	170		402
		$T_3(O,O,O)$	21d	QF-1/EGS	115-125		475
		$T_4(N,O,O,O)$	44n	OV-1	130→	19.94 MU	350
				OV-17	130→	19.80 MU	
			41,45	SE-30	175→300		69
	(ASB)	$T_3(O,O,O)$	21d	F-60	100→200	18.80 MU	148
	Normetanephrine		21				336
			21pya	SE-30	180		401
			21py	SE-30	200	1.66/moty	701
				SE-30	220	1.56/moty	

Table 7-3. Hydroxyamines (cont'd.)

Formula	Compound	Silylation	Method (Yield %)	Stat. Phase	Temp.	Retention Data, Physical Constants	Ref.
$C_9H_{13}NO_3$	Normetanephrine		21d	QF-1/EGS	115–125		475
		$T_2(O,O)$	36n	SE-30	130→	20.86 MU (Ac der.)	349
				OV-1	130→	20.87 MU (Ac der.)	
				OV-17	130→	23.43 MU (Ac der.)	
				SE-30	130→	18.93 MU (HFB der.)	
				OV-17	130→	19.34 MU (HFB der.)	
				Mass Spec.			
		$T_2(O,O)$	36n	OV-1	130→	17.87 MU	350
				OV-17	130→	19.43 MU	
		$T_3(N,O,O)$	44n	OV-1	130→	18.77 MU	350
				OV-17	130→	19.46 MU	
		$T_4(N,N,O,O)$	36–44n	OV-1	130→	21.41 MU	350
				OV-17	130→	21.54 MU	
		$T_2(O,O)$ (ASB)	21d	F-60	100→200	19.50 MU	148
$C_9H_{14}N_2O_2$	1-(p-Aminophenyl)-2-amino-1,3-propanediol		25	SE-30	100→260		714
$C_{10}H_{12}N_2O$	5-Hydroxytryptamine (ASB)	$T_1(O)$	21d	F-60	100→200	21.80 MU	148
$C_{10}H_{13}NO_2$	N-Acetyltyramine		25	F-60	100→250		348
$C_{10}H_{15}NO$	Ephedrine	$T_1(O)$	41,45	SE-30	175→300		69
	(ASB)	$T_1(O)$	21d	F-60	100→200	13.90 MU	148
$C_{10}H_{15}NO_2$	3,4-Dimethoxyphenyl-ethylamine	$T_1(N)$	44n	OV-1	130→	16.93 MU	350
				OV-17	130→	19.10 MU	
		$T_2(N,N)$	44n	OV-1	130→	19.78 MU	350
				OV-17	130→	21.35 MU	
$C_{10}H_{15}NO_3$	Metanephrine		21				336
			21py	SE-30	200	1.66/moty	701
					220	1.56/moty	
			21pya	SE-30	180		401

Table 7-3. Hydroxyamines (cont'd.)

Formula	Compound	Silylation	Method (Yield %)	Stat. Phase	Temp.	Retention Data, Physical Constants	Ref.
$C_{10}H_{15}NO_3$	Metanephrine		21d	QF-1/EGS	115/125		475
		$T_2(O,O)$	21sg	DC-1107	170	0.80/epin	402
		$T_2(O,O)$	35n	SE-30	130→	21.23 MU (Ac der.)	349
				OV-1	130→	21.28 MU (Ac der.)	
				OV-17	130→	23.58 MU (Ac der.)	
				SE-30	130→	19.32 MU (HFB der.)	
				OV-17	130→	19.90 MU (HFB der.)	
				Mass Spec.			
		$T_2(O,O)$	36n	OV-1	130→	17.98 MU	350
				OV-17	130→	19.36 MU	
		$T_3(N,O,O)$	44n	OV-1	130→	19.36 MU	350
				OV-17	130→	19.41 MU	
	(ASB)	$T_2(O,O)$	21d	F-60	100→200	18.20 MU	148
$C_{11}H_{11}NO$	4-Amino-2-methyl-1-naphthol (HCl) (Vitamin K_5)		25k	STAP	140		174
$C_{16}H_{33}NO_2$	C_{16}-Sphingosine		25	SE-30	160	0.40/sph	593
$C_{16}H_{35}NO_2$	C_{16}-Dihydro-sphingosine	$T_2(O,O)$	25	SiO	207	0.62/sph	396
$C_{17}H_{35}NO_2$	C_{17}-Sphingosine		25	SE-30	160	0.62/sph	593
$C_{17}H_{37}NO_2$	C_{17}-Dihydro-sphingosine	$T_2(O,O)$	25	SiO	207		396
$C_{18}H_{35}NO_2$	Anhydro-C_{18}-dehydro-phytosphingosine		25	SE-30	220 / 230	0.66/hsph / 0.69/hsph	150
$C_{18}H_{37}NO_2$	Anhydro-C_{18}-phyto-sphingosine		25	SE-30	220 / 230	0.72/hsph / 0.74/hsph	150
	C_{18}-Sphingosine		25	SE-30	210,220 / 230	0.88/hsph / 0.89/hsph	150

Table 7-3. Hydroxyamines (cont'd.)

Formula	Compound	Silyl-ation	Method (Yield %)	Stat. Phase	Temp.	Retention Data, Physical Constants	Ref.
$C_{18}H_{37}NO_2$	C_{18}-Sphingosine		25	SE-30	180	3.68/mst	266
			25	SE-30	160		593
			25	SE-30	214	3.61/mst	726
			25	SE-52			403
	threo-C_{18}-Sphingosine	$T_2(O,O)$	25	SE-30	220	1.71/hsph, 0.82/ahsp	150
	erythro-C_{18}-Sphingosine	$T_2(O,O)$	25	SE-30	220	1.88/hsph, 0.90/ahsp	150
$C_{18}H_{37}NO_3$	C_{18}-Dehydrophytosphingosine		25	SE-30	210 220 230	1.51/hsph 1.48/hsph 1.45/hsph	150
$C_{18}H_{39}NO$	Sphingine (2-amino-octadecanol)		25	SE-30	210	0.53/hsph	150
$C_{18}H_{39}NO_2$	C_{18}-Dihydro-sphingosine		25	SE-30	210 230	32.0' 15.0'	150
			25	SE-30	160		593
			25	SE-30	180	1.14/sph, 4.19/mst	266
			25	SE-52	214		403
			22py	SiO	207		396
	erythro-C_{18}-Dihydro-sphingosine	$T_2(O,O)$	25	SE-30	220	2.09/hsph	150
	threo-C_{18}-Dihydro-sphingosine	$T_2(O,O)$	25	SE-30	220	1.80/hsph, 0.86/ahsp	150
$C_{18}H_{39}NO_3$	C_{18}-Phytosphingosine		25	SE-30	210 220 230	1.65/hsph 1.61/hsph 1.56/hsph	150
			25	Mass Spec.			397

Table 7-3. Hydroxyamines (cont'd.)

Formula	Compound	Silylation	Method (Yield %)	Stat. Phase	Temp.	Retention Data, Physical Constants	Ref.
$C_{19}H_{37}NO_2$	3-O-Methyl-C_{18}-sphingosine		25	SE-30	160		593
$C_{19}H_{39}NO_2$	1,3-Dihydroxy-2-amino-nonadecene		25	SiO			398
	3-O-Methylsphingosine		25	SE-30	210	0.73/hsph	150
	3-O-Methylsphingosine		25	SE-30	180	0.83/sph, 3.08/mst	266
	3-O-Methyl-C_{18}-dihydrosphingosine		25	SE-30	210	0.80/hsph	150
$C_{19}H_{41}NO_2$	1,3-Dihydroxy-2-amino-nonadecane		25	SiO			398
$C_{19}H_{41}NO_3$	2-Amino-1,3,4-trihydroxy-nonadecane	$T_3(O,O,O)$	25	SiO			398
$C_{20}H_{39}NO_3$	N-Acetylsphingosine	$T_2(O,O)$	25	SE-30, Mass Spec.			267
$C_{20}H_{41}NO_2$	C_{20}-Sphingosine		25	SE-30	210, 220, 230	1.76/hsph, 1.71/hsph, 1.66/hsph	150
	erythro-C_{20}-Sphingosine	$T_2(O,O)$	25	SE-30	220	3.58/hsph, 1.72/ahsp	150
	threo-C_{20}-Sphingosine	$T_2(O,O)$	25	SE-30	220	3.26/hsph, 1.56/ahsp	150
$C_{20}H_{41}NO_3$	N-Acetyldihydrosphingosine	T_2	25	Mass Spec.			267
	N-Acetylsphingosine	T_2	25	Mass Spec.			781
$C_{20}H_{41}NO_4$	N-Acetylphytosphingosine	T_3	25	Mass Spec.			781

Table 7-3. Hydroxyamines (cont'd.)

Formula	Compound	Silyl-ation	Method (Yield %)	Stat. Phase	Temp.	Retention Data, Physical Constants	Ref.
$C_{20}H_{43}NO_2$	C_{20}-Dihydro-sphingosine		25	SE-30	210 230	2.00/hsph 1.87/hsph	150
$C_{20}H_{43}NO_3$	C_{20}-Phyto-sphingosine		25	SE-30	210 220 230	3.32/hsph 3.11/hsph 2.88/hsph	150
	2-Amino-1,3,4-tri-hydroxyeicosane		25	SE-30	180→220		151
			25	SiO			398
$C_{21}H_{45}NO_3$	19-Methyl-C_{20}-phyto-sphingosine		25	SE-30	230	3.58/hsph	150
			25	SE-30 Mass Spec.			151

TABLE 7-4. INDOLES

Formula	Compound	Silyl-ation	Method (Yield %)	Stat. Phase	Temp.	B.P./mm; M.P., Retention Data	Ref.
C_8H_7N	Indole	T_1	16x(55%)			b 121°/12; m 37-38°	73
		T_1	24				224
C_8H_7NO	5-Hydroxyindole	$T_2(O,N)$	43	OV-1, OV-17			347
C_8H_9N	Indoline	T_1	24				224
$C_{10}H_9NO_2$	Indoleacetic acid	$T_1(O)$	25	F-60	90 pr	16.70 MU	347
		$T_1(O)$	25	10% F-60		16.70 MU	182
				1% F-60		16.62 MU	
		$T_2(N,O)$	43	F-60	90 pr	16.70 MU	347
			25	SE-52	160	3.44/phba	334
$C_{10}H_9NO_3$	5-Hydroxyindole-acetic acid	$T_1(O)$	25	F-60	215 pr	22.00 MU	347
		$T_2(O,O)$	25	10% F-60		22.00 MU	182
				1% F-60		22.00 MU	
		T_3	43	F-60	215 pr	22.51 MU	347
$C_{10}H_{11}NO$	Tryptophol	$T_1(O)$	25	10% F-60		18.00 MU	182
				1% F-60		18.12 MU	
		$T_1(O)$	25	F-60	90 pr	18.00 MU	347
		$T_2(N,O)$	43	F-60	90 pr	19.13 MU	
$C_{10}H_{11}NO_2$	5-Hydroxytryptophol	$T_2(O,O)$	25	10% F-60		21.24 MU	182
				1% F-60		21.20 MU	
$C_{10}H_{12}N_2O$	5-Hydroxytryptamine	$T_1(O)$	21t,21k	NGS	215		340
				F-60	182		
				F-60-Z	182	5.29/anth	
	(ASB)	$T_1(O)$	21a	F-60-Z	182	5.29/anth	332
	(ASB)	$T_1(O)$	21d	F-60	182	21.80 MU	148
$C_{11}H_9NO_2$	Indoleacrylic acid	$T_2(N,O)$	25	10% F-60	100→200	23.76 MU	182
				1% F-60		23.72 MU	

Table 7-4. Indoles (cont'd.)

Formula	Compound	Silylation	Method (Yield %)	Stat. Phase	Temp.	B.P./mm; M.P., Retention Data	Ref.
$C_{11}H_9NO_3$	Indolepyruvic acid	T_3 (N,COOH, enol)	25	10% F-60 1% F-60		24.64 MU 24.52 MU	182
$C_{11}H_{11}NO_2$	Indolepropionic acid	T_1(O)	25	F-60	90 pr	20.00 MU	347
		T_1(O)	25	10% F-60 1% F-60		20.00 MU 20.00 MU	182
	5-Methoxyindole-acetic acid	T_2(N,O)	43	F-60	90 pr	20.89 MU	347
		T_1(O)	25	10% F-60 1% F-60		21.12 MU 21.20 MU	182
$C_{11}H_{11}NO_3$	Indolelactic acid	T_2(O,O)	25	10% F-60 1% F-60		21.34 MU 21.32 MU	182
		T_2(O,O)	25	F-60	90 pr	21.34 MU	347
		T_3 (N,O,O)	43	F-60	90 pr	22.00 MU	347
	Methyl 5-hydroxy-indoleacetate	T_1(O)	25	F-60	100→250	0.60/mpam	348
		T_1(O)	21py	10% F-60 1% F-60		21.18 MU 21.30 MU	182
$C_{11}H_{13}NO_2$	5-Methoxytryptophol	T_1(O)	25	10% F-60 1% F-60		20.32 MU 20.32 MU	182
		T_1(O) T_2(N,O)	25 43	F-60 F-60	205 pr 205 pr		347
$C_{12}H_{11}NO_3$	Methyl indole-pyruvate	T_1 (enol)	21py	10% F-60 1% F-60		22.80 MU 22.82 MU	182
		T_2 (N,enol)	21py	10% F-60 1% F-60		23.70 MU 23.58 MU	182
$C_{12}H_{13}NO_2$	Indolebutyric acid	T_1(O)	25	10% F-60 1% F-60		21.26 MU 21.18 MU	182

Table 7-4. Indoles (cont'd.)

Formula	Compound	Silyl-ation	Method (Yield %)	Stat. Phase	Temp.	B.P./mm; M.P., Retention Data	Ref.
$C_{12}H_{13}NO_2$	Indolebutyric acid	$T_1(O)$	25	F-60	90 pr	21.26 MU	347
		$T_2(N,O)$	43	F-60	90 pr	21.25 MU	347
$C_{12}H_{13}NO_3$	Methyl indolelactate	$T_1(O)$	21py	10% F-60		20.48 MU	182
				1% F-60		20.48 MU	
$C_{12}H_{16}N_2$	N,N-Dimethyl-tryptamine	T_1	43,44	OV-17	140→300		336
$C_{12}H_{16}N_2O$	4-Hydroxy-N,N-di-methyltryptamine	$T_1(O)$	21	F-60-Z			336
		$T_1(O)$	21k	F-60-Z	182	2.89/anth	332, 340
	5-Hydroxy-N,N-di-methyltryptamine	$T_1(O)$	21	F-60-Z	182	3.19/anth	336
		$T_1(O)$	21t,21k	F-60-Z NGS	216	3.21/anth	332, 340
		$T_1(O)$ $T_2(N,O)$	43 44	OV-17 OV-17	140→300 140→300		336
	6-Hydroxy-N,N-di-methyltryptamine	$T_1(O)$	21	F-60-Z	182	3.70/anth	336
		$T_1(O)$	21k	F-60-Z NGS	216	3.74/anth	332, 340
	7-Hydroxy-N,N-di-methyltryptamine	$T_1(O)$	21	F-60-Z	182	2.23/anth	336
		$T_1(O)$	21k	F-60-Z NGS	216	1.72/anth	332, 340
$C_{14}H_{20}N_2O$	5-Hydroxy-N,N-di-ethyltryptamine	$T_1(O)$	21t,21k	F-60-Z NGS	182 216	5.10/anth 3.96/anth	332, 340

8

Amino Acids and Related Compounds

8-1. INTRODUCTION

Amino acids can form two products on silylation as the carboxyl group is silylated more easily than the amino group.

$$RCH\underset{\underset{NH_2}{|}}{-}C\overset{\overset{O}{\parallel}}{\underset{OH}{\diagdown}} \quad \rightarrow \quad RCH\underset{\underset{NH_2}{|}}{-}C\overset{\overset{O}{\parallel}}{\underset{OTMS}{\diagdown}} \quad \rightarrow \quad RCH\underset{\underset{\underset{TMS}{|}}{NH}}{-}C\overset{\overset{O}{\parallel}}{\underset{OTMS}{\diagdown}}$$

I   II

The silyl ester (I) is the chief product under mild conditions, as with hexa-methyldisilazane (HMDS) alone (645, 646). The amino group usually requires a stronger donor and has been silylated by N-trimethylsilyldiethyl-amine (TMSDEA) or by N,O-bis(trimethylsilyl) acetamide (BSA) to yield the silylamine–silyl ester (II). Other functional groups will also react, hydroxy and sulfhydryl groups as well as other amino and carboxyl func-tions. The extent of involvement of the guanidino group of arginine is not known. Glycine is the only amino acid reported as silylated twice on the amino group (323). The N-silylated derivatives, like other silylamines, hydrolyse very readily and must be carefully protected from moisture.

8-2. SILYLATION

All the common amino acids have been silylated. The products have been distilled except for arginine and cystine. Silylated arginine is not thermostable, and cystine is difficult to silylate; however the GC of the TMS derivatives of both of these amino acids has recently been reported (559, 898). Asparagine and glutamine also can be silylated (898).

Esterification of an amino acid by HMDS is readily accomplished in refluxing toluene (645, 653) and is hastened by the addition of an acid catalyst (646). The reaction is complete when the amino acid has dissolved. Prolonged treatment with HMDS, at least of the neutral amino acids, yields N-silylated esters as well (76, 645). A small amount of the disilyl derivative can be quickly converted to the silyl ester by passing ammonia through the reaction solution (653), which reverses the preparation reaction.

$$
2RCH\underset{\overset{|}{\underset{\overset{|}{TMS}}{NH}}}{\overset{O}{-C}\diagdown_{OTMS}} + NH_3 \rightarrow 2RCH\underset{\overset{|}{NH_2}}{\overset{O}{-C}\diagdown_{OTMS}} + Me_3SiNHSiMe_3
$$

Birkofer *et al.* (82) reported that dipeptides were silylated by HMDS to N-silyldipeptide silyl esters. They found that β-linked derivatives were thermostable but that α-linked dipeptide derivatives on distillation cyclized to diketopiperazines. Rühlmann *et al.* (655), however, silylated a series of glycyl and alanyl dipeptides with TMSDEA and distilled most of the products in good yield. Glycylglycine (654), depending on the amount of TMSDEA taken, yields disilylated derivatives of glycine anhydride or diketopiperazine, along with hexamethyldisilazane.

Boiling TMCS converts amino acids to silyl ester hydrochlorides in high yields (325):

$$
RCH\underset{\overset{|}{NH_2}}{\overset{O}{-C}\diagdown_{OH}} + Me_3SiCl \rightarrow RCH\underset{\overset{|}{NH_3Cl}}{\overset{O}{-C}\diagdown_{OTMS}}
$$

Silylation either of amino acid metal salts with TMCS (639, 640) or of amino acid hydrochlorides with TMCS and base (650) yields fully silylated derivatives.

The usual reagent for complete silylation of amino acids has been TMSDEA (Methods 33 and 34). The reaction is a silylamine-amine exchange, which depends upon the elimination of diethylamine. An acid catalyst may be used.

$$
R\!-\!CH\underset{\overset{|}{NH_2}}{\overset{O}{-C}\diagdown_{OH}} + 2TMS\!-\!NH(Et_2)_2 \rightarrow R\!-\!CH\underset{\overset{|}{\underset{\overset{|}{TMS}}{NH}}}{\overset{O}{-C}\diagdown_{OTMS}} + Et_2NH
$$

Conditions have been studied by Rühlmann *et al.* (642, 645) and by Smith *et al.* (513, 743). The former workers heated a 30% excess of

TMSDEA with an amino acid until no more diethylamine (b. p. 56°) distilled, then distilled the product from the residue. The latter (513) heated the amino acid with 100% excess TMSDEA, with or without acidic catalyst, under reflux for one hour, diluted with benzene and analysed by GC. Yields are shown in the table. Evidently the equilibrium is far to the right and the uncatalysed reaction is slow.

Ref.	Catalyst	Leucine	Serine	Aspartic Acid
642	None	92%	97%	93%
513	None	74	71	61
513	Trichloroacetic acid	98	93	80
513	Silica-alumina	99	94	87

Nony et al. (559) adapted the TMSDEA process to the preparation of protein hydrolysate samples for GC on DC-200. A large excess of reagent in xylene was taken and diethylamine was allowed to distill off for four hours. Cystine and arginine peaks appeared in the chromatogram.

Klebe et al. (42) found BSA to be a very convenient reagent for analytical samples. In acetonitrile near the boil it gave clear solutions with 22 amino acids, singly or in mixtures, in 10 to 30 min. Analysis of the reaction mixtures by GC on SE-30 showed sharp, single peaks for all except arginine, which decomposed.

Gehrke et al. (898) silylated with bis(TMS)trifluoroacetamide in acetonitrile at various temperatures and time periods, and analysed on 3% DC-550. Results were reproducible for 19 amino acids, asparagine, and glutamine, under proper conditions; arginine did not respond. Glycine, glutamic acid and glutamine required mild conditions to avoid multiple products.

8-3. GAS CHROMATOGRAPHY

Rühlmann and Giesecke (644) first reported the gas chromatographic separation of one acidic and seven neutral amino acid persilyl derivatives. They used a column with 30% silicone stationary phase at 165°, and obtained results of only 0.5% average error. However, when Rühlmann and Michael (651, 653) extended this study to other amino acids severe problems of forepeaks, tailing and overlapping peaks were encountered. Best results were only semiquantitative. Cysteine and lysine derivatives decomposed on the column and histidine gave an unusable peak. The use of a nonpolar column (CNSi) was no improvement. Other than persilyl derivatives were tried (653). It was hoped that N-TMS ethyl esters (647, 649) with boiling points 15° to 20° lower than the corresponding TMS esters, would chromatograph more readily, but there was little difference in retention time, and no advantage otherwise.

The TMS amino acid esters were more promising. They were made using HMDS as mentioned (653). They are more stable to hydrolysis than the persilyl derivatives and have shorter retention times on a nonpolar silicone column. The peaks were well shaped, without forepeaks. Indeed, it was found that the forepeaks observed with the persilyl compounds were due to these TMS amino acid esters, from partial desilylation of the persilyl compounds on the column. The silicone column temperature was isothermal, between 160° and 240°, depending on the volatility of ester. The lysine ester decomposed, arginine gave no ester and histidine and tryptophan esters were not volatile enough. The polarity of the extra nitrogen atoms of these compounds may account for instability or poor volatility. We may assume that the α-amino group in all amino acid TMS esters is made less polar by hydrogen bonding to the carbonyl. Cysteine sulfhydryl was not silylated under the conditions used and apparently was oxidized in the column, eluting as the cystine derivative.

When an amino acid sample was silylated with BSA and analysed by GC on an SE-30 column (422), silylated glycine and alanine could not be separated from TMS-acetamide. However, if, instead of BSA, the silyl donor was bis(trimethylsilyl)trifluoroacetamide, the N-TMS-trifluoroacetamide formed was more volatile, and did not interfere with the early TMS amino acid peaks (898).

8-4. MISCELLANEOUS

Aminobenzoic acids were readily silylated and analysed by GC (182, 640). Tyrosine, thyronine and their iodinated derivatives were silylated in 97-100% yields with BSA, 69-97% yields with HMDS–TMCS (709). Chromatographic separation was complete in 37 minutes on SE-30. The 4'-hydroxy groups of 3,5-diiodothyronine, 3,5,3'-triiodothyronine and thyroxine were not silylated, probably because of the nonplanar shape of the molecule (709). Others assumed silylation of *all* functional groups (carboxyl, amino, and phenolic), as only single peaks were obtained on GC (19).

The mass spectrometry of silyl amino acid derivatives has been investigated by Teeter (774) and is described in section 3-6.

The hydroxy groups of serine and threonine amino acid derivatives have been protected by silylation, usually with HMDS, while the amino and carbonyl functions have been otherwise involved. In work with silylated N-carboxyanhydrides of serine and threonine the O-TMS group was conveniently hydrolyzed during the peptide synthesis (189). β-Hydroxy-α-amino acid methyl esters were O-silylated with boiling HMDS prior to N-acylation with N-trifluoroacetyl-L-prolylchloride (288). For gas chromatographic analysis of N-trifluoroacetyl dipeptide methyl esters the hydroxy groups were first silylated (860). The same protective procedure was used for N-dinitrophenyl-serine, -threonine and -hydroxyproline amino acid methyl esters for analysis by GC (359, 891).

The following tables list amino acids, their sodium salts, and hydrochlorides (Tables 8-1) and amino acid derivatives in which the amino group, the carboxyl group, or both are substituted (Table 8-2). All the T_2 silylation in Table 8-1 indicates N,O-bis(TMS) derivatives unless otherwise marked.

TABLE 8-1. AMINO ACIDS[1]

Formula	Compound	Silylation	Method (Yield %)	B.P./mm; M.P.	n_D^t	Stat. Phase, Temp., Retention Data	Ref.
$C_2H_5NO_2$	Glycine	$T_1(O)$	21u	b 89-90/22			646, 653
			15b-14 (75%) 21-14 (65%)	b 97/22	1.4229^{20}		640
		T_2		b 80/10	1.4207^{20}		76
		T_2	35 (73%) 33 (95%)				641
		T_2	33 (88%)	b 85/15	1.4216^{20}	SiO, 160°, 1.02/alan	642, 651
			33 (82%)	b 88/15		DC-200, 92→200°, 1.06/alan	743
			33			DC-200, 100→220°	742
			33x			DC-200, 100→220°	559
			41,45			SE-30, 175→300°	69
		T_3 (N,N,O)	34 (44%)	b 108-109/12	1.4346^{20}		323
	(HCl)	T_2	14,33 (65%)			SE-30, 117°, 5.8'	650
$C_2H_7NO_3S$	Taurine		43d			SE-30, 117°, 5.8'; 128°, 3.3'	147
$C_3H_7NO_2$	Alanine	$T_1(O)$	11 (94%)	m 152 (HCl)			325
		$T_1(O)$	17* (61%)	b 138-141/15	1.4405^{20}		324
		$T_1(O)$	21u	b 66-67/15		SiO, 160°, 2.57'	646, 653
			21	m 80-82		SiO, 160°	645

[1]Includes hydrochlorides and metal salts.
*Product is N-formyl TMS ester.

Table 8-1. Amino Acids (cont'd.)

Formula	Compound	Silyl-ation	Method (Yield %)	B.P./mm; M.P.	n_D^t	Stat. Phase, Temp., Retention Data	Ref.
$C_3H_7NO_2$	Alanine	T_2	14 (71%)				325
		T_2	14b				814
		T_2	15b–14 (66%)	b 37/3	1.4177^{20}		640
		T_2	21–14 (67%)		1.4165^{20}		76
		T_2	35 (34%) 33 (95%)				641
		T_2	33 (91%)	b 76/15	1.4174^{20}	SiO, 160°, 4.35'	642, 651
			33 (61%)	b 76/15		DC–200, 92→200°	743
			33x			DC–200, 100→220°	559
			41,45			SE–30, 175→300°	69
		T_2	24			Mass Spec.	774
	(HCl)	T_2	14,33				650
	β-Alanine	$T_1(O)$	21u	b 92–93/18 m 90–92		SiO, 160°, 1.38/alan	646, 653
		T_2	33 (92%)	b 42/0.1	1.4238^{20}		642
			33x			DC–200, 100→220°	559
	Sarcosine	$T_1(O)$	21t	b 63–64/15		SiO, 160°, 1.19/alan	653
		T_2	33 (87%)	b 93/25, 57/3	1.4228^{20}	SiO, 160°, 1.20/alan	642, 651
$C_3H_7NO_2S$	Cysteine	$T_1(O)$	11 (98%) 14 (78%)	b 189 (HCl)			325
		$T_1(O)$	21u 21t	b 124–126/16 m 198–203 (dec.)		SiO, 200°, 20.31/alan	653
		T_3	33 (90%)	b 78/0.1, 111/4	1.4559^{20}	SiO, 200°, 6.52/alan	642, 651

Table 8-1. Amino Acids (cont'd.)

Formula	Compound	Silyl-ation	Method (Yield %)	B.P./mm; M.P.	n_D^t	Stat. Phase, Temp., Retention Data	Ref.
$C_3H_7NO_2S$	Cysteine		41,45			SE-30, 175→300°	69
		(HCl)	43d			SE-30, 105°, 6.6'; 117°, 3.5'; 128°, 1.8'	147
$C_3H_7NO_3$	Serine	T_3	21(73%)	b 84/0.2	1.4559^{20}		71
		T_1(COOH)	11(91%)	m 146 (HCl)			325
		T_2(O,O)	21u	b 116-117/18, m 120 (dec.)		SiO, 160°, 4.77/alan	646, 653
		T_3	12u(75%)	b 78/0.5	1.4230^{20}		71
		T_3	14(70%)				325
			22(22%), 23(63%), 33(71%), 34(72-94%)				513
		T_3	33(97%)	b 73/0.4, 88/4	1.4229^{20}	SiO, 160°, 3.53/alan	642, 651
			33(50%)	b 114/4		DC-200, 92→200°, 3.07/alan	743
			33			DC-200, 100→220°	742
			33x			DC-200, 100→220°	559
			41,45			SE-30, 175→300°	69
		T_3	24			Mass Spec.	774
$C_3H_7NO_4S$	Cysteine sulfinic acid (hydrate)		43d			SE-30, 117°, 5.8'; 128°, 3.5'	147
			43d			SE-30, 117°, 9.8'; 128°, 4.6'	147

Table 8-1. Amino Acids (cont'd.)

Formula	Compound	Silyl-ation	Method (Yield %)	B.P./mm; M.P.	n_D^t	Stat. Phase, Temp., Retention Data	Ref.
$C_4H_7NO_4$	Aspartic acid	$T_2(O,O)$	17*(70%)	b 127-28/0.06	1.4481^{20}		324
		$T_2(O,O)$	21u	b 139-140/15 m 143-149		SiO, 180°, 8.14/alan	646, 653
			22(16%) 23(55%) 33(61%) 34(70-87%)				513
		T_3	33(93%)	b 74/0.1, 116/4	1.4307^{20}	SiO, 200°, 5.46/alan	642, 651
			33(95%)	b 113/4		DC-200, 4.70/alan	743
			33x			DC-200, 100→220°	559
			41,45			SE-30, 175→300°	69
		T_3	24			Mass Spec.	774
$C_4H_9NO_3$	Threonine	$T_2(O,O)$	21u	b 116-118/16 m 173-174 (dec.)		SiO, 160°, 5.74/alan	646, 653
		T_3	33(90%)	b 75-78/0.2	1.4252^{20}		646
			33x			DC-200, 100-220°	559
			41,45			SE-30, 175→300°	69
		T_3	43n	b 60-62/0.2			422
$C_5H_9NO_2$	Proline	$T_1(O)$	21u	b 98/17 m 115-120		SiO, 160°, 3.25/alan	646, 653
		T_2	14b				814
		T_2	33(87%)	b 56/0.1, 77/3	1.4395^{20}	SiO, 160°, 2.71/alan	642, 651
			33(76%)	b 87/5.5		DC-200, 2.63/alan	743
			33x			DC-200, 100→220°	559

*Product is N-formyl TMS ester

Table 8-1. Amino Acids (cont'd.)

Formula	Compound	Silyl-ation	Method (Yield %)	B.P./mm; M.P.	n_D^t	Stat. Phase, Temp., Retention Data	Ref.
$C_5H_9NO_2$	Proline		41,45			SE-30, 175→300°	69
		T_2	24			Mass Spec.	774
$C_5H_9NO_3$	Hydroxyproline	T_2(O,O)	21u	b 129-130/10		SiO, 200°, 8.6/alan	646, 653
		T_3	33(93%)	b $75/10^{-3}$	1.4370^{20}	SiO, 200°, 5.46/alan	642, 651
$C_5H_9NO_4$	Glutamic acid	T_1	11(93%)	m 171 (HCl)		SE-30, 175→300°	325
		T_2(O,O)	17*(52%)	b 135-136/0.1	1.4510^{20}		324
		T_2(O,O)	21u	b 175-178/16		SiO, 200°, 9.25/alan	646, 653
			14(61%)				325
		T_3	33(93%)	b 115/1.1	1.4390^{20}	SiO, 200°, 5.46/alan	642, 651
			33x			DC-200, 100→220°	559
			41,45			SE-30, 175→300°	69
		T_3	24			Mass Spec.	774
$C_5H_{11}NO_2$	Norvaline	T_1(O)	21u	b 102-103/22, 48-49/0.1, m 119-123	1.4230^{20}	SiO, 160°, 2.23/alan	646
		T_2	33(96%)	b 58/0.6, 68/3			642, 651
	Valine	T_1(O)	21u	b 73-74/12		SiO, 160°, 1.99/alan	646, 653
		T_1(O)	37(47%)	b 73-74/12, m 111-113		SiO, 160°, 2.09/alan	645

*Product is N-formyl TMS ester.

Table 8-1. Amino Acids (cont'd.)

Formula	Compound	Silyl-ation	Method (Yield %)	B.P./mm; M.P.	n_D^t	Stat. Phase, Temp., Retention Data	Ref.
$C_5H_{11}NO_2$	Valine	T_2	21-14 (77%)	b 93/10	1.4226^{20}		76
		T_2	33(97%)	b 98/15	1.4229^{20}	SiO, 160°, 1.85/alan	642, 651
			33(78%)	b 104/10		DC-200, 1.72/alan	743
			33x			DC-200, 100→220°	559
			41,45			SE-30, 175→300°	69
$C_5H_{11}NO_2S$	Methionine	$T_1(O)$	21u	b 136-137/15 m 183-193 (dec.)		SiO, 180°, 7.87/alan	646, 653
		T_2	33(94%)	b 90-91/0.2	1.4553^{20}		646
		T_2	33	b 94/3	1.4549^{20}	SiO, 200°, 5.46/alan	651
			33(89%)	b 134/5		DC-200, 4.72/alan	743
			33x			DC-200, 100→220°	559
			41,45			SE-30, 175→300°	69
			43d			SE-30, 105°, 5.6'; 117°, 2.8'; 128°, 1.5'	147
$C_5H_{11}NO_2Se$	Seleno-methionine	T_2	24			Mass Spec.	774
			43d			SE-30, 105°, 7.6'; 117°, 3.8'; 128°, 2.0'	147
$C_5H_{11}NO_3S$	Methionine sulfoxide		43d			SE-30, 117°, 10.5'; 128°, 5.5'	147
$C_5H_{11}NO_4S$	Methionine sulfone		43d			SE-30, 117°, 14.3'; 128°, 7.6'	147
$C_6H_9N_3O_2$	Histidine	$T_1(O)$	21u	b 130-135/0.03			653
			33	b 115/10⁻³	1.4644^{20}		651

Table 8-1. Amino Acids (cont'd.)

Formula	Compound	Silyl-ation	Method (Yield %)	B.P./mm; M.P.	n_D^t	Stat. Phase, Temp., Retention Data	Ref.
$C_6H_9N_3O_2$	Histidine		33x			DC-200, 100→220°	559
			41,45			SE-30, 175→300°	69
$C_6H_{12}N_2O_4S_2$	Cystine		33x			DC-200, 100→220°	559
			43d			SE-30, 170°, 9.8' 180°, 6.0'	147
$C_6H_{12}N_2O_4Se_2$	Seleno-cystine		43d			SE-30, 170°, 15.8' 180°, 9.5'	147
$C_6H_{13}NO_2$	ε-Aminocaproic acid	T_2	15b-14 (54%)	b 114/2.5	1.4331^{20}		640
		T_2	24			Mass Spec.	774
$C_6H_{13}NO_2$	Isoleucine	$T_1(O)$	21u	b 98-99/18 m 112-114		SiO, 160°, 3.23/alan	653
		$T_1(O)$	37(47%)				645
		T_2	15b-14 (65%)	b 64/7	1.4267^{20}		640
		T_2	33(93%)	b 108/15	1.4268^{20}	SiO, 160°, 2.68/alan	642, 651
			33x			DC-200, 100→220°	559
		T_2	33,35 (79,56%)				641
			41,45			SE-30, 175→300°	69
		T_2	24			Mass Spec.	774
$C_6H_{13}NO_2$	Leucine	$T_1(O)$	11(94%)	m 138 (HCl)			325
		$T_1(O)$	17*(74%)	b 125-126/1.5	1.4441^{20}		324
		$T_1(O)$	21u	b 93/15		SiO, 160°, 2.84/alan	646, 653

*Product is N-formyl TMS ester.

Table 8-1. Amino Acids (cont'd.)

Formula	Compound	Silylation	Method (Yield %)	B.P./mm; M.P.	n_D^t	Stat. Phase, Temp., Retention Data	Ref.
$C_6H_{13}NO_2$	Leucine	$T_1(O)$	37(49%)	b 93/15, m 118-121			645
		T_2	14(89%)				325
		T_2	33, 15b-14(80%)	b 63/0.8	1.4244^{20}		639
		T_2	21-14(82%)		1.4236^{20}		76
		T_2	24-14b (92%)	b 104/17			77
			22(37%) 23(67%) 33(74%) 34(60-99%)				513
		T_2	33	b 63/0.8	1.4244^{20}	SiO, 160°, 2.34/alan	642, 651
			33(87%)	b 108/10		DC-200, 2.07/alan	743
			33x			DC-200, 100→220°	559
			41,45			SE-30, 175→300°	69
		T_2	24			Mass Spec.	774
	Norleucine	T_2	24			Mass Spec.	774
$C_6H_{13}NO_2S$	Ethionine	T_2	24			Mass Spec.	774
$C_6H_{14}N_2O_2$	Lysine	$T_1(O)$	11(69%)	m 217 (HCl)			325
		T_1	21u	b 102-3/0.01, m 79-89			646, 653
		T_3	14(36%)	b 110-12/0.001	1.4384^{20}		325
		T_3	33(91%)	b 97/10⁻³	1.4385^{20}		642, 651
			33(81%)	b 147/4		DC-200, 6.67/alan	743
			41,45			SE-30, 175→300°	69

Table 8-1. Amino Acids (cont'd.)

Formula	Compound	Silyl-ation	Method (Yield %)	B.P./mm; M.P.	n_D^t	Stat. Phase, Temp., Retention Data	Ref.
$C_6H_{14}N_2O_2$	Lysine	T_3 (N,N,O)	24			Mass Spec.	774
$C_6H_{14}N_4O_2$	Arginine		33x			DC-200, 100→220	559
$C_7H_7NO_2$	o-Aminobenzoic acid	T_2	15b-14 (47%)	b 104/7, m 34	1.5348^{20}		640
		T_2	25			10% F-60, 14.80 MU; 1% F-60, 14.78 MU	182
	p-Aminobenzoic acid	T_2	15b-14 (50%)	b 125/0.6	1.5416^{20}		640
		T_2	25			10% F-60, 18.38 MU; 1% F-60, 18.38 MU	182
$C_7H_7NO_3$	2-Amino-3-hydroxy-benzoic acid	T_1(O)	24			Mass Spec.	774
		T_2	25			10% F-60, 17.62 MU; 1% F-60, 17.58 MU	182
$C_8H_{12}N_2O_3S$	6-Aminopenicillanic acid	T_2	21(10%)				65
$C_9H_9I_2NO_3$	3,5-Diiodotyrosine	T_3	25(80%), 43n(98%)	b 135-138/2		SE-30, 125→250	709
			43n,43py			OV-1	19
$C_9H_{10}INO_3$	3-Iodotyrosine	T_3	25(87%), 43n(98%)	b 125-127/2		SE-30, 125→250	709
			43n,43py			OV-1	19
$C_9H_{11}NO_2$	Phenylalanine	T_1(O)	21u			SiO, 200, 11.35/alan	651
		T_1(O)	37(42%)	b 134/11, m 148-154			645

Table 8-1. Amino Acids (cont'd.)

Formula	Compound	Silyl-ation	Method (Yield %)	B.P./mm; M.P.	n_D^t	Stat. Phase, Temp., Retention Data	Ref.
$C_9H_{11}NO_2$	Phenylalanine	T_2	35(59%) 33(75%)				641
		T_2	33(96%)	b 110/1.1	1.4853^{20}	SiO, 200 , 8.57/alan	642, 651
			33(91%)	b 145/5		DC-200, 5.72/alan	743
			33x			DC-200, 100→220	559
			41,45			SE-30, 175→300	69
		T_2	24			Mass Spec.	774
$C_9H_{11}NO_3$	Tyrosine	$T_2(O,O)$	21u	b 194-196/21 m 170 (dec.)		SiO, 240 , 32.37/alan	646, 653
		T_3	25,43n (97%)	b 112-115/2		SE-30, 125→250	709
			43n,43py			OV-1	19
		T_3	33(82%)	b 103/10^{-4}	1.4680^{20}	SiO, 240 , 8.2/alan	642, 651
			33x			DC-200, 100→220	559
			41,45			SE-30, 175→300	69
$C_{11}H_{12}N_2O_2$	Tryptophan	T_1	21u	b 159-162/0.1			646
		T_3	33(58%)	b 145-46/0.04	1.5082^{20}		646
			33x			DC-200, 100→220	559
		T_3	43n	b 140-142/0.2			422
			24			Mass Spec.	774

Table 8-1. Amino Acids (cont'd.)

Formula	Compound	Silyl-ation	Method (Yield %)	B.P./mm; M.P.	n_D^t	Stat. Phase, Temp., Retention Data	Ref.
$C_{15}H_{11}I_4NO_4$	Thyroxine	$T_2(N,O)$	25(82%) 43n(98%)	b 235-237/2		SE-30, 125→250	709
			43n,43py			OV-1	19
$C_{15}H_{12}I_3NO_4$	3,5,3'-Triiodo-thyronine	$T_2(N,O)$	25(69%) 43n(98%)	b 220-222/2		SE-30, 125→250	709
			43n,43py			OV-1	19
$C_{15}H_{13}I_2NO_4$	3,5-Diiodothyronine	T_2	25(95%) 43n(98%)	b 191-194/2		SE-30, 125→250	709
$C_{15}H_{15}NO_4$	Thyronine		43n,43py			OV-1	19

TABLE 8-2. AMINO ACID DERIVATIVES[1]

Formula	Compound	Silyl-ation	Method (Yield %)	B.P./mm; M.P.	n_D^t	Stat. Phase, Temp., Retention Data	Ref.
$C_4H_5NO_4$	Serine N-carboxy-anhydride						189
$C_4H_6N_2O_2$	Glycine anhydride	T1, T2	35(1%), 14b(98%), 33u(97%)	b 135-136/17, m 96-97			654
$C_4H_7NO_3$	N-Acetylglycine		25			10% F-60, 13.16 MU; 1% F-60, 13.64 MU	182
			25,43			F-60, 90°→, 13.16 MU; F-60, 90°→, 13.87 MU	347
$C_4H_9NO_2$	Glycine ethyl ester	T1	11	b 66-70/12			74
		T1	18e(34%)	b 66-70/12			75
	(HCl)	T1	14e(74%), 14c(70%), 35(84%)	b 68-70/13, b 71-74/14	1.4210^{20}		648
$C_5H_6F_3NO_3$	N-TFA-alanine	(HCl) T1	14e			SiO, 160°, 5.55'	652
$C_5H_7NO_4$	Threonine N-carboxy-anhydride	T1	21u			SiO, 180°	653
$C_5H_9NO_3$	N-Acetylalanine	T1	21u			SiO, 180°	189
$C_5H_{10}N_2O_3$	Glycylalanine	T1	33(81%)	b 126-130/0.1			653
		T2					655
	Glycyl-β-alanine	T2	21(68%)	b 138/0.025			82
$C_5H_{11}NO_2$	Alanine ethyl ester (HCl)	T1	33(97%)	b 71/18	1.4183^{20}	SiO, 160°, 5.66'	649
		T1	14e				652
		T1	35e(95%)	b 78-80/22	1.4181^{20}		648

[1]The amino or carbonyl function is substituted, or both.

Table 8-2. Amino Acid Derivatives (cont'd.)

Formula	Compound	Silyl-ation	Method (Yield %)	B.P./mm; M.P.	n_D^t	Stat. Phase, Temp., Retention Data	Ref.
$C_5H_{11}NO_2$	β-Alanine ethyl ester	T_1	18e(55%)	b 96-100/14			75
	(HCl)	T_1	33(47%)	b 87/16	1.4253^{20}		649
	Betaine (HCl)	T_1	14e			SiO, 160°, 8.05'	652
	(HCl)	T_1	18(59%)				325
$C_5H_{11}NO_3$	Serine ethyl ester (HCl)	T_1	14e		1.4251^{20}	SiO, 160°, 21.53'	652
		T_2	33(84%)	b 114/13			649
$C_6H_{10}N_2O_2$	Alanine anhydride	T_2	14b(99%)	b 113-114/15	1.4439^{20}		654
$C_6H_{12}N_2O_3$	Alanylalanine	T_2	33(80%)	b 130/2	1.4410^{20}		655
	N-Methylalanyl-glycine	T_3 (N,N',O)	48f				417
$C_6H_{13}NO_2$	Ethyl α-amino-butyrate (HCl)	T_1	14e		1.4221^{20}	SiO, 160°, 8.20'	652
		T_1	33(87%)	b 77/14			649
	Ethyl β-amino-butyrate	T_1	18e	b 90-95/20			75
$C_6H_{13}NO_2$	Ethyl α-aminoiso-butyrate (HCl)	T_1	14e	b 74-75/15	1.4249^{20}	SiO, 160°, 7.50'	652
		T_1	33(74%)				649
$C_6H_{13}NO_2S$	Methionine methyl ester	T_1	33(92%)	b 88/0.1	1.4674^{20}		649
$C_7H_{11}N_3O_2$	Histidine methyl ester (HCl)	T_2	33(80%)	b 115-18/0.01	1.4736^{20}		649
$C_7H_{11}NO_5$	N-Acetyl-L-glutamic acid		25			10% F-60, 17.84 MU 1% F-60, 17.60 MU	182

Table 8-2. Amino Acid Derivatives (cont'd.)

Formula	Compound	Silyl-ation	Method (Yield %)	B.P./mm; M.P.	n_D^t	Stat. Phase, Temp., Retention Data	Ref.
$C_7H_{13}NO_2$	Proline ethyl ester (HCl)	T_1	33(80%)	b 92-93/13	1.4439^{20}		649
		T_1	14e			SiO, 160°, 15.70'	652
$C_7H_{13}NO_3$	N-Acetyl norvaline	T_1	21u			SiO, 180°	653
	N-Acetyl valine	T_1	21u			SiO, 180°	653
$C_7H_{14}N_2O_3$	Glycylvaline	T_2	33(83%)	b 127-128/0.04 m 30-31.5	1.4512^{20}		655
$C_7H_{15}NO_2$	D,L-Norvaline ethyl ester	T_1	18e(74%)	b 81-82/19			75
	(HCl)	T_1	33(96%)	b 55-56/0.25	1.4250^{20}		649
	Valine ethyl ester (HCl)	T_1	33(90%)	b 88/17	1.4243^{20}		649
		T_1	35e(72%)	b 94-97/23	1.4242^{20}		648
		T_1	14e			SiO, 160°, 10.95'	652
$C_7H_{15}NO_2S$	Methionine methyl ester (HCl)	T_1	14e			SiO, 190°, 10.70'	652
$C_7H_{16}N_2O_2$	Lysine methyl ester (HCl)	T_2	33(28%)	b 91-95/0.04	1.4624^{20}		649
$C_8H_8N_2O_3$	Nicotinuric acid		43			F-60, 18.86 MU	647
$C_8H_{12}F_3NO_3$	N-TFA-leucine	T_1	21u			SiO, 180°	653
$C_8H_{15}NO_3$	N-Acetylleucine	T_1	21u			SiO, 180°	653
$C_8H_{15}NO_4$	Aspartic acid di-ethyl ester (HCl)	T_1	33(81%)	b 88-89/0.3	1.4350^{20}		649
		T_1	14e			SiO, 190°, 12.25'	652
$C_8H_{16}N_2O_3$	Alanylvaline	T_2	33(70%)	b 123/0.1 m 80-84			655
	Glycylisoleucine	T_2	33(75%)	b 147/0.1	1.4518^{20}		655
	Glycylleucine	T_2	33(80%)	b 137/0.35	1.4522^{20}		655

Table 8-2. Amino Acid Derivatives (cont'd.)

Formula	Compound	Silyl-ation	Method (Yield %)	B.P./mm; M.P.	n_D^t	Stat. Phase, Temp., Retention Data	Ref.
$C_8H_{17}NO_2$	Isoleucine ethyl ester (HCl)	T_1	33(95%)	b 110/15	1.4292^{20}		649
		T_1	14e			SiO, 160°, 16.45'	652
	Leucine ethyl ester (HCl)	T_1	18e(51%)	b 107-112/12			75
	(HCl)	T_1	33(76%)	b 102-104/19	1.4259^{20}		649
	(HCl)	T_1	14e			SiO, 160°, 14.20'	652
	Norleucine ethyl ester (HCl)	T_1	33(78%)	b 102/15	1.4277^{20}		649
	(HCl)	T_1	14e			SiO, 160°, 17.10'	652
$C_9H_9NO_3$	Hippuric acid	T_1	16z(30%)		1.5171^{20}		309
		T_1	25			10% F-60, 18.40 MU 1% F-60, 18.60 MU	182
			25			SE-52, 160°, 2.53/phba	334
			25,43			F-60, 18.40 MU F-60, 18.27, 18.44 MU	347
$C_9H_9NO_4$	Salicyluric acid	T_2	25			10% F-60, 20.82 MU 1% F-60, 20.88 MU	182
			25,43			F-60, 20.82 MU F-60, 20.92 MU	347
$C_9H_{13}F_3N_2O_5$	N-TFA-L-seryl-L-alanine methyl ester	$T_1(O)$	21	m 64.5-66		SiO, 190°, 0.64/mmy 222°, 0.66/mmy ApM, 190°, 0.26/mmy 222°, 0.29/mmy	860
$C_9H_{17}NO_4$	Glutamic acid diethyl ester (HCl)	T_1	33(88%)	b 102-103/0.5	1.4382^{20}		649
	(HCl)	T_1	14e			SiO, 190°, 13.65'	652
$C_9H_{18}N_2O_3$	Alanylisoleucine	T_2	33(45%)	b 134/0.8 m 68-72			655

Table 8-2. Amino Acid Derivatives (cont'd.)

Formula	Compound	Silylation	Method (Yield %)	B.P./mm; M.P.	n_D^t	Stat. Phase, Temp., Retention Data	Ref.
$C_9H_{18}N_2O_3$	Alanylleucine	T_2	33(72%)	b 100/0.0008 m 63	1.4472^{20}		655
$C_{10}H_{10}N_2O_2S$	Serine phenylthiohydantoin	$T_2(N,O)$	43d			DC-560, 165°	588
$C_{10}H_{11}NO_3$	N-Benzoylalanine	T_1	17(55%)	b 184-188/4 m 69			309
$C_{10}H_{11}NO_4$	N-Benzoyl-β-alanine	T_1	17(60%)	b 209-212/3			309
	Anisuric acid	T_2	25			10% F-60, 21.24 MU; 1% F-60, 21.24 MU	182
	N-Carbobenzoxyglycine	T_1	15e(40%)	b 148/0.5			76
	o-Methoxyhippuric acid	T_2	25			10% F-60, 1% F-60	182
	Methyl salicylurate	T_1	25			10% F-60, 19.56 MU; 1% F-60, 19.60 MU	182
$C_{10}H_{12}N_3O_7$	DNP-serine methyl ester	T_1	25			SE-30, 204°, 11.2'; 214°, 25.9'; XE-60, 210°, 13.2'; 185°, 17.7'; XE-61, 207°, 19.35'	359
$C_{10}H_{15}F_3N_2O_5$	N-TFA-L-threonyl-L-alanine methyl ester	$T_1(O)$	21	m 134-136		SiO, 190°, 0.60/mmy; 222°, 0.65/mmy; ApM, 190°, 0.23/mmy; 222°, 0.26/mmy	860
$C_{11}H_{12}N_2O_2S$	Threonine phenylthiohydantoin	$T_2(N,O)$	43d			DC-560, 160°	588
$C_{11}H_{13}NO_4$	N-Carbobenzoxyalanine	T_1	15e(36%)	b 129/0.16			76

Table 8-2. Amino Acid Derivatives (cont'd.)

Formula	Compound	Silylation	Method (Yield %)	B.P./mm; M.P.	n_D^t	Stat. Phase, Temp., Retention Data	Ref.
$C_{11}H_{13}N_3O_7$	DNP-threonine methyl ester	T_1	25			SE-30, 204°, 11.2'; 214°, 25.9'; XE-60, 210°, 11.3'; XE-61, 185°, 15.4'; 206°, 18.75'	359
$C_{11}H_{14}N_2O_3$	Glycylphenylalanine	T_2	33 (13%)	b 155/0.09 m 96–97			655
$C_{11}H_{15}F_3N_2O_5$	N-TFA-L-prolylserine methyl ester	T_1(O)	21			PGA, 185°, D 5.6', L 6.85'	288
	N-TFA-L-seryl-L-proline methyl ester	T_1(O)	21	m 71–72		SiO, 190°, 1.58/mmy; 222°, 1.46/mmy; ApM, 190°, 210°, 0.76/mmy, 222°, 0.75/mmy	860
$C_{11}H_{15}NO_2$	Phenylalanine ethyl ester (HCl)	T_1	33 (82%)	b 92/0.1	1.48292°		649
		T_1	14e			SiO, 190°, 24.60'	652
$C_{11}H_{15}NO_3$	Tyrosine ethyl ester (HCl)	T_2	33 (65%)	b 125/10⁻³	1.47632°		649
		T_2	14e			SiO, 230°, 15.50'	652
$C_{11}H_{17}F_3N_2O_5$	N-TFA-L-seryl-L-valine methyl ester	T_1(O)	21	b 100/0.5		SiO, 201°, 0.97/mmy; 221°, 0.95/mmy; ApM, 190°, 0.41/mmy; 210°,222°, 0.43/mmy	860

Table 8-2. Amino Acid Derivatives (cont'd.)

Formula	Compound	Silyl-ation	Method (Yield %)	B.P./mm; M.P.	n_D^t	Stat. Phase, Temp., Retention Data	Ref.
$C_{11}H_{17}F_3N_2O_5S$	N-TFA-L-seryl-L-methionine methyl ester	$T_1(O)$	21	b 140/0.5		SiO, 201°, 3.10/mmγ; 222°, 2.72/mmγ; ApM, 201°, 1.80/mmγ; 222°, 1.62/mmγ	860
$C_{12}H_9N_3O_7$	DNP-hydroxyproline methyl ester	T_1	25			SE-30, 204°, 15.35'; 221°, 30.1'; XE-60, 210°, 17.0'; XE-61, 185°, 26.0'; 213°, 22.9'	359
$C_{12}H_{12}F_3NO_4$	N-TFA-tyrosine methyl ester	$T_1(O)$	21			SiO, 225°, 1.23/mmγ	860
$C_{12}H_{14}N_2O_2$	Tryptophan methyl ester (HCl)	T_1	33(84%)	b 158-159/0.08	1.5283^{20}		649
$C_{12}H_{15}NO_4$	N-Carbobenzoxy-β-aminobutyric acid	T_1	15e(67%)	b 150-152/0.17			76
$C_{12}H_{16}N_2O_3$	Alanylphenylalanine	T_2	(88%)	b 149-150/0.07	1.4873^{20}		655
$C_{12}H_{17}F_3N_2O_5$	N-TFA-L-prolylhomoserine methyl ester	$T_1(O)$	21			PGA, 185°, D 9.0'; L 11.05'	288
	N-TFA-L-prolylallothreonine methyl ester	$T_1(O)$	21			PGA, 185°, D 5.4'; L 6.25'	288
	N-TFA-L-prolyl-threonine methyl ester	$T_1(O)$	21			PGA, 185°, D 5.1'; L 6.25'	288

Table 8-2. Amino Acid Derivatives (cont'd.)

Formula	Compound	Silyl-ation	Method (Yield %)	B.P./mm; M.P.	n_D^t	Stat. Phase, Temp., Retention Data	Ref.
$C_{12}H_{17}F_3N_2O_5$							
	N-TFA-L-threonyl-L-proline methyl ester	$T_1(O)$	21	m 142-143		SiO, 190°, 1.61/mmy; 222°, 1.50/mmy; ApM, 190-222°, 0.73/mmy	860
$C_{12}H_{19}F_3N_2O_5$							
	N-TFA-L-seryl-L-isoleucine methyl ester	$T_1(O)$	21	m 48-50		SiO, 190°, 1.33/mmy; 222°, 1.23/mmy; ApM, 190°, 0.59/mmy; 222°, 0.58/mmy	860
	N-TFA-L-seryl-L-leucine methyl ester	$T_1(O)$	21	m 90-91		SiO, 190°, 1.22/mmy; 222°, 1.14/mmy; ApM, 190-222°, 0.54/mmy	860
	N-TFA-L-threonyl-L-valine methyl ester	$T_1(O)$	21	m 103-105		SiO, 190°, 0.93/mmy; 222°, 0.92/mmy; ApM, 190°, 0.36/mmy; 222°, 0.39/mmy	860
$C_{12}H_{19}F_3N_2O_5S$							
	N-TFA-L-threonyl-L-methionine methyl ester	$T_1(O)$	21	m 103-104		SiO, 201°, 2.88/mmy; 222°, 2.49/mmy; ApM, 201°, 1.52/mmy; 222°, 1.40/mmy	860
$C_{12}H_{22}N_2O_2$	Leucine anhydride	T_2	14b(92%)	b 145-146/15	1.4575^{20}		654
$C_{13}H_{17}NO_4$	N-Carbobenzoxyvaline	T_1	15e(48%)	b 132-133/0.13			76
$C_{13}H_{17}F_3N_2O_5$	N-TFA-L-prolyl-hydroxy-proline methyl ester	$T_1(O)$	21			PGA, 185°, D 18.3', L 22.1'	288

Table 8-2. Amino Acid Derivatives (cont'd.)

Formula	Compound	Silylation	Method (Yield %)	B.P./mm; M.P.	n_D^t	Stat. Phase, Temp., Retention Data	Ref.
$C_{13}H_{19}F_3N_2O_5$	N-TFA-L-prolyl-β-hydroxyvaline methyl ester					PGA, 185°, D 6.6', L 8.05'	288
$C_{13}H_{21}F_3N_2O_5$	N-TFA-L-threonyl-L-isoleucine methyl ester	$T_1(O)$	21	m 94-95		SiO, 190°, 1.25/mmy; 222°, 1.17/mmy; ApM, 190°, 0.52/mmy; 222°, 0.53/mmy	860
	N-TFA-L-threonyl-L-leucine methyl ester	$T_1(O)$	21	m 148-149		SiO, 190°, 1.15/mmy; 222°, 1.09/mmy; ApM, 190°, 0.46/mmy; 222°, 0.48/mmy	860
$C_{14}H_{19}NO_4$	N-Carbobenzoxy-leucine	T_1	15e(58%)	b 145-148/0.15			76
$C_{14}H_{19}F_3N_2O_7$	N-TFA-L-prolyl-β-hydroxyglutamic acid dimethyl ester	$T_1(O)$	21			PGA, 185°, D 27.0', L 29.7'	288
$C_{15}H_{17}F_3N_2O_5$	N-TFA-L-alanyltyrosine methyl ester	$T_1(O)$	21			SiO, 225°, 5.4/mmy	860
	N-TFA-L-seryl-L-phenylalanine methyl ester	$T_1(O)$	21	m 84-85		SiO, 190°, 4.47/mmy; 210°, 3.82/mmy; ApM, 201°, 2.73/mmy; 222°, 2.44/mmy	860

Table 8-2. Amino Acid Derivatives (cont'd.)

Formula	Compound	Silyl-ation	Method (Yield %)	B.P./mm; M.P.	n_D^t	Stat. Phase, Temp., Retention Data	Ref.
$C_{16}H_{19}F_3N_2O_5$	N-TFA-L-threonyl-L-phenylalanine methyl ester	$T_1(O)$	21	m 110-111		SiO, 201°, 4.10/mmy 222°, 3.56/mmy ApM, 201°, 2.31/mmy 222°, 2.09/mmy	860
$C_{18}H_{23}F_3N_2O_5$	N-TFA-tyrosyl-L-isoleucine methyl ester	$T_1(O)$	21			SiO, 225°, 9.5/mmy	860

9

Amides and Ureas

9-1. ALIPHATIC AND AROMATIC ACID AMIDES

Preparative scale silylation of amides has usually been carried out with TMCS and triethylamine, in good yield. With one mole of TMCS in the cold one TMS group is easily introduced (79, 186); with a large excess of TMCS and long heating a second TMS group may be introduced (422).

$$
CH_3C\overset{O}{\underset{NH_2}{\big\langle}} \xrightarrow[\text{TEA}]{\text{TMCS}} CH_3C\overset{O}{\underset{NH-TMS}{\big\langle}} \xrightarrow{\text{TMCS}} CH_3C\overset{O-TMS}{\underset{N-TMS}{\big\langle}}
$$

The evidence for the structure of the bis(TMS) product has been discussed (section 4-4). Its formation is analagous to the silylation of N-halo-acetamides (68, 192):

$$
CH_3C\overset{O}{\underset{NHX}{\big\langle}} \xrightarrow{\text{BSA}} CH_3C\overset{OTMS}{\underset{NX}{\big\langle}} \qquad X = Br, Cl
$$

Klebe and co-workers silylated acetanilides with BSA (420, 422) in acetonitrile, obtaining complete reaction in 10-30 minutes at 70-80°. These derivatives were studied for silyl exchange between O and N and for their silyl donor properties (422).

Chloramphenicol and related compounds have been silylated with HMDS–TMCS in pyridine (608, 714, 890) and the products analysed via GC on SE-30. It was assumed that only the two hydroxyl groups were silylated, never the acetamido group or an amino group. From the evidence in the preceding paragraph, the use of BSA here should give interesting results with these compounds.

9-2. CYCLIC AMIDES AND IMIDES

These compounds are grouped together because their silylation is irregular and most of them do not fit other categories listed. The silylation of these compounds proceeds sometimes to O-silyl, sometimes to N-silyl derivatives. As discussed in section 4-4, the usual result is an increase in aromaticity (or stability) of the hetero ring .

9-3. UREAS AND CARBAMIDES

Ureas and related compounds have been silylated in various ways. There is no difficulty in introducing a TMS group into each amino (or imino) group of urea, thiourea, guanidine, or carbamate esters. The potent silyl donor, N-TMS-N,N'-diphenylurea, was used by Klebe (413) most effectively on many of these compounds. The by-product of silylation, diphenylurea, was usually insoluble and hence readily removed from the main silylation product. Unfortunately, this solid reagent with its solid product is not so convenient for analytical work as are the liquid silylators.

TABLE 9-1. ALIPHATIC AND AROMATIC ACID AMIDES

Formula	Compound	Silyl-ation	Method (Yield %)	B.P./mm; M.P.	n_D^t	Stat. Phase, Temp., Retention Data	Ref.
CH_3NO	Formamide	T_1	35	b 84-85/21			186
		T_2	14	b 71-73/35	1.4395^{20}		418
C_2H_4BrNO	N-Bromoacetamide	$T_1(O)$	43(81%)	b 54-55/10.5	1.4642^{20}		192
C_2H_4ClNO	N-Chloroacetamide	$T_1(O)$	48(76%)	b 38-39/10.5	1.4375^{20}		64,192
		$T_1(O)$	43(91%)				
C_2H_5NO	Acetamide	T_1	14b(90%)	b 84/13			79
		T_1	21(80%)	b 124/83-84			598
				m 48-49			
		T_1	35(96%)	b 185-186			186
				m 52-54			
		T_1	14b(83%)	b 84-85			272
			21(80%)	m 46			
		T_2	14(80%)	b 71-73/35			422
		T_2	14b(61%)	b 67.5/30	1.4179^{20}		272
	N-Methylformamide	T_1	14b(96%)	b 64/12, 75/20	1.4408^{20}		192
$C_2H_5NO_2$	Hydroxyacetamide		11				375
C_3H_5NO	Acrylamide	T_1	14b				186
		T_1	14b(85%)	b 105-106/22			272
				m 85-86			
		T_2	14	b 73.5/22			80
C_3H_7NO	N-Methylacetamide	T_1	14b(76%)	b 48-49/11	1.4379^{24}		186
		T_1	14b(91%, 47%)	b 52.8-3.3/11.5, 57/14, 67/22	1.4392^{20} 1.4379^{24}		192, 272
		T_1	14e(53%)	b 154/770	1.4382^{20}		234
	Propionamide	T_1	21(73%)	b 132/98-100			598
				m 66-67			

Table 9-1. Aliphatic and Aromatic Acid Amides (con't'd.)

Formula	Compound	Silyl-ation	Method (Yield %)	B.P./mm; M.P.	n_D^t	Stat. Phase, Temp., Retention Data	Ref.
$C_4H_5NO_2$	Succinimide	$T_1(N)$	14u(94%)	b 108-109/10.5, 120-121/18	1.4740^{20} 1.4745^{20}		192
C_4H_7NO	Methylacrylamide	$T_1(N)$	21(83%)	b 72-73/2	1.4749^{20}		598
$C_4H_7NO_2$	N-Hydroxymethyl-acrylamide	T_1	14b	m 65-68			186
			25			C-20M, 190°, 4.6'	895
C_4H_8BrNO	N-Bromoisobutyramide	T_1	48(77%) 43(72%)	b 70-72/10	1.4592^{20}		192
C_4H_9NO	Acetimino ethyl ether	T_1	14b(52%)	b 57.5/40	1.4174^{20}		272
	N-Ethylacetamide	T_1	14b(31%)	b 69.5-70.5/30	1.4384^{20}		272
C_5H_9NO	N-Vinylpropionamide	$T_1(O)$	14b(70%)	b 47.5-48.2/11.5	1.4401^{20}		272
$C_5H_{11}NO$	N-Ethylpropionamide	T_1	14b(41%)	b 64-64.5/11.8	1.4409^{20}		272
C_7H_6ClNO	N-Chlorobenzamide	$T_1(O)$	48(66%) 48(75%)	b 70-72/0.15	1.5261^{20}		68, 192
		T_1	48(46%)	b 70-72/0.15	1.5261^{20}		192
C_7H_7NO	Benzamide	T_1	14b(52%) 35(96%)	m 118-120			186
		T_1	21(90%)	m 117-121			598
		T_1	21(82%)	b 148-150/11.5 m 118			272
$C_7H_8N_2O$	Anthranilic acid amide	T_2	14b(79%)	b 131-133/1.1 m 126-128			272
$C_8H_5NO_2$	Phthalimide	$T_1(N)$	14u(87%)	b 151-155/10.5 m 67.5			192
C_8H_8ClNO	m-Chloroacetanilide	$T_1(N)$ T_1	43n 43n	b 64-66/0.2			422 422
	p-Chloroacetanilide	T_1	43n	b 61-63/0.2			422

Table 9-1. Aliphatic and Aromatic Acid Amides (cont'd.)

Formula	Compound	Silyl-ation	Method (Yield %)	B.P./mm; M.P.	n_D^t	Stat. Phase, Temp., Retention Data	Ref.
$C_8H_8N_2O_3$	m-Nitroacetanilide	T_1	43n	b 85-88/0.2			422
	p-Nitroacetanilide	T_1	43n	m 64-67			422
C_8H_9NO	Acetanilide	T_1	43n				420
$C_9H_{11}NO$	Benzimino ethyl ether	T_1	14b(78%)	b 108.5-09/11.5	1.4948^{20}		272
	m-Methylacetanilide	T_1	43n	b 53-55/0.2			422
	p-Methylacetanilide	T_1	43n, 43py	b 50-53/0.2		SE-30, 100→300°, 8.6', 7.5'	422
$C_9H_{11}NO_2$	m-Methoxyacetanilide	T_1	43n,	b 69-70/0.3		SE-30, 100→300°, 10.8'	422
	p-Methoxyacetanilide	T_1	43n	b 75-76/0.2			422
$C_9H_{11}NS$	Thiopropionic acid anilide	T_1	14b(54%)	b 80-82/0.0005 m 64-66			272
$C_9H_{19}NO_4$	Pantothenyl alcohol		23g			SE-30, 185°	869
$C_{11}H_{11}Br_3N_2O_5$	N-Tribromoacetyl-p-nitrophenylserinol		25			SE-30, 100→260°	714
$C_{11}H_{11}Cl_3N_2O_5$	N-Trichloroacetyl-p-nitrophenylserinol		25			SE-30, 100→260°	714
$C_{11}H_{11}F_3N_2O_5$	N-Trifluoroacetyl-p-nitrophenylserinol		25			SE-30, 110→260°	714
$C_{11}H_{12}BrClN_2O_5$	N-Bromochloroacetyl-p-nitrophenylserinol		25			SE-30, 110→260°	714
$C_{11}H_{12}Br_2N_2O_5$	N-Dibromoacetyl-p-nitrophenylserinol		25			SE-30, 110→260°	714

Table 9-1. Aliphatic and Aromatic Acid Amides (cont'd.)

Formula	Compound	Silyl-ation	Method (Yield %)	B.P./mm; M.P.	n_D^t	Stat. Phase, Temp.•, Retention Data	Ref.
$C_{11}H_{12}Cl_2N_2O_5$	Chloroamphenicol		25			SE-30, 110→260	714
		T_2	25			SE-30, 225 , 1.31/mcap QF-1, 225 , 1.19/mcap XE-60, 225 , 1.33/mcap	608
$C_{11}H_{12}F_2N_2O_5$	N-Difluoroacetyl-p-nitrophenylserinol	T_2	25			SE-30, 205 , 5.1'	890
$C_{11}H_{12}N_2O_6$	N-Glyoxalyl-p-nitro-phenylserinol		25			SE-30, 110→260°	714
$C_{11}H_{13}BrN_2O_5$	N-Monobromoacetyl-p-nitrophenylserinol		25			SE-30, 110→260°	714
$C_{11}H_{13}ClN_2O_5$	Monochloro-chloro-amphenicol		25			SE-30, 110→260°	714
		T_2	25			SE-30, 225°, QF-1, XE-60	608
$C_{11}H_{13}FN_2O_5$	N-Monofluoroacetyl-p-nitrophenylserinol		25			SE-30, 110→260°	714
$C_{11}H_{14}N_2O_5$	N-Acetyl-p-nitro-phenylserinol		25			SE-30, 110→260°	714
$C_{12}H_{15}Cl_2NO_4$	N-Dichloroacetyl-p-methoxyphenylserinol		25			SE-30, 110→260°	714

Table 9-1. Aliphatic and Aromatic Acid Amides (cont'd.)

Formula	Compound	Silyl-ation	Method (Yield %)	B.P./mm; M.P.	n_D^t	Stat. Phase, Temp., Retention Data	Ref.
$C_{12}H_{15}Cl_2NO_5S$	N-Dichloroacetyl-p-methanesulfonyl-phenylserinol		25			SE-30, 110→260	714
$C_{13}H_{14}Cl_2N_2O_6$	Chloroamphenicol 3-acetate	T_1	25			SE-30, 205 , 1.39/dcap	890
$C_{13}H_{18}N_2O_5$	N-Dimethylacetyl-p-nitrophenylserinol		25			SE-30, 110→260	714
$C_{16}H_{17}KN_2O_4S(H_2O)$	Penicillin G (Potassium salt)	T_1	23e				752
$C_{18}H_{37}NO$	Stearamide	T_1	35				358

TABLE 9-2. CYCLIC AMIDES AND IMIDES

Formula	Compound	Silylation	Method	Yield %	B.P./mm; M.P.	n_D^t	Analysis	Ref.
$C_3H_3NO_2S$	Thiazolidin-2,4-dione	$T_2(N,O)$	21					272
$C_3H_4N_2O_2$	Hydantoin	$T_2(N,N)$	21				IR	272
$C_4H_4N_2O_2$	Maleic hydrazide (Tetrahydropyridazin-3,6-dione)	$T_1(O)$	22py		m 63-65		C-20M, 190°, 6.11; SE-30, 100°, 4.72	893
		$T_2(O,O)$	14b	75	b 120-121/11.5 m 70		C,H,N	272
$C_4H_5NO_2$	Succinimide	$T_1(N)$	14u	94	b 108-109/10.5 120-121/18	1.4740^{20} 1.4745^{20}		192
		$T_1(N)$	21	83	b 72-73/2	1.4749^{20}	IR, C,H,N,Si	598

Table 9-2. Cyclic Amides and Imides (cont'd.)

Formula	Compound	Silyl-ation	Method	Yield %	B.P./mm, M.P.	n_D^t	Analysis	Ref.
$C_4H_6N_2O_2$	Diketopiperazine	T_2(N,N)	34	0.5	b 135-136/17		IR, C,H,N,Si	654
			14b	98	m 96-97			422
		T_2(N,N)	43n,43d					
		T_2(N,N)	47n				C,H,N	418
C_4H_7NO	2-Pyrrolidone	T_1(N)	14b	80	b 77-81/6			186
		T_1(N)	14u	84	b 77-81/6, 99/18			192
C_5H_5NO	α-Pyridone	T_1(O)	14				IR	272
$C_5H_6N_2O_2$	1-Methyl-3-hydroxy-pyridazin-6-one	T_1(0-3)	14b	65	b 122-123/11.5 m 35-36		C,H,N	272
C_5H_9NO	δ-Valerolactam	T_1	33	98	b 79-80/12	1.46902^{20}	C,H,N,Si	654
			15e	25				

Table 9-2. Cyclic Amides and Imides (cont'd.)

Formula	Compound	Silylation	Method	Yield %	B.P./mm, M.P.	n_D^t	Analysis	Ref.
C_6H_7NO	2,3-Dihydroazepin-2-one	T_1 (N or O)	14b	72	b 72-73/11	1.4926^{20}	NMR, C,H,N	272
$C_6H_{11}NO$	Caprolactam	T_1 (N) T_1	14 33 14b 14e	82 95 39 78	b 103.5-104/12 b 111-111.5/16	1.4681^{20} 1.4700^{20}	IR, C,H,N C,H,N,Si	272 654
$C_6H_{11}NS$	Thiocaprolactam	T_1 (N)	14b	31	b 97-98/1	1.5412^{20}	IR, C,H,N	272
$C_8H_5NO_2$	Phthalimide	T_1 (N) T_1 (N)	14u 43n	87	b 151-155/10.5 m 67.5			192 422

Table 9-2. Cyclic Amides and Imides (cont'd.)

Formula	Compound	Silyl-ation	Method	Yield %	B.P./mm, M.P.	n_D^t	Analysis	Ref.
$C_8H_6N_2O$	2-Hydroxyquin-oxaline	$T_1(O)$	14u		b 74/0.005 m 32-33		C,H,N, UV	607
		$T_1(O)$	14u					583
$C_8H_6N_2O_2$	Tetrahydrophthala-zine-1,4-dione	$T_2(O,O)$	14b	69	b 140-141/0.6 m 54		NMR, C,H,N	272
	Tetrahydroquinazo-lin-2,4-dione	$T_2(O,O)$	14b	78	b 91-93/0.001 m 62		C,H,N	272
	Tetrahydroquinoxa-line-2,3-dione	$T_2(O,O)$	21				IR, NMR	272
C_8H_7NO	Oxindole	$T_2(N,O)$	43b		b 85-90/0.5			418
		$T_2(N,O)$	43n		b 98-100			422

Table 9-2. Cyclic Amides and Imides (cont'd.)

Formula	Compound	Silyl-ation	Method	Yield %	B.P./mm, M.P.	n_D^t	Analysis	Ref.
$C_9H_8N_2O$	2-Keto-3-methyl-di-hydroquinoxaline	$T_1(N)$	14u				UV	583
		$T_1(N)$	14u		b 101/0.2 m 62-64		C,H,N, UV	607
$C_9H_8N_2O_2$	2-Methyl-4-hydroxy-1,2-dihydrophthala-zin-1-one	$T_1(O-4)$	14b	52	b 118-118.5/0.5 m 81-82		C,H,N	272
	1-Phenyl-pyrazolin-3,5-dione	$T_2(O,O)$	21				IR	272
$C_{10}H_{11}NO$	Homodihydrocarbo-styril	T_1 (N or O)	43n 43py	66,94	b 60-61/0.1			422
		T_1 (N or O)	43n					420

-5

TABLE 9-3. UREAS AND CARBAMIDES

Formula	Compound	Silylation	Method (Yield %)	Physical Constants	Stat. Phase, Column Temp., Retention Data	Ref.
CH_4N_2O	Urea	T_1	35(89%)	m 168-171		186
		T_2(N,N')	21(98%)	m 222-224		832
CH_4N_2S	Thiourea	T_2(N,N')	14t(60%)	m 156		84
		T_2(N,N')	47n(82%)	m 155-158		413
CH_5N_3	Guanidine	T_3	47n(72%)	b 40/0.5; n_D^{20} 1.4450		413
CH_5N_3O	Semicarbazide	T_2(1,4)	21(18%)			834
$C_2H_4N_2O_2$	Hydroxyurea		25		C-20M, 190°	895
$C_2H_6N_2O_2$	N-(Hydroxymethyl)-urea	T_2(N,O)	14e(40%)	m 71-72		36
$C_3H_5Cl_3N_2O_2$	Chloralurea	T_1(O)	11f(76%)	m 132-134		308
$C_3H_6N_2O$	N,N'-Ethyleneurea	T_1	35b	m 118-120		186
		T_2		m 67-68.5		186
$C_3H_7NO_2$	Urethane	T_1	14b	b 170-175 n_D^{25} 1.4184		186
			35b	b 172-175		
$C_3H_7NO_3$	Methyl N-(hydroxymethyl)-carbamate		25		C-20M, 190°, 1.6', 1.0', 0.6'	895
$C_3H_8N_2O$	N,N'-Dimethylurea	T_1	47n(79%)	m 125-129		413
		T_1	35b(85%)	m 77-79		186
		T_1	47n(100%) 37n(3-10%)			413
$C_3H_8N_2O_3$	N,N'-Bis(hydroxymethyl)urea	T_2(O,O)	23s,25		C-20M, 190°	895
			14e(44%)	m 98		36
$C_4H_9NO_3$	2-Methoxyethyl carbamate		25		C-20M, 190°	895

Table 9-3. Ureas and Carbamides (cont'd.)

Formula	Compound	Silylation	Method (Yield %)	Physical Constants	Stat. Phase, Column Temp., Retention Data	Ref.
$C_5H_6Cl_6N_2O_3$	Dichloralurea	T_2	11f(91%)	m 180-181		308
$C_5H_{11}NO_3$	Ethyl N-β-hydroxy-ethyl carbamate		25		C-20M, 190°	895
$C_5H_{12}N_2O_3$	N,N'-Bis(hydroxy-ethyl)urea		25		C-20M, 190°	895
$C_7H_7NO_2$	Phenyl carbamate	T_1	21	m 54-59		217
$C_8H_{10}N_2O$	N-Phenyl-N'-methylurea	T_2	43n			420
$C_8H_{16}N_4O_6$	Strepurea		25		DEGS, 70→220°	618
$C_8H_{18}N_6O_4$	Streptidine		25		DEGS, 70→220°	618
$C_9H_{10}Cl_2N_2O$	N,N-Dimethyl-N'-3,4-dichlorophenyl-urea	T_1	25		QF-1, 130°, 0.56/ippc SE-30, 130°, 0.90/ippc C-20M, 170°.	228
$C_9H_{11}ClN_2O$	N,N-Dimethyl-N'-4-chlorophenylurea	T_1	25		QF-1, 130°, 0.22/ippc SE-30, 130°, 0.35/ippc C-20M, 170°, 0.28/ippc	228
$C_9H_{11}NO_2$	3-Ethoxyphenyl carbamate	T_1	21			217
$C_9H_{12}N_2O$	N-(p-Tolyl)-N'-methylurea	T_2	43n			420
		T_1	43n	m 79-81		422
$C_{10}H_{12}NO_2Cl$	Isopropyl N-3-chlorophenyl-carbamate		22py		QF-1, 130°, 2.4/ippc SE-30, 130°, 2.5/ippc C-20M, 170°, 2.9/ippc	228

Table 9-3. Ureas and Carbamides (cont'd.)

Formula	Compound	Silyl-ation	Method (Yield %)	Physical Constants	Stat. Phase, Column Temp., Retention Data	Ref.
$C_{10}H_{13}NO_2$	Isopropyl N-phenyl carbamate	T_1	22py		QF-1, 130°, 3.50' SE-30, 130°, 2.70' C-20M, 170°, 4.05'	228
	2-Isopropylphenyl carbamate	T_1	21	m 64-70		217
	3-Isopropylphenyl carbamate	T_1	21	m 55-57		217
$C_{10}H_{13}NO_2S$	4-Methylthio-3,5-xylenyl carbamate	T_1	21	m 84-89		217
$C_{11}H_9NO_2$	1-Naphthyl carbamate	T_1	21	m 93-96		217
$C_{12}H_{11}NO_2$	1-Naphthyl N-methylcarbamate	T_1	22py		QF-1, 130°, 1.0/ippc SE-30, 130°, 1.4/ippc C-20M, 170°, 0.41/ippc	228
$C_{12}H_{18}NO_2$	4-Dimethylamino-3,5-dimethylphenyl N-methylcarbamate	T_1	22py		QF-1, 130°, 0.42, 0.79/ippc SE-30, 130°, 1.0, 0.35/ippc C-20M, 170°, 1.2, 4.0/ippc	228
$C_{13}H_{12}N_2O$	N,N'-Diphenylurea	T_2	43			418
$C_{13}H_{12}ClNO_2$	o-Chlorophenyl N-p-tolylcarbamate	T_1	22py, 42		SE-30, 175°	231
	m-Chlorophenyl N-p-tolylcarbamate	T_1	22py, 42		SE-30, 175°	231
	p-Chlorophenyl N-p-tolylcarbamate	T_1	22py, 42		SE-30, 175°	231

10

Carbohydrates

The silylation of carbohydrates offers no particular problem as they are polyols and hydroxy groups are easiest of all to silylate. Only sugar amines and phosphates present any difficulty. With the usual excess of reagent taken all hydroxy groups are rapidly silylated under mild conditions.

The reader seeking background information in this area is referred to the comprehensive paper of Sweeley, Bentley, Makita and Wells (764), which presents a thorough discussion of the preparation and separation by gas chromatography of the silyl derivatives of over a hundred carbohydrates and related substances.

10-1. SILYLATION

As the following tables in this chapter show, relatively few workers have investigated the bulk preparation of silylated carbohydrates. Nearly all of these used TMCS in pyridine (Method 13) or TMCS and pyridine in formamide and hexane (Method 17). The latter method of silylation was first used by Kerr (407) on starch, and its application extended by Henglein et al. (307, 310, 314) to monosaccharides and uronic acids. TMCS in pyridine has been used with sugar alcohols (104, 545, 740, 754) as well as with other sugar derivatives.

Yields of distilled silylated products (78, 104, 158, 305, 307, 310, 477, 545, 595, 671, 754) were excellent, in the 65-95% range. Elemental analyses were satisfactory. The products were usually colorless viscous oils (477, 698), stable in solution in organic solvents to washing with water (887). NMR spectra have been reported for TMS derivatives of α-glucose and α-rhamnose (500, 501), xylose anomers (305) and various flavonoid glycosides (500, 501, 502, 625). Sprung (754) found the distillation of hexitol silyl ethers a useful means of purification and separation of hexitols from lower polyols.

The almost universal derivatization procedure (Method 25) for carbohydrate analysis by GC is the simple method developed by Sweeley et al. (764) in which the reagent is HMDS–TMCS (2:1) in pyridine. These

workers determined the optimum ratio of HMDS to TMCS using methyl
α-glucopyranoside as a model compound. Exact proportions were not
critical and good results were obtained over a considerable range. The
sugar dissolved and the reaction was complete, usually in a few minutes.
Sometimes warming was required to dissolve the sample. The small amount
of precipitate, presumably ammonium chloride, which formed upon addition of TMCS, in no way interfered with GC analysis and no attempt was
made to remove it. The reaction mixture was used directly for analysis
by GC.

The completion of the reaction can be shown by obtaining on GC a
single peak from a pure anomer, or two peaks from a known mixture of
two components. If not all hydroxy groups are silylated, many peaks will
result from partial silylation products. This is not the case ordinarily and
the reaction should be considered as quantitative. Partial silylation occurs
only when insufficient reagent is taken. Such conditions have been studied
by Kim, Bentley and Sweeley (408), who used either HMDS–TMCS in
pyridine or N-TMS-acetamide; the latter reagent was described by Birkofer et al. (78). Many of the partial derivatives of glucose were identified.
Hydroxyls at C-1, C-2 and C-6 are particularly reactive (408). Effects of
differences in reaction rates or steric factors could not be assessed from
the data obtained.

In general, the silylation reaction is rapid and the anomeric composition
of the products agrees well with the starting material where the HMDS–
TMCS–pyridine formula is used (764). This composition was calculated
on the basis of peak areas obtained on analysis of the silylated mixture by
GC. Results with samples obtained from aqueous equilibrium solutions
were close to those determined by other means.

Hot pyridine effects a different equilibrium mixture: a different ratio of
α and β forms and an increase in the γ component. This so-called γ-com-
ponent from D-galactose mutarotated in pyridine was silylated and shown
by gas chromatography on a nitrile-silicone column to consist of two compounds. These were identified by polarimetry, IR and NMR as the α and β
anomers of trimethylsilyl 2,3,5,6-tetra-O-(trimethylsilyl)-D-galactofurano-
side (7, 710).

In an effort to obtain consistent yields for quantitative work with tri-
and tetrasaccharides in corn syrup, Brobst and Lott (111, 489) replaced
the TMCS of the Sweeley formula with trifluoroacetic acid as catalyst.
This modified method accommodated water, up to 50% of the sample
weight, they claimed, and no ammonium chloride was deposited. Tedious
drying of samples was thus avoided. This method has been applied to the
quantitative determination of wort and beer carbohydrates (508) and to
wood pulp hydrolysates (168). It is essential for good results that the

trifluoroacetic acid be added last (110) and carefully, as the reaction is vigorous (110, 168). Bentley and Botlock (54) were unable to obtain complete silylation by this procedure. Silylation was complete, however, using 5-μl samples of aqueous sugar solution and an HMDS–TMCS–pyridine (1:1:4) reagent (1 ml).

Other reagents have been used for carbohydrates. N,O-Bis(trimethyl-silyl)-acetamide (BSA) in pyridine causes anomerization of hexoses (760). The chromatogram from one sugar may contain four or five peaks, whose relative areas will vary with time. Another reagent, N-TMS-imidazole, appears to react with great rapidity in pyridine, as it causes less anomerization than does the HMDS–TMDS–pyridine formula, produces higher yields with di- and trisaccharides, and leads to slightly higher yields in the presence of water (110) in comparison with the procedure of Brobst and Lott (111).

Halomethyldimethylsilyl and dimethylsilyl (DMS) ethers have been prepared under conditions analagous to the preparation of the corresponding TMS compounds. On analysis by GC the retention time of the halo compounds was several times greater, that of DMS derivatives about half, in comparison with the corresponding TMS compounds. This indicates that the DMS derivatives of oligosaccharides might be particularly useful. Further details are given in section 13-2.

10-2. GAS CHROMATOGRAPHY

The multiplicity of peaks obtained in GC analyses of carbohydrate TMS ethers increases the problems of resolution. For sure identification, Sweeley et al. (764) made analyses on both polar and non-polar phases, such as SE-52 and EGS, respectively. These, with SE-30, NGS and QF-1 have been the most used phases for carbohydrate TMS derivatives. The relation of molecular conformation to order of elution has been studied (220, 764).

Early attempts at quantitative work yielded results of 5 to 10% accuracy (62, 610, 768), based on comparison of the combined anomer peak areas with the area from standard amounts of sugar. The use of internal standards (20, 289, 677) gave results of about 1% accuracy.

Sawardeker and Sloneker (677) found that a Carbowax 20M column caused much less tailing of pyridine peaks than SE-52 or EGS columns, on which pyridine tailing obscured pentose and methylpentose peaks. Other investigators have had similar difficulty with pyridine and have removed it by washing a chloroform solution of the silylated sugar with water (887) or by vacuum evaporation (62).

Several investigators attempted to reduce the complexity of the chromatograms caused by anomers. They made other derivatives before silylation so that each sugar then gave one peak. By reduction of aldoses to
alditols and silylation of the alditols, Sloneker and Sawardeker (735) were
able to resolve and determine as many as eight common sugars with 2%
accuracy. Morrison and Perry (534) oxidized neutral aldoses to aldonic
acids. These were converted to lactones, which were silylated and chromatographed. Determinations were accurate to about 1%. Glucose formed
two lactones and was conveniently determined enzymatically and removed
before the oxidation.

10-3. THIN LAYER CHROMATOGRAPHY

Thin layer chromatography of TMS sugars has been investigated on
silica gel (295, 393, 465, 595). Kärkkäinen *et al.* (393) thus fractionated
sugar mixtures into neutral sugars, amino sugars and uronic acids before
analysis by GC, and separated the anomers of some neutral sugars. Lehrfeld (465) resolved mixtures of silylated (1) α,β-D-glucose and methyl
α,β-D-glucopyranoside, and (2) α,β-maltose and methyl α,β-maltoside.
Protection from the atmospheric moisture was necessary for good results.
Experiments with exposure to air showed the order of stability: methyl
TMS-α-D-glucopyranoside $>$ TMS-α,β-D-glucose $>$ methyl TMS-β-D-
glucopyranoside. The relative instability of the β-glucoside was attributed
to the exposed equatorial methoxyl group.

10-4. CARBOHYDRATE DERIVATIVES

Carbohydrate components of complex natural substances have been
determined as methyl glycosides that result from methanolysis of the
original substance. The methyl glycosides are readily separated from the
methanolysis products and silylated for analysis by GC. This procedure has
been applied to glycolipids (573, 724, 768, 792, 886, 887), bacterial
polysaccharides (366, 887, 888), blood group substances (485, 486),
saponins (789), and wood (783). Amino sugars present can be determined similarly (768).

Aldonic, aldaric and alduronic acids are completely silylated using the
HMDS–TMCS–pyridine method (579, 605). Depending on pretreatment
of the acid, silylated lactones may be formed as well as silyl esters. Aldonic
acids, for instance, may form both 1,4- and 1,5-lactones (579). Ascorbic
acid appears to form two products, but under severe conditions only the
tetrasilyl derivative is formed, as shown by mass spectra (812).

Most amino sugars covered by this review have been silylated as N-acyl derivatives. Glucosamine and galactosamine were silylated directly by several investigators using HMDS–TMCS in pyridine. The products were successfully analysed by GC, but no proof of N-silylation was given. It is likely that no N-silylation occurred, as other amines have been little or only slowly affected by this reagent (513, 894). Indeed, Sweeley and Vance (767) showed by mass spectrometry that the product of galactosamine silylation is the tetra-O-TMS derivative; the amino group remains free. The TMS derivative of the methyl ester of neuraminic acid 2-O-methyl ketal is entirely analagous (767), *i.e.,* the amino group is not silylated with HMDS–TMCS in pyridine.

Sugar phosphates and ribonucleotides have been silylated and analysed by GC (Table 10-9). It seems to have been assumed that the phosphoric acid group of simple sugar phosphates has been fully silylated (302, 347, 357) since phosphoric acid itself can be silylated with TMCS (302) and phenylphosphoric acid is converted to bis(TMS) phosphate by HMDS–TMCS (301). More direct proof of the esterification of sugar phosphates by silylating agents was not given. However, strong silylation conditions have been used—HMDS–TMCS at reflux (302), and BSA (347)—and it is likely that esterification has occurred, to impart the volatility necessary for GC. In ribonucleosides such as adenosine and cytidine silylation of all free hydroxyl groups of the ribose part as well as the 6-amino group of the pyrimidine ring occurred.

In the following carbohydrate tables deoxy sugars are classed with the corresponding non-deoxy compounds.

TABLE 10-1. SIMPLE CARBOHYDRATES

Formula	Compound	Silylation	Method (Yield %)	Stat. Phase	Column Temp.	Retention Data, Physical Constants	Ref.
$C_3H_6O_3$	Glyceraldehyde	T_2	25	SE-52	125	0.44/gu	764
				EGS	140	0.25/marp	
$C_4H_8O_4$	Erythrose	T_3	25	SiO	125→250	0.23/gu	491
				SE-52	140	0.10, 0.12, 0.14/gu	764
				EGS	140	0.29, 0.35/marp	
$C_5H_{10}O_4$	5-Deoxylyxose	T_3	25	NGS	170	0.226, 0.286/mmgu	355
	2-Deoxyribose		25	SE-30	180	0.204/ga	160
				SE-52	170	0.183/ga	
				ApL	210	0.309/ga	
		T_3	25	SE-52	140	0.16/gu	764
				EGS	140	0.49/marp	
				DEGS	70→220	0.72/gu	618
				JXR	175	0.426/gu	761
$C_5H_{10}O_5$	Pentaerythrose		25	SE-30	125→326		758
							282
	Apiose		25	SiO	135→240	10.0', 14.0'	616
	Arabinose	T_4	17(62%)	JXR		b 168-170°/7; n_D^{27} 1.4319	477
		T_4	25	SE-30	180	β 0.332/ga	160
				SE-52	170	β 0.323/ga	
				ApL	210	β 0.413/ga	
		T_4	13	ApL	180	α 0.49, β 0.41/xy	220
			23hs	SE-52	160	α 0.30, β 0.26, γ 0.34/gu	168
		T_4	25	SE-52	140	0.33, 0.38, β 0.28/gu	764
				EGS	140	1.31, 1.10, β 0.97/marp	
			25	SE-52, EGS	100→190		130
			25	DEGS	70→220	0.78/gu	618
			25	JXR	175	0.205/gu	761

Table 10-1. Simple Carbohydrates (cont'd.)

Formula	Compound	Silylation	Method (Yield %)	Stat. Phase	Column Temp.	Retention Data, Physical Constants	Ref.
$C_5H_{10}O_5$	Arabinose	T_4	25	JXR	140→210	β 0.34/miss β 0.26/sin β 0.24/min	488
			25	XF-1105 XF-1112 OS-138 15% BDS 3.5% BDS	122 150 160 142 140	0.28, 0.32, β 0.25/gu 0.30, 0.36, 0.39, β 0.28/gu 0.42, 0.49, β 0.32/gu 0.35, 0.41, β 0.26/gu 0.53, 0.56, β 0.38/gu	62
			25	SiO	125→250	0.56, 0.58/gu	491
				Mass Spec.			162
	Lyxose	T_4	13	ApL	180	α 0.39, β 0.53/xy	220
			25	ApL SE-52 SE-30	210 170 180	α 0.381, β 0.532/ga α 0.300, β 0.387/ga β 0.410/ga	160
			25	NGS SE-52	170 140	α 0.41/mmgu β 0.26, 0.33/gu	355
			25	SE-52 EGS	140 140	β 0.26, 0.33/gu 0.94, 1.42, β 1.26/marp	764
	Ribose	T_4	13	ApL	180	α 0.48, β 0.52/xy	220
			25	ApL SE-30 SE-52	210 180 170	0.485, 0.529, 0.590/ga 0.404, 0.438/ga 0.375, 0.400/ga	160
			22s,25	0.3% SE-52 0.05% SE-52	115 120	0.698/gu 0.255/gu	22
		T_4	25	SE-52 EGS	140 140	0.27, 0.32, 0.35/gu 1.22, 1.33, 1.48/marp	764
		T_4	25	EGS	160	0.38, 0.41/mgap	610
		T_4	22s,25	EGS	150	0.672/gu	22

Table 10-1. Simple Carbohydrates (cont'd.)

Formula	Compound	Silyl-ation	Method (Yield %)	Stat. Phase	Column Temp.	Retention Data, Physical Constants	Ref.
$C_5H_{10}O_5$	Ribose		25	DEGS	70→220	0.78/gu	618
			22s,25	DEGS	135	0.609, 0.687/gu	22
			25	SiO	125→250	0.65, 0.67/gu	491
			25	C-20M	15.8', 17.4'		677
			25	TLC			393
			25	SE-30	195	2.070, 2.156/mddc	55
	Ribose-d_6		25	SE-30	195	2.037, 2.124/mddc	55
	Ribulose	T_4	25	SE-52	140	0.23, 0.25, 0.33, 0.35/gu	764
	Xylose	T_4	17(65%)			b 191-193°/8; n_D^{27} 1.4386	477
			25	ApL	210	α 0.737/ga	160
				SE-30	180	α 0.514/ga	
				SE-52	170	α 0.499/ga	
		T_4	13	ApL	180	α 0.73/xy	220, 221
		T_4	25	SE-52	140	α 0.43, 0.54/gu	56,
				EGS	140	2.11, α 1.64/marp	764
			22s,25	EGS	150	0.707/gu	22
			23hs	SE-52	160	α 0.41, β 0.53, γ 0.28, 0.29/gu	168
			24s	SE-52	190	0.17/van	168
			25	SE-52	242		674
			22s,25	0.3% SE-52	115	0.730/gu	22
				0.05% SE-52	120	0.250/gu	
			25	DEGS	70→220	0.94/gu	618
			22s,25	DEGS	135	0.673/gu	22
			25	JXR	175	0.291/gu	761
		T_3	25	SiO	125→250	0.50, 0.52/gu	491

Table 10-1. Simple Carbohydrates (cont'd.)

Formula	Compound	Silyl-ation	Method (Yield %)	Stat. Phase	Column Temp.	Retention Data, Physical Constants	Ref.
$C_5H_{10}O_5$	Xylose	T_4	25	JXR	140→210	0.55/miss, 0.44/sin, 0.41/min	488
			25	XF-1105	122	0.26, 0.26, 0.50, α 0.37/gu	62
				XF-1112	150	0.32, 0.34, 0.59, α 0.46/gu	
				OS-138	160	0.38, 0.38, 0.80, α 0.58/gu	
				15% BDS	142	0.29, 0.31, 0.54, α 0.41/gu	
				3.5% BDS	140	0.43, 0.43, 1.00, α 0.69/gu	
			25	SE-30	195	3.509/mddc	55
			25	TLC, SE-30	150		393
	Xylose-d$_6$		25	SE-30	195	3.456/mddc	55
$C_6H_{12}O_4$	Digitoxose	T_3	25	SE-52	140	0.18/gu	764
				EGS	140	0.51/marp	
$C_6H_{12}O_5$	2-Deoxygalactose	T_4	25	SE-52	140	0.42, 0.45, 0.53/gu	764
				EGS	150	0.59/gu	
	2-Deoxyglucose	T_4	25	JXR	175	0.426/gu	761
	6-Deoxyglucose	T_4	25	SE-52	140	0.16, 0.25, 0.46, 0.64/gu	764
			25	SE-30	180	α 0.528, β 0.724/ga	160
				SE-52	170	α 0.517, β 0.724/ga	
				ApL	210	α 0.704, β 1.000/ga	
	Fucose	T_4	25	SE-30	155		95
			25	SE-30	180	α 0.445/ga	160
				SE-52	170	α 0.418/ga	
				ApL	210	α 0.571/ga	
		T_4	25	SE-52	140	0.33, 0.38, 0.45/gu	764
				EGS	150	0.25/gu	
				C-1540	140	0.42/gu	
		T_4	25	EGS	160	0.33, 0.36, 0.50/mgap	610
			25	DEGS	70→220	0.80/gu	618
			25	BDS	180→200	6.08'	352

Table 10-1. Simple Carbohydrates (cont'd.)

Formula	Compound	Silylation	Method (Yield %)	Stat. Phase	Column Temp.	Retention Data, Physical Constants	Ref.
$C_6H_{12}O_5$	Fucose		25	BDS	142	0.24, β 0.26, 0.38/gu	62
				XF-1112	150	0.30, β 0.37, 0.45/gu	
			25	TLC; SE-30	150		393
			25	JXR	175	0.256/gu	761
			25	SE-30	195	α 2.357, β 2.789/mddc	55
	Fucose-d$_8$		25	SE-30	195	α 2.311, β 2.755/mddc	55
	Rhamnose	T$_4$	17(65%)			b 178-182°/7; n_D^{25} 1.4370	477
			41,45		175→300		69
			25	SE-30	180	α 0.363/ga	160
				SE-52	170	α 0.343/ga	
				ApL	210	α 0.417/ga	
			23s,25	SE-52	115	5.6'	405
			22s,25	0.3% SE-52	115	0.755/gu	22
				0.05% SE-52	120	0.705/gu	
		T$_4$	25	SE-52	140	0.30/gu	764
				EGS	150	0.20/gu	
				C-1540	140	0.33/gu	
			22s,25	EGS	150	0.764/gu	22
			25	DEGS	70→220	0.75/gu	618
			22s,25	DEGS	135	0.543/gu	22
				Mass Spec.			162
	Rhamnose-d$_8$		25	SE-30	195	α 1.906, β 2.627/mddc	55
			25	SE-30	195	α 1.871, β 2.589/mddc	55
$C_6H_{12}O_6$	Allose	T$_5$	25	EGS	170	β 2.08/gu	764
				C-1540	140	0.79/gu	
	Altrose	T$_5$	25	SE-52	140	0.65, 0.68, β 0.94/gu	764
				EGS	150	0.63, 0.75, β 1.16/gu	

Table 10-1. Simple Carbohydrates (cont'd.)

Formula	Compound	Silyl-ation	Method (Yield %)	Stat. Phase	Column Temp.	Retention Data, Physical Constants	Ref.
$C_6H_{12}O_6$	Fructose	T_5	17(79%)			b 125-130°/0.01; n_D^{20} 1.4328	307
			25h	SE-30	150	β 0.73/gu	570
			25	SE-30	180	0.856/ga	160
				SE-52	170	0.800/ga	
				ApL	210	0.817/ga	
			23s	0.05% SE-52	119 pr	8.8'	405
			25	0.3% SE-52	175 pr	9.6'	
			22s,25	0.3% SE-52	115	0.650/gu	22
				0.05% SE-52	120	0.750/gu	
		T_5	25	SE-52	140	0.69/gu	764
				EGS	150	0.56/gu	
				C-1540	140	0.60/gu	
			22s,25	EGS	150	0.646/gu	22
			25	DEGS	70→220	0.89/gu	618
			22s,25	DEGS	135	0.848/gu	22
			25	SiO	125→250	0.87/gu	491
			25	XF-1105	122	0.69, 0.69, 0.82, 1.23/gu	62
				OS-138	160	0.50, 0.54, 0.77, 1.00/gu	
				BDS	142	0.62, 0.65, 0.72, 1.42/gu	
		T_5	13f	ApM, SiO	230→240		871
		T_5	13f	ApM, SiO	230→240		871
	Galactose	T_5	17(76%)	SE-30	175→300	b 128-138°/0.01; n_D^{20} 1.4342	307
			41,45	SE-30	250	0.65, 0.78, 0.90/mgup	69
			25	SE-52	160	α 0.87, β 1.07, γ 0.74/gu	768
			23hs	SE-52	140	0.76, 1.08, α 0.88/gu	168
		T_5	25	EGS	150	0.91, 1.38, α 1.03/gu	764
				XE-60	128	0.91/gu	

Table 10-1. Simple Carbohydrates (cont'd.)

Formula	Compound	Silylation	Method (Yield %)	Stat. Phase	Column Temp.	Retention Data, Physical Constants	Ref.
$C_6H_{12}O_6$	Galactose		22s,25	0.3% SE-52	115	α 0.698, β 0.850/gu	22
				0.05% SE-52	120	α 0.813, β 0.875/gu	610
			25	EGS	160	1.10, 1.25, 1.58/mgap	22
			22s,25	EGS	150	α 1.06, β 0.880/gu	618
				DEGS	135	α 0.652, β 1.109/gu	352
			25	DEGS	70→220	0.99/gu	62
				BDS	180→200	10.90'	
			25	XF-1105	122	0.78, 1.20, α 0.92/gu	
				XF-1112	150	0.77, 1.15, 1.82, α 0.91/gu	
				OS-138	160	0.65, 1.06, α 0.74/gu	
				15% BDS	142	0.88, 1.34, 2.01, α 1.00/gu	
				3.5% BDS	140	0.77, 1.25, α 0.88/gu	
			25	NGS	156	1.10/mguf	737
				C-6000	140	1.13/mguf	
			25	TLC; SE-30	150		393
			25	C-20M	170	25.8', 28.6', 41.4'	677
			25	JXR	175	0.590/gu	761
			25	SiO	125→250	0.95/gu	491
		T_5	25	XF-1150	155	4 peaks, NMR study	7
			25	XE-60	145	α 15.6', β 21.4'	678
				Mass Spec.			162
	Glucose	T_4	42py (73%)			b 117°/0.01	77
			42 (98%)			b 115°/0.08	77, 78
			17 (80%)			b 135-140°/0.007	314
			24py	SE-30	130, 140→275		54, 111
		T_5	25h, 24py, 44py	TLC			465

Table 10-1. Simple Carbohydrates (cont'd.)

Formula	Compound	Silylation	Method (Yield %)	Stat. Phase	Column Temp.	Retention Data, Physical Constants	Ref.
C₆H₁₂O₆	Glucose		25h	SE-30	150	β 1.58/gu	570
		T₅	41,45	SE-30	175→300		69
			13	SE-30	60→200	0.82/mdgu	105
				SE-30, ApM	215		739
		T₅	13f	ApM, SiO	230-240		871
		T₅	25,42	XE-60 SE-30	170 170	α 0.58/βgu α 0.61/βgu	408
			25	SE-30 SE-52 ApL	180 170 210	α 1.124, β 1.655/ga α 1.139, β 1.185/ga α 1.278, β 1.974/ga	160
			23s,25	0.05% SE-52 3% SE-52 SE-30	119 pr 175 pr 135 pr	α 14.0', β 15.0' α 13.0' α 4.4', β 6.4'	405
		T₅	23hs	SE-52	160	β 1.63, γ 0.82/gu	168
			25	SE-52	140 210	β 1.55, 1.57/gu β 1.22/gu	56, 764
		T₅	24py	SE-52	180		112, 508
		T₅	25	SE-52	180		385
			22s,25	0.3% SE-52 0.05% SE-52	115 120	β 1.460/gu β 1.187/gu	22
		T₅	25	SE-52 EGS	140 150	α 1.09, β 1.71/mgup α 1.06, β 2.06/mgup	768
		T₅	25	EGS	160	1.20, 2.14/mgap	610
			22s,25	EGS DEGS	150 135	β 1.295/gu β 1.26/gu	22
			25	DEGS	70→220	β 1.07/gu	618

Table 10-1. Simple Carbohydrates (cont'd.)

Formula	Compound	Silyl-ation Method (Yield %)	Stat. Phase	Column Temp.	Retention Data, Physical Constants	Ref.
$C_6H_{12}O_6$	Glucose	T_5	XF-1105	122	β 1.88/gu	62
		25	XF-1112	150	β 1.70/gu	
			OS-138	160	β 1.74/gu	
			15% BDS	142	β 1.82/gu	
			3.5% BDS	140	β 1.94/gu	
		T_5	JXR	140→210	α 0.71, β 0.87/min	488
		25	SE-30; TLC	150		393
		25	SiO	125→250	1.02, 1.21/gu	491
		25	C-6000	140	1.32/mguf	737
			PPE	175	1.16/mguf	
		T_5	C-20M	150	α 3,1', β 5.5'	383
		25	C-20M	145		173
		T_5	C-20M	170	35.2', 67.0'	677
		25	QF-1		α, β peaks	40
		T_5	C-1540	140	β 1.73/gu	764
		25	XE-60	128	β 1.99/gu	
			EGS	150	β 1.94/gu	
		25	XE-60	145	α 16.1', β 30.5'	678
		25	SE-30	195	α 5.469, β 8.177/mddc	55
		25	Mass Spec.			766
		25	Mass Spec.			162
	Glucose-d_7	25	SE-30	195	α 5.385, β 7.964/mddc	55
		25	Mass Spec.			766
	Gulose	T_5	SE-52	140	0.66, 0.95, α 0.74/gu	764
		25	EGS	150	0.84, 2.11, α 0.95/gu	
	Mannose	13	SE-30, ApM	215		739
		23hs	SE-52	160	α 0.68, β 1.04, γ 0.36/gu	168

Table 10-1. Simple Carbohydrates (cont'd.)

Formula	Compound	Silyl-ation	Method (Yield %)	Stat. Phase	Column Temp.	Retention Data, Physical Constants	Ref.
$C_6H_{12}O_6$	Mannose		25	SE-30	180	α 0.792, β 1.225/ga	160
				SE-52	170	α 0.777, β 1.185/ga	
				ApL	210	α 0.762, β 1.349/ga	
		T_5	25	SE-52	140	0.70, β 1.08/gu	764
				EGS	150	0.62, β 1.31/gu	
			22s,25	0.3% SE-52	115	1.08/gu	22
				0.05% SE-52	120	0.825/gu	
				EGS	150	1.14/gu	
				DEGS	135	0.480, 0.652/gu	
			25	EGS	160	0.79, 1.52/mgaP	610
			25	DEGS	70→220	0.97/gu	618
			25	XF-1105	122	0.68, β 1.16/gu	62
				XF-1112	150	0.68, β 1.17/gu	
				OS-138	160	0.53, β 0.89/gu	
				1.5% BDS	142	0.62, β 1.30/gu	
				3.5% BDS	140	0.62, β 1.11/gt	
			25	TLC; SE-30	150	0.475/gu	393
			25	JXR	175	20.2', 38.0'	761
			25	C-20M	170		677
			25	SE-30	195	α 4.563, β 7.030/mddc	55
			25	Mass Spec.			162
	Mannose-d$_7$		25	SE-30	195	α 4.518, β 6.962/mddc	55
	Sorbose	T_5	25	SE-52	140	0.85/gu	764
				EGS	150	0.69/gu	
				C-1540	140	0.82/gu	
			25	ApL	210	1.134/ga	160
	Talose	T_5	25	SE-52	140	1.13, α 0.86/gu	764
				EGS	150	1.06, 1.51, α 1.22/gu	
			25	STAP	150	α 0.58/agup	353

Table 10-1. Simple Carbohydrates (cont'd.)

Formula	Compound	Silyl-ation	Method (Yield %)	Stat. Phase	Column Temp.	Retention Data, Physical Constants	Ref.
$C_7H_{12}O_7$	Sedoheptulosan	T_6	25	SE-30	175→250		870
$C_7H_{14}O_6$	2-Deoxy-D-manno-heptose	T_5	25	EGS,XF-1112 NGSb	162 162	1.42, 2.10/mgup 1.52, 1.80, 2.89/mgup	577, 578
$C_7H_{14}O_7$	D-glycero-D-galacto-Heptose	T_6	25	SE-52	140 210	4.27/gu 1.77, 2.50, 3.08, 3.54/gu	764
	D-glycero-D-gulo-Heptose		25	ApL SE-30 SE-52	210 180 170	α 1.730/ga α 2.232/ga α 2.373/ga	160
		T_6	25	SE-52	140 210	2.29, 2.39/gu 1.62, 2.92/gu	56, 764
	D-glycero-L-manno-Heptose			SE-52	200	17.0', 21.0'	888
	d-manno-Heptulose	T_6	25	SE-30	175→250		870
	Sedoheptulose	T_6	25	SE-52 EGS	140 170	1.12/gu 2.22/gu	764
$C_9H_{18}O_9$	D-erythro-L-galacto-Nonulose	T_8	25	SE-52	275		704
$C_{10}H_{18}O_9$	3-O-β-L-Arabinopyrano-syl-L-arabinose		25	ApK SE-30	210 210	0.47, 0.37/suc 1.10, 0.67, 0.74/suc	574
	3-O-β-D-Xylopyrano-syl-D-xylose		25	ApK SE-30	210 210	0.95, 1.20, 0.76/suc 0.56, 0.92, 0.42/suc	574
	4-O-β-D-Xylopyrano-syl-D-xylose		25	ApK SE-30	210 210	1.65/suc 0.89, 0.69/suc	574
$C_{11}H_{20}O_{10}$	3-O-β-D-Galactopyrano-syl-L-arabinose		25	ApK SE-30	210 210	1.03/suc 0.96, 0.80, 1.19/suc	574

Table 10-1. Simple Carbohydrates (cont'd.)

Formula	Compound	Silyl-ation	Method (Yield %)	Stat. Phase	Column Temp.	Retention Data, Physical Constants	Ref.
$C_{12}H_{22}O_9$	2-O-α-L-Fucopyrano-syl-L-fucose		25	ApK	210	0.71/suc	574
				SE-30	210	0.51/suc	
	3-O-α-L-Fucopyrano-syl-L-fucose		25	ApK	210	0.67/suc	574
				SE-30	210	0.46, 0.95/suc	
	4-O-α-L-Fucopyrano-syl-L-fucose		25	ApK	210	0.81, 0.63/suc	574
				SE-30	210	0.57/suc	
$C_{12}H_{22}O_{11}$	Cellobiose		25	ApK	210	2.32, 1.33/suc	574
				SE-30	210	1.73, 1.19/suc	
		T_8	25	SE-52	210	α 11.9, β 16.6/gu	764
					250	β 1.14, 1.37/suc	
			25	Ucon	195		887
		T_8	25	Mass Spec.			162
	3-O-β-D-Galactopy-ranosyl-D-galactose		25	ApK	210	1.00/suc	574
				SE-30	210	1.00, 1.97/suc	
	6-O-β-D-Galactopyrano-syl-D-galactose		25	ApK	210	1.57, 2.32/suc	574
				SE-30	210	2.50/suc	
	Gentiobiose	T_8	25	SE-52	210	22.6/gu	764
			25	Ucon	225		887
	Isomaltose		24py	QF-1	150→350		40
			25	SE-52	150		508
	Lactose		25	SE-30	150		393
		T_8	25	SE-30	175→250	10.5/gu	890
		T_8	25	SE-52	210		764
			25	Ucon	195		887

Table 10-1. Simple Carbohydrates (cont'd.)

Formula	Compound	Silyl-ation	Method (Yield %)	Stat. Phase	Column Temp.	Retention Data, Physical Constants	Ref.
$C_{12}H_{22}O_{11}$	Lactose		25	TLC; SE-30	150		393
		T_8	25	Mass Spec.			162
	Laminaribose		25	ApK / SE-30	210 / 210	2.42, 2.00/suc ; 1.62/suc	574
			25	SE-30	150		570
		T_8	25	Mass Spec.			162
	Maltose	T_8	13			b 164-168°/0.14	305
			25	SE-30	150		393
			25	ApK / SE-30	210 / 210	1.58, 2.31/suc ; 1.40/suc	574
		T_8	24py	SE-30,52	pr		111, 112, 508
			25	SE-30; TLC	150		393
		T_8	25	SE-52	210 / 250	α 11.7, β 13.1/gu ; β 1.16/suc	56, 764
		T_8	25h,24py, 44py	TLC			465
			25	Ucon	195		887
			13	QF-1	160→220	α, β peaks	271
			25	Mass Spec.			162
	4-O-β-D-Mannopyrano-syl-L-glucose		25	ApK / SE-30	210 / 210	1.45/suc ; 1.31/suc	574
	4-O-β-D-Mannopyrano-syl-D-mannopyranose		25	ApK / SE-30	210 / 210	1.37, 2.01/suc ; 1.03, 1.40/suc	574
	Melibiose	T_8	25	SE-52	210	15.1, 19.0, 20.0/gu	764

Table 10-1. Simple Carbohydrates (cont'd.)

Formula	Compound	Silylation	Method (Yield %)	Stat. Phase	Column Temp.	Retention Data, Physical Constants	Ref.
$C_{12}H_{22}O_{11}$	Sucrose	T_8	13			b 190-200°/0.04; n_D^{20} 1.4434	158
			17(62%)			b 208-210°/0.07; n_D^{20} 1.4434	307
			25	SE-30	150		393
			25	SE-30	250 pr		827
			24py	SE-52	150→350		508
		T_8	25	SE-52	210 / 250	10.4/gu / 2.3'	764
			25	SE-52	242	3.28/pin	674
			25	TLC; SE-30	150		393
			25	EGS / SE-52	155 / 160		849
			25	SiO	125→250	2.43/gu	491
			25	Ucon	195		887
			13	QF-1	135→210		271
		T_6	48				417
	Trehalose	T_8	25	Ucon	225		547
		T_8	25	SE-52	210	13.5/gu	764
	Turanose	T_7	25	SE-52	210	12.7/gu	764
$C_{18}H_{32}O_{16}$	Gentianose	T_{11}	25	SE-52	210 / 250	138.0/gu / 8.10/suc	764
	Maltotriose		24py	SE-30	pr		111
			24py	SE-52	pr		111, 112, 508
	Manninotriose		25	SE-30 / QF-1	160→285 / 250		827

Table 10-1. Simple Carbohydrates (cont'd.)

Formula	Compound	Silylation Method (Yield %)	Stat. Phase	Column Temp.	Retention Data, Physical Constants	Ref.
$C_{18}H_{32}O_{16}$	Melezitose	25	SE-52	210 / 250	120.5/gu / 7.98/suc	764
		25	QF-1 / SE-30	250 / 160→285		827
	Planteose	25	SE-52	210 / 250	133.5/gu / 8.12/suc	764
	Raffinose	25	SE-30	150		393
		25	SE-30 / QF-1	290 pr / 250		827
		25	TLC; SE-30	150		393
		25	SE-52	210 / 250	99.0/gu / 6.4/suc	56, 764
		22s,25	0.05% SE-52 / 3% SE-52	225 / 275	19.5' / 15.6'	22
$C_{24}H_{42}O_4$	Maltotetraose	24py	SE-30	pr		111
		24py	SE-52	pr		111, 112, 508
	Stachyose	25	SE-52	250	52.4/suc	56, 764
Polysac.	Cellulose	13	2-3 TMS groups/unit			695
	Dextrin	17				307
	Pectin	17	0.9 TMS groups/unit			314
	Starch	17	2 TMS groups/unit			407

TABLE 10-2. METHYL SUBSTITUTED SUGARS

Formula	Compound	Silylation	Method	Stat. Phase	Column Temp.	Retention Data, Physical Constants,	Ref.
$C_6H_{12}O_4$	Methyl 5-deoxy-arabinofuranoside	T_2	25	BDS	145		660
	Methyl 5-deoxy-ribofuranoside	T_2	25	BDS	145		660
	Methyl 5-deoxy-xylofuranoside	T_2	25	BDS	145		660
$C_6H_{12}O_5$	Methyl arabino-furanoside	T_2	25	SE-52	135		275
		T_3	13	ApL	180	α 0.40, β 0.38/xy	220
		T_3	25	SE-30	200	0.24, 0.29, 0.33/mgup	889
				NGS	170	0.36, 0.38, 0.44, 0.48/mgup	
				Ucon	200	0.32, 0.35, 0.40/mgup	
		T_3	25	SE-52	140	α 0.21, β 0.20/gu	764
				EGS	140	β 0.78/marp, α 10.85'	162
				Mass Spec.			
	2-O-Methylarabinose	T_3	25	BDS	150	0.37, 0.52/mgup	485
	5-O-Methylarabinose	T_3	25	BDS	150	0.43, 0.51/mgup	485
	Methyl lyxofuranoside	T_3	25	NGSb	170	α 0.582/mmgu	355
		T_3	13	ApL	180	α 0.37, β 0.42/xy	220
		T_3	25	SE-30	200	0.25, 0.30, 0.34/mgup	889
				NGS	170	0.38, 0.40/mgup	
				Ucon	200	0.32, 0.38/mgup	
	Methyl riboside	T_3	13	ApL	180	α 0.39, β 0.43/xy	220
		T_3	25	SE-30	200	0.33/mgup	889
				NGS	170	0.42/mgup	
				Ucon	200	0.34, 0.37/mgup	
	2-O-Methylxylose	T_3	25	SE-52	50→125		703
		T_3	25	JXR	140→210	0.36, miss, 0.28/sin, 0.26/min	488

Table 10-2. Methyl Substituted Sugars (cont'd.)

Formula	Compound	Silyl-ation	Method	Stat. Phase	Column Temp.	Retention Data, Physical Constants	Ref.
$C_6H_{12}O_5$	3-O-Methylxylose	T_3	25	SE-52	50→125		703
	4-O-Methylxylose	T_3	25	SE-52	50→125		703
	Methyl xyloside		25	SE-30	200	0.44, 0.47/mgup	889
				NGS	170	0.64, 0.71/mgup	
				Ucon	200	0.52, 0.58/mgup	
			13	ApL	180	α 0.69, β 0.77/xy	220
		T_3	25	EGS	140	α 1.29, β 1.44/marp	764
				SE-52	140	α 0.31, β 0.34/gu	
$C_7H_{12}O_5$	Methyl 6-deoxygluco-pyranosid-5-ene	T_3	25	SE-52		b 110-115°/0.3; m 40-41°	463
$C_7H_{12}O_6$	Methyl glucopyrano-sid-5-ene	T_3					462
$C_7H_{14}O_5$	2,3-Di-O-methylxylose	T_2	25	SE-52	50→125		703
	Methyl fucopyranoside		25	SE-30	150	α 0.34, β 0.37/mgap	96
			25	SE-30	200	0.32, 0.36, 0.39/mgup	889
				NGS	170	0.36, 0.45, 0.57/mgup	
				Ucon	200	0.35, 0.39, 0.45/mgup	
	Methyl 3-O-methyl-D-xyloside		25	SE-30	200	0.33/mgup	635
	Methyl rhamnoside		25	SE-30	200	0.33/mgup	889
				NGS	170	0.33, 0.36, 0.40/mgup	
				Ucon	200	0.33, 0.37/mgup	
		T_3	41,45	SE-30 Mass Spec.	175→300		69
							162
$C_7H_{14}O_6$	Methyl alloside		25	SE-30	200	0.49, 0.65, 0.73/mgup	889
				NGS	170	0.45, 0.64/mgup	
				Ucon	200	0.56, 0.69/mgup	

Table 10-2. Methyl Substituted Sugars (cont'd.)

Formula	Compound	Silyl-ation	Method	Stat. Phase	Column Temp.	Retention Data, Physical Constants	Ref.
$C_7H_{14}O_6$	Methyl altroside		25	SE-30	200	0.46, 0.52, 0.57, 0.65, 0.77/mgup	889
				NGS	170	0.40, 0.46, 0.56, 0.77, 1.56/mgup	
				Ucon	200	0.45, 0.49, 0.60, 0.75, 0.88, 0.97, 1.18/mgup	
	Methyl galacto-furanoside		25	Ucon	200	α 0.79/mgup	889
	Methyl galacto-pyranoside	T_4	13			α,b 114-115°/0.23 n_D^{25} 1.4373	305
						β,b 113°/0.2; n_D^{25} 1.4378	
			25	SE-30	150	β 1.15/mgap	96
			25	SE-30	160	α 0.68, β 0.78, γ 0.91/mgup	767
		T_4	13	SE-30	200	0.70, 0.81, 0.91/mgup	889
				NGS	170	0.69, 0.78, 1.03/mgup	
				Ucon	200	0.66/mgup	
			25	SE-52	140	α 0.72, β 0.82/gu	764
				EGS	150	α 0.80, β 1.08/gu	
			25	17% EGS	150	α 15'	610
				15% EGS	160	α 15'	
			25	Ucon	190	7.6', 8.8', 10.9'	403
			25	Ucon	200	α 0.76, β 0.92/mgup	889
		T_4	25	SE-52	140	α 0.78, β 0.89, γ 0.67/mgup	768
				EGS	150	α 0.85, β 0.15/mgup	
				Mass Spec.			162
	3-O-Methylgluco-furanose	T_4	17	TLC		b 117°/10⁻⁴; n_D^{20} 1.4338	595

Table 10-2. Methyl Substituted Sugars (cont'd.)

Formula	Compound	Silylation	Method	Stat. Phase	Column Temp.	Retention Data, Physical Constants	Ref.
$C_7H_{14}O_6$	Methyl gluco-furanoside		25	Ucon	200	α 0.68/mgup	889
	Methyl gluco-pyranoside	T_3	13	C-20M	203	α 1.49/mgin, 2.07/dpm	519
			42py			b 109-110°/0.1	78
		T_4	13			b 115-120°/0.25; n_D^{22} 1.4410	356
		T_4	13f	TLC		b 126-127°/0.08; n_D^{20} 1.4368	595
		T_4	13	ApM	220	α b 109-110°/0.1; n_D^{25} 1.4415; β b 118-120°/0.2; n_D^{25} 1.4419	305
		T_4	25	SE-30	160	β 1.12/mgup	768
		T_4	25	SE-30	160	β 1.13/mgup, α 12'	767
		T_4	41,45	SE-30	175→300		69
			25	SE-30	200	α 1.08/mgup	889
				NGS	170	α 1.06/mgup	
				Ucon	200	β 1.07/mgup	
		T_4	25	SE-52	140	α 0.92, β 1.07/gu	764
				EGS	150	α 0.94, β 1.01/gu	
		T_4	25	JXR	140→210	α 0.91/miss, 0.73/sin, 0.67/sin	488
		T_4	13	C-20M	203	α 0.37/mqin, 0.53/dpm	519
			25,25h, 24py,44py	TLC			465
				Mass Spec.			162
	2-O-Methylglucose	T_4	25	C-20M	150	α 1.08, β 1.50/gu	191
	3-O-Methylglucose	T_4	17	C-20M	150	b 117°/10⁻⁴; n_D^{20} 1.4338	595
		T_4	25	SE-52	140	0.56/gu	764
				EGS	150	0.53/gu	

Table 10-2. Methyl Substituted Sugars (cont'd.)

Formula	Compound	Silylation	Method	Stat. Phase	Column Temp.	Retention Data, Physical Constants	Ref.
$C_7H_{14}O_6$	3-O-Methylglucose		25	C-20M	150	α 0.76, β 1.25/gu	191
				C-20M	160	α 0.44, β 0.72/mgup	191
	4-O-Methylglucose		25	C-20M	150	α 0.90, β 1.67/gu	457
	6-O-Methylglucose	T_4	25	QF-1			191
				C-20M	150	α 1.52, β 1.85/gu	191
	Methyl guloside		25	SE-30	200	0.45, 0.58, 0.61, 0.64/mgup	889
				NGS	170	0.55, 0.59, 0.74, 0.87/mgup	
				Ucon	200	0.49, 0.54, 0.68/mgup	
	Methyl idoside		25	SE-30	200	0.60/mgup	889
				NGS	170	1.32/mgup	
				Ucon	200	0.64, 0.80/mgup	
		T_4	25	SE-52	140	α 0.75, β 0.64/gu	764
				EGS	150	α 0.89, β 0.73/gu	
	Methyl manno-pyranoside	T_4	13	ApM	220	b 109-110°/0.23; n^{20}_D 1.4419	305
			25	SE-30	150	α 0.83, β 0.96/mgaP	96
			25	SE-30	200	0.54, 0.70, 0.80, 0.89/mgup	889
				NGS	170	0.47, 0.57, 0.71, 0.84/mgup	
				Ucon	200	0.88, α 0.64, β 0.73/mgup	
		T_4	25	SE-52	140	α 0.59, β 0.67/gu	764
				EGS	150	α 0.54, β 0.70/gu	
		T_4	25	JXR	140→210	0.72/miss, 0.58/sin, 0.54/min	488
		T_4	25	C-20M	145		173
			22d	SE-30,UCW-98			867
				Mass Spec.			162
	Methyl taloside		25	SE-30	200	0.58, 0.76/mgup	889
				NGS	170	0.72, 0.78/mgup	
				Ucon	200	0.70, 0.82/mgup	

Table 10-2. Methyl Substituted Sugars (cont'd.)

Formula	Compound	Silylation	Method	Stat. Phase	Column Temp.	Retention Data, Physical Constants	Ref.
$C_8H_{16}O_5$	2,3,4-Tri-O-methyl-apiose	T_1		NGSb	150	0.316, 0.355/mmgu	354
	2,3,4-Tri-O-methyl-xylose	T	25	SE-52	50→125		703
	Methyl 3,4-di-O-methyl-D-xyloside		25	SE-30			635
$C_8H_{16}O_7$	Methyl D-glycero-D-galacto-heptoside		25	SE-30 / NGS / Ucon	200 / 170 / 200	1.40, 1.82, 1.93, 2.06/mgup / 1.07, 1.71, 2.04/mgup / 1.13, 1.21, 1.86, 2.04/mgup	889
	Methyl D-glycero-L-galacto-heptoside		25	SE-30 / NGS / Ucon	200 / 170 / 200	1.28, 1.92/mgup / 1.05, 1.28, 1.61/mgup / 1.15, 1.41, 1.59/mgup	889
	Methyl L-glycero-D-gluco-heptoside		25	SE-30 / NGS / Ucon	200 / 170 / 200	1.56, 1.79/mgup / 1.10, 1.63/mgup / 1.02, 1.26, 1.51/mgup	889
$C_9H_{18}O_6$	Methyl 2,3-di-O-methyl galactoside		25	PPE / BDS	185 / 160	0.76, 0.87/mgup / 0.79/mgup	486
	Methyl 2,4-di-O-methyl galactoside		25	PPE / BDS	185 / 160	0.94/mgup / 0.99, 1.02/mgup	486
	Methyl 3,4-di-O-methyl galactoside		25	PPE / BDS	185 / 160	0.98/mgup / 1.33, 1.67/mgup	486
	Methyl 4,6-di-O-methyl galactoside		25	PPE / BDS	185 / 160	0.88, 1.07/mgup / 0.83, 1.16/mgup	486
	2,3,4-Tri-O-methyl-mannose	$T_2(1,6)$	25	QF-1 / NGS	130 / 128 / 140	5.8' / 7.8' / 4.6'	458

Table 10-2. Methyl Substituted Sugars (cont'd.)

Formula	Compound	Silyl-ation	Method	Stat. Phase	Column Temp.	Retention Data, Physical Constants	Ref.
$C_9H_{18}O_6$	3,4,6-Tri-O-methyl-mannose	$T_2(1,2)$	25	NGS	140	3.2'	458
					128	4.9'	
				QF-1	130	4.7'	
$C_{10}H_{20}O_6$	Methyl 2,3,4-tri-O-methylgalactoside		25	PPE	185	1.25/mgup	486
				BDS	160	1.42/mgup	
	Methyl 2,4,6-tri-O-methylgalactoside		25	PPE	185	0.70, 0.79/mgup	486
				BDS	160	0.65, 0.75/mgup	
	Methyl 3,4,6-tri-O-methylgalactoside		25	PPE	185	0.97, 1.07/mgup	486
				BDS	160	0.99, 1.19/mgup	
	Methyl 2,3,4-tri-O-methyl-D-glucoside		25	SE-30			635
	Methyl 2,3,4-tri-O-methylmannoside	T(6)	25	NGS	128	7.8'	458
	Methyl 3,4,6-tri-O-methylmannoside	T(2)	25	NGS	128	5.6'	458
$C_{13}H_{24}O_{11}$	Methyl β-cellobioside	T_7	25	SE-52	210	13.1/gu	764
	Methyl β-maltoside	T_7	25	SE-52	210	11.6/gu	764
	Methyl maltoside		25h, 24py, 44py	TLC			465

TABLE 10-3. MISCELLANEOUS GLYCOSIDES

Formula	Compound	Silyl-ation	Method	Stat. Phase	Column Temp.	Retention Data, Physical Constants	Ref.
$C_8H_{14}O_6$	Vinyl glucopyranoside	T_4	25	SE-52	50→150		575
$C_8H_{16}O_6$	Ethyl glucopyranoside	T_4	25	SE-52	50→150		575
$C_{10}H_{16}KNO_9S_2$	Sinigrin	T_4	25,26	SE-30	175 / 188 / 203	6.35' / 3.4' / 1.9'	255
$C_{12}H_{16}O_6$	Phenylglucoside	T_4	25	SE-52	140 / 210	β 7.16/gu / β 3.23, 3.62, 2.54/gu	764
$C_{12}H_{16}O_7$	Arbutin	T_5	25,26	SE-30	188 / 203 / 243	8.2' / 4.2' / 1.2'	255
			23s,25	SE-52	255 pr	6.5'	405
			22s,25	SE-30 / SE-52	250 / 260	4.3'	22
$C_{13}H_{18}O_7$	Salicin	T_5	25,26	SE-30	203 / 243	3.7' / 1.3'	255
$C_{14}H_{20}O_7$	Homoarbutin methyl ether	T_4	25,26	SE-30	188 / 203	7.6' / 3.5'	255
	Isohomoarbutin methyl ether	T_4	25,26	SE-30	188 / 203	7.0' / 3.3'	255
$C_{15}H_{16}O_9$	Daphnin	T_5	25,26	SE-30	203 / 243	7.4' / 3.0'	255
	Esculin	T_5	25,26	SE-30	203 / 243	10.5' / 3.9'	255
		T_5	25				500, 502
		T_5	25	SE-52	250	3.2/suc	56

carb gly 2

Table 10-3. Miscellaneous Glycosides (cont'd.)

Formula	Compound	Silylation	Method	Stat. Phase	Column Temp.	Retention Data, Physical Constants	Ref.
$C_{15}H_{16}O_9$	Esculin	T_5	25	SE-52	250	3.2/suc	764
$C_{15}H_{22}O_9$	Aucubin	T_5	21d,25	UCW-98		4.98/cina	867
		T_6	25,26	SE-30	203	2.9'	255
					243	1.7'	
$C_{16}H_{18}O_9$	Scopolin	T_4	21d,25	UCW-98		5.03/cina	867
$C_{16}H_{18}O_{10}$	Fraxin	T_5	25,26	SE-30	203	8.5'	255
					243	3.3'	
$C_{16}H_{21}O_{11}$	Monotropein	T_7	25,26	SE-30	203	7.6'	255
					243	2.6'	
$C_{18}H_{34}O_6$	Sorbitan monolaurate	T_3	25	SE-52	100→300		759
$C_{19}H_{26}O_{12}$	Gaultherin	T_6	25,26	SE-30	203	5.8'	255
$C_{20}H_{27}NO_{11}$	Amygdalin	T_7	25,26	SE-30	243	9.0'	255
$C_{21}H_{20}O_{10}$	Apigenin 7-glucoside	T_6	25				500, 502
	Emodin glucoside	T_6	25,26	SE-30	243	8.0'	255
	Homovitexin	T_7	25	SE-30	300	4.1, 5.4/camp	569
	Saponaretin	T_7	25				333
		T_7	25				500
		T_7	25				700
	Vitexin	T_7	25				500, 700
$C_{21}H_{20}O_{11}$	Homoorientine	T_7	25	SE-30	285	2.8, 4.0/camp	569
					300	3.6, 3.7/camp	
		T_8	25	SE-30	285	10.0, 9.0/camp	569
					300	5.4, 7.1/camp	
	Luteolin 7-glucoside	T_7	25				500, 502

Table 10-3. Miscellaneous Glycosides (cont'd.)

Formula	Compound	Silyl-ation	Method	Stat. Phase	Column Temp.	Retention Data, Physical Constants	Ref.
$C_{21}H_{20}O_{11}$	Orientine	T_8	25	SE-30	285, 300	3.8/camp, 2.6/camp	569
	Orobol 7-glucoside	T_7	25				500, 502
	Quercitrin		23s,25	SE-30, SE-52	250 pr, 255 pr	13.8', 27.7'	405
		T_7	25				500, 501
$C_{21}H_{20}O_{12}$	Hyperin	T_7	22s,25	SE-30, SE-52	250, 260	4.23/arbn, 5.00/arbn	22
		T_8	25				500, 502
$C_{21}H_{20}O_{13}$	Myricetin 3-β-galactoside	T_8	25				627
		T_9					384
$C_{21}H_{21}ClO_{10}$	Pelargonidin 3-glucoside chloride	T_7	22s,25	SE-30, SE-52, DEGS, QF-1	210, 210, 195, 215	0.220/mlgs, 0.635/mlgs, 0.865/mlgs, 1.126/mlgs	22
			23s,25	SE-30	215 pr	7.0'	405
$C_{21}H_{21}ClO_{11}$	Cyanidin 3-glucoside chloride	T_8	22s,25	SE-30, SE-52, QF-1, DEGS	210, 210, 215, 195	0.826/mlgs, 1.770/mlgs, 1.253/mlgs, 1.008/mlgs	22

Table 10-3. Miscellaneous Glycosides (cont'd.)

Formula	Compound	Silyl-ation	Method	Stat. Phase	Column Temp.	Retention Data, Physical Constants	Ref.
$C_{21}H_{21}ClO_{12}$	Delphinidin 3-gluco-side chloride	T_9	22s,25	SE-30 SE-52 QF-1 DEGS	210 210 215 195	0.694/mlgs 0.833/mlgs 1.373/mlgs 1.323/mlgs	22
			23s,25	SE-30 SE-52	210 pr 210 pr	23.6' 8.0'	405
$C_{21}H_{24}O_{10}$	Phloridzin	T_7	25	SE-52	250	7.3/suc	764
$C_{22}H_{22}O_{11}$	Scoparin	T_7	25	NMR			333
	Tectoridin	T_6	25	NMR			500, 501
$C_{22}H_{22}O_{12}$	Isorhamnetin 3-β-galactoside	T_7	25	NMR			628
$C_{22}H_{23}ClO_{12}$	Petunidin 3-gluco-side chloride	T_8	23s,25	SE-52 SE-30	210 pr 210 pr	8.8' 26.8'	405
			22s,25	SE-30 SE-52 QF-1 DEGS	210 210 215 195	0.788/mlgs 0.916/mlgs 0.845/mlgs 0.665/mlgs	22
$C_{22}H_{24}O_{10}$	Sakuranin	T_5	25	NMR			500
$C_{22}H_{26}O_{12}$	Catalposide	T_6	25,26	SE-30	203 243	26.9' 11.1'	255
$C_{22}H_{42}O_6$	Sorbitan mono-palmitate	T_3	25	SE-52			759
$C_{23}H_{25}ClO_{12}$	Malvidin 3-glucoside chloride		23s,25	SE-52 SE-30	210 pr 210 pr	9.6' 34.0'	405

Table 10-3. Miscellaneous Glycosides (cont'd.)

Formula	Compound	Silyl-ation	Method	Stat. Phase	Column Temp.	Retention Data, Physical Constants	Ref.
$C_{23}H_{25}ClO_{12}$							
	Malvidin 3-glucoside chloride	T_7	22s,25	SE-30 SE-52 QF-1 DEGS	210 210 215 195	34.0' 9.6' 14.2' 11.9'	22
$C_{23}H_{28}O_{11}$							
	Paenoiflorin	T_5	25,26	SE-30	203 243	24.9' 7.4'	255
$C_{24}H_{26}O_{12}$							
	Pendulin	T_5	25	NMR			500, 502
$C_{24}H_{26}O_{13}$							
	Iridin	T_6	25	NMR			500, 502
$C_{24}H_{44}O_6$							
	Sorbitan monooleate	T_3	25	SE-52			759
$C_{24}H_{46}O_6$							
	Sorbitan monostearate	T_3	25	SE-52			759
$C_{27}H_{30}O_{14}$							
	Apigenin 7-neo-hesperidoside	T_8	25	NMR			625
	Sphaerobioside	T_8	25				626
$C_{27}H_{30}O_{15}$							
	Kaempferol 7-neo-hesperidoside	T_9	25	NMR			625
	Luteolin 7-rhamno-glucoside	T_9	25	NMR			500, 502
	Saponarin	T_{10}	25	NMR			333
	Violanthin	T_{11}	25	NMR			333
$C_{27}H_{30}O_{16}$							
	Lucenin-1		25	NMR			700
	Rutin		23s,25	SE-30 SE-52	255 pr 250 pr	4.2' 2.2'	405
		T_{10}	25	NMR			500, 501

Table 10-3. Miscellaneous Glycosides (cont'd.)

Formula	Compound	Silyl-ation	Method	Stat. Phase	Column Temp.	Retention Data, Physical Constants	Ref.
$C_{27}H_{30}O_{16}$	Rutin	T_{10}	22s,25	SE-30 / SE-52	250 / 260	1.107/arbn / 1.116/arbn	22
$C_{27}H_{31}ClO_{17}$	Delphinidin diglucoside chloride		23s,25				405
$C_{27}H_{32}O_{14}$	Naringin	T_8	25	NMR			500, 501
$C_{28}H_{32}O_{15}$	Diosmin	T_8	25	NMR			625
$C_{28}H_{32}O_{16}$	Isorhamnetin 3-rhamno-galactoside	T_9		NMR			628
	Isorhamnetin 3-rutinoside	T_9	25	NMR			628
	Tamarixetin 7-neo-hesperidoside	T_9	25	NMR			625
	Tamarixetin 7-rutinoside	T_9	25	NMR			625
$C_{28}H_{34}O_{15}$	Hesperidin (rhamnose-glucose)		23s,25	SE-52	255 pr	16.4'	405
		T_8	25	NMR			500, 501
		T_8	22s,25	SE-30 / SE-52	250 / 260	1.815/arbn / 1.388/arbn	22
	Neohesperidin	T_8	25	NMR			500
$C_{33}H_{40}O_{19}$	Robinin	T_{11}	25	NMR			628
$C_{46}H_{66}O_7$	Phlei-xanthophyll	T_5	25				316
$C_{58}H_{94}O_{27}$	Cyclamine		25				788

TABLE 10-4. O-SUBSTITUTED SUGARS, ANHYDRIDES

Formula	Compound	Silyl-ation	Method (Yield %)	Stat. Phase	Column Temp.	Retention Data, Physical Constants	Ref.
$C_6H_8O_4$	1,4:3,6-Dianhydro-glucopyranose	T_1	13	Ester	124		144
		T_1	13	PDDS,NP-10	124		262
	1,4:3,6-Dianhydro-mannopyranose	T_1	13	PDDS,NP-10	124		262
		T_1	13				51
$C_6H_{10}O_5$	1,6-Anhydrogalacto-furanose	T_3	25	SE-52	145	α 18.8', β 16.2';	678
				XE-60	145	α 12.2', β 10.2';	
				EGS	168	α 7.4', β 5.8';	
				C-20M	160	α 8.5', β 6.5'	
	1,6-Anhydrogalacto-pyranose	T_3	25	STAP	150	β 0.67/agup	353
	1,6-Anhydrogluco-furanose	T_3	13	Ester	124		144
		T_3	13	PDDS,NP-10	124		262
		T_3	25	SE-52	145	β 24.1'	678
				XE-60	145	β 19.8'	
				EGS	168	β 11.4'	
				C-20M	160	β 12.0'	
	1,6-Anhydrogluco-pyranose	T_3	42(96%)			b 93°/0.04	78
		T_3	25	STAP	150	β 12.8'	353
		T_3	13	PDDS,NP-100	124	α, β peaks	262
		T_3	25	SE-52	145	β 20.1'	678
				XE-60	145	β 14.2'	
				EGS	168	β 9.0'	
				C-20M	160	β 10.2'	
		T_3		Mass Spec.			320

Table 10-4. O-Substituted Sugars, Anhydrides (cont'd.)

Formula	Compound	Silyl-ation	Method (Yield %)	Stat. Phase	Column Temp.	Retention Data, Physical Constants	Ref.
$C_6H_{10}O_5$	1,6-Anhydro-mannopyranose	T_3	13	PDDS, NP-10	124	α, β peaks	262
		T_3	25	STAP	150	β 0.86/agup	353
	1,6-Anhydrotalo-pyranose	T_3	25	STAP	150	β 0.98/agup	353
	Idosan	T_5	25	SE-52	140	0.50/gu	764
				EGS	150	0.66/gu	
$C_8H_{12}O_5$	1,2-O-Isopropylidene-α-D-ribo-pentodialdo-1,4-furanose-3-t	T_1	25	EGS			331
$C_8H_{13}IO_4$	5-Deoxy-5-iodo-1,2-O-isopropylidene-xylo-furanose	T_1	13			b 72-74°/0.006; n_D^{25} 1.4861	305
$C_8H_{14}O_6$	4,6-Ethylideneglucose	T_5	25	SE-52	140	α 0.54/gu	764
$C_8H_{16}O_7$	2-O-Hydroxyethyl-glucose	T_5	24py	SE-52	180	α, β peaks	489
	3-O-Hydroxyethyl-glucose	T_5	24py	SE-52	180	α, β peaks	489
	6-O-Hydroxyethyl-glucose	T_5	24py	SE-52	195	α, β peaks	489
			25	QF-1	170→250		604
				SE-30	210→250		
				Mass Spec.			
$C_9H_{14}O_5$	1,6-Anhydro-3,4-O-isopropylidenegalacto-pyranose	T_1	25	STAP	150	β 1.25/agup	353
	1,6-Anhydro-2,3-O-isopropylidene-mannopyranose	T_1	25	STAP	150	β 1.25/agup	353

Table 10-4. O-Substituted Sugars, Anhydrides (cont'd.)

Formula	Compound	Silyl-ation	Method (Yield %)	Stat. Phase	Column Temp.	Retention Data, Physical Constants	Ref.
$C_9H_{14}O_5$	1,6-Anhydro-2,3-O-isopropylidene-talopyranose	T_1	25	STAP	150	β 0.98/agup	353
	1,6-Anhydro-3,4-O-iropropylidene-talopyranose	T_1	25	STAP	150	β 0.98/agup	353
$C_9H_{16}O_6$	2-O-Allyl-D-gluco-pyranose		25	SE-52	180→220		632
	3-O-Allyl-D-gluco-pyranose		25	SE-52	180→220		632
	6-O-Allyl-D-gluco-pyranose		25	SE-52	180→220		632
	1,2-Isopropylidene-allofuranose-3-t	T_3	25	EGS			331
	1,2-O-Isopropylidene fructopyranose	T_3	11(35%)	TLC		b 90°/10⁻⁴; n_D^{20} 1.4458	595
	1,2-O-Isopropylidene glucofuranose	T_3	13(36%)			b 101-102°/0.1; n_D^{25} 1.4401	305
	1,2-O-Isopropylidene glucofuranose	T_3	17(73%)	TLC		b 112°/0.15; n_D^{20} 1.4416	595
$C_9H_{18}O_8$	O-(2,3-Dihydroxy-propyl)-glucose		24py	SE-52	125→275		490
$C_9H_{18}O_8S$	2-O-Methylsulfonyl-ethyl-D-glucopyranose		25	QF-1	200,218		633
	2-O-Methylsulfonyl-ethyl-D-glucose		25	ApM	200	0.68, 0.84/mseg	134,
				QF-1	200	0.65, 0.755/mseg	634
				XE-60	190	0.63, 0.76/mseg	
				SE-52	200	0.702, 0.851/mseg	

Table 10-4. O-Substituted Sugars, Anhydrides (cont'd.)

Formula	Compound	Silyl-ation	Method (Yield %)	Stat. Phase	Column Temp.	Retention Data, Physical Constants	Ref.
$C_9H_{18}O_8S$	3-O-Methylsulfonyl-ethyl-D-glucose		25	SE-52 ApM QF-1 XE-60	200 200 200 190	0.537, 0.83/mesg 0.449, 0.77/mseg 0.49, 0.72/mseg 0.40, 0.685/mseg	134, 634
	6-O-Methylsulfonyl-ethyl-D-glucose		25	SE-52 ApM QF-1 XE-60	200 200 200 190	0.833/mseg 0.78/mseg 0.88/mseg 0.784/mseg	134, 634
	6-O-Methylsulfonyl-ethyl-D-glucopyranose		25	QF-1	200,218		633
$C_{10}H_{18}O_6$	1,2-O-Isopropylidene-3-O-methyl gluco-furanose	T_2	17(58%)	TLC		b 120°/10⁻⁴; n_D^{20} 1.4408	595
$C_{10}H_{20}O_7$	2-O-Ethoxyethyl glucose	T_4	24py	SE-52	215		489
$C_{10}H_{20}O_8$	2-O-Hydroxyethoxy-ethyl glucose	T_5	24py	SE-52	205		489
	6-O-Hydroxyethoxy-ethyl glucose	T_5	25	QF-1 SE-30 Mass Spec.	170→250 210-250		604
$C_{12}H_{20}O_5$	Methyl 2,3-O-cyclo-hexylidenexyloside	T_1	25	NGSb	150	2.7/mxyp	87
	Methyl 3,4-O-cyclo-hexylidenexyloside	T_1	25	NGSb	150		87
$C_{12}H_{20}O_6$	1,2,4,5-Di-O-iso-propylidenefructo-pyranose	T_1	17(52%)	TLC		m 65-66°	595

Table 10-4. O-Substituted Sugars, Anhydrides (cont'd.)

Formula	Compound	Silyl-ation	Method (Yield %)	Stat. Phase	Column Temp.	Retention Data, Physical Constants	Ref.
$C_{12}H_{20}O_6$	2,3,4,5-Di-O-iso-propylidenefructo-pyranose	T_1	11p(69%)	TLC		b 106°/0.06; n_D^{20} 1.4437	595
	1,2,5,6-Di-O-iso-propylidenegluco-furanose	T_1	17(73%)	TLC		m 44-45°	595
$C_{12}H_{24}O_9$	6-O-Glucosyltri-ethylene glycol	T_5	25	QF-1 SE-30 Mass Spec.	170→250 210-250		604
$C_{12}H_{24}O_{10}$	Di-O-(2,3-dihydroxy-propyl)glucose		24py	SE-52	125→275		490
$C_{12}H_{25}NO_6$	2-O-(2-Diethylamino-ethyl)-glucose	T_4	25	XE-60 SE-52	140 210	0.57, 0.82/dmgu 0.76, 0.87/dmgu	615
	2-O-(2-Diethylamino-ethyl)-D-glucose		25	XE-60	140		632
	3-O-(2-Diethylamino-ethyl)-glucose	T_4	25	SE-52 XE-60	210 140	0.61, 0.84/dmgu 0.40, 0.61/dmgu	615
	3-O-(2-Diethylamino-ethyl)-D-glucose		25	XE-60	140		632
	6-O-(2-Diethylamino-ethyl)-glucose	T_4	25	SE-52 XE-60	210 140	0.80, 1.00/dmgu 0.60, 1.00/dmgu	615
	6-O-(2-Diethylamino-ethyl)-D-glucose		25	XE-60	140		632
$C_{13}H_{18}O_6$	2-O-Benzylglucose	T_4	25	SE-30	220	α 2.65, β 3.43/gu	408
	3-O-Benzylglucose	T_4	25	SE-30	220	α 2.24, β 3.26/gu	408
		T_4	42 (97%) 42py (84%)			b 143°/0.04 b 142°/0.03	78

Table 10-4. O-Substituted Sugars, Anhydrides (cont'd.)

Formula	Compound	Silyl-ation	Method (Yield %)	Stat. Phase	Column Temp.	Retention Data, Physical Constants	Ref.
$C_{13}H_{18}O_6$	4-O-Benzylglucose	T_4	25	SE-30	220	α 2.37, β 3.48/gu	408
	6-O-Benzylglucose	T_4	25	SE-30	220	α 3.26, β 3.97/gu	408
		T_4	25(80%)			b 156°/0.03	408
$C_{14}H_{18}O_6$	Methyl 4,6-benzyli-denegalactoside	T_2	25	SE-52	210	α 2.77, β 3.00/gu	764
	Methyl 4,6-benzyli-dene-α-glucoside	T_2	13(41%)	SE-52	140	b 148-150°/0.15	305
		T_2	25	SE-52	210	α 4.67/gu α 3.15/gu	764
	Methyl 4,6-benzyli-deneidoside	T_2	25	SE-52	210	α 2.96, β 3.11, 2.52/gu	764
$C_{14}H_{20}O_{10}$	2,3,4,6-Tetracetyl-glucose	T_1	42(96%)			b 120°/10⁻⁴; m 98°	78
$C_{14}H_{28}O_{10}$	6-O-Glucosyltetra-ethylene glycol	T_5	25	QF-1 SE-30 Mass Spec.	170→250 210→250		604
$C_{15}H_{20}O_6$	Methyl 3-methyl-4,6-benzilideneidoside	T_1	25	SE-52	210	β 1.93/gu	764
$C_{16}H_{20}O_6$	1,2-O-Isopropylidene-3,5-O-benzylidene-glucofuranose	T_1	17(58%)	TLC		m 92°	595
$C_{16}H_{26}O_6$	Methyl 3,5,6-tri-O-allyl-D-gluco-furanoside	T_1	25	XE-60	150	5.8', 6.25'	134

Table 10-4. O-Substituted Sugars, Anhydrides (cont'd.)

Formula	Compound	Silyl-ation	Method (Yield %)	Stat. Phase	Column Temp.	Retention Data, Physical Constants	Ref.
$C_{16}H_{32}O_{11}$	6-O-Glucosyl penta-ethylene glycol	T_5	25	QF-1 SE-30 Mass Spec.	170→250 210→250		604
$C_{20}H_{20}O_6$	1,2;3,5-Di-O-benzyli-dene-α-D-gluco-furanose	T_1	25	XE-60	200→235		134
$C_{25}H_{26}O_6$	6-Trityl-glucose	T_4	42py (90%)			m 110°	78

TABLE 10-5. SUGAR ACIDS AND ACID DERIVATIVES

Formula	Compound	Silyl-ation	Method (Yield %)	Stat. Phase	Column Temp.	Retention Data, Physical Constants	Ref.
$C_4H_6O_4$	Erythrono-1,4-lactone	T_2	25	SE-30	140	0.10/gun	580
				SE-52	150	0.11/gun	
				QF-1	170	0.35/gun	
				DC-560/EGSP-Z	185	0.16/gun	
				NGS	165	0.54/gun	
				XE-60	150	0.41/gun	
				C-1540	160	0.28/gun	
				ECNSS	140	0.93/gun	
				EGSS-Y	150	0.77/gun	
				HiEff	150	0.64/gun	
				EGS	180	0.46/gun	
		T_2	25	SE-30	120		581
				Mass Spec.			
	Threono-1,4-lactone	T_2	25	SE-30	140	0.08/gun	580
				SE-52	150	0.09/gun	
				QF-1	170	0.23/gun	
				DC-560/EGSP-Z	185	0.13/gun	
				NGS	165	0.29/gun	
				XE-60	150	0.20/gun	
				ECNSS	140	0.37/gun	
				EGSS-Y	150	0.40/gun	
				HiEff	150	0.30/gun	
		T_2	25	SE-30	120		581
				Mass Spec.			
$C_5H_8O_4$	2-Deoxyerythropentono-1,4-lactone	T_2	25	NGSb	170	0.694/rb	534
				C-20M	155	0.407/rb	
$C_5H_8O_5$	Arabinono-1,4-lactone	T_3	25(75%)	NGSb	170	0.681/rb	534
				C-20M	155	0.733/rb	
		T_3	25	SE-30	140	0.25/gun	580
				SE-52	150	0.27/gun	
				QF-1	170	0.41/gun	
				DC-560/EGSP-Z	185	0.33/gun	
				NGS	165	0.48/gun	

Table 10-5. Sugar Acids and Acid Derivatives (cont'd.)

Formula	Compound	Silyl-ation	Method (Yield %)	Stat. Phase	Column Temp.	Retention Data, Physical Constants	Ref.
$C_5H_8O_5$	Arabinono-1,4-lactone	T_3	25	XE-60	150	0.38/gun	580
				C-1540	160	0.28/gun	
				ECNSS	140	0.50/gun	
				EGSS-Y	150	0.55/gun	
				HiEff	150	0.44/gun	
				EGS	180	0.34/gun	
		T_3	25	NGSb	170	0.092/aarl	579
		T_3	25	SE-30	140		581
				Mass Spec.			
	Arabinono-1,5-lactone	T_3	25	SE-30	140	0.29/gun	580
		T_3	25	SE-30	180		581
				Mass Spec.			
	Arabinonolactone	T_3	25	XF-1112	155→195		728
		T_3	25	SE-52	140	0.31/gu	764
	Lyxono-1,4-lactone	T_3	25	NGSb	170	1.58/rb	534
				C-20M	155	1.42/rb	
		T_3	25	SE-30	140	0.40/gun	580
				SE-52	150	0.45/gun	
				QF-1	170	0.81/gun	
				DC-560/EGSP-Z	185	0.51/gun	
				NGS	165	1.17/gun	
				XE-60	150	1.08/gun	
				ECNSS	140	1.66/gun	
				EGSS-Y	150	1.27/gun	
				HiEff	150	1.17/gun	
		T_3	25	NGSb	170	0.207/aarl	579
		T_3	25	SE-30	140	1.58/arlt	581
				Mass Spec.			
	Ribono-1,4-lactone	T_3	25	NGSb	170	1.000/rb	534
				C-20M	155	1.000/rb	
						m 83-84°	

Table 10-5. Sugar Acids and Acid Derivatives (cont'd.)

Formula	Compound	Silyl- ation	Method (Yield %)	Stat. Phase	Column Temp.	Retention Data, Physical Constants	Ref.
$C_5H_8O_5$	Ribono-1,4-lactone	T_3	25	SE-30	140	0.31/gun	580
				SE-52	150	0.35/gun	
				QF-1	170	0.64/gun	
				DC-560/EGSP-Z	185	0.42/gun	
				NGS	165	0.75/gun	
				XE-60	150	0.73/gun	
				C-1540	160	0.42/gun	
				ECNSS	140	1.05/gun	
				EGSS-Y	150	0.86/gun	
				HiEff	150	0.79/gun	
				EGS	180	0.53/gun	
		T_3	25	SE-30	140	1.23/arlt	581
				Mass Spec.			
	Ribonolactone		25	SE-52	140	0.36/gu	764
			25	NGSb	170	0.167/aarl	579
	Xylono-1,4-lactone	T_3	25	NGSb	170	0.794/rb	534
				C-20M	155	0.911/rb	
		T_3	25	SE-30	140	0.27/gun	580
				SE-52	150	0.30/gun	
				QF-1	170	0.54/gun	
				DC-560/EGSP-Z	185	0.36/gun	
				NGS	165	0.58/gun	
				XE-60	150	0.51/gun	
				C-1540	160	0.34/gun	
				ECNSS	140	0.69/gun	
				EGSS-Y	150	0.66/gun	
				HiEff	150	0.57/gun	
				EGS	180	0.42/gun	
			25	NGSb	170	0.108/aarl	579
		T_3	25	SE-30	140	1.05, 1.03/arlt	581
				Mass Spec.			
	Xylono-1,5-lactone	T_3	25	SE-30	140	0.31/gun	580

Table 10-5. Sugar Acids and Acid Derivatives (cont'd.)

Formula	Compound	Silylation	Method (Yield %)	Stat. Phase	Column Temp.	Retention Data, Physical Constants	Ref.
$C_5H_8O_5$	Xylono-1,5-lactone	T_3	25	SE-30	180		581
				Mass Spec.			
	Xylonolactone	T_3	25	XF-1112	155→195		728
$C_5H_{10}O_6$	Arabinonic acid	T_5	25	SE-52	140	0.33, 0.58/gun	764
				SE-30	140	0.63/gun	580
				Mass Spec.			
	Xylonic acid	T_5	25	SE-30	140	0.57/gun	580
				Mass Spec.			
$C_6H_6O_6$	Glucaric acid-1,4:3,6-dilactone	T_2	25	SE-30	170	2.2/eryl	605
				SE-52	190	2.8/eryl	
	Mannaric acid-1,4:3,6-dilactone	T_2	25	SE-30	170	4.0/eryl	605
				SE-52	190	5.3/eryl	
$C_6H_8O_6$	Ascorbic acid		25	SE-30	70→350	one peak	536
				10% F-60	100→250	19.92 MU	182
				1% F-60		20.00 MU	
			43	OV-17	194 pr		347
			25	DEGS	70→220	1.39/gu	618
		T_4	25,42	SE-30	170	1.66, 2.06/octd	812
				Mass Spec.			
			25	SE-52	140	1.25/gu	764
	Glucurono-1,4-lactone	T_3	17(77%)			b 110-113°/0.002	310
	Glucuronolactone		25	SE-30	150		393
			25	SE-30	140		467
		T_3	25	SE-30	170	3.0, 3.2/eryl	605
				SE-52	190	3.6/eryl	
				XE-60	180	6.6, 7.3/eryl	

Table 10-5. Sugar Acids and Acid Derivatives (cont'd.)

Formula	Compound	Silylation	Method (Yield %)	Stat. Phase	Column Temp.	Retention Data, Physical Constants	Ref.
$C_6H_8O_6$	Guluronolactone	T_3	25	SE-30 / SE-52	170 / 190	2.2, 2.8, 4.8/eryl / 2.4, 3.2, 4.4/eryl	605
	Mannuronolactone	T_3	25	SE-30 / SE-52	170 / 190	fur α 3.1, β 4.1/eryl / fur α 3.6, β 4.7/eryl	605
$C_6H_8O_7$	Glucaro-1,4-lactone	T_4	25	SE-30 / SE-52	170 / 190	5.6/eryl / 5.5/eryl	605
	Glucaro-3,6-lactone	T_4	25	SE-30 / SE-52	170 / 190	6.3/eryl / 6.1/eryl	605
$C_6H_{10}O_5$	Fucono-1,4-lactone	T_3	25	NGSb / C-20M	170 / 155	0.758/rb / 0.781/rb	534
	Rhamnono-1,4-lactone	T_3	25	NGSb / C-20M	170 / 155	1.65/rb / 1.35/rb	534
$C_6H_{10}O_6$	Altrono-1,4-lactone	T_4	25	NGSb / C-20M	170 / 155	2.03/rb / 2.95/rb	534
	Galactono-1,4-lactone	T_4	25	NGSb / C-20M	170 / 155	1.53/rb / 3.12/rb	534
		T_4	25	SE-30	140	0.92/gun	580
				SE-52	150	0.98/gun	
				QF-1	170	0.88/gun	
				DC-560/EGSP-Z	185	0.95/gun	
				NGS	165	0.95/gun	
				XE-60	150	0.95/gun	
				C-1540	160	0.84/gun	
				ECNSS	140	0.98/gun	
				EGSS-Y	150	0.96/gun	
				HiEff	150	0.90/gun	
				EGS	180	0.80/gun	
		T_4	25	JXR	140→210	0.91/miss, 0.72/sin, 0.66/min	488
			25	NGSb	170	0.213/aarl	579
		T_4	25	SE-30 / SE-52	170 / 190	4.5/eryl / 4.3/eryl	605

Table 10-5. Sugar Acids and Acid Derivatives (cont'd.)

Formula	Compound	Silylation	Method (Yield %)	Stat. Phase	Column Temp	Retention Data, Physical Constants	Ref.
$C_6H_{10}O_6$	Galactono-1,4-lactone	T_4	25	SE-30	180		581
				Mass Spec.			764
	Galactonolactone		25	SE-52	140	α 0.97/gu	728
	Glucono-1,4-lactone	T_4	25	XF-1112	155→195		534
		T_4	25	NGSb	170	1.64/rb	580
				C-20M	155	3.77/rb	
		T_4	25	SE-30, ECNSS	140	18.9'	579
				SE-52, XE-60	150		
				QF-1	170		
				DC-560/EGSP-Z	185		
				NGS	165		
				C-1540	160		
				EGSS-Y, HiEff	150		
				EGS	180		
				NGSb	170	0.274/aarl	
			22s,25	0.05% SE-52	115	5.00'	22
				3% SE-52	150	7.25'	
		T_4	25	SE-30	170	4.6/eryl	605
				SE-52	190	4.5/eryl	
		T_4	25	SE-30	180		581
				Mass Spec.			
	Glucono-1,5-lactone	T_4	25	XF-1112	155→195		728
			25	SE-52	140	0.98/gu	764
		T_4	25	SE-30	170	0.93/gun	580
		T_4	25	SE-30	170	4.4/eryl	605
				SE-52	190	4.4/eryl	
		T_4	25	SE-30	180		581
				Mass Spec.			
	Gulono-1,4-lactone	T_4	25	NGSb	170	2.36/rb	534
				C-20M	155	4.32/rb	

Table 10-5. Sugar Acids and Acid Derivatives (cont'd.)

Formula	Compound	Silyl-ation	Method (Yield %)	Stat. Phase	Column Temp.	Retention Data, Physical Constants	Ref.
$C_6H_{10}O_6$	Gulono-1,4-lactone		25	NGSb	170	0.401/aarl	579
		T_4	25	SE-30	140	1.03/gun	580
				SE-52	150	1.15/gun	
				QF-1	170	1.12/gun	
				DC-560/EGSP-Z	185	1.13/gun	
				NGS	165	1.51/gun	
				XE-60	150	1.69/gun	
				C-1540	160	1.17/gun	
				ECNSS	140	1.80/gun	
				EGSS-Y	150	1.44/gun	
				HiEff	150	1.52/gun	
				EGS	180	1.16/gun	
		T_4	25	JXR	140→210	0.96/miss, 0.76/sin, 0.70/min	488
		T_4	25	SE-30	170	5.0/eryl	605
				SE-52	190	5.0/eryl	
		T_4	25	SE-30	180		581
				Mass Spec.			
	Gulonolactone		25	SE-52	140	α 1.08/gu	764
				EGS	170	α 3.03/gu	
	Idono-1,4-lactone	T_4	25	NGSb	170	1.88/rb	534
				C-20M	155	3.82/rb	
		T_4	25	SE-30	170	5.2/eryl	605
				SE-52	190	4.9/eryl	
			25	NGSb	170	0.322/aarl	579
	Idonolactone		25	SE-52	140	1.05/gu	764
	Mannono-1,4-lactone	T_4	25	NGSb	170	3.07/rb	534
				C-20M	155	4.74/rb, m 69-70°	
		T_4	25	SE-30	170	6.5/eryl	605
				SE-52	190	6.3/eryl	

Table 10-5. Sugar Acids and Acid Derivatives (cont'd.)

Formula	Compound	Silylation	Method (Yield %)	Stat. Phase	Column Temp.	Retention Data, Physical Constants	Ref.
$C_6H_{10}O_6$	Mannono-1,4-lactone	T_4	25	SE-30	160	1.29/gun	580
				SE-52	150	1.50/gun	
				QF-1	170	1.40/gun	
				DC-560/EGSP-Z	185	1.40/gun	
				NGS	165	1.91/gun	
				XE-60	150	2.06/gun	
				ECNSS	140	2.20/gun	
				EGSS-Y	150	1.80/gun	
				HiEff	150	1.78/gun	
		T_4	25	NGSb	170	0.512/aarl	579
	Mannono-1,5-lactone	T_4	25	Mass Spec.			581
							580
	Mannonolactone	T_4	25	XF-1112	155→195		728
	Talono-1,4-lactone	T_4	25	SE-52	140	1.47/gu	764
				NGSb	170	2.01/rb	534
				C-20M	155	3.33/rb	
						m 70-71°	
		T_4	25	SE-52	150	1.19/gun	580
				QF-1	170	1.49/gun	
				DC-560/EGSP-Z	185	1.13/gun	
				NGS	165	1.35/gun	
				XE-60	150	1.73/gun	
				ECNSS	140	1.84/gun	
				EGSS-Y	150	1.40/gun	
				HiEff	150	1.48/gun	
		T_4	25	SE-30 Mass Spec.	180		581
	Talonolactone		25	SE-52	140	α 1.16/gu	764
				EGS	170	α 3.07/gu	
$C_6H_{10}O_7$	Galacturonic acid	T_5	17(76%)	SE-30	178	α 5.9', β 7.3', γ 4.5'	862
						b 112-114°/0.001	310
						n_D^{20} 1.4388	

Table 10-5. Sugar Acids and Acid Derivatives (cont'd.)

Formula	Compound	Silyl-ation	Method (Yield %)	Stat. Phase	Column Temp.	Retention Data, Physical Constants	Ref.
$C_6H_{10}O_7$	Galacturonic acid		25	ApL SE-30 SE-52	210 180 170	0.923, 1.414/ga 1.414/ga 1.540/ga	160
		T_5	25	SE-30	170	fur α 4.5, β 5.9/eryl pyr α 6.4, β 8.3/eryl	605
				SE-52	190	fur α 4.1, β 5.5/eryl pyr α 6.0, β 7.7/eryl	
	Glucuronic acid		25	SE-30	178	α 5.7', β 7.1'	862
			21d,22d	SE-30,UCW-98			867
		T_5	25	SE-30; TLC	150		393
		T_5	25	SE-30	140		468
			25	ApL SE-30 SE-52	210 180 170	1.648, 2.204/ga 1.464, 1.984/ga 1.634, 2.177/ga	160
		T_5	25	SE-30	170	fur 5.3/eryl pyr α 6.8, β 9.2/eryl	605
				SE-52	190	fur 4.9/eryl pyr α 6.3, β 7.8/eryl	
	(K salt)	T_5	17(69%)			b 130-134°/0.01 n_D^{20} 1.4402	310
	Guluronic acid	T_5	25	SE-30 SE-52	170 190	4.8/eryl 4.4/eryl	605
	Iduronic acid	T_5	25	SE-30	150		393
			25	SE-30	140		467, 468
	Mannuronic acid		25	Ap	180		600
		T_5	25	SE-30 SE-52	170 190	pyr α 4.4, β 6.7/eryl pyr α 4.1, β 6.1/eryl	605
$C_6H_{10}O_8$	Galactaric acid	T_6	25	SE-30 SE-52	170 190	9.5/eryl 8.4/eryl	605

Table 10-5. Sugar Acids and Acid Derivatives (cont'd.)

Formula	Compound	Silyl-ation	Method (Yield %)	Stat. Phase	Column Temp.	Retention Data, Physical Constants	Ref.
$C_6H_{10}O_8$	Glucaric acid (or K salt)	T_6	25	SE-30 SE-52	170 190	8.3/eryl 7.4/eryl	605
	Mannaric acid (K salt)	T_6	25	SE-30 SE-52	170 190	6.5/eryl 6.2/eryl	605
$C_6H_{12}O_7$	Galactonic acid	T_6	25	SE-30 SE-52	170 190	8.2/eryl 6.8/eryl	605
	Gluconic acid	T_6	25	SE-30 SE-52	170 190	8.1/eryl 6.9/eryl	605
		T_6	25	SE-30 Mass Spec.	170	1.72/gun	580
	Gulonic acid	T_6	25	SE-30 SE-52	170 190	6.9/eryl 6.1/eryl	605
	Idonic acid	T_6	25	SE-30 SE-52	170 190	8.6/eryl 7.4/eryl	605
	Mannonic acid	T_6	25	SE-30 SE-52	170 190	7.2/eryl 6.1/eryl	605
		T_6	25	SE-30 Mass Spec.	170	1.53/gun	580
$C_7H_{10}O_6$	Methyl glucosidurono-1,4-lactone	T_2	17(76%)			b 114-115°/0.01	310
		T_2	25	SE-30 SE-52	170 190	fur α 2.1, β 2.4/eryl fur α 2.5, β 2.7/eryl	605
	Methyl glucosidurono-lactone		25	F-60	90→250	17.98 MU	371
	Methyl mannosidurono-1,4-lactone	T_2	25	SE-30 SE-52	170 190	fur α 2.1, β 3.0/eryl fur α 2.6, β 3.7/eryl	605
	Methyl mannosidurono-3,6-lactone		25	SE-52	190		685

Table 10-5. Sugar Acids and Acid Derivatives (cont'd.)

Formula	Compound	Silyl-ation	Method (Yield %)	Stat. Phase	Column Temp.	Retention Data, Physical Constants	Ref.
$C_7H_{12}O_6$	Methyl (methyl lyxo-furanosid)uronate	T_2	25	NGS	170	α 1.25/mmgu	355
$C_7H_{12}O_7$	D-glycero-D-galacto-Heptono-I,4-lactone	T_5	25	NGSb C-20M	170 155	2.81/rb 7.52/rb	534
	D-glycero-D-gulo-Heptono-I,4-lactone	T_5	25	NGSb C-20M	170 155	4.56/rb 10.52/rb	534
		T_5	25	SE-52	150	3.10/gun	580
		T_5	25	SE-52	210	α 2.00/gu	764
		T_5	25	SE-30 Mass Spec.	180		581
	D-glycero-L-manno-Heptono-I,4-lactone	T_5	25	NGSb C-20M	170 155	4.44/rb 8.46/rb	534
		T_5	25	SE-52	150	3.10/gun	580
		T_5	25	SE-30 Mass Spec.	180		581
	D-glycero-D,L-talo-Heptono-I,4-lactone	T_5	25	NGSb C-20M	170 155	2.92/rb 8.30/rb	534
	Methyl galacturonate	T_4	25	SE-30	170	fur α 4.3, β 3.2/eryl pyr α 4.8, β 5.0/eryl	605
				SE-52	190	fur α 4.2, β 3.1/eryl pyr α 4.7, β 5.0/eryl	
	Methyl galactosiduronic acid	T_4	25	SE-30	170	fur α 3.7, β 3.4/eryl pyr α 5.4, β 6.0/eryl	605
				SE-52	190	fur α 3.7, β 3.4/eryl pyr α 5.4, β 5.8/eryl	

Table 10-5. Sugar Acids and Acid Derivatives (con't'd.)

Formula	Compound	Silyl-ation	Method (Yield %)	Stat. Phase	Column Temp.	Retention Data, Physical Constants	Ref.
$C_7H_{12}O_7$	Methyl glucosiduronic acid	T_4	25	SE-30	170	fur α 4.0, β 4.0/eryl pyr α 6.1, β 6.1/eryl	605
				SE-52	190	fur α 4.1, β 4.0/eryl pyr α 5.9, β 5.9/eryl	
	Methyl mannosiduronic acid	T_4	25	SE-30	170	fur α 4.9/eryl pyr α 3.7, β 4.2/eryl	605
				SE-52	190	fur α 4.7/eryl pyr α 3.7, β 4.2/eryl	
$C_8H_{12}O_6$	Ethyl glucosidurono-lactone	T_2	25	F-60	90→250	18.18 MU	371
$C_8H_{14}O_7$	Methyl (methyl galacto-sid) uronate	T_3	25	SE-30	170	fur α 3.0, β 2.5/eryl pyr α 3.9, β 4.0/eryl	605
				SE-52	190	fur α 3.1, β 2.6/eryl pyr α 4.1, β 4.3/eryl	
	Methyl (methyl gluco-sid) uronate	T_3	25	F-60	90→250	α 19.40 MU, β 19.53 MU	371
		T_3	11f(81%)			b 114-116°/0.01 n_D^{20} 1.4484	310
	Methyl (methyl gluco-sid) uronate	T_3	25	SE-30	170	fur α 3.0, β 3.0/eryl pyr α 4.8, β 4.8/eryl	605
				SE-52	190	fur α 3.1, β 2.9/eryl pyr α 4.9, β 4.7/eryl	
	Methyl (methyl manno-sid) uronate	T_3	25	SE-30	170	fur α 3.0, β 3.5/eryl pyr α 2.6, β 3.0/eryl	605
				SE-52	190	fur α 2.9, β 3.5/eryl pyr α 2.7, β 3.2/eryl	
$C_9H_{16}O_7$	Methyl (ethyl gluco-sid) uronate	T_3	25	F-60	90→250	α 19.70, β 19.86 MU	371

Table 10-5. Sugar Acids and Acid Derivatives (cont'd.)

Formula	Compound	Silylation	Method (Yield %)	Stat. Phase	Column Temp.	Retention Data, Physical Constants	Ref.
$C_{10}H_{18}O_7$	Ethyl (ethyl glucosid) uronate		25	F-60	90→250	α 20.10, β 20.25 MU	371
$C_{11}H_{14}N_2O_8$	Methyl (uracil glucosid)uronate		25				362
$C_{12}H_{16}N_2O_8$	Methyl (thymine glucosid)uronate		25				362
$C_{12}H_{20}O_{11}$	Cellobionolactone		25	SE-52	210	14.86/gu	764
	Lactobiono-1,4-lactone		25	SE-52	210	14.92/gu	764
	Maltobiono-1,4-lactone		25	SE-52	210	14.38/gu	764
	Melibionolactone		25	SE-52	210	18.6/gu	764
$C_{13}H_{15}NO_8$	Methyl (p-nitrophenyl glucopyranosid)uronate	T_3	25	SE-30 SE-52 QF-1 CNSi NGS	220 220 220 220 220	10.00/mpg 10.64/mpg 12.36/mpg 12.87/mpg 6.59/mpg	362, 773
$C_{13}H_{16}O_7$	Methyl (phenyl-C^{14}-glucosid) uronate	T_3	25	2% SE-30 5% SE-30	250		423
	Methyl (phenyl glucosid)uronate	T_3	25	SE-30 SE-52 QF-1 CNSi NGS	220 220 220 220 220	2.64/mpg 2.36/mpg 1.91/mpg 2.49/mpg 0.84/mpg	362, 773
$C_{13}H_{22}O_7$	Methyl (cyclohexyl glucopyranosid)uronate	T_3	25	SE-30 SE-52 QF-1 CNSi NGS	220 220 220 220 220	2.32/mpg 2.11/mpg 1.25/mpg 2.13/mpg 0.51/mpg	362, 773

Table 10-5. Sugar Acids and Acid Derivatives (cont'd.)

Formula	Compound	Silyl- ation	Method (Yield %)	Stat. Phase	Column Temp.	Retention Data, Physical Constants	Ref.
$C_{14}H_{18}O_7$	Methyl (benzyl gluco- pyranosid)uronate	T_3	25	SE-30 SE-52 QF-1 CNSi NGS	220 220 220 220 220	3.34/mpmg 3.20/mpmg 1.93/mpmg 3.20/mpmg 1.03/mpmg	362, 773
$C_{15}H_{15}NO_7$	8-Hydroxyquinolinyl glucosiduronic acid		43	OV-1	241 pr		347
$C_{16}H_{16}O_7$	1-Naphthyl glucosid- uronic acid		43	OV-1	239 pr		347
	2-Naphthyl glucosid- uronic acid		43	OV-1	244 pr		347
$C_{17}H_{18}O_7$	Methyl (1-naphthyl-1- C^{14} glucosid)uronate	T_3	25	2% SE-30 5% SE-30	270 275		423
$C_{17}H_{20}O_9$	Methyl (hydroxycamphor glucopyranosid)uronate	T_3	25	SE-30 SE-52 QF-1 CNSi NGS	220 220 220 220 220	8.27/mpg 8.21/mpg 8.64/mpg 9.34/mpg 3.11/mpg	362, 773
$C_{17}H_{28}O_7$	Methyl (bornyl gluco- pyranosid)uronate	T_3	25	SE-30 SE-52 QF-1 CNSi NGS	220 220 220 220 220	4.08/mpg 3.71/mpg 2.18/mpg 3.71/mpg 0.78/mpg	362, 773
	Methyl (bornylglucosid) uronate-C^{14}	T_3	25	2% SE-30	245 pr		423

TABLE 10-6. SUGAR ALCOHOLS

Formula	Compound	Silylation	Method (Yield %)	Stat. Phase	Column Temp.	Retention Data, Physical Constants	Ref.
$C_3H_8O_3$	Glycerol	T_3	13 (90%)			b 96°/10; n_D^{20} 1.4149	754
		T_3	13b (77%)			b 78-81°/2; n_D^{20} 1.4148	104
		T_3		SKT-V, SKT		b 96-97°/10 n_D^{20} 1.4108	811
		T_3	13	ApM SE-30	205 184		739
		T_3	41,45	SE-30	175→300		69
		T_3	25	SE-52	100→300	0.257/gyp	759
		T_3	25	SE-52	125	0.04/gu	764
		T_3	25	10% F-60 1% F-60	100→250 100→250	13.16 MU 13.06 MU	182
			25	DEGS	70→220	0.66/gu	618
			25	JXR	120→325		662
			25	SE-30	130 pr		91
			25	SE-30	65→180	5.5'	734
$C_4H_{10}O_4$	Erythritol	T_4	25	SE-30	160 pr		91
		T_4	13 (90%)			b 99°/1.1	754
		T_4	13	ApM, SE-30	210		739
		T_4	41,45	SE-30	175→300		69
			25	SE-52 EGS	140 140	0.16/gu 0.49/gu	764
$C_5H_{10}O_4$	1,4-Anhydroribitol	T_3	25	Ucon	192	4.5'	366
	1,4-Anhydroxylitol	T_3	13 (63%)			b 96-97°/1; m -57° n_D^{20} 1.4300	545

Table 10-6. Sugar Alcohols (cont'd.)

Formula	Compound	Silyl-ation	Method (Yield %)	Stat. Phase	Column Temp.	Retention Data, Physical Constants	Ref.
$C_5H_{12}O_4$	Pentaerythritol	T_4	13 (90%)			b 128-129°/5 n_D^{20} 1.4179	754
		T_4	13,23	SE-30	125→275	b 150°/17	740
		T_4	25	SE-30	125→326		758
$C_5H_{12}O_5$	Apiitol	T_5	25	JXR	135→240		616
	Arabinitol	T_5	13	ApL	180	0.54/xy	220
			25	SE-52	140	0.46/gu	764
				EGS	140	2.14/marp	
				C-1540	140	0.36/gu	
				XE-60	205	0.46/gu	
			25	JXR	175	0.332/gu	761
		T_5	25	JXR	140→210	0.63/miss, 0.51/sin, 0.48/min	488
	Ribitol	T_5	13	ApL	180	1.06/arl. 0.57/xy	220
			13	SE-30	210		739
			25	SE-52	140	0.46/gu	764
				EGS	140	2.06/marp	
			25	JXR	175	0.338/gu	761
			25	Ucon	192	6.0'	366
	Xylitol	T_5	13 (83%)			b 112-113°/1; m -53° n_D^{20} 1.4250	545
		T_5	13	ApL	180	0.91/arl, 0.49/xy	220
			25	SE-30	145→257	9.0'	380
			25	SE-52	140	0.42/gu	764
				EGS	140	2.08/marp	
				C-1540	140	0.36/gu	
				XE-60	205	0.44/gu	

Table 10-6. Sugar Alcohols (cont'd.)

Formula	Compound	Silylation	Method (Yield %)	Stat. Phase	Column Temp.	Retention Data, Physical Constants	Ref.
$C_5H_{12}O_5$	Xylitol		25	JXR	175	0.327/gu	761
		T_5	25	JXR	140→210	0.60/miss, 0.48/sin, 0.46/min	488
			25c	Ucon			887
$C_6H_{10}O_4$	3,5-O-Methylene-1,4-anhydroxylitol	T_1	13 (79%)			b 80-81°/3; m 10-11° n_D^{20} 1.4515	545
$C_6H_{12}O_5$	2,4-O-Methylenexylitol	T_3	13 (88%)			b 111°/1; m 15-16° n_D^{20} 1.4412	545
$C_6H_{14}O_5$	1,4-Anhydro-D-sorbitol		25	SE-30	145→257		380
	Fucitol		25	BDS, SE-30, NGS	180→210	8.33'	352
			25c	Ucon			887
	Rhamnitol	T_5	25	JXR	140→210	0.73/miss, 0.58/sin, 0.55/min	488
$C_6H_{14}O_6$	Allitol		25	SE-52, EGS, XE-60	140, 150, 205	1.24/gu, 1.39/gu, 0.86/gu	764
	Altritol		25	SE-52, EGS, XE-60	140, 150, 205	1.30/gu, 1.59/gu, 0.93/gu	764
	Galactitol	T_6	13 (90%)			b 149°/1.6	754
		T_6	25	SE-30	175		208
			25	SE-30	160	1.01/srbl	761
		T_6	25	SE-30, QF-1	270		827
			25	SE-52, EGS	140, 150	1.28/gu, 1.38/gu	764
			25	SE-52, EGS	160, 155		849

Table 10-6. Sugar Alcohols (cont'd.)

Formula	Compound	Silyl- ation	Method (Yield %)	Stat. Phase	Column Temp.	Retention Data, Physical Constants	Ref.
$C_6H_{14}O_6$	Galactitol	T_6	25	10% F-60	100→250	20.00 MU	182
				1% F-60	100→250	20.18 MU	
		T_6	25	JXR	140→210	1.09/miss, 0.87/sin, 0.80/min	488
			25	BDS	180→210	12.47'	352
			25h	XF-1105		1.38/gu	62
				OS-138		0.62/gu	
				BDS		1.39/gu	
				XF-1112		1.27/gu	
	Mannitol	T_6	13(90%)			b 149°/1.7; n_D^{20} 1.4310	754
			25	SE-30	160	0.96/srbl	761
		T_6	25	SE-30			767
		T_6	13	SE-30	210		739
			25	SE-52	140	1.21/gu	764
				EGS	150	1.31/gu	
				XE-60	205	0.84/gu	
			25	EGS	158		846
		T_6	25	10% F-60	100→250	19.90 MU	182
				1% F-60	100→250	20.00 MU	
			25c	Ucon	70→220		887
			25	DEGS	70→220	1.04/gu	618
		T_6	25	JXR	140→210	1.07/miss, 0.85/sin, 0.79/min	488
	Sorbitol	T_6	13(90%)			b 145°/1.2; n_D^{20} 1.4310	754
			25	SE-30	160		761
			25	SE-30	145→257		380
			25	SE-52	170		717

Table 10-6. Sugar Alcohols (con't.)

Formula	Compound	Silylation	Method (Yield %)	Stat. Phase	Column Temp.	Retention Data, Physical Constants	Ref.
$C_6H_{14}O_6$	Sorbitol		25	SE-52	140	1.24/gu	764
				EGS	150	1.42/gu	91
				SE-30	195 pr		182
		T_6	25	10% F-60	100→250	20.00 MU	
				1% F-60		20.12 MU	
			25	DEGS	70→220	1.04/gu	618
		T_6	25	JXR	140→210	1.09/miss, 0.86/sin, 0.79/min	488
			25h	XF-1105	122	1.38/gu	62
				OS-138	160	0.62/gu	
				BDS	142	1.39/gu	
				XF-1112	150	1.24/gu	
$C_7H_{14}O_7$	3-O-Methylglucitol		25	C-20M	150	0.85/gu, 0.86/gl	191
					160	0.47/gu, 0.96/gl	
$C_8H_8O_5$	2,3,4-Tri-O-methyl-apiitol			NGSb	150	0.206/mmgu	354
$C_9H_{18}O_8$	1-O-D-Galactopyrano-sylglycerol	T_6	25	Vers	225	α, β peaks	203
	1-O-D-Glucopyranosyl-glycerol		25	GESF-96	165	α, β peaks	201
	1-O-L-Arabinofurano-syl-D-threitol	T_7	25	Vers	255		203
	2-O-D-Xylofuranosyl-D-erythritol		25	GESF-96	165		201
$C_{10}H_{20}O_7$	1-Deoxy-2-O-β-L-rhamno-pyranosyl-D-erythritol	T_5	25	GESF-96	180		202
	1-Deoxy-3-O-L-rhamno-pyranosyl-D-erythritol	T_5	25	GESF-96	180		202
$C_{10}H_{20}O_9$	1-O-D-Galactopyranosyl-D-threitol		25	Vers	255	α, β peaks	203

Table 10-6. Sugar Alcohols (cont'd.)

Formula	Compound	Silylation	Method (Yield %)	Stat. Phase	Column Temp.	Retention Data, Physical Constants	Ref.
$C_{10}H_{20}O_9$	2-O-D-Galactopyranosyl-D-threitol		25	Vers	255	α, β peaks	203
	1-O-α-D-Glucopyranosyl-erythritol		25	GESF-96	190		201
	2-O-α-D-Glucopyranosyl-D-erythritol		25	GESF-96	190	α, β peaks	201
	1-O-D-Mannopyranosyl-erythritol	T_7	23	GESF-96	235		204
	2-O-α-D-Mannopyranosyl-D-erythritol	T_7	23	GESF-96	235		204
	4-O-β-D-Xylopyranosyl-D-xylitol		25	ApK SE-30	210 210	β 0.58/suc β 0.46/suc	574
$C_{11}H_{24}O_6$	1,3,4,5,6-Penta-O-methylmannitol		25	NGS	137		458
$C_{12}H_{24}O_9$	3-O-α-L-Fucopyranosyl-L-fucitol		25	ApK SE-30	210 210	α 0.92/suc α 0.75/suc	574
	4-O-α-L-Fucopyranosyl-L-fucitol		25	ApK SE-30	210 210	0.83/suc 0.69/suc	574
$C_{12}H_{24}O_{11}$	Cellobiitol		25	ApK SE-30	210 210	1.50/suc 1.70/suc	574
	α-D-Glucopyranosyl-D-fructitol		25	ApK SE-30	210 210		574
	Laminaribiitol		25	ApK SE-30	210 210	2.0/suc 1.90/suc	574

Table 10-6. Sugar Alcohols (cont'd.)

Formula	Compound	Silyl-ation	Method (Yield %)	Stat. Phase	Column Temp.	Retention Data, Physical Constants	Ref.
$C_{12}H_{24}O_{11}$	Maltitol		25	ApK SE-30	210 210	1.86/suc 1.90/suc	574
	4-O-β-D-Mannopyranosyl-L-gulitol		25	SE-30	210	2.0/suc	574
	4-O-β-D-Mannopyranosyl-D-mannitol		25	ApK SE-30	210 210	1.90/suc 2.0/suc	574
	Melibiitol		25	SE-30	210	2.7/suc	574
$C_{16}H_{30}O_{11}$	L-Rhamnopyranosyl-(1→4)-L-rhamnopyranosyl-(1→3)-1-deoxy-D-erythritol	T_7	25	GESF-96	180		202

TABLE 10-7. AMINO SUGARS

Formula	Compound	Silyl-ation	Method (Yield %)	Stat. Phase	Column Temp.	Retention Data, Physical Constants	Ref.
$C_6H_{13}NO_4$	6-Deoxyallosamine		25	SE-30	60→200	0.79/mdgu	105
	6-Deoxygalactosamine		25	SE-30	60→200	0.79/mdgu	105
	6-Deoxyglucosamine		25	SE-30	60→200	0.82/mdgu	105
	6-Deoxygulosamine		25	SE-30	60→200	0.74/mdgu	105
	6-Deoxymannosamine		25	SE-30	60→200	0.84/mdgu	105
$C_6H_{13}NO_5$	Galactosamine		25	QF-1 SE-30	144 170 205	1.04, 1.20/gu 0.79/gu 0.81/gu	394
			25	SE-30	140	0.79/gu	466
			25	SE-52	140	0.79/gu	764
			25	SE-30 Mass Spec.	160	α 0.56, β 0.58, γ 0.63/mgup	767
			25	TLC; SE-30	150		393
	(HCl)		21d	ApM	170	0.63/βgu	599
	Glucosamine		25	QF-1 SE-30	144 170 205	1.18, 1.29/gu 0.90, 1.13/gu 0.93, 1.10/gu	394
			25	SE-30	140		466, 468
			25	SE-52	140 150	0.91/gu 1.15/gu	764
			25	TLC; SE-30	150		393
			25	SE-30	100→200	2.4/perl	470
	(HCl)		21d	ApM	170	0.73/βgu	599
	Mannosamine		25	SE-30	100→200	2.0/perl	470
$C_8H_{15}NO_6$	N-Acetylgalactosamine	T_4	25			m 144°	165
		T_4	25	SE-30	160	1.72, 2.12, 2.32/mgup	768

Table 10-7. Amino Sugars (cont'd.)

Formula	Compound	Silylation	Method (Yield %)	Stat. Phase	Column Temp.	Retention Data, Physical Constants	Ref.
C$_8$H$_{15}$NO$_6$	N-Acetylgalactosamine		25	SE-30; TLC	150		393
			25	SE-30	200	2.3/mgap	96
			25	BDS	180→200	21.0'	352
		T$_4$	25	NGSb	190	α 1.78/adgl	576
			25	SE-52	140	2.34/gu	764
					160	2.08/gu	
					170	8.45/gu	
		T$_4$	25	EGS	150	6.83, 8.70/mgap	610
			25	DEGS	70→220	1.61/gu	618
			25	NGA	193		430
	N-Acetylglucosamine		25	BDS	150	21.63'	352
		T$_4$	25	SE-52			591
		T$_4$	25	NGSb	190	α 2.17/adgl; m 162°	576
			25	NGSb	190		535
			25	TLC; SE-30	150		393
		T$_4$	25	SE-30	200	α 2.4, β 2.2/mgap	96
		T$_4$	25	EGS	150	8.5, 12.7/mgap	610
			25	DEGS	70→220	1.67/gu	618
			25	SE-30	70→350	13.6'	516
				DEGS	70→220	11.9'	
			25	SE-52	140	2.62/gu	764
					160	2.27/gu	
					170	8.39/gu	
			25	EGS			
			25	NGA	193		430
			25	DEGS	70→220		617
	N-Acetylmannosamine		25	SE-52	160	1.71/gu	764
				EGS	170	5.14/gu	

Table 10-7. Amino Sugars (cont'd.)

Formula	Compound	Silyl-ation	Method (Yield %)	Stat. Phase	Column Temp.	Retention Data, Physical Constants	Ref.
$C_8H_{15}NO_6$	N-Acetylmannosamine		25	SE-52			594
$C_8H_{17}NO_6$		T_4	25	SE-52			591
	2-Acetamido-2-deoxy-galactitol	T_5	25	NGSb	190	1.04/adg1	576
		T_5	25	BDS	180→210	21.0'	352
	2-Acetamido-2-deoxy-glucitol	T_5	25	NGA	193	8.0'	430
		T_5	25	NGSb	190		576
		T_5	25	BDS	180→210	17.5'	352
	2-Acetamido-2-deoxy-mannitol	T_5	25	BDS	180→210	17.8'	352
$C_9H_{17}NO_6$	Methyl-2-acetamido-2-deoxygalactopyranoside	T_3	25	SE-30	150	2.3/mgap	96
$C_9H_{17}NO_7$	N-Carboethoxy-galactosamine	T_4	25	ApL	130→210		561
	N-Carboethoxyglucosamine	T_4	25	ApL	130→210		561
$C_{11}H_{19}NO_9$	N-Acetylneuraminic acid		25	SE-30	160	125.0'	145
$C_{11}H_{21}NO_8$	Methyl neuraminate 2-O-methyl ketal	T_4	25	SE-30 Mass Spec.	160	4.1/mgup	767
$C_{12}H_{15}Cl_2NO_5$	N-(3,4-Dichlorophenyl)-glucosylamine	T_4	25	C-20M	195	20.4'	383, 755
$C_{12}H_{16}ClNO_5$	N-(4-Chlorophenyl)-glucosylamine	T_4	25	C-20M	190	11.5'	383
$C_{12}H_{21}NO_9$	Methyl N-acetyl-neuraminate	T_4	25	SE-30	160	10.3/gu	768

Table 10-7. Amino Sugars (cont'd.)

Formula	Compound	Silyl-ation	Method (Yield %)	Stat. Phase	Column Temp.	Retention Data, Physical Constants	Ref.
$C_{12}H_{21}NO_9$	Methyl N-acetyl-neuraminate		25	SE-52	160	7.25/gu	764
			25	SE-30	150→200	3.3/mgap	96
$C_{13}H_{23}NO_9$	Methyl N-acetylneuramin-ate 2-O-methyl ketal	T_4	25	SE-30	160	4.3/gu	768
			25	SE-30	160	41.0'	145
$C_{14}H_{17}Cl_2NO_7$	N-(3-Carbomethoxy-2,5-dichlorophenyl)-glucosylamine	T_4	25	C-20M	210	17.7'	383
$C_{14}H_{19}NO_7$	N-(3-Carbomethoxy-phenyl)glucosylamine	T_4	25	C-20M	205	13.2'	383
$C_{15}H_{21}NO_6$	Benzyl 2-acetamido-2-deoxy-α-D-mannofurano-side	T_3	25	SE-52			591, 594
	Benzyl 2-acetamido-2-deoxy-α-D-manno-pyranoside	T_3	25	SE-52			594

TABLE 10-8. NUCLEOSIDES AND RELATED COMPOUNDS

Formula	Compound	Silylation	Method (Yield %)	Stat. Phase	Column Temp.	Retention Data, Physical Constants	Ref.
$C_9H_{11}FN_2O_5$	5-Fluorodeoxyuridine		25	SE-30	214	8.7'	296
$C_9H_{11}FN_2O_6$	5-Fluorouridine		25	SE-30	214	12.0'	296
$C_9H_{12}N_2O_5$	Deoxyuridine		25	SE-30	214	8.7'	296
					254	2.1'	
		T_2 (3',5')	25	DC-430	230	0.46/adns	671
					250	0.50/adns	
$C_9H_{12}N_2O_6$	Uridine	T_3 (2',3',5')	25	DC-430	210	8.7'; m 39-44°	671
		T_4 (2',3',5',6')	25	DC-430	238 pr	18.9'	622
					230	0.65/adns	
					250	0.66/adns	
					210	8.7'	
			25	SE-30	209	12.9'	296
					214	12.0'	
			43n	SE-30	234 pr		268
			25	DC-430	140→255		300
$C_9H_{13}N_3O_5$	Cytidine	T_4 (2',3',5',6')	25	DC-430	230	1.91/adns	671
					250	1.69/adns	
			25	SE-30	209	3.9'	296
			25	DC-430	140→255		300
$C_{10}H_{12}N_4O_4$	7-Ribofuranosyl-7H-purine		25	SE-30	212		529
	9-Ribofuranosyl-9H-purine		25	SE-30	212		529
$C_{10}H_{12}N_4O_5$	Inosine	T_3 (2',3',5')	23 (98%)		220	m 265-266°.	671
		T_4 (2',3',5',6')	25	DC-430	230	8.45'	671
					230	0.95/adns	
					250	0.89/adns	

Table 10-8. Nucleosides and Related Compounds (cont'd.)

Formula	Compound	Silylation	Method (Yield %)	Stat. Phase	Column Temp.	Retention Data, Physical Constants	Ref.
$C_{10}H_{12}N_4O_5$	Inosine		25	SE-30	242	6.0'	296
$C_{10}H_{12}N_4O_6$	Xanthosine		25	SE-30	242	8.4'	296
		T_5 (2',3',5',2,6)	25	DC-430	230 250 220	1.33/adns 1.20/adns 12.2'	671
$C_{10}H_{13}N_5O_3$	Deoxyadenosine	T_3 (3',5',6)	25	SE-30	242 254	5.1' 3.6'	296
			25	DC-430	230 250	0.84/adns 0.87/adns	671
$C_{10}H_{13}N_5O_4$	Adenosine	T_3 (2',3',5')	25	SE-30	209 242 254	21.6' 6.0' 5.4'	296
		T_3 (2',3',5')	25(99%)	DC-430	238	7.5'; m 36-37°	622
		T_3	25	SE-30	228 249 225 240	12.9' 6.2' 10.2' 7.9'	295
				XE-60			
				TLC			
		T_4 (2',3',5',6)	25	SE-30	228 249 225 240	14.7' 6.7' 6.8' 4.5'	295
				XE-60			
				TLC			
		T_4 (2',3',5',6)	25	DC-430	246 pr 238 230 250	21.8' 8.9' 11.0' 5.2'	671
			43n	SE-30	260 pr		268
			25	DC-430	140→255		300

Table 10-8. Nucleosides and Related Compounds (cont'd.)

Formula	Compound	Silyl-ation	Method (Yield %)	Stat. Phase	Column Temp.	Retention Data, Physical Constants	Ref.
$C_{10}H_{13}N_5O_4$	Deoxyguanosine		25	SE-30	242 254	9.9' 6.6'	296
		T_4 (3',5',2,6)	25	DC-430	250	1.47/adns	671
$C_{10}H_{13}N_5O_5$	Guanosine	T_5 (2',3',5',2,6)	25	DC-430	254 pr 230 250 230	24.4' 1.80/adns 1.55/adns 9.7'	671
			25	SE-30	209 242	38.4' 10.5'	296
			43n	SE-30	265 pr		268
			25	DC-430	140→255		300
$C_{10}H_{13}N_5O_7S$	Adenosine-5'-sulfate		25	SE-30	249	6.2'	295
$C_{10}H_{14}N_2O_6$	Thymidine	T_2 (3',5')	25(99%)	DC-430	210	6.9'; m 108-109°	671
		T_3 (3',5',6)	25	DC-430	230 250	0.54/adns 0.55/adns	671
			25	SE-30	214 254	9.6' 2.6'	296
			43n	SE-30	230 pr		268
$C_{11}H_{12}BrN_3O_4$	6-Bromo-β-D-ribofurano-syl-1H-imidazo[4,5-b]-pyridine		25	SE-30	212		529
	6-Bromo-β-D-ribofurano-syl-3H-imidazo[4,5-b]-pyridines		25	SE-30	212		529

Table 10-8. Nucleosides and Related Compounds (cont'd.)

Formula	Compound	Silyl-ation	Method (Yield %)	Stat. Phase	Column Temp.	Retention Data, Physical Constants	Ref.
$C_{11}H_{12}ClN_3O_4$							
	1-β-D-Ribofuranosyl-1H-4-chloroimidazo[4,5-c] pyridine		25	SE-30	212		529
	3-β-D-Ribofuranosyl-3H-4-chloroimidazo[4,5-c] pyridine		25	SE-30	212		529
$C_{11}H_{13}N_3O_4$	1-β-D-Ribofuranosyl-1H-imidazo[4,5-b]pyridine		25	SE-30	212		529
	1-β-D-Ribofuranosyl-1H-imidazo[4,5-c] pyridine		25	SE-30	212		529
	3-β-D-Ribofuranosyl-3H-imidazo[4,5-b] pyridine		25	SE-30	212		529
	3-β-D-Ribofuranosyl-3H-imidazo[4,5-c] pyridine		25	SE-30	212		529
$C_{11}H_{13}N_3O_5$	1-β-D-Ribofuranosyl-1H-imidazo[4,5-b]pyridine-4-oxide		25	SE-30	212		529
	3-β-D-Ribofuranosyl-3H-imidazo[4,5-b]pyridine-4-oxide		25	SE-30	212		529
$C_{11}H_{14}N_2O_8$	Methyl (uracil glucopyrano-sid) uronate		25				362
$C_{11}H_{15}N_5O_3S$	5'-Thiomethyladenosine		25	SE-30	231 249	13.3' 8.0'	295
$C_{12}H_{13}N_3O_6$	1-β-D-Ribofuranosyl-1H-5-nitrobenzimidazole		25	SE-30			529

Table 10-8. Nucleosides and Related Compounds (cont'd.)

Formula	Compound	Silyl-ation	Method (Yield %)	Stat. Phase	Column Temp.	Retention Data, Physical Constants	Ref.
$C_{12}H_{13}N_3O_6$	3-β-D-Ribofuranosyl-3H-5-nitrobenzimidazole		25	SE-30			529
$C_{12}H_{16}N_2O_8$	Methyl (thymine gluco-pyranosid) uronate		25				362
$C_{12}H_{17}N_5O_3S$	5'-Thioethyladenosine		25	SE-30	231	15.1'	295
$C_{13}H_{16}N_2O_5$	1-β-D-Ribofuranosyl-1H-5-methoxybenzimidazole		25	SE-30			529
$C_{13}H_{16}N_2O_5$	3-β-D-Ribofuranosyl-3H-5-methoxybenzimidazole		25	SE-30			529
$C_{13}H_{17}N_5O_5$	Adenosine-5'-monopropionate		25	SE-30	249	9.0'	295
$C_{15}H_{23}N_6O_5S$	S-Adenosylmethionine		25	SE-30			295
$C_{17}H_{27}NO_8$	N-(3,4,6-Tri-O-acetyl-D-glucopyranosyl)-piperidine	T_1	25	XE-60 / SE-30	170 / 170		408

TABLE 10-9. PHOSPHATES AND NUCLEOTIDES

Formula	Compound	Silyl-ation	Method (Yield %)	Stat. Phase	Column Temp.	Retention Data, Physical Constants	Ref.
$C_3H_7O_7P$	2-Phosphoglyceric acid		23	DC-430	160 190 218		302
	3-Phosphoglyceric acid		23	DC-430	160 190 218		302
$C_3H_9O_6P$	Glycerophosphoric acid		43	OV-17	170→260		347
			23	DC-430	160 190 218		302
$C_4H_9O_7P$	Erythose-4-phosphate	T_4	23	DC-430	190 218	4.25', 6.05', 7.10', 1.4', 1.8', 2.1'	302
$C_5H_{11}O_8P$	Ribose-5-phosphate	T_5	23	DC-430	225	12.2'	302
$C_6H_{13}O_9P$	Fructose-6-phosphate	T_6	23	DC-430	190 218	21.0', 6.55'	302
	Glucose-1-phosphate	T_6	23	DC-430	160 190 218	0.82', 8.6', 18.9', 0.35', 2.75', 5.7', 0.2', 1.17', 2.3'	302
		T_6	43	OV-1 OV-17	271 pr 271 pr		347
	Glucose-6-phosphate	T_6	23	DC-430	218	10.3'	302
		T_6	43	OV-1 OV-17	257 pr 230 pr		347

Table 10-9. Phosphates and Nucleotides (cont'd.)

Formula	Compound	Silyl-ation	Method (Yield %)	Stat. Phase	Column Temp.	Retention Data, Physical Constants	Ref.
$C_8H_{15}O_9P$	Dimethyl 1,4-gluconolactone-6-phosphate	T_3	25	HiEff	172		847
$C_8H_{17}O_8P$	Dimethyl 2-deoxyglucose-6-phosphate	T_3	25	HiEff	172	1.00/pgun	847
$C_8H_{17}O_9P$	Dimethyl fructose-1-phosphate	T_4	25	HiEff	172	0.54, 0.72/pgun	847
	Dimethyl fructose-6-phosphate	T_4	25	HiEff	172	0.64/pgun	847
	Dimethyl galactose-6-phosphate	T_4	25	HiEff	172	0.98/pgun	847
	Dimethyl glucose-6-phosphate	T_4	25	HiEff, EGS	172	1.56, 1.93/pgun	847
	Dimethyl mannose-6-phosphate	T_4	25	HiEff, EGS	172	0.78/pgun	847
$C_9H_{13}N_2O_9P$	Uridine-3' (or 2')-phosphate		23	DC-430	250 / 265	5.5' / 3.5'	301
	Uridine-5'-phosphate		23	DC-430	250 / 265	7.3' / 4.4'	301
			43n	SE-30	270 pr		268
$C_9H_{14}N_3O_8P$	Cytidine-5'-phosphate		23	DC-430	250,265		301
$C_{10}H_{13}N_4O_8P$	Inosine-5'-phosphate		23	DC-430	250 / 265	10.0' / 6.0'	301
$C_{10}H_{14}N_5O_6P$	Deoxyadenosine-5'-phosphate		25	SE-30	249	6.2'	295
$C_{10}H_{14}N_5O_7P$	Adenosine-2'-phosphate		25	SE-30	231	6.6'	295
	Adenosine-3'-phosphate		25	SE-30	231	7.0'	295

Table 10-9. Phosphates and Nucleotides (cont'd.)

Formula	Compound	Silyl-ation Method (Yield %)	Stat. Phase	Column Temp.	Retention Data, Physical Constants	Ref.
$C_{10}H_{14}N_5O_7P$	Adenosine-3'(or 2')-phosphate	23	DC-430	250 / 265	9.05' / 5.6'	301
	Adenosine-5'-phosphate	25	SE-30	228 / 249	17.0' / 8.2'	295
		23	DC-430	250 / 265	11.8' / 7.1'	301
		43n	SE-30	276 pr		268
$C_{10}H_{14}N_5O_8P$	Guanosine-3'(or 2')-phosphate	23	DC-430	250 / 265	12.0' / 7.3'	301
	Guanosine-5'-phosphate	23	DC-430	250 / 265	14.3' / 8.65'	301
$C_{10}H_{15}N_2O_9P$	Thymidine-5-phosphate	23	DC-430	250 / 265	6.3' / 4.05'	301
$C_{10}H_{15}N_5O_{10}P_2$	Adenosine-5'-diphosphate	25	SE-30	249	8.1'	295
$C_{10}H_{16}N_5O_{13}P_3$	Adenosine-5'-triphosphate	25	SE-30	249		295
$C_{10}H_{22}O_{12}P_2$	Tetramethyl fructose-1,6-diphosphate	25 T_3	HiEff, EGS	188	6.96, 8.53/pgun	847
$C_{21}H_{27}N_7O_{14}P_2$	Nicotinamide adenine dinucleotide	25	SE-30	228 / 249	14.0' / 6.0'	295

11

Steroids

The separation of free steroids by gas chromatography became practical in 1960 when VandenHeuvel, Sweeley, and E. C. Horning (810), using a 1-3% coating of stationary phase instead of the usual 10-20%, found that most steroids and stationary phases were stable at the lower temperatures permitted. A number of reviews on the separation and determination of steroids by gas chromatography (E. C. Horning, VandenHeuvel and co-workers, 338, 341, 344, 345, 346, 807, 808; Kuksis, 448; Sjovall, 729) describe the use of steroid TMS ethers. The use of silyl derivatives frequently offers further improvements in volatility, resolution, peak shape and in reduction of column loss (324, 498, 796, 848). Introduction of the silyl group may accentuate minor differences between closely related substances, so that the derivatives may be satisfactorily separated by gas chromatography (GC).

11-1. SILYLATION

For analysis other than by GC small scale preparations of a dozen steroid TMS ethers have been made (131, 193, 474, 482, 623, 843). The products were crystalline solids with fairly sharp melting points; most melted in the 100-150° range. Some were purified by TLC or recrystallized. Carbon values tended to be low. The ethers hydrolysed only slowly with water (482). Infrared absorption spectra are given (193, 482) and show absence of free hydroxyl.

The most used procedure for the silylation of steroids for GC was that described by Luukkainen, VandenHeuvel, Haahti and Horning (498). The sample was treated in tetrahydrofuran (THF) with HMDS and TMCS (Method 26) and allowed to stand overnight. The solvents were removed and the residue extracted with hexane. The mixture was centrifuged and the hexane solution evaporated. The resulting product was dissolved in THF for analysis by GC.

Lau (456) found the reaction in THF to require 15 hr for completion at room temperature, 3 hr at 56°, a temperature often used (636). Small amounts of water adversely affected the yield *only* if the reaction mixture was heated.

Other solvents frequently used in place of THF were pyridine or chloro-form (Methods 25 and 23c). It was shown by Wells and Makita (848) that cholesterol in THF required 2-5 hr for complete reaction, whereas methyl cholanates in pyridine required only 10 min (504), in each case the 3α-hydroxyl being silylated. Often solvents were removed and the residue taken up in hexane or other solvent for injection. Ammonium chloride from the silylation remained on the wall of the vessel so that centrifuging was not necessary (807).

Other silylation reagents have been little used. However, BSA has recently found application as a selective reagent for polyhydroxy steroids such as cortisone derivatives (155, 339, 351, 809) and cardenolides (515). The relatively unhindered hydroxyl groups (3β, 12β, 16β, 20α, 21) are silylated with HMDS–TMCS or BSA alone (uncatalysed reaction). 11β-Hydroxyl groups and some tert-17α-hydroxyls are silylated when BSA–TMCS is used (catalysed reaction). All hydroxyl groups react when BSA–TMCS–TSIM is used. Further details are given in sections 11-9 and 11-10.

Double derivatives of ketonic hydroxysteroids have been made by ketoxime formation with O-methylhydroxylamine followed by silylation of the steroid hydroxyl groups, as described by Fales and Luukkainen (218). The O-methoxime (MO) results from reaction of the steroid in pyridine with excess methylhydroxylamine hydrochloride, held overnight at room temperature. Silylation is effected by the addition of HMDS to the mixture. (The HMDS is catalysed by the HCl present.) Keto groups at C-3 and C-17 react to form MO derivatives but 11-keto groups do not react. If a solution of free O-methylhydroxylamine in ether is used, only the C-3 keto group reacts. Retention time of an MO derivative was found higher than the parent on a nonpolar column, lower on a polar column. MO-TMS derivatives of 17-ketosteroids and 17-hydroxycorticosteroids show over-lapping peaks when analysed on 1% SE-30 (219). MO, TMS and MO-TMS derivatives were compared with the parent steroid on SE-30 and NGS columns (218). Whereas MO derivatives of cortisone and related compounds decompose during GC, the MO-TMS derivatives are stable (263, 264). This permits the determination of C_{19} and C_{21} human urinary steroids in a single run. 16-Keto and some 3-keto structures give MO isomers of the *syn/anti* type (351).

Chambaz *et al.* (155a) studied the formation of enol TMS ethers from keto steroids under different silylation conditions of reaction time and reagent composition. Yields of the silyl ethers varied from zero for andros-terone (HMDS–TMCS–DMF) to 59% for testosterone (TSIM–BSA–TMCS), both reactions at room temperature for 20 hr. With BSA–TMCS (1:1) at room temperature, the order of reaction rate was 4-ene-3-one > 20-one > 17-one. More severe reaction conditions (BSA–TMCS, 60°,

72 hr) for testosterone produced additional compounds shown to be androstenes containing two trimethylsiloxy groups and a ketone group. It was therefore suggested that for analytical work on ketosteroids methoxime-TMS derivatives should be used.

Halomethyldimethylsilyl and dimethylsilyl ethers have been prepared under reaction conditions of the corresponding TMS compounds. The halo compounds have been analysed by GC using electron capture detectors. The dimethylsilyl derivatives have slightly lower retention times than the corresponding TMS derivatives on non-polar columns. Further details are given in Chapter 13.

11-2. GAS CHROMATOGRAPHY

The liquid phases ordinarily used for steroids have the following relative polarities as summarized by Kuksis (448): CHDMS > NGS > EGSS-X, -Y,-Z > QF-1 > XE-60 > SE-52 > SE-30 in agreement with Hartman and Wotiz (299), who conclude: CHDMS $\cong$ NGSb > XE-60 > SE-60. The retention times of silyl ethers on SE-30 are generally greater than for free steroids; on CHDMS, NGS, XE-60 and EGSS-X,-Y,-Z retention times are usually less than for free steroids (807). However there are exceptions (299, 799). The newer phases, OV-1 (nonpolar) and OV-17 (polar), have high thermostability and are especially useful for programmed procedures (339).

Mixed phases were considered advantageous (381, 521, 522, 542). Nonpolar SE-30 was mixed with a polar phase, either XE-60 or NGS, before coating the support. The phase ratio can be changed to obtain the best separation (522). Nair *et al.* (542) found that the addition of NGS to SE-30 improved the selectivity of the column in distinguishing unsaturation. They observed that the combination separates steroids better than either phase separately.

The measurement of relative retention time by steroid number (SN) involves a most useful concept developed by VandenHeuvel and Horning (290, 806), and is dscribed in section 2-8. The analagous methylene unit (MU) designation originally applied to aliphatic amines and alcohols has also been used for steroids (345, 808). These measurement systems provide precise retention standards, reproducible and suitable for comparison between laboratories.

11-3. THIN-LAYER AND COLUMN CHROMATOGRAPHY

TLC of steroid TMS ethers has been extensively investigated by Brooks and co-workers (122, 123, 124, 126, 841). The low polarity of these derivatives enhances their mobility and facilitates elution. They are relatively stable to hydrolysis at neutral pH and can be recovered from silica gel plates in 85-95% yields, even in 1 ng-1 μg quantities (126, 841). Losses from hydrolysis or adsorption are slight and relatively constant.

Gottfried (279) separated various TMS ethers of aldosterone and cortisol on silica gel G. Lindgren and Svahn (474) separated triterpene and sterol TMS ethers more readily than the acetates by TLC on silica gel impregnated with silver nitrate. Column chromatography on silicic acid was also useful in separating hydroxysteroid TMS ethers from hydroxyketosteroid TMS ethers prior to GC (124).

11-4. STEROLS

Wells and Makita (848) developed the optimum conditions for the quantitative silylation of cholesterol with HMDS–TMCS–THF. For GC they used a nitrile-silicone column at 235° with an argon ionization detector. This procedure was applied to the fecal sterols: coprostanol, cholesterol, 7-cholestene-3β-ol, and methostenol, whose detector responses were found to be linear for 1-6 μg samples. Recoveries of added amounts of pure sterols were 94-98%.

Fumagalli and his associates found that desmosterol (24-dehydrocholesterol) can be satisfactorily separated from cholesterol on a phenylmethylsiloxane polymer column (253, 568). However, for the determination of submicrogram amounts of desmosterol in the presence of much larger quantities of cholesterol, it was advantageous to convert the sterols first to silyl derivatives (794), which for maximum precision were chromatographed in carbon disulfide solution (795).

Miettinen et al. (527) found that the results of GC of fecal sterols on a variety of stationary phases were 20-40% less than theoretical. With the silyl derivatives, however, results were quantitative and peak area responses over a 0.06-120 μg range were proportional to the original sterol weights. DC-560 and SE-30 columns were most effective for separation. Preliminary TLC separation preceded silylation for GC.

Food and fecal sterols of subjects on controlled diets were identified as silyl derivatives by Eneroth et al. (211). They silylated one mg of saponified extracts with HMDS in dimethylformamide (DMF). Reaction was complete at room temperature overnight for 3-hydroxysteroids. The ethers were injected directly from the reaction mixture or extracted first by heptane from the DMF solution. Analysis was made on a SE-30 column coupled with a mass spectrometer, which greatly assisted in identification of the sterol.

Nair et al. (537, 538, 539) studied the GC of vitamins D_2 and D_3 and their derivatives on a biphase column SE-52/SE-949 (the latter a polar

cyanoethyl-methyl polysiloxane) at 213°. Thermal cyclization of each vitamin and its silyl derivative to pyro and isopyro derivatives occurred during
GC, giving peaks quantitatively related to the parent compounds, thus
estimation could be achieved. Silyl derivatives were better resolved than
the parent compounds or trifluoroacetates. Biological samples were thus
assayed following saponification, extraction, precipitation and column chromatography. Related sterols did not interfere. Similar procedures for vitamin D_2 in the presence of vitamin A are described (815, 828).

Many plant sterols have been analysed as their silyl ethers (426, 428,
523, 526, 636, 664, 665). Knights (426) examined 15 plant sterols and
their silyl ethers by GC–MS and discussed their fragmentation. He
observed the characteristic cleavage of 5-en-3-ol steroid TMS ethers involving loss of 129 mass units, as discussed in section 3-5. Rozanski (636)
quantified the determination of the soybean sterols, campesterol, β-sitosterol,
and stigmasterol, as their silyl derivatives, measuring ratios of peak areas
before and after addition of a known amount of one of the sterols to the
sample, or by using cholesterol as an internal standard. The relative
responses of these sterols to the flame ionization detector differ significantly.
In comparison with the free sterols or their acetates, the silyl derivatives
on 2% SE-52 at 230° had somewhat longer retention times but produced
very symmetrical peaks and were more stable in stainless steel columns.

VandenHeuvel (798) prepared chloromethyldimethylsilyl (CMDMS)
and dimethylsilyl (DMS) as well as TMS derivatives of cholesterol epimers.
He observed retention times on GC to be CMDMS > TMS > DMS for
both polar and nonpolar phases. However, the difference between DMS
and TMS derivative retention times was not great (761, 798).

11-5. BILE ACIDS

The silylation of bile acids has been carried out on methyl esters only.
This has been the form in which the bile acids obtained from natural
sources has been purified before silylation. Methyl esters prepared from
bile (690) or fecal extracts (209, 210, 284) were purified by TLC; methyl
esters from bile acids obtained from serum (668), cellular material (564)
or gallstones (329) were purified by column chromatography.

Silylation of the various hydroxy groups of bile acid methyl esters does
not proceed uniformly. Equatorial hydroxyls at 3α, 6α, 7β, and 12β, as well
as 3β (axial) are silylated easily with HMDS in acetone (668), or in
dimethylformamide (209, 210, 690) or in dioxane with TMCS (107).
Axial hydroxyls at 7α and 12α do not react under these conditions. The
number of TMS groups introduced affects the retention time on GC step-
wise, so that the relative retention on QF-1 or XE-60 indicates the number

of groups silylated (107, 209). This partial silylation procedure was developed as an aid to identification.

The silylation of all hydroxy groups of bile acid methyl esters has been carried out using HMDS—TMCS—pyridine (Method 25) (284, 504) and the results have been quantified by GC. Makita and Wells (504) obtained 92-98% recoveries of added amounts of bile acids, using a 0.5% Hi-Eff-8B column. (A nitrile-silicone column was found inadequate.) Grundy et al. (284) obtained results with an accuracy of 3%. Their best separations were obtained on Hi-Eff-8B and QF-1 columns. 3-Keto bile acid esters yielded by-products presumed to be enol TMS ethers, which were satisfactorily estimated by GC.

The use of BSA in silylation of di- and trihydroxy methyl cholanates produced multiple peaks (564). When retention on SE-30 was compared, each chloromethyldimethylsilyl group substituted for TMS in a derivative molecule doubled the retention time (800).

When pyridine was used as a reaction solvent with HMDS—TMCS (504) a 10-minute reaction at room temperature effected complete silylation; with tetrahydrofuran as solvent, 2 hr was required. As pyridine was believed to promote the formation of secondary products from 3-ketosteroids, presumably by reaction with their enol forms, the use of dimethylformamide was suggested (527).

11-6. ESTROGENS

The application of silylation to the analysis of estrogens and their metabolites was pioneered by Luukkainen et al. (498, 499) and further developed in a series of papers by Adlercreutz and Luukkainen (12, 13, 15, 17). The advantages of silylation here, especially for the highly polar polyhydroxy steroids, were pronounced. The severe tailing of free estriol (E_3), for instance, was almost absent from the tris(TMS) derivative; retention times on selective phases were shorter and resolution was improved. (See Fig 2-1.)

The silylation reagent generally used was HMDS—TMCS in chloroform, tetrahydrofuran (Method 26), or pyridine (Method 25) and the mixture was warmed for several hours or allowed to stand overnight at room temperature. In tetrahydrofuran Lau (456) found the reaction complete for estrone (E_1), estradiol (E_2) and E_3. In the usual procedure the sample was then evaporated and the residue was dissolved in hexane for analysis.

A variety of column phases were used. On SE-30, nonselective, retention of the estrogen TMS ethers was longer than for the free compounds; the order of elution was E_1, E_2, E_3 (128, 522, 531). On selective phases such as QF-1, XE-60, or NGS, retention of the silyl derivatives was shorter than for the free steroids and the order of elution was E_2, E_3, E_1. This elution order was also observed with mixed selective and nonselective phases (381, 520, 521, 542). These biphases were used to vary the separation behavior of certain steroid mixtures.

Double derivatives obtained by methylation of the phenolic C-3 hydroxyl group and silylation of any other hydroxyls has been studied (13, 17, 176, 495). The 3-methoxy compounds are normally obtained in the Brown method of purification of estrogen extracts. They, as well as their silyl derivatives, may be analysed by GC, which double characterization is an important aid in identification. This method is especially helpful when applied to late pregnancy urine samples, where the background material may be troublesome (176). Another double derivative used is the methoxime–TMS ether for ketonic steroids, such as estrone (218).

Over thirty estrogens and metabolites are of interest in working with biological samples (17). Many of these occur in pregnancy urine or bile. The sharp increase in estriol in late pregnancy and its evaluation for diagnosis has caused much interest in its specific determination (487, 680, 681, 682, 683, 684). The silyl derivative was analysed on a 2% XE-60 column using tritiated estriol as an internal standard. Schindler *et al.* (683) studied the effects of urine specific gravity and the presence of sugar or other substances on estriol recovery.

Mass spectrometry of urinary estrogen TMS derivatives was briefly discussed and the identification of a previously unknown estrogen confirmed (497). The SN values for urinary estrogen TMS derivatives were determined (381) and the variation of these values with different stationary phases and functional groups studied (691).

11-7. ANDROSTANES

Silylation has simplified the gas chromatographic analysis of the three principal human urinary 17-ketosteroids: androsterone (A), etiocholanolone (E), and dehydroepiandrosterone (DHEA). Because of poor separation, GC of the free steroids requires the use of two columns, but their silyl ethers can be separated on one. For this, 2% XE-60, a nitrile-silicone polymer, is the phase commonly used. VandenHeuvel, *et al.* (801) applied this method to the analysis of urine samples. Urine hydrolysis extracts could be silylated directly, or after prepurification by column chromatography or TLC. Retention times were shorter than expected from molecular weights and response was linear with mass. The method was sensitive to 0.01 µg and the precision was 0.5%. Pregnanediol could be estimated at the same time. France *et al.* (235) concluded that estimation at the 0.05 µg level was possible.

Curtius and Müller (181) evaluated ten different procedures for urine hydrolysis for routine steroid determination. They found that hydrolysis with β-glucuronidase combined with ether extraction at pH 0.8 was the best method. VandenHeuvel (799) has studied the GC of 17-ketoglucuronoside TMS ethers. A routine procedure for estimation of urinary 11-deoxy-17-ketosteroids was developed by Solomon *et al.* (746). Hydrolysis extracts were purified by chromatography with silicic acid, silylated, then analysed on a biphase column, SE-30/NGS (2:1). The determination of 17-ketosteroids and related compounds in the blood is also described (567, 669, 730, 731, 732, 733, 818).

The relationship between structure and retention time for androstane steroids and their silyl derivatives as well as the influence of groups has been examined in detail (156, 299). 11β-Hydroxyl groups are silylated by HMDS–TMCS–pyridine (124) but not by HMDS–pyridine hydrochloride–pyridine (264). Mass spectrometry of the TMS ethers has been studied (121, 193, 732, 818).

The gas chromatographic analysis of urinary A, E, and DHEA as their silyl derivatives has been investigated by many workers (60, 236, 382, 411, 464, 629). These three 17-ketosteroids along with 11β-hydroxy-A, 11-keto-E and 2 progesterone metabolites were separated on XE-60, Hi-Eff-8B (298), or NGS (177, 637). Creech (177) recovered 95-100% of added steroids in quantitation studies. Barrett and McNeil (60) obtained the ethers in better than 95% yields. Preliminary TLC purification of the free steroids on silica gel separated them into groups of different polarity which were separately silylated for GC (60, 412, 614).

The determination of testosterone by silylation requires prepurification from the 17-ketosteroids. This has been accomplished by column chromatography (338, 667, 884) or by TLC (259). Vestergaard *et al.* (817) found that E-TMS has the same retention on XE-60 as the testosterone derivative, and separated these compounds by column chromatography prior to GC. These workers also prepared crystalline testosterone-TMS and observed that the isolated material was quite stable to hydrolysis. A sample in hexane in contact with water for one week lost only 10% by GC. No testosterone peak or other new peaks appeared.

The pronounced tendency of 4-ene-3-one ketosteroids, such as testosterone, to form enol TMS ethers, particularly under strong reaction conditions, was studied by Chambaz *et al.* (155a). Other ketosteroids (20-one or 17-one) can also enolize. Further details are given in section 11-1.

For electron capture detection Thomas and co-workers (778, 779, 780, 830) prepared chloromethyldimethylsilyl ethers of the 11-deoxy-17-ketosteroids. They were found more thermostable than the corresponding TMS derivatives on 0.6% XE-60 but not as effective as steroid chloroacetates for electron capture detection. The bromomethyldimethylsilyl steroids, however, were superior in this regard, although their retention times were five times greater than those of the corresponding TMS derivatives. Vanden-Heuvel (798) examined chloromethyldimethylsilyl (CMDMS) and di-methylsilyl (DMS) derivatives of epimers and observed on GC that retention was of the order CMDMS > TMS > DMS.

11-8. PREGNANES

The determination of the metabolites of progesterone as silyl derivatives is similar to the procedure for 17-ketosteroids, as described in section 11-8. Indeed, pregnanediol (Pd) and pregnanetriol (Pt) may be determined along with them (177, 181, 298, 614). Hydrolysis and extraction from urine, prepurification by column or thin layer chromatography, silylation and conditions for GC were much the same. Using pure compounds, Curtius (180) was able to separate silyl ethers of Pd, Pt, allopregnanediol, pregnanolone, pregnanetriolone, and the three major ketosteroids.

The relative retention times of the acetates, propionates and silyl ethers of all eight 17β-pregnane-3,20-diols were compared on QF-1 (157). Five of these were identified in the bile of pregnant women through GC of their acetates and silyl ethers on four different columns (11). In the gas chro-matographic analysis of silyl ethers of five triols on XE-60, 5α compounds separated well from 5β, but were not well resolved among themselves (292).

In the determination of Pd and Pt on DC-200 or SE-30, nonpolar columns, it is necessary to first separate them from the 17-ketosteroids by TLC (409, 603). If NGS or XE-30 columns are used it is not necessary to prepurify (180). Hammond and Leach devised a routine urinary Pd assay based on this procedure, which yielded recoveries in excess of 90% (293).

The mass spectrometry of the bis(TMS) ether of 5β-pregnane-3α,20α-diol and the TMS ether of 3α-hydroxy-5β-pregnane-20-one is discussed (16). 20-Trimethylsiloxypregnanes characteristically yield the fragment, m/e 117, $CH_3-CH\overset{+}{O}SiMe_3$ (123).

11-9. CORTICOSTEROIDS

The 11β-hydroxyl group, present in many corticosteroids, is sterically hindered and less easily silylated than a 3α-hydroxyl. Brooks et al. (124) silylated 5β-androstan-3α,11β-diol-17-one with HMDS-TMCS (5:1) in pyridine at room temperature overnight. Complete reaction of the 11β-hydroxyl required this length of time. Chambaz and Horning (155) treated the same steroid with various reagents for 20 hours at room temperature with formation of mono- or di-TMS ethers or both as shown:

Reagent	Position(s) silylated	
	3α	$3\alpha,11\beta$
HMDS	X	
HMDS–TMCS, 50:1	X	
25:1	X	X
10:1		X
BSA	X	
BSA–TMCS, 10:1		X
TSIM	X	X
TSIM–TMCS, 10:1		X

During gas chromatography cortisone and related 17α-hydroxy steroids suffer a nonquantitative loss of 17β-side chain to yield the corresponding 17-ketosteroid (805). The 20-MO derivative also decomposes (218) but Gardiner and Horning (264) found that the silylated MO derivatives are stable to GC on 1% SE-30. This allowed the separation of urinary keto-steroids and corticosteroids in a single determination. Following the reaction of the steroid fraction with methoxylamine hydrochloride in pyridine the addition of HMDS brought about silylation. Although, as was shown by mass spectrometry, 11β-hydroxy, 17α-hydroxy and 11-keto groups did not react (264), conversion of the 20-keto-21-hydroxy side chain to the 20-MO-21-TMS derivative was sufficient to stabilize the steroid for GC.

VandenHeuvel et al. (809) found that MO derivatives of 17α-hydroxy-20-keto-C_{21}-steroids were dehydrated on analysis by GC. This was prevented, and a more volatile derivative obtained, by silylating the 17α-hydroxy group with BSA catalysed by TMCS (339). Identity of the product was proved by mass spectrometry. The 17α-trimethylsiloxy-20-keto derivative was not stable in GC.

Silylation by HMDS-based reagents has given different results for 11β- and tert-17α-hydroxyl groups (264, 279, 297, 623). The addition of HMDS to a C-20 methoxime in pyridine–pyridine hydrochloride solution did not silylate the hindered 11β- or 17α-hydroxyls, as shown by GC–MS (264), yet HMDS–TMCS (5:1) reacted (124). Rosenfeld (623), using HMDS–TMCS in pyridine, reported the pentasilyl ether of cortol (5β-pregnane-$3\alpha,11\beta,17\alpha,20\alpha,21$-pentol), which was isolated by TLC and found by IR to be practically free of hydroxyl. Analysis of the product showed carbon 1.2% high and silicon 0.5% low for the pentasilyl derivative. Under even milder silylating conditions, HMDS–TMCS in THF, both positions in question were believed to be silylated (297). Testing for completion of reaction by TLC showed that the 17α-hydroxyl took longer than the 11β-hydroxyl to react. Gottfried (279) reported that bis and tris(TMS) derivatives were obtained from cortisol and HMDS—TMCS in pyridine but that only mono substitution occurred when chloroform was the solvent. The silylation results shown in the Table 11-6 indicate the views of the original authors.

When silylation is carried out with BSA-based reagents the hindered 11β- and 17α-hydroxyls can be selectively silylated. With BSA alone these groups are not silylated (155, 339); with BSA—TMCS (catalysed reaction), 11β-hydroxyl groups and tert-17α-hydroxyl groups of 17α-hydroxy-20-keto-C_{21}-steroids react (155, 809). All hydroxyl groups of the cortol series are silylated by TSIM—BSA—TMCS (3:3:2) at 60° (155). Pyridine was used as a solvent when the steroid was not readily soluble in the silylating reagent. Programmed separations were made with these derivatives on OV-1 and OV-17 columns. Upon quantification accuracy was found to be 1%; precision, 0.5%. On examination by mass spectrometry, cortol-$(TMS)_3$, -$(TMS)_4$ and -$(TMS)_5$ ethers showed the calculated molecular ion m/e values (155).

11-10. GLYCOSIDES AND AGLYCONES

Glucuronides of 17-ketosteroids and pregnanediol have been converted to methyl esters, silylated and analysed by GC (372, 799). Temperatures approaching 300° were used, with SE-30, OV-1 and OV-17 columns.

Ouabain and digoxigenin digitoxosides have been silylated and chromatographed on SE-30 at 285° and 300° (868). At 300° there is 2-10% decomposition of the glucoside TMS ethers. Quantification of the aglycone TMS ethers with 3-8% accuracy was achieved following hydrolysis of the glycosides. Column temperature was 285° on SE-30 (868); earlier results had been obtained at 228° with approximately 40' elution time (377).

Maume, Wilson and Horning (515) studied the selective silylation of cardenolides, dihydrodigoxigenin, digitoxigenin, digoxigenin and gitoxigenin. They found that HMDS—TMCS—pyridine silylated 3β-, 12β- and 16β-hydroxyls. BSA—pyridine or BSA—TMCS—pyridine (faster than BSA—pyridine alone) reacted with these groups and the C-23 enol of the lactone ring. TSIM—BSA—TMCS in pyidine at 60° silylated all hydroxyl groups, including 14β and the lactone enol. These various derivatives were chromatographed on 1% SE-30 programmed from 200°. The mass spectrometry of digitoxigenin TMS ethers was presented and discussed.

Five bufadienolides from Ch'an Su were purified by column chromatography, silylated and separated on 1.5% SE-30 at 235° (666).

11-11. TRITERPENES

Of the triterpenoid alcohols reported as silyl derivatives (58, 61, 360, 427, 718), a few (360) contained more than one hydroxyl group. These polyhydroxy terpenes as free steroids gave peaks with much tailing, which was eliminated by silylation. From the unsaponifiable fraction of wood, Lindgren and Svahn (474) separated a group of triterpene alcohols by GC and TLC of their silyl ethers. TLC on silver nitrate-treated silica gel yielded fractions with only a small amount of hydrolysed material.

For the greatest convenience, an attempt is made in the following tables to classify steroids both by structure and by biological activity, which is not possible. Triterpenes can be considered sterols, for instance, and some pregnanes will be found with the corticosteroids. The author apologizes for any confusion caused by this arrangement.

TABLE 11-1. STEROLS

Formula	Compound	Method	Stat. Phase	Temp.	Retention Data, Physical Constants	Ref.
$C_{27}H_{42}O$	5,7,24-Cholestatrien-3β-ol	26	SE-30	211		254
$C_{27}H_{44}O$	7-Dehydrocholesterol (5,7-Cholestadien-3β-ol)	26	SE-30	211		254
			CNSi	213		254
		22d	QF-1			227
		26	SE-30	230	2.17/chn	253
			F-60	210	2.30/chn	
			QF-1	230	3.66/chn	
			PhSi	215	4.26/chn	
			NGS	225	9.51/chn	
			CHDMS/PVP	230	8.18/chn	
		43	SE-52/XE-60	215	2.62/chn	537
		26	QF-1	225	1.96/chn	628
		26	XE-60	200	2.99/chn	664
		22c	SE-52	213	2.78/chn	538
			SE-52/949	225	2.62/chn	
		25	OV-17	254	1.17, 2.33/chn	761
		26	XE-60	235	2.56/chn	848
	Desmosterol	25	F-60	100→250	31.24 MU	182
	(5,24-Cholestadien-3β-ol)	26	SE-30	230	2.12/chn	253
			F-60	210	2.38/chn	
			QF-1	230	3.70/chn	
			PhSi	215	4.20/chn	
			NGS	225	8.90/chn	
			CHDMS/PVP	230	7.64/chn	
		26	NGS	225	2.65/chn	568
		26	SE-30	211		254
			CNSi	213		

Table 11-1. Sterols (cont'd.)

Formula	Compound	Method	Stat. Phase	Temp.	Retention Data, Physical Constants	Ref.
$C_{27}H_{44}O$	Desmosterol	26	F-60	225	2.83/chn	424
			FS-1265	225	2.0/chn	
			NGS	225	2.72/chn	
			HiEff	225	2.62/chn	
		26	QF-1	225	1.87/chn	628
		26	XE-60	200	2.82/chn	664
			EZSP	215	2.92/chn	
			XE-30			665
			SE-30			
			XE-60/NGS			
			SE-30	225		744
			QF-1, CNSi			
		25	OV-17	254	2.41, 1.03/chn	761
			PhSi	230		794
		26	XE-60	235	2.48/chn	848
		26	SE-30	211		254
			CNSi	213		
	7,24-Cholestadien-3β-ol					
	Isopyrovitamin D₃	43	SE-52/XE-60	215	2.25/chn	537, 539
	Previtamin D₃	43	SE-52/XE-60	215	1.53, 2.25/chn	537, 539
	Pyrovitamin D₃	43	SE-52/XE-60	215	1.53/chn	537, 539
	5,6-trans-Vitamin D₃	43	SE-52/XE-60	215	2.83/chn	537, 539
	Vitamin D₃ - Cholecalciferol (9,10-Seco-5,7,10(19)-cholestatrien-3β-ol)	43	OV-1-OV-17	230		347
		43	SE-52	225	1.52, 2.22/chn	537, 539
			SE-52/XE-60	215	1.53, 2.25/chn	
		22c	SE-52	225	1.52, 2.22/chn	538
			SE-52/XE-60	213	1.56, 2.37/chn	

Table 11-1. Sterols (cont'd.)

Formula	Compound	Method	Stat. Phase	Temp.	Retention Data, Physical Constants	Ref.
$C_{27}H_{44}O$	Zymosterol (5α-Cholest-8(9),24-dien-3β-ol)	26	SE-30	211		254
			CNSi	213		
$C_{27}H_{44}O_2$	7-Ketocholesterol (5-Cholesten-3β-ol-7-one)	22d	SE-30	235	4.74/chn	125
			QF-1	220	6.00/ch1	227
$C_{27}H_{46}O$	4-Cholesten-3β-ol		SE-30	205	2.40/chn	121
			Mass Spec.			120
	7-Cholesten-3β-ol	23c	SE-30	250		426
			Mass Spec.			
		26	SE-30	230	2.21/chn	253
			F-60	210	2.31/chn	
			QF-1	230	3.64/chn	
			PhSi	215	4.03/chn	
			NGS	225	8.26/chn	
			CHDMS/PVP	230	6.91/chn	
			HiEff	225		425
		23c	SE-30	225	3.06/chn	427
			DC-560	225	2.15/chn	
			FS-1265	225	2.48/chn	
			HiEff	225	3.06/chn	
			HiEff/PVP	225		
		23c	SE-30	230/250		428
			Mass Spec.			
		22	F-60	225	3.06/chn	424
			FS-1265	225	2.15/chn	
			NGS	225	2.69/chn	
			HiEff	225	2.48/chn	
		26	QF-1	225	1.98/chn	628
		26	XE-60	200	2.84/chn	664
			EZSP	215	2.52/chn	
		26	XE-60	235	2.52/chn	848

Table 11-1. Sterols (cont'd.)

Formula	Compound	Method	Stat. Phase	Temp.	Retention Data, Physical Constants	Ref.
$C_{27}H_{46}O$	8-Cholesten-3β-ol	26	EZSP	215	2.18/chn	664
	Cholesterol (5-Cholesten-3β-ol)	13j			m 129-130°	482
		25h (91%)	XE-60	205→245	11.0'	474
			TLC		m 128.5-129°	
		33	Mass Spec.		m 130°	843
		26	Mass Spec.		m 121-123°	193
		25	XE-60	205→245	15.0'	58
		26	QF-1	207	0.67/chl	212
			SE-30	214	1.27/chl	
		22d	QF-1	220	4.4'	227
		26	SE-30	230	1.95/chn	253
			F-60	210	2.10/chn	
			QF-1	230	3.39/chn	
			PhSi	215	3.32/chn	
			NGS	225	6.85/chn	
			CHDMS/PVP	230	6.18/chn	
		43	SE-52/949	225	2.38/chn	537
			SE-52/XE-60	215	2.37/chn	
		26	NGS	225	2.10/chn	568
		43	OV-1	180→	30.79 MU	339
			OV-17	180→	32.09 MU	
		26	SE-52	230	2.48/chn, 0.78/cmpl	636
		25	QF-1	212	2.05/chn	818
			SE-30	220	2.45/chn	
		25	F-60	100→250	30.80 MU	182
		21d	QF-1	200	0.71/chl	211
			SE-30	195	1.26/chl	
			Mass Spec.			

Table 11-1. Sterols (cont'd.)

Formula	Compound	Method	Stat. Phase	Temp.	Retention Data, Physical Constants	Ref.
$C_{27}H_{46}O$	Cholesterol (5-Cholesten-3β-ol)	23c	SE-30	225	2.45/chn	427
			DC-560	225	2.52/chn	
			FS-1265	225	1.87/chn	
			HiEff	225	2.07/chn	
			HiEff/PVP	225	2.60/chn	
		26	F-60	225	2.52/chn	424
			FS-1265	225	1.87/chn	
			NGS	225	2.29/chn	
			HiEff	225	2.07/chn	
		25	SE-30	200–280		126, 841
			TLC			
		26	SE-30	205	1.95/chn	498
			PhSi	207	3.32/chn	
			QF-1	195	3.39/chn	
			NGS	210	6.85/chn	
		25	XE-60	225	6.4'	522
			XE-30	225	37.4'	
			XE-60/SE-30	225	12.7'	
		22c	SE-52	213	2.46/chn	538
			SE-52/949	225	2.38/chn	
		26	QF-1	225	1.75/chn	628
		26	XE-60	220	2.43/chn	664
			EZSP	215	2.14/chn	
		25	OV-17	254	1.99/chn	761
		23	SE-30	235	2.36/chn	798
			EGSS-Z	205	2.31/chn	
			SE-30	205	2.52/chn	121
			Mass Spec.			
		23c	SE-30	230/250		428
			Mass Spec.			
		26	XE-60	235	2.12/chn	848

Table 11-1. Sterols (cont'd.)

Formula	Compound	Method	Stat. Phase	Temp.	Retention Data, Physical Constants	Ref.
$C_{27}H_{46}O$	Cholesterol (5-Cholesten-3β-ol)	23c	SE-30	250		426
			Mass Spec.			120
		26,42	Mass Spec.			193
	Epicholesterol (5-Cholesten-3α-ol)	23	SE-30	235	1.82/chn	798
			EGSS-Z	205	1.64/chn	
	Lathosterol (5α-Cholest-7-en-3β-ol)	26	SE-30	211		254
			CNSi	213		
			F-60	240	1.15*/chl	285
			QF-1		1.12*/chl	
	Zymostenol (8-Cholesten-3β-ol)	26	SE-30	211		254
			CNSi	213		
$C_{27}H_{46}O_2$	7β-Hydroxycholesterol (5-Cholesten-3β,7β-diol)	22d	QF-1	220	1.30/chl	227
	20α-Hydroxycholesterol (5-Cholesten-3β,20α-diol)	25	XE-60/SE-30	225	20.8'	522
			XE-60	225	7.2'	
	26-Hydroxycholesterol (5-Cholesten-3β,26-diol)		SE-30	235	6.30/chn	125
			Mass Spec.			
	20α,22β-Dihydroxycholesterol (5-Cholesten-3β,20α,22β-triol)	25	XE-60/SE-30	225	29.3'	522
			XE-60	225	14.2'	
$C_{27}H_{48}O$	5α-Cholestan-1-ol	43	HiEff	200	α 0.77, β 1.18/chn	318
	5α-Cholestan-2-ol	43	HiEff	200	α 1.81, β 1.50/chn	318
	Cholestanol (5α-Cholestan-3β-ol)	21d	QF-1	200	1.07*/chl	211
			SE-30	195	0.98*/chl	
			Mass Spec.			
		26	QF-1	207	1.07*/chl	212
			SE-30	214	1.01*/chl	

*Calculated from author's data.

Table 11-1. Sterols (cont'd.)

Formula	Compound	Method	Stat. Phase	Temp.	Retention Data, Physical Constants	Ref.
C$_{27}$H$_{48}$O	Cholestanol (5α-Cholestan-3β-ol)	26	SE-30	205	2.61/chn	498
			PhSi	207	2.38/chn	
			QF-1	195	2.40/chn	
			NGS	210	2.14/chn	
		26	QF-1	225	1.86/chn	628
		26	XE-60	235	2.17/chn	848
	5α-Cholestan-4α-ol	43	HiEff	200	2.24/chn	318
	5α-Cholestan-6α-ol	43	HiEff	200	1.96/chn	318
	5α-Cholestan-7-ol	43	HiEff	200	1.40/chn	318
		43	HiEff	200	α 1.41, β 0.698/chn	318
	5β-Cholestan-4β-ol	43	HiEff	200	1.41/chn	318
	5β-Cholestan-6β-ol	43	HiEff	200	1.03/chn	318
	Coprostanol (5β-Cholestan-3β-ol)	21d	QF-1	200	0.74*/chl	211
			SE-30	195	0.76*/chl	
			Mass Spec.			
		26	QF-1	207	0.77*/chl	212
			SE-30	214	0.77*/chl	
		25	HiEff	245		364
		22d	QF-1, XE-60	240		527
			SE-30, HiEff			
			DC-560			
		22c	SE-52	213	2.52/chn	538
			SE-52/949	225	2.42/chn	
		26	QF-1	225	1.47/chn	627
		26	XE-60	235	1.57/chn	848
	Dihydrocholesterol	25	XE-60	205-245		474
			TLC			

*Calculated from author's data.

Table 11-1. Sterols (cont'd.)

Formula	Compound	Method	Stat. Phase	Temp.	Retention Data, Physical Constants	Ref.
$C_{27}H_{48}O$	Dihydrocholesterol	22d	QF-1	220	1.97/chn	227
	Epicholestanol (5α-Cholestan-3α-ol)	26	SE-30	205	3.06/chn	498
			PhSi	207	3.18/chn	
			QF-1	195	5.79/chn	
			NGS	210		
		43	HiEff	200	1.38/chn	318
		43	SE-52/949	225	2.42/chn	537
		26	QF-1	225	1.89/chn	628
	Epicoprostanol (5β-Cholestan-3α-ol)	25	QF-1	207	0.80*/chl	212
			SE-30	214	0.81*/chl	
			QF-1	212	1.69/chn	818
			SE-30	220	2.05/chn	
		43	HiEff	200	1.83/chn	318
$C_{27}H_{48}O_3$	Cholestan-3β,5α,6β-triol	22d	QF-1	220	2.20/chl	227
		25	SE-30 TLC	200→280		126
$C_{28}H_{44}O$	Ergosterol (5,7,22-Ergostatrien-3β-ol)	13b				482
		22c	SE-30	225	2.96/chn	427
			DC-560	225	3.24/chn	
			FS-1265	225	2.28/chn	
			HiEff	225	3.05/chn	
		22c	SE-52	213	3.15/chn	538
			SE-52/949	225	2.85/chn	
		43	SE-52/949	225	2.85/chn	537
		26	QF-1	225	2.14/chn	628
	Isopyrovitamin D_2	43	SE-52/XE-60	215	2.52/chn	537, 539
		22py	BDS	160→200		828

*Calculated from author's data.

Table 11-1. Sterols (cont'd.)

Formula	Compound	Method	Stat. Phase	Temp.	Retention Data, Physical Constants	Ref.
$C_{28}H_{44}O$	5,6-trans-Vitamin D_2	43	SE-52/XE-60	215	3.10/chn	537, 539
	Vitamin D_2 (Calciferol)	43	OV-17	220→		347
			OV-1	230→		
		22c	SE-52	213	1.77, 2.75/chn	538
			SE-52/949	225	1.69, 2.51/chn	
		22py	BDS	160→200		828
		43	SE-52/949	225	1.69, 2.51/chn	537
			SE-52/XE-60	215	1.68, 2.52/chn	539
	Previtamin D_2	43	SE-52/XE-60	215	1.68, 2.52/chn	537, 539
	Pyrovitamin D_2	43	SE-52/XE-60	215	1.68/chn	537, 539
		22py	BDS	160→200		828
$C_{28}H_{46}O$	Dihydrotachysterol	43	SE-52/949	225	1.90/chn	537
		22c	SE-52	213	2.07/chn	538
			SE-52/949	225	1.90/chn	
	Brassicasterol (24β-Methyl-5,22-cholestadien-3β-ol)	23c	DC-560	225	2.94/chn	427
			FS-1265	225	2.05/chn	
			HiEff	225	2.12/chn	
			SE-30	234	1.12/chn	213
			Mass Spec.			
	7-Ergosten-3β-ol (24β-Methyl-5α-cholest-7-en-3β-ol)	26	EZSP	215	2.46/chn	664
		26	F-60	225	4.1/chn	424
			FS-1265	225	2.75/chn	
			NGS	225	3.47/chn	
			HiEff	225	3.38/chn	
	14-Ergosten-3β-ol (24β-Methyl-5α-cholest-14-en-3β-ol)	26	F-60	225	3.71/chn	424
			FS-1265	225	2.4/chn	
			NGS	225	3.03/chn	
			HiEff	225	2.78/chn	

Table 11-1. Sterols (cont'd.)

Formula	Compound	Method	Stat. Phase	Temp.	Retention Data, Physical Constants	Ref.
$C_{28}H_{46}O$	22-Ergosten-3β-ol (24β-Methyl-5α-cholest-22-en-3β-ol)	26	NGS	225	2.28*/chn	424
			HiEff	225	2.16*/chn	426
	24-Methylenecholesterol (5,24(28)-Ergostadien-3β-ol)	23c	SE-30	250		428
			Mass Spec.	230,250		
	24-Methylene-7-cholesten-3β-ol (7,24(28)-Ergostadien-3β-ol)	23c	SE-30	250		426
		23c	SE-30	230,250		428
			Mass Spec.			
$C_{28}H_{48}O$	Campesterol (24α-Methyl-5-cholesten-3β-ol)	21d	QF-1	200	1.31*/chl	211
			SE-30	195	1.32*/chl	
			Mass Spec.			
		26	SE-52	230	3.19/chn	636
		23c	SE-30	250		426
			Mass Spec.			
		23c	SE-30	230,250		428
			Mass Spec.			
		22d	DC-560	240		527
			QF-1, SE-30			
			XE-60, HiEff			
			F-60	240	1.34*/chl	285
			QF-1		1.29*/chl	
		26	SE-30	235	1.29/chl	666
	4α-Methostenol (4α-Methyl-5α-cholest-7-en-3β-ol)	26	SE-30	211		254
			CNSi	213		
		26	XE-60	235	3.04/chn	848
		26	F-60	240	1.47*/chl	285
			QF-1		1.29*/chl	

*Calculated from author's data.

Table 11-1. Sterols (cont'd.)

Formula	Compound	Method	Stat. Phase	Temp.	Retention Data, Physical Constants	Ref.
$C_{28}H_{48}O$	4β-Methostenol (4β-Methyl-5α-cholest-7-en-3β-ol)	42	Mass Spec.		m 103-105°	193
	24-Methostenol (24-Methyl-5α-cholest-7-en-3β-ol)	23c	SE-30 Mass Spec.	230,250		428
	4α-Methyl-8-cholesten-3β-ol	26	XE-60	235	2.71/chn	848
	24-Methyl-5α-cholestan-3β-ol	23c	SE-30 Mass Spec.	230,250		428
	24α-Methyl-5α-cholestan-3β-ol	21d	QF-1 SE-30	200 195	1.39*/chl 1.32*/chl	211
	24α-Methyl-5β-coprostan-3β-ol (24α-Methyl-5β-cholestan-3β-ol)	21d	QF-1 SE-30 Mass Spec.	200 195	1.00*/chl 1.03*/chl	211
		22d	DC-560 QF-1, SE-30 XE-60, HiEff	240		527
$C_{29}H_{48}O$	24-Ethylidene-7-cholesten-3β-ol	23c	SE-30 Mass Spec.	230,250		428
		23c	SE-30 Mass Spec.	250		426
	Fucosterol (24-Ethylidene-5-cholesten-3β-ol)	23c	SE-30 Mass Spec.	250		426
		23c	SE-30 DC-560 FS-1265 HiEff HiEff/PVP EGSP-Z	225 225 225 225 225 200	4.16/chn 4.42/chn 3.05/chn 3.80/chn 5.55/chn 4.88/chn	427
			SE-30 Mass Spec.	234	1.67/chn	213

*Calculated from author's data.

Table 11-1. Sterols (cont'd.)

Formula	Compound	Method	Stat. Phase	Temp.	Retention Data, Physical Constants	Ref.
C₂₉H₄₈O	Fucosterol (24-Ethylidene-5-cholesten-3β-ol)	23c	SE-30 Mass Spec.	250		426
	29-Isofucosterol	23c	SE-30 DC-560 FS-1265 HiEff	225 225 225 225	4.27/chn 4.44/chn 3.00/chn 3.93/chn	427
		23c	SE-30 Mass Spec.	230,250		428
	4α-Methyl-24-methylene-7-cholesten-3β-ol	25	XE-60 TLC	205→245		474
	Stigmasterol (24α-Ethyl-5,22-cholestadien-3β-ol)	13b			m 143-144°	482
		21d	QF-1 SE-30 Mass Spec.	200 195	1.36*/chl 1.49*/chl	211
		23c	SE-30 DC-560 FS-1265 HiEff HiEff/PVP	225 225 225 225 225	3.56/chn 3.71/chn 2.50/chn 2.70/chn 3.82/chn	427
		26	SE-52	230	3.51/chn, 1.1/cmpl	636
		26	QF-1 SE-30 Mass Spec.	207 214	1.35*/chl 1.45*/chl	212
		26	F-60 FS-1265 NGS HiEff	225 225 225 225	3.71/chn 2.50/chn 2.90/chn 2.72/chn	424
		26	QF-1	225	2.28/chn	628
		26	EZSP	215	2.98/chn	664

*Calculated from author's data.

Table 11-1. Sterols (cont'd.)

Formula	Compound	Method	Stat. Phase	Temp.	Retention Data, Physical Constants	Ref.
$C_{29}H_{48}O$	Stigmasterol (24α-Ethyl-5,22-cholestadien-3β-ol)		F-60	240	1.47*/chl	285
			QF-1		1.36*/chl	
$C_{29}H_{50}O$	24-Ethylcholest-7-en-3β-ol (24-Ethyl-7-cholesten-3β-ol)	23c	SE-30	230,250		428
			Mass Spec.			
	24β-Ethyl-5α-cholest-22-en-3β-ol		QF-1	207	0.97/chl	212
			SE-30	214	1.87/chl	
	24β-Ethyl-5β-cholest-22-en-3α-ol		QF-1	207	1.08*/chl	212
			SE-30	214	1.20*/chl	
	24β-Ethyl-5β-cholest-22-en-3β-ol		QF-1	207	0.91/chl	212
			SE-30	214	1.85/chl	
	β-Sitosterol (24α-Ethyl-5-cholesten-3β-ol)	21d	QF-1	200	1.69*/chl	211
			SE-30	195	1.70*/chl	
			Mass Spec.			
			SE-30	218		523
			QF-1	207	1.61*/chl	212
			SE-30	214	1.71*/chl	
			Mass Spec.			
		43	SE-52/949	225	3.82/chn	537
		26	SE-52	230	3.95/chn, 1.25/cmpl	636
		26	F-60	225	4.27/chn	424
			FS-1265	225	3.0/chn	
			NGS	225	3.5/chn	
			HiEff	225	3.4/chn	
		22c	SE-52	213	4.26/chn	538
			SE-52/949	225	3.82/chn	
		26	EZSP	215	3.47/chn	664
		26	SE-30	235	1.64/chl	666
		25	SE-52	242	3.71/pin	674
		26	XE-60	235	3.34/chn	848

*Calculated from author's data.

Table 11-1. Sterols (cont'd.)

Formula	Compound	Method	Stat. Phase	Temp.	Retention Data, Physical Constants	Ref.
$C_{29}H_{50}O$	β-Sitosterol (24α-Ethyl-5-cholesten-3β-ol)	23c	SE-30 Mass Spec.	250		426
	α-Sitosterol (24α-Ethyl-5-cholesten-3α-ol)		F-60 QF-1	240	1.75*/chl 1.56*/chl	285
			SE-30	218		523
	5β-Stigmastenol (24α-Ethyl-5β-cholest-22-en-3β-ol)	22d	DC-560, SE-30 QF-1, SE-30 XE-60, HiEff	240		527
$C_{29}H_{52}O$	24β-Ethyl-5α-cholestan-3β-ol	23c	SE-30 Mass Spec.	230,250		428
		21d	QF-1 SE-30 Mass Spec.	200 195	1.80*/chl 1.70*/chl	211
	24β-Ethyl-5β-cholestan-3β-ol	21d	QF-1 SE-30 Mass Spec.	200 195	1.25*/chl 1.30*/chl	211
	5β-Sitostanol (24α-Ethyl-5β-cholestan-3β-ol)	22d	DC-560, SE-30 QF-1, SE-30 XE-60, HiEff	240		527
$C_{30}H_{50}O$	Citrostadienol (4α-Methyl-5α-stigmasta-7,24(28)-dien-3β-ol)	25	XE-60	205→245		474
		23c	DC-560 FS-1265 HiEff HiEff/PVP EGSP-Z	225 225 225 225 200	7.72/chn 4.45/chn 6.59/chn 8.90/chn 7.70/chn	427

*Calculated from author's data.

Table 11-1. Sterols (cont'd.)

Formula	Compound	Method	Stat. Phase	Temp.	Retention Data, Physical Constants	Ref.
$C_{30}H_{50}O$	Dihydroagnosterol (4,4,14α-Trimethyl-5α-cholesta -7,9(11)-dien-3β-ol)		SE-30 Mass Spec.	225	3.70/chn	121
	Lanosterol (4,4,14α-Trimethyl-5α-cholesta -8,24-dien-3β-ol)		SE-30 Mass Spec.	225	4.30/chn	121
		26	QF-1	225	2.56, 2.72/chn	628
		26	XE-60	235	3.37/chn	848
		25	XE-60 TLC	205→245		474
$C_{30}H_{52}O$	8(9)-Lanosten-3β-ol (4,4,12α-Trimethyl-5α-cholest- 8(9)-en-3β-ol)	26	FS-1265 NGS HiEff	225 225 225	2.95/chn 2.90/chn 2.43/chn	424

*Calculated from author's data.

TABLE 11-2. BILE ACIDS

Formula	Compound	Method	Stat. Phase	Temp.	Retention Data, Physical Constants	Ref.
$C_{25}H_{38}O_4$	Methyl 3,12-diketocholanate	25	F-60, SE-30, QF-1, XE-60, HiEff	240		284
$C_{25}H_{38}O_5$	Methyl 3α-hydroxy-7,12-diketocholanate	25	HiEff	280	3.20/mkdc	504
$C_{25}H_{40}O_2$	Methyl 3β-hydroxy-5-cholenate	33			m 73°	843
$C_{25}H_{40}O_3$	Methyl 3-ketocholanate	25	F-60, SE-30, QF-1, XE-60, HiEff	240		284
$C_{25}H_{40}O_4$	Methyl 3α-hydroxy-12-ketocholanate	25	HiEff	245	5.16/mcho	504
	Methyl 3α-hydroxy-12-ketocholanate	25	F-60, SE-30, QF-1, XE-60, HiEff	240		284
	Methyl 7-ketolithocholate	21d	QF-1	230	1.08/mdch	690
	(Methyl 3α-hydroxy-5β-cholanate)	25	HiEff	245	5.45/mcho	504
		25	SE-30	238	3.28/chn	800
$C_{25}H_{40}O_5$	Methyl 3,7-dihydroxy-12-ketocholanate	25	F-60, SE-30, QF-1, XE-60, HiEff	240		284
	Methyl 3α,7α-dihydroxy-12-ketocholanate	25	HiEff	245	4.01/mcho	504
	Methyl 3α,12α-dihydroxy-7-ketocholanate	25	HiEff	245	4.10/mcho	504
	Methyl 3α,12α-dihydroxy-7-keto-5β-cholanate	23g	QF-1; TLC; Mass Spec.	253		716
	Methyl 7-ketodeoxycholate (Methyl 3α,12α-dihydroxycholate)	25	SE-30 HiEff	245		364

Table 11-2. Bile Acids (cont'd.)

Formula	Compound	Method	Stat. Phase	Temp.	Retention Data, Physical Constants	Ref.
$C_{25}H_{40}O_5$	Methyl 7-ketodeoxycholate (Methyl 3α,12α-dihydroxycholate)	25	F-60, QF-1, XE-60, HiEff	240		284
$C_{25}H_{42}O_3$	Methyl 3-hydroxycholanate	25	HiEff	245	α 1.77, β 1.42/mcho	504
	Methyl 3α-hydroxy-5α-cholanate		HiEff QF-1	215 190		329
	Methyl 7α-hydroxycholanate	23g	XE-60	240	1.15/mcho	107
		25	SE-30	238	1.49/chn	800
	Methyl 7β-hydroxycholanate	25	SE-30	238	1.71/chn	800
	Methyl 12α-hydroxycholanate	23g	XE-60	240	1.10/mcho	107
		25	SE-30	238	1.42/chn	800
	Methyl lithocholate (Methyl 3α-hydroxy-5β-cholanate)	23g	XE-60	240	1.75/mcho	107
		25	SE-30	238	2.14/chn	800
		25	F-60, SE-30, QF-1, XE-60, HiEff	240		284
		25	SE-30, HiEff	245		364
		26	XF-1150	225		471
		25	CHDMS	230		544
		43	FS-1265 FS-1265/ SE-30/NGS	210 210	0.30/mdch 0.20/mdch	564
		21d	QF-1	230	0.30/mdch	690
		23g	QF-1; TLC; Mass Spec.	253		716
$C_{25}H_{42}O_4$	Methyl chenodeoxycholate (Methyl 3α,7α-dihydroxy-5β -cholanate)	23g	XE-60	240	T_1 (3) 5.37, T_2 1.87/mcho	107

Table 11-2. Bile Acids (cont'd.)

Formula	Compound	Method	Stat. Phase	Temp.	Retention Data, Physical Constants	Ref.
$C_{25}H_{42}O_4$	Methyl chenodeoxycholate (Methyl 3α,7α-dihydroxy-5β-cholanate)	25	F-60, SE-30, QF-1, XE-60, HiEff	240		284
		25	CHDMS	230		544
		43	FS-1265 FS-1265/ SE-30/NGS	210 210	0.35, 0.80/mdch 0.22, 0.50/mdch	564
		21a	CNSi QF-1	225 221	0.48/mdch 0.65/mdch	668
		25	SE-30	238	2.64/chn	800
		21d	QF-1	230	0.64/mdch	690
		26	XF-1150	225		471
		23g	XE-60	240	T_1(3) 4.70, T_2 1.72/mcho	107
	Methyl deoxycholate (Methyl 3α,12α-dihydroxy-5β-cholanate)	26	XF-1150	225		471
		25	F-60, SE-30, QF-1, XE-60, HiEff	240		284
		21d	HiEff SE-30	245		364
		25	CHDMS	230		544
		43	FS-1265 FS-1265/ SE-30/NGS	210 210	0.32, 0.60/mdch 0.22, 0.45/mdch	564
		21a	QF-1 CNSi	221 225	0.57/mdch 0.42/mdch	668
		25	SE-30	238	2.25/chn	800
		25	HiEff	245	1.30/mcho	504
		23g	XE-60	240	T_1(3) 2.72, T_2 1.13/mcho	107

Table 11-2. Bile Acids (cont'd.)

Formula	Compound	Method	Stat. Phase	Temp.	Retention Data, Physical Constants	Ref.
$C_{25}H_{42}O_4$	Methyl deoxycholate (Methyl 3α,12α-dihydroxy-5β-cholanate)	23g	QF-1; TLC; Mass Spec.	253		716
	Methyl 3α,7α-dihydroxy-5β-cholanate	23g	QF-1; TLC; Mass Spec.	253		716
	Methyl 3α,7β-dihydroxy-5β-cholanate	23g	QF-1; TLC; Mass Spec.	253		716
	Methyl 3α,12α-hydroxy-5α-cholanate		HiEff QF-1	215 190		329
	Methyl 'α'-hydodeoxycholate (Methyl 3α,6α-dihydroxy-5β-cholanate)	23g	XE-60	240	T_1(3) 6.47, T_1(6) 5.40, T_2 2.00/mcho	107
		43	FS-1265	210	0.36/mdch	564
			FS-1265/SE-30/NGS	210	0.26/mdch	
		25	HiEff	245	1.64/mcho	504
		25	SE-30	238	2.81/chn	800
	Methyl 'β'-hydodeoxycholate (Methyl 3α,6β-dihydroxy-5β-cholanate)	43	FS-1265	210	0.35/mdch	564
			FS-1265/SE-30/NGS	210	0.24, 0.56/mdch	
	Methyl 12-ketolithocholate	25	HiEff SE-30	245		364
	Methyl ursodeoxycholate (Methyl 3α,7β-dihydroxy-5β-cholanate)	23g	XE-60	240	T_1(3) 5.30, T_2 2.17/mcho	107
		43	FS-1265	210	0.34, 0.62/mdch	564
			FS-1265/SE-30/NGS	210	0.28, 0.54/mdch	
		21d	QF-1	230	0.37/mdch	690

Table 11-2. Bile Acids (cont'd.)

Formula	Compound	Method	Stat. Phase	Temp.	Retention Data, Physical Constants	Ref.
$C_{25}H_{42}O_4$	Methyl ursodeoxycholate (Methyl 3α,7β-dihydroxy-5β-cholanate)	25	HiEff	245	7α 1.40, 7β 2.04/mcho	504
		25	SE-30	238	3.04/chn	800
$C_{25}H_{42}O_5$	Methyl cholate (Methyl 3α,7α,12α-trihydroxy-5β-cholanate)	23g	XE-60	240	$T_1(3)$ 14.1, $T_2(3,7)$ 4.30, $T_2(3,12)$ 4.30, T_3 1.57/mcho	107
		26	XE-1150	225		471
		25	F-60, SE-30, QF-1, XE-60, HiEff	240		284
		25	CHDMS	230	0.36, 0.60, 1.25/mdch	544
		43	FS-1265	210		564
			FS-1265/ SE-30/NGS	210	0.23, 0.47, 1.34/mdch	
		21a	QF-1 CNSi	221 225	1.24/mdch 1.27/mdch	668
		21d	QF-1	230	1.26/mdch	690
		25	HiEff	245	0.97/mcho	504
		25	SE-30	238	2.70/chn	800
	Methyl 3α,6α,7-trihydroxycholanate	25	HiEff	245	7α 1.31, 7β 2.61/mcho	504
	Methyl 3α,6β,7-trihydroxycholanate	25	HiEff	245	7α 0.93, 7β 1.58/mcho	504

Table 11-2. Bile Acids (cont'd.)

Formula	Compound	Method	Stat. Phase	Temp.	Retention Data, Physical Constants	Ref.
$C_{25}H_{42}O_5$	Methyl 3α,6α,7α-trihydroxy-cholanate	43	FS-1265 FS-1265/ SE-30/NGS	210 210	0.45, 0.61/mdch 0.31, 0.47/mdch	564
	Methyl 3α,6α,7β-trihydroxy-cholanate	43	FS-1265 FS-1265/ SE-30/NGS	210 210	0.67/mdch 0.51/mdch	564
	Methyl 3α,7α,12α-trihydroxy-5β-cholanate	23g	QF-1 TLC Mass Spec.	253		716
$C_{27}H_{45}NO_4$	Methyl glycolithocholate (5β-Cholan-3α-ol-24-oyl-glycine methyl ester)	25	SE-30, QF-1	245		294
$C_{27}H_{45}NO_5$	Methyl glycodeoxycholate (5β-Cholan-3α,12α-diol-24-oyl-glycine methyl ester)	25	SE-30, QF-1	245		294
$C_{27}H_{46}O_6$	Methyl glycocholate (5β-Cholan-3α,7α,12α-triol-24-oyl-glycine methyl ester)	25	SE-30, QF-1	245		294

TABLE 11-3. ESTROGENS

Formula	Compound	Method	Stat. Phase	Temp.	Retention Data, Physical Constants	Ref.
$C_{18}H_{18}O_2$	Equilenin (1,3,5(10),6,8-Estrapentaen-3-ol-17-one)	26	SE-30	250	0.69/chn, 25.6 SN	381
			SE-30/XE-60	250	1.02/chn	
			SE-30	205	0.67/chn	499
			PhSi	207	1.84/chn	
			QF-1	195	2.55/chn	
			NGS	210	4.80/chn	
$C_{18}H_{20}O_2$	Estra-1,3,5(10),6-tetraen-3-ol-17-one	26	SE-30	250	0.56/chn	381
			SE-30/XE-60	250	0.79/chn, 24.6 SN	
	Equilin (1,3,5(10),7-Estratetraen-3-ol-17-one)	26	SE-30	205	0.54/chn	499
			PhSi	207	1.27/chn	
			QF-1	195	1.80/chn	
			NGS	210	2.81/chn	
$C_{18}H_{20}O_3$	6-Ketoestrone (Estratrien-3-ol-6,17-dione)	22py, 26	QF-1	203	5.30/chn	12
			XE-60	205	3.64/chn	
			Z	195	11.80/chn	
			F-60	230	1.14/chn	
		26	SE-30	220	29.1 SN	691
			XE-60	215	36.5 SN	
			NGSb, HiEff	198	37.0 SN	
	16-Ketoestrone (Estratrien-3-ol-16,17-dione)	22py, 26	QF-1	203	2.32/chn	12
			XE-60	205	2.32/chn	
			Z	195	5.02/chn	
			F-60	230	1.18/chn	
$C_{18}H_{22}O$	1,3,5(10),16-Estratetraen-3-ol	22py	SE-30 Mass Spec.	190		782
		23z	MS-2211	185	4.18/mpam	129
			FS-1265	205	3.11/mpam	
			NGSb	230	4.94/mpam	
	Estratrien-16-one (oxime)	25	SE-30	220	0.33/chn, 23.2 SN	546
			OV-17	220	0.59/chn	

Table 11-3. Estrogens (cont'd.)

Formula	Compound	Method	Stat. Phase	Temp.	Retention Data, Physical Constants	Ref.
$C_{18}H_{22}O$	Estratrien-17-one (oxime)	25	SE-30	220	0.34/chn, 23.0 SN	546
			OV-17	220	0.49/chn	15
$C_{18}H_{22}O_2$	11-Dehydro-17α-estradiol (1,3,5(10),11-Estratetraen-3,17α-diol)	26	F-60, Z, QF-1, XE-60			
			Z	195	0.85/chn	496
			F-60	223	0.53/chn	
			SE-30	226	0.54/chn	
			Mass Spec.			497
	Estratrien-2-ol-17-one	26	SE-30	250	0.80/chn	381
			SE-30/XE-60	250	1.05/chn	
	Estratrien-3-ol-16-one	26	QF-1	205	2.40/estl	128
			SE-30	210	0.80/estl	
	Estrone (Estratrien-3-ol-17-one)	22py, 26	QF-1	203	1.58/chn	12
			XE-60	205	1.37/chn	
			Z	195	3.44/chn	
			F-60	230	0.60/chn	
		22c	JXR	185	3.14/pga	795
			SE-52	200	3.87/pga	
		23h	XE-60	225	2.10/chn	291
		22py	SE-30	225	0.241/chl	521
			SE-30/XE-60	235	0.363/chl	
		25	XE-60	220	2.09/andn, 2.00/chn	681
		26	QF-1	205	2.10/estl	128
			SE-30	210	0.75/estl	
		22	Emb.	240	0.52/chn	176
		26	SE-30	223	0.54/chn	218
			NGS	223	2.67/chn	
			Mass Spec.			
		26	SE-30	250	0.54/chn	381
			SE-30/XE-60	250	0.78/chn, 24.4 SN	

Table 11-3. Estrogens (cont'd.)

Formula	Compound	Method	Stat. Phase	Temp.	Retention Data, Physical Constants	Ref.
$C_{18}H_{22}O_2$	Estrone (Estratrien-3-ol-17-one)	26	XE-60	212	0.80/andn	495
			QF-1	180		
			SE-30	190	1.33/andn	
			NGS	203-216		
		26	SE-30	205	0.52/chn	498,
			PhSi	207	1.21/chn	499
			QF-1	195	1.83/chn	
			NGS	210	2.67/chn	
		26	QF-1	258	1.60/chn	531
			SE-30	258	0.51/chn	
		26	SE-30/NGS	197	2.00/andn	542
		26	SE-30	220	26.1 SN	691
			XE-60	215	31.7 SN	
			NGSb	205	30.3 SN	
			QF-1	198	30.5 SN	
			HiEff	220	30.5 SN	
	(MO)	26	SE-30	223	0.64/chn	218
			NGS	223	1.75/chn	
			Mass Spec.			
$C_{18}H_{22}O_3$	2-Hydroxyestrone (Estratrien-2,3-diol-17-one)	26	QF-1	205	2.8/estl	128
			SE-30	210	1.3/estl	
		26	SE-30	250	1.04/chn	381
			SE-30/XE-60	250	1.04/chn, 24.9 SN	
	16α-Hydroxyestrone (Estratrien-3,16α-diol-17-one)	22py, 26	QF-1	203	1.76/chn	12
			XE-60	205	1.74/chn	
			Z	195	3.53/chn	
			F-60	230	0.98/chn	
		26	SE-30	250	0.88/chn	381
			SE-30/XE-60	250	1.11/chn, 25.9 SN	

Table 11-3. Estrogens (cont'd.)

Formula	Compound	Method	Stat. Phase	Temp.	Retention Data, Physical Constants	Ref.
C$_{18}$H$_{22}$O$_3$	16α-Hydroxyestrone (Estratrien-3,16α-diol-17-one)	26	SE-30	205	0.98/chn	499
			PhSi	207	1.76/chn	
			QF-1	198	2.02/chn	
			NGS	210	2.71/chn	
		26	0.75% SE-30	205	10.4'	883
			3% SE-30	239	10.5'	
			QF-1	195	8.5'	
		26	SE-30	220	27.7 SN	691
			XE-60	215	31.8 SN	
			NGSb	205	30.7 SN	
			QF-1	198	30.5 SN	
			HiEff	220	27.7 SN	
	16β-Hydroxyestrone (Estratrien-3,16β-diol-17-one)	26	SE-30	220	28.1 SN	691
			XE-60	215	31.6 SN	
			NGSb	205	32.4 SN	
			QF-1	198	31.4 SN	
			HiEff	220	31.1 SN	
	6-Ketoestradiol (Estratrien-3,17β-diol-6-one)	26	QF-1	205	4.1/estl	128
			SE-30	210	1.9/estl	
		22py, 26	QF-1	203	3.02/chn	12
			XE-60	205	2.43/chn	
			Z	195	3.80/chn	
			F-60	230	1.38/chn	
		26	SE-30	220	28.8 SN	691
			XE-60	215	32.5 SN	
			NGSb	205	32.2 SN	
			QF-1	198	33.0 SN	
			HiEff	220	31.5 SN	
		26	SE-30	223	1.00/chn	218
			NGS	223	3.11/chn	
	(MO)	26	SE-30	223	1.18/chn	218
			NGS	223	2.20/chn	
			Mass Spec.			

Table 11-3. Estrogens (cont'd.)

Formula	Compound	Method	Stat. Phase	Temp.	Retention Data, Physical Constants	Ref.
$C_{18}H_{22}O_3$	16-Ketoestradiol (Estratrien-3,17β-diol-16-one)	26	QF-1	205	3.1/estl	128
			SE-30	210	1.6/estl	
		26	SE-30	250	0.97/chn	381
			SE-30/XE-60	250	1.25/chn, 26.0 SN	
		26	SE-30	205	1.00/chn	499
			PhSi	207	1.94/chn	
			QF-1	198	2.94/chn	
			NGS	210	3.93/chn	
		26	SE-30	220	28.2 SN	691
			XE-60	215	32.1 SN	
			NGSb	205	33.0 SN	
			QF-1	198	31.9 SN	
			HiEff	220	31.3 SN	
		22py, 26	QF-1	203	2.26/chn	12
			XE-60	205	2.12/chn	
			Z	195	4.02/chn	
			F-60	230	1.08/chn	
		26	SE-30	223	0.99/chn	218
			NGS	223	3.10/chn	
		26	SE-30	223	1.17/chn	218
	(MO)		NGS	223	2.15/chn	
			Mass Spec.			
$C_{18}H_{24}O$	Estratrien-17β-ol	26	QF-1	205	0.38/estl	128
			SE-30	210	0.34/estl	
	17-Deoxoestrone (Estratrien-3-ol)	26	QF-1	205	0.43/estl	128
			SE-30	210	0.37/estl	
		26	SE-30	220	22.7 SN	691
			XE-60	215	23.1 SN	
			NGSb	205	23.8 SN	
			QF-1	198	23.7 SN	
			HiEff	220	24.2 SN	
		26	QF-1	258	0.61/chn	531
			SE-30	258	0.46/chn	

Table 11-3. Estrogens (cont'd.)

Formula	Compound	Method	Stat. Phase	Temp.	Retention Data, Physical Constants	Ref.
$C_{18}H_{24}O_2$	16α-Estradiol (Estratrien-3,16α-diol)	26	QF-1	205	0.92/estl	128
			SE-30	210	0.94/estl	
		26	SE-30	250	0.62/chn	381
			SE-30/XE-60	250	0.66/chn, 24.5 SN	
		23h	XE-60	225	0.885/chn	291
	Estradiol (Estratrien-3,17β-ol)	22c	JXR	185	4.16/pga	795
			SE-52	200	4.61/pga	
		26	QF-1	205	6.1'	128
			SE-30	210	10.0'	
		22py, 26	QF-1	203	0.85/chn	12
			XE-60	205	0.79/chn	
			Z	195	1.07/chn	
			F-60	230	0.70/chn	
		26	SE-30	220	25.8 SN	691
			XE-60	215	26.2 SN	
			NGSb	205	26.6 SN	
			QF-1	198	26.5 SN	
			HiEff	220	26.2 SN	
		22	Emb.	240	0.66/chn	176
		26	SE-30	250	0.67/chn, 24.5 SN	381
			SE-30/XE-60	250	0.70/chn, 24.5 SN	
		26	Z	195	1.04/chn	496
			F-60	223	0.67/chn	
			SE-30	226	0.66/chn	
		26	SE-30	205	0.68/chn	499
			PhSi	207	0.82/chn	
			QF-1	198	0.87/chn	
			NGS	210	0.97/chn	
		22py	SE-30	225	10.6'	522
			XE-60	225	2.7'	
			XE-60/SE-30	225	4.1'	

Table 11-3. Estrogens (cont'd.)

Formula	Compound	Method	Stat. Phase	Temp.	Retention Data, Physical Constants	Ref.
$C_{18}H_{24}O_2$	Estradiol (Estratrien-3,17β-ol)	26	QF-1	258	T_1 0.89/chn	531
					T_2 0.63/chn	
					T_2 0.65/chn	
			SE-30	258		542
		26	SE-30/NGS	197	1.44/andn	497
		22py	Mass Spec.			
		24py	TLC			122
	Estratrien-3,17α-diol	26	QF-1	205	0.89/estl	128
			SE-30	210	0.90/estl	
		22py,	QF-1	203	0.76/chn	12
		26	XE-60	205	0.70/chn	
			Z	195	0.90/chn	
			F-60	230	0.62/chn	
		26	SE-30	220	25.4 SN	691
			XE-60	215	25.6 SN	
			NGSb	205	25.7 SN	
			QF-1	198	26.5 SN	
			HiEff	220	25.2 SN	
		26	SE-30	250	0.61/chn, 24.6 SN	381
			SE-30/XE-60	250	0.62/chn, 24.6 SN	
		26	Z	195	0.85/chn	496
			F-60	223	0.59/chn	
			SE-30	226	0.62/chn	
		26	SE-30	205	0.60/chn	499
			PhSi	207	0.72/chn	
			QF-1	198	0.77/chn	
			NGS	210	0.81/chn	
		22py	SE-30	225	9.4'	522
			XE-60	225	2.3'	
			XE-60/SE-30	225	3.8'	
			Mass Spec.			497

Table 11-3. Estrogens (cont'd.)

Formula	Compound	Method	Stat. Phase	Temp.	Retention Data, Physical Constants	Ref.
$C_{18}H_{24}O_3$	6α-Hydroxy-17β-estradiol (Estratrien-3,6α,17β-triol)	26	SE-30	220	27.4 SN	691
			XE-60	215	28.0 SN	
			NGSb	205	27.8 SN	
			QF-1	198	28.4 SN	
			HiEff	220	26.5 SN	
	7α-Hydroxy-17β-estradiol (Estratrien-3,7α,17β-triol)	26	SE-30	220	25.9 SN	691
			XE-60	215	26.0 SN	
			NGSb	205	25.7 SN	
			QF-1	198	26.5 SN	
			HiEff	220	24.3 SN	
	16-Epiestriol (Estratrien-3,16β,17β-triol)	22py, 26	QF-1,	203	1.58/chn	12
			XE-60	205	1.59/chn	
			Z	195	1.76/chn	
			F-60	230	1.30/chn	
		26	QF-1	205	2.1/estl	128
			SE-30	210	2.3/estl	
		26	SE-30	220	28.6 SN	691
			XE-60	215	29.6 SN	
			NGSb	205	29.0 SN	
			QF-1	198	31.0 SN	
			HiEff	220	28.0 SN	
		26	QF-1	200		471
		26	0.75% SE-30	205	15.9'	883
			3% SE-30	239	15.1'	
			QF-1	195	7.7'	
		26	SE-30	205	1.50/chn	499
			PhSi	207	1.56/chn	
			QF-1	198	1.84/chn	
			NGS	210	1.57/chn	
		26	SE-30	250	1.31/chn	381
			SE-30/XE-60	250	1.34/chn, 26.8 SN	

Table 11-3. Estrogens (cont'd.)

Formula	Compound	Method	Stat. Phase	Temp.	Retention Data, Physical Constants	Ref.
$C_{18}H_{24}O_3$	16,17-Epiestriol (Estratrien-3,16β,17α-triol)	22py, 26	QF-1	203	1.20/chn	12
			XE-60	205	1.16/chn	
			Z	195	1.28/chn	
			F-60	230	1.04/chn	
		26	SE-30	220	27.6 SN	691
			XE-60	215	28.0 SN	
			NGSb	205	27.5 SN	
			QF-1	198	28.3 SN	
			HiEff	220	26.2 SN	
	17-Epiestriol (Estratrien-3,16α,17α-triol)	26	SE-30	220	28.1 SN	691
			XE-60	215	28.9 SN	
			NGSb	205	28.4 SN	
			QF-1	198	28.4 SN	
			HiEff	220	27.1 SN	
		22py, 26	QF-1	203	1.36/chn	12
			XE-60	205	1.36/chn	
			Z	195	1.54/chn	
			F-60	230	1.14/chn	
		26	SE-30	205	1.33/chn	499
			PhSi	207	1.44/chn	
			QF-1	198	1.54/chn	
			NGS	210	1.32/chn	
	Estriol (Estratrien-3,16α,17β-triol)	22py	SE-30	225	0.545/chl	521
			SE-30/XE-60	235	0.563/chl	
		22c	JXR	185	8.78/pga	795
			SE-52	200	9.94/pga	
		25	XE-60	220	1.44/andn, 1.37/chn	681
			MeSiO	243	2.55/estn	590
		26	XE-60	193	1.43/chn	10
			NGS	207	1.70/chn	
		43	OV-1	235		487

Table 11-3. Estrogens (cont'd.)

Formula	Compound	Method	Stat. Phase	Temp.	Retention Data, Physical Constants	Ref.
$C_{18}H_{24}O_3$	Estriol (Estratrien-3,16α,17β-triol)	23h	XE-60	225	1.38/chn	291
		26	QF-1	205	1.7/estl	128
			SE-30	210	2.10/estl	
		22py,	QF-1	203	1.40/chn	12
		26	XE-60	205	1.34/chn	
			Z	195	1.64/chn	
			F-60	230	1.23/chn	
		22	Emb.	240	1.26/chn	176
		26	SE-30	250	1.22/chn, 26.9 SN	381
			SE-30/XE-60	250	1.24/chn	
		26	SE-30	205	1.38/chn	498
			PhSi	207	1.54/chn	
			QF-1	195	1.58/chn	
			NGS	210	1.41/chn	
		26	SE-30	220	28.2 SN	691
			XE-60	215	28.8 SN	
			NGSb	205	28.9 SN	
			QF-1	198	29.0 SN	
			HiEff	220	26.9 SN	
		26	SE-30	205	1.38/chn	499
			PhSi	207	1.54/chn	
			QF-1	198	1.58/chn	
			NGS	210	1.41/chn	
		26	QF-1	258	1.50/chn	531
			XE-30	258	1.50/chn	
		26	SE-30/NGS	197	2.59/andm	542
	2-Hydroxy-17β-estradiol (Estratrien-2,3,17β-triol)	26	QF-1	205	1.3/estl	128
			SE-30	210	1.7/estl	
	6α-Hydroxy-17β-estradiol (Estratrien-3,6α,17β-triol)	26	QF-1	205	1.6/estl	128
			SE-30	210	1.7/estl	

Table 11-3. Estrogens (cont'd.)

Formula	Compound	Method	Stat. Phase	Temp.	Retention Data, Physical Constants	Ref.
$C_{18}H_{24}O_3$	6β-Hydroxy-17β-estradiol (Estratrien-3,6β,17β-triol)	26	F-60, Z, QF-1, XE-60			15
	11β-Hydroxy-17β-estradiol (Estratrien-3,11β,17β-triol)	26	F-60, Z, QF-1, XE-60			15
$C_{18}H_{24}O_4$	Estra-2,3,16α,17β-tetrol	26	SE-30 / SE-30/XE-60	250 / 250	1.90/chn / 1.82/chn	381
$C_{19}H_{24}O_2$	11-Dehydro-17α-estradiol 3-methyl ether (3-Methoxy-1,3,5,11-estratetraen 3,17α-diol)	26	XE-60 / Z / F-60 / SE-30	200 / 195 / 223 / 226	0.61/chn / 1.02/chn / 0.45/chn / 0.44/chn	496
$C_{19}H_{24}O_3$	2-Methoxyestrone (2-Methoxyestratrien-3-ol-17-one)	26	QF-1 / SE-30	205 / 210	3.4/estl / 1.1/estl	128
		26	QF-1	200		471
		26	SE-30 / PhSi / QF-1 / NGS	205 / 207 / 198 / 210	0.78/chn / 2.05/chn / 2.88/chn / 4.35/chn	499
		26	0.75% SE-30 / 3% SE-30 / QF-1	205 / 239 / 195	8.3' / 8.7' / 12.1'	883
		26	F-60, Z, QF-1, XE-60			15
		26	SE-30 / XE-60 / NGSb / QF-1 / HiEff	220 / 215 / 205 / 198 / 220	27.6 SN / 32.5 SN / 34.2 SN / 32.3 SN / 32.4 SN	691
$C_{19}H_{26}O_2$	3-Methoxyestratrien-17α-ol	22c, 22py	QF-1 / SE-30 / XE-60 / Z / F-60	194 / 227 / 195 / 195 / 227	0.66/mesl, 0.50/chn / 0.51/mesl, 0.70/chn / 0.68/mesl, 1.02/chn / 1.11/mesl, 0.15/chn / 0.52/mesl	14, 496

Table 11-3. Estrogens (cont'd.)

Formula	Compound	Method	Stat. Phase	Temp.	Retention Data, Physical Constants	Ref.
$C_{19}H_{26}O_2$	3-Methoxyestratrien-17β-ol	22	Emb.	225	0.52/chn	176
			NGA	190	0.90/chn	
		26	XE-60	212		495
			QF-1	180		
			SE-30	190		
		26	QF-1	258	0.89/chn	531
			SE-30	258	0.54/chn	
		26	XE-60	200	0.80/chn	496
			Z	195	1.20/chn	
			F-60	223	0.57/chn	
			SE-30	226	0.56/chn	
$C_{19}H_{26}O_3$	2-Methoxyestradiol (2-Methoxyestratrien-3,17β-diol)	22py, 26	QF-1	203	1.30/chn	12
			XE-60	295	1.26/chn	
			Z	195	1.92/chn	
			F-60	230	0.99/chn	
		22	Emb.	225,240		176
			NGA	190		
		26	QF-1	200		471
		26	SE-30	220	27.3 SN	691
			XE-60	215	28.5 SN	
			NGSb	205	29.1 SN	
			QF-1	198	28.4 SN	
			HiEff	220	28.0 SN	
		26	QF-1	205	1.5/estl	128
			SE-30	210	1.5/estl	
$C_{19}H_{26}O_3$	3-Methoxyestratrien-16α,17β-diol	22	Emb.	225	1.04/chn	176
			NGA	190	1.80/chn	
		26	XE-60	212		495
			QF-1	180		
			XE-30	190		

Table 11-3. Estrogens (cont'd.)

Formula	Compound	Method	Stat. Phase	Temp.	Retention Data, Physical Constants	Ref.
$C_{19}H_{26}O_4$	2-Methoxyestriol (2-Methoxyestratrien-3,16α,17β-triol)	22py, 26	QF-1 XE-60 Z F-60	203 295 195 230	2.12/chn 2.08/chn 2.74/chn 1.86/chn	12
		26	SE-30 QF-1	210 205	2.9/estl 3.3/estl	128
		26	QF-1	200		471
$C_{20}H_{24}O_2$	Ethynyl estradiol (17α-Ethynylestratrien-3,17β-diol)	25	SE-30	260		98, 772
$C_{20}H_{26}O_3$	3-Acetoxyestradiol (3-Acetoxyestratrien-17β-ol)	26	QF-1 SE-30	258 258	1.7/chn 0.68/chn	531

TABLE 11-4. ANDROSTANES

Formula	Compound	Method	Stat. Phase	Temp.	Retention Data, Physical Constants	Ref.
$C_{18}H_{26}O_2$	19-Nortestosterone (19-Nor-4-androsten-17β-ol-3-one)	22py	SE-30 SE-30/XE-60	225 235	0.225/chl 0.367/chl	521
		22py	SE-30 XE-60 SE-30/XE-60	225 225 225	8.4' 6.7' 6.5'	522
		25			m 118-120°	131
		26	QF-1 SE-30	258 258	2.1/chn 0.78/chn	531
$C_{18}H_{28}O_2$	19-Nor-4-androsten-17β-ol	25				131
$C_{19}H_{26}O_2$	1,4-Androstdien-17β-ol-3-one	25			m 101-104°	131
	4-Androsten-3,17-dione (3,17-oxime)	22c	JXR SE-52	185 200	4.23/pga 5.16/pga	795
		25	NGS SE-30	210 225	1.80/chn 1.16/chn	123
$C_{19}H_{26}O_3$	4-Androsten-16α-ol-3,7-dione	22py	SE-30 XE-60 SE-30/XE-60	225 225 225	13.5' 25.8' 18.5'	522
$C_{19}H_{28}O$	5,16-Androstdien-3β-ol	22z	MS-2211 FS-1265 NGSb	185 205 230	3.53/mpam 2.14/mpam 3.11/mpam	129
$C_{19}H_{28}O_2$	4-Androsten-17(α or β)-ol-3-one	22c	JXR SE-52	185 200	α 3.11, β 3.82/pga α 3.84, β 4.65/pga	795
	5-Androsten-3β-ol-16-one (oxime)	25	SE-30 OV-17	220 220	0.85/chn, 26.4 SN 0.96/chn	546
	9(11)-Androsten-3-ol-17-one	22c	XE-60	210		816
	Dehydroepiandrosterone (5-Androsten-3β-ol-17-one)	22	XE-60 SE-30 NGS HiEff	262 251 231 242	1.36/chn 0.56/chn 0.84/chn 1.14/chn	298

Table 11-4. Androstanes (cont'd.)

Formula	Compound	Method	Stat. Phase	Temp.	Retention Data, Physical Constants	Ref.
$C_{19}H_{28}O_2$	Dehydroepiandrosterone (5-Androsten-3β-ol-17-one)	26	CNSi	202	1.57/chn	801
			NGS	212	1.44/chn	
			QF-1	195	1.28/chn	
			SE-30	205	0.46/chn	
		25	XE-60		1.34/chn	180
		22	XE-60	225	0.85/preg	181
			QF-1	210	0.85/preg,0.473/test	
		25	10% F-60	100→250	25.54 MU	182
			1% F-60		25.14 MU	
		26	SE-30	223	0.49/chn	218
			NGS	223	1.38/chn	
			Mass Spec.			
		22c	QF-1	187	2.51/ando; m 147-51°	411
		26	SE-30/NGS	198	1.38/andn	542
		22c	SE-30/NGS	205	0.67/chn	746
		22c	HiEff		2.14/ando	776
			HiEff/JXR		2.32/ando	
		25	QF-1	215	1.39/chn	818
			SE-30	225	0.46/chn	
			Mass Spec.			
		22z	XE-60	225	1.33/chn	291
		25	SE-30	225	0.196/chl	521
			SE-30/XE-60	235	0.267/chl	
		22c	JXR	185	2.78/pga	795
			SE-52	200	3.19/pga	
		25	SE-30	210		124
			TLC			
		22c	NGS	195	2.20/ando	412
			XE-60	195	2.20/ando	

Table 11-4. Androstanes (cont'd.)

Formula	Compound	Method	Stat. Phase	Temp.	Retention Data, Physical Constants	Ref.
$C_{19}H_{28}O_2$	Dehydroepiandrosterone (5-Androsten-3β-ol-17-one)	43	OV-1	180→	24.90 MU	339
			OV-17		27.85 MU	
		22c	SE-30	210	0.87/test	669
			XE-60	216	0.67/test	
		26	XE-60	210	1.08/chn	614
		26	XE-60	222	1.30/chn	603
			QF-1	222	1.30/chn	
			DC-200	222	0.52/chn	
		25	SE-30	219	0.48/chn	409
			XE-60	208	1.41/chn	
		22c	XE-60/SE-30		0.89/chn	321
		26	XE-60	218	1.30/chn	236
		22c	XE-60	195	1.47/chn	46
		22h	XE-60	223	1.30/chn	235
		25	SE-30	195	0.75/chn	382
			XE-60	210	1.19/chn	206
		26	STAP	230	16.0'	560
		25	SE-30	250	1.15/andn	799
			NGS	240	0.34/andn	
		25	SE-30 Mass Spec.	216		766
		26	SE-30	210	0.456/chn	622
			NGS	210	1.480/chn, 24.32 SN	
	(MO)	43	OV-1	180→	25.63 MU	339
			OV-17		28.17 MU	
	(MO)	26	SE-30	223	0.58/chn	218
			NGS	223	0.91/chn	
			Mass Spec.			

Table 11-4. Androstanes (cont'd.)

Formula	Compound	Method	Stat. Phase	Temp.	Retention Data, Physical Constants	Ref.
$C_{19}H_{28}O_2$	Dehydroepiandrosterone (oxime) (5-Androsten-3β-ol-17-one)	25	SE-30	220	0.79/chn, 26.2 SN	546
			OV-17	220	0.80/chn	121
	Epitestosterone (4-Androsten-17α-ol-3-one)		NGS	220	1.87/chn	
			SE-30	225	0.63/chn	
			Mass Spec.			
		23	XE-60	210	2.00/chn	206
			SE-30	235	0.54/chn	798
			EGSS	205	2.11/chn	
		25	TLC			123
	(MO)	43	OV-1		26.00 MU	351
			OV-17		28.31 MU, 28.52 MU	
	(MO)	25	TLC			123
	(oxime)	25	TLC		T_2(3,oxime)	123
	Testosterone (5-Androsten-17β-ol-3-one)	26	NGS	220	2.32/chn	121
			SE-30	225	0.69/chn	
			Mass Spec.			
		26	SE-30	223	0.66/chn	218
			NGS	223	2.40/chn	
		22py	SE-30	225	9.8'	522
			XE-60	225	7.7'	
			SE-30/XE-60	225	7.4'	
		26	XE-60	210	2.35/chn	206
			QF-1	258	2.1/chn	531
			SE-30	258	0.79/chn	
		22c	SE-30	210	1.18/test	667
			SE-30/NGS	215	1.21/test	
			XE-60	216	1.25/test	
		22c	SE-30/NGS	205	0.97/chn	746
			JXR	190	0.66/chn; m 89-90°	780

Table 11-4. Androstanes (cont'd.)

Formula	Compound	Method	Stat. Phase	Temp.	Retention Data, Physical Constants	Ref.
$C_{19}H_{28}O_2$	Testosterone (5-Androsten-17β-ol-3-one)	23	SE-30	235	0.64/chn	798
			EGSS-Z	205	2.62/chn	
		25	SE-30	225	0.258/chl	521
			SE-30/XE-60	235	0.438/chl	
		26	SE-30	210	0.620/chn	622
			NGS	210	2.45/chn, 25.4 SN	
		25	TLC			123
	(MO)	26	SE-30	210	0.700/chn	622
			NGS	210	1.42, 1.60/chn, 25.80 SN	
	(MO)	26	SE-30	223	0.73/chn	218
			NGS	223	1.50/chn	
			Mass Spec.			
	(MO)	43	OV-1		26.45 MU	351
			OV-17		28.85 MU, 29.12 MU	
	(MO)	25	TLC			123
	(oxime)	25	TLC		T_2(3,oxime)	123
$C_{19}H_{28}O_3$	5α-Androstan-3α-ol-11,17-dione	25	QF-1	215	2.32/chn	818
			SE-30	225	0.48/chn	
	5β-Androstan-3α-ol-11,17-dione	25	QF-1	215	2.36/chn	818
			SE-30	225	0.49/chn	
		26	XE-60	225		292
		22	XE-60	262	2.40/chn	298
			NGS	231	1.36/chn	
			HiEff	242	2.03/chn	
	(MO)	43	OV-1		26.01 MU	351
			OV-17		28.85 MU	
	Androstan-16α-ol-3,17-dione	25	SE-30	225	0.364/chl	521
			SE-30/XE-60	235	1.025/chl	

Table 11-4. Androstanes (cont'd.)

Formula	Compound	Method	Stat. Phase	Temp.	Retention Data, Physical Constants	Ref.
$C_{19}H_{28}O_3$	4-Androsten-6β,11β-diol-17-one	22c	XE-60	240	1.28/andr	46
			SE-52	210	1.93/andr	
	5-Androsten-3β,16α-diol-17-one	25	QF-1	215	1.46/chn	818
			SE-30	225	0.84/chn	
			Mass Spec.			339
		43	OV-1	180→	27.26 MU	
			OV-17	180→	29.18 MU	
	(MO)	21py	SE-30			337
	(MO)		SE-30	225		123
			Mass Spec.			339
		43	OV-1	180→	27.32 MU	
			OV-17	180→	29.04 MU	
	5-Androsten-3β,17β-diol-16-one	22c	SE-52	200	6.64/pga	795
			JXR	185	5.89/pga	
		25	QF-1	215	1.84/chn	818
			SE-30	225	0.94/chn	
		25	TLC			124
	(MO)	21py	SE-30			337
	(MO)		SE-30			123
			Mass Spec.			
	(MO)		SE-30	190→250		263
			Mass Spec.			
	19-Hydroxytestosterone	26	SE-30/NGS	230		526
	(4-Androsten-17β,19-diol-3-one)	22py	SE-30	225	0.430/chl	521
			SE-30/XE-60	235	0.692/chl	
		22py	SE-30	225	16.2'	522
			XE-60	225	10.7'	
			SE-30/XE-60	225	10.3'	

Table 11-4. Androstanes (cont'd.)

Formula	Compound	Method	Stat. Phase	Temp.	Retention Data, Physical Constants	Ref.
$C_{19}H_{28}O_3$	11-Ketoandrosterone (Androstan-3α-ol-11,17-dione)	22	XE-60	225	1.42/preg	181
			QF-1	210	1.435/preg	
		22z	XE-60	225	2.51/chn	291
		26	STAP	230	1.46/dean	560
		25	SE-30	219	0.46/chn	410
			XE-60	208	2.38/chn	
		43	OV-1	180→	25.03 MU	339
			OV-17	180→	28.46 MU	
	(MO)	43	OV-1	180→	26.00 MU	339
			OV-17	180→	28.86 MU	
	(oxime)	25	NGS	210	T_2(3,17-oxime)	123
	11-Ketoetiocholanolone (5β-Androstan-3α-ol-11,17-one)	22c	NGS	215	4.15/ando	412
			XE-60	215	4.10/ando	
		43	OV-1	180→	25.15 MU	339
			OV-17	180→	28.59 MU	
		25	SE-30	219	0.47/chn	410
			XE-60	208	2.78/chn	
		22c	XE-60	195	3.21/chn	46
		22	XE-60	225	1.655/preg	181
			QF-1	210	1.451/preg	
		26	STAP	230	1.63/dean	560
		26	XE-60	210	1.85/chn	614
		26	QF-1	222	2.14/chn	603
			XE-60		2.66/chn	
			DC-200		0.63/chn	
		22c	SE-30/NGS	205	0.89/chn	746
	(MO)	43	OV-1	180→	26.10 MU	339
			OV-17	180→	28.85 MU	
	(oxime)	25	NGS	210	T_2[3,oxime(17)]	123

Table 11-4. Androstanes (cont'd.)

Formula	Compound	Method	Stat. Phase	Temp.	Retention Data, Physical Constants	Ref.
$C_{19}H_{28}O_4$	5-Androsten-3β,11β,16α-triol-17-one (MO)	25	SE-30	225		123
$C_{19}H_{30}O$	5α-Androstane-17-one (oxime)	25	SE-30	225	0.36/chn	123
			NGS	210	0.38/chn	
	4-Androsten-17β-ol	25	SE-30		m 133-135°	131
		26	SE-30	210	0.224/chn	622
			NGS	210	0.232/chn, 22.0 SN	
	16-Androsten-3-ol	22z	MS-2211	185	α 3.05, β 4.60/mpam	129
			GS-1265	205	α 1.78, β 2.32/mpam	
			NGSb	230	α 2.21, β 3.10/mpam	
	16-Androsten-3α-ol	21py	SE-30			337
		43	OV-1	180→	21.61 MU	339
			OV-17	180→	22.73 MU	
	5β-Androst-16-en-3α-ol	22z	MS-2211	185	2.97/mpam	129
			FS-1265	205	1.95/mpam	
			NGSb	230	2.61/mpam	
$C_{19}H_{30}O_2$	5α-Androstan-3β-ol-16-one (MO)	43	OV-1		26.00 MU, 28.56 MU	351
			OV-17		28.60 MU	
	(oxime)	25	SE-30	220	0.86/chn, 26.4 SN	546
			OV-17	220	0.95/chn	
	5α-Androstan-17α-ol-3-one	22	SE-30	260	0.60/chn	299
			XE-60	260-262	1.16/chn	
			NGS	232	0.94/chn	
			HiEff	238	1.09/chn	
	5α-Androstan-17β-ol-3-one	22	SE-30	260	0.64/chn	299
			XE-60	260-262	1.32/chn	
			NGS	232	1.07/chn	
			HiEff	238	1.27/chn	
		26	SE-30	210	0.506/chn, 24.70 SN	622
			NGS	210	1.600/chn	
		25	TLC			123

Table 11-4. Androstanes (cont'd.)

Formula	Compound	Method	Stat. Phase	Temp.	Retention Data, Physical Constants	Ref.
$C_{19}H_{30}O_2$	5α-Androstan-17β-ol-3-one	22c	JXR SE-52	185 200	3.05/pga 3.56/pga	795
	(MO)	26	SE-30 NGS	210 210	0.662/chn, 25.60 SN 1.120/chn	622
		25	TLC			123
	(MO)	25	TLC (oxime)		T_2(3,oxime)	123
	5β-Androstan-17α-ol-3-one	22	SE-30 XE-60 NGS HiEff	260 260-262 232 238	0.47/chn 0.91/chn 0.62/chn 0.81/chn	299
	5β-Androstan-17β-ol-3-one	22	SE-30 XE-60 NGS HiEff	260 260-262 232 238	0.59/chn 1.18/chn 0.91/chn 1.13/chn	299
		26	SE-30 NGS	210 210	0.450/chn, 24.30 SN 1.330/chn	622
	(MO)	26	SE-30 NGS	210 210	0.551/chn, 25.0 SN 0.980/chn	622
	13α-Androstan-3β-ol-16-one (oxime)	25	SE-30 OV-17	220 220	0.68/chn 0.73/chn	546
	13α-Androstan-3β-ol-17-one (oxime)	25	SE-30 OV-17	220 220	0.58/chn 0.53/chn	546
	14β-Androstan-3β-ol-16-one (oxime)	25	SE-30 OV-17	220 220	0.70/chn 0.75/chn	546
	14β-Androstan-3β-ol-17-one (oxime)	25	SE-30 OV-17	220 220	0.81/chn 0.79/chn	546
	4-Androsten-3β,17β-diol		SE-30 Mass Spec.	205	0.580/chn	121
		22c	JXR SE-52	185 200	3.58/pga 3.74/pga	795

Table 11-4. Androstanes (cont'd.)

Formula	Compound	Method	Stat. Phase	Temp.	Retention Data, Physical Constants	Ref.
$C_{19}H_{30}O_2$	5-Androsten-3β,17-diol	25	QF-1	215	α 0.48, β 0.57/chn	818
			SE-30	225	α 0.53, β 0.61/chn	
			Mass Spec.			
	5-Androsten-3β,17β-diol	22c	JXR	185	α 3.07, β 3.70/pga	795
			SE-52	200	α 3.10, β 3.81/pga	
			SE-30	205	0.605/chn	121
			Mass Spec.			
		22py, 24py	TLC			122, 124
		43	OV-1	180→	25.86 MU	339
			OV-17	180→	26.80 MU	
		22c	XE-60	195	0.71/ando	412
		22py	SE-30	225	9.9'	522
			XE-60	225	10.7'	
			SE-30/XE-60	225	9.6'	
		26	SE-30	210	0.600/chn	622
			NGS	210	0.500/chn, 25.30 SN	
			QF-1	200		661
			Mass Spec.			
			QF-1	215	0.57/chn	732
			SE-30	225	0.61/chn	
			Mass Spec.			
	Androsterone (5α-Androstan-3α-ol-17-one)	22	XE-60	262	1.02/chn	298
			SE-30	251	0.47/chn	
			NGS	231	0.60/chn	
			HiEff	242	0.78/chn	
		26	CNSi	202	1.09/chn	801
			NGS	212	0.94/chn	
			QF-1	195	1.03/chn	
			SE-30	205	0.37/chn	
		26	XE-60	218	0.94/chn	236

Table 11-4. Androstanes (cont'd.)

Formula	Compound	Method	Stat. Phase	Temp.	Retention Data, Physical Constants	Ref.
$C_{19}H_{30}O_2$	Androsterone (5α-Androstan-3α-ol-17-one)	25	SE-30	250	0.94/ando	799
			NGS	240	0.22/ando	321
		22c	XE-60/SE-30		0.64/chn	409
		25	SE-30	219	0.49/chn	603
			XE-60	208	0.99/chn	
		26	QF-1	222	1.25/chn	
			XE-60	222	0.94/chn	
			DC-200	222	0.56/chn	
		26	XE-60	210	0.81/chn	614
			XE-60	210	0.88/chn	206
		22c	SE-30	210	0.71/chn	669
			XE-60	216	0.49/test	
		22c	SE-30	195	1.56/ando	412
			XE-60		1.44/ando	
			NGS			
		22c	SE-30/NGS	205	0.48/chn	746
		26	STAP	230	0.673/dean	560
			XE-60	223	0.94/chn	235
		22c	XE-60	195	1.01/chn	46
			SE-52			
		26	SE-30	210	0.362/chn, 23.60 SN	622
			NGS	210	0.915/chn	
		22	XE-60	225	0.612/preg	181
			QF-1	210	0.685/preg	
		25	XE-60	100→250	0.96/chn	180
		25	10% F-60		24.76 MU	182
			1% F-60		24.44 MU	
		26	SE-30	223	0.41/chn	218
			NGS	223	0.96/chn	
			Mass Spec.			

Table 11-4. Androstanes (cont'd.)

Formula	Compound	Method	Stat. Phase	Temp.	Retention Data, Physical Constants	Ref.
$C_{19}H_{30}O_2$	Androsterone	22c	QF-1	187	1.97/ando; m 84-86°	411
	(5α-Androstan-3α-ol-17-one)	43	OV-1	180→	24.21 MU	339
			OV-17	180→	26.81 MU	
		25	SE-30	150→300		372
			Mass Spec.			
		26	SE-30/NGS	198	19.90'	542
		25	QF-1	215	1.13/chn	818
			SE-30	225	0.38/chn	
			Mass Spec.			
		22c	HiEff		1.33/ando	776
			HiEff/JXR		1.58/ando	
		22	SE-30	260	0.47/chn	299
			XE-60	260	0.87/chn	
			NGS	232	0.58/chn	
			HiEff	238	0.74/chn	
		22c	JXR	185	2.22/pga	795
			SE-52	200	2.48/pga	
		22z	XE-60	225	0.96/chn	291
		22py, 24py	TLC			122, 123
	(MO)	25	TLC			124
		26	NGS	223	0.64/chn	218
			SE-30	223	0.48/chn	
			Mass Spec.			
	(MO)	26	SE-30	210	0.452/chn, 24.30 SN	622
			NGS	210	0.625/chn	
	(MO)	43	OV-1	180→	25.01 MU	339
			OV-17	180→	27.15 MU	
	(MO)	22py, 24py	TLC			122, 123

Table 11-4. Androstanes (cont'd.)

Formula	Compound	Method	Stat. Phase	Temp.	Retention Data, Physical Constants	Ref.
$C_{19}H_{30}O_2$	Androsterone (oxime) (5α-Androstan-3α-ol-17-one)	22py, 24py	TLC		$T_1(3)$ $T_2(3,\text{oxime})$	122, 123
		22z	XE-60	225	1.41/chn	291
	Epiandrosterone (5α-Androstan-3β-ol-17-one)	25	SE-30 Mass Spec.	216		766
		26	SE-30	210	0.474/chn, 24.50 SN	622
			NGS	210	1.466/chn	
		22	SE-30	260	0.55/chn	299
			XE-60	260	1.16/chn	
			NGS	232	0.91/chn	
			HiEff	238	1.2/chn	
		26	CNSi	202	1.62/chn	801
			NGS	212	1.44/chn	
			QF-1	195	1.44/chn	
			SE-30	205	0.48/chn	
			NGA	225	1.22/chn	306
		22c	JXR	185	2.90/pga	795
			SE-52	200	3.30/pga	
		22	XE-60	225		181
			QF-1	210	0.531/test	
		25	QF-1	215	1.55/chn	732, 818
			SE-30	225	0.48/chn	
			Mass Spec.			
		22c	HiEff		2.15/ando	776
			HiEff/JXR		2.30/ando	
		26	XE-60	218	1.35/chn	236
		22c	SE-30/NGS	205	0.68/chn	746
		43	OV-1	180→	25.02 MU	339
			OV-17	180→	27.85 MU	
		22c	NGS	195	2.20/ando	412
			XE-60	195	2.23/ando	

Table 11-4. Androstanes (cont'd.)

Formula	Compound	Method	Stat. Phase	Temp.	Retention Data, Physical Constants	Ref.
$C_{19}H_{30}O_2$	Epiandrosterone (MO) (5α-Androstan-3β-ol-17-one)	43	OV-1 OV-17	180→ 180→	25.71 MU 28.19 MU	339
	(MO)	26	SE-30 NGS	210 210	0.570/chn, 25.10 SN 0.970/chn	622
	Epietiocholanolone (5β-Androstan-3β-ol-17-one)	25	QF-1 SE-30 Mass Spec.	215 225	1.15/chn 0.37/chn	818
		22	XE-60	260	0.86/chn	299
		26	SE-30 NGS	210 210	0.362/chn, 23.60 SN 0.915/chn	622
		26	SE-30 CNSi NGS QF-1	205 202 212 195	0.37/chn 1.07/chn 0.94/chn 1.04/chn	801
			NGA	225	0.75/chn	306
		22c	JXR SE-52	185 200	2.17/pga 2.39/pga	795
	(MO)	26	SE-30 NGS	210 210	0.440/chn, 24.25 SN 0.625/chn	622
	Etiocholanolone (5β-Androstan-3α-ol-17-one)	22c	NGA-Z	225	0.98/chn	306
		22c	SE-30 XE-60	210 216	0.75/test 0.63/test	669
		26	XE-60	210	0.89/chn	614
		26	QF-1 XE-60 DC-200	222 222 222	1.25/chn 1.14/chn 0.60/chn	603
		22	XE-60 SE-30 NGS HiEff	262 251 231 242	1.18/chn 0.50/chn 0.73/chn 0.98/chn	298

Table 11-4. Androstanes (cont'd.)

Formula	Compound	Method	Stat. Phase	Temp.	Retention Data, Physical Constants	Ref.
$C_{19}H_{30}O_2$	Etiocholanolone (5β-Androstan-3α-ol-17-one)	22c	JXR	185	2.37/pga	795
			SE-52	200	2.66/pga	409
		25	SE-30	219	0.41/chn	321
			XE-60	208	1.21/chn	
		22c	XE-60/SE-30		0.75/chn	412
		22c	NGS	195	1.87/ando	339
			XE-60	195	1.81/ando	
		43	OV-1	180→	24.41 MU	780
			OV-17	180→	27.12 MU	
		26	XE-60	190	1.06/chn	236
		22c	XE-60	218	1.14/chn	46
			XE-60	195	1.25/chn	235
			SE-52			
		22h	XE-60	223	1.14/chn	382
		25	SE-30	195	0.64/chn	560
			XE-60			
		26	STAP	230	0.798/dean	180
		25	XE-60	225	1.16/chn	181
		22	XE-60	225	0.730/preg	182
			QF-1	210	0.754/preg	
		25	10% F-60	100→250	25.06 MU	411
			1% F-60	100→250	24.76 MU	
		22c	QF-1	187	2.24/ando	206
			XE-60	210	1.00/chn	542
		26	SE-30/NGS	198	1.17/andn	746
		22c	SE-30/NGS	205	0.56/chn	776
		22c	HiEff		1.81/ando	
			HiEff/JXR		1.95/ando	

Table 11-4. Androstanes (cont'd.)

Formula	Compound	Method	Stat. Phase	Temp.	Retention Data, Physical Constants	Ref.
$C_{19}H_{30}O_2$	Etiocholanolone (5β-Androstan-3α-ol-17-one)	25	QF-1	215	1.24/chn	818
			SE-30	225	0.39/chn	
			Mass Spec.			
		26	SE-30	205	0.39/chn	801
			CNSi	202	1.34/chn	
			NGS	212	1.22/chn	
			QF-1	195	1.12/chn	
		22	SE-30	260	0.46/chn	299
			XE-60	260	0.94/chn	
			NGS	232	0.72/chn	
			HiEff	238	1.03/chn	
		26	SE-30	210	0.390/chn	622
			NGS	210	1.250/chn, 23.85 SN	
			XE-60	190	1.06/chn	780
		25	SE-30	150→300		372
			Mass Spec.			
		22z	XE-60	225	1.13/chn	291
		25	SE-30	220		124
			TLC			
		26	SE-30	210	0.479/chn	622
	(MO)		NGS	210	0.825/chn, 24.60 SN	
		43	OV-1	180→	25.22 MU	339
	(MO)		OV-17	180→	27.32 MU	
			SE-30	190→250		263
	(MO)		Mass Spec.			
$C_{19}H_{30}O_3$	5-Androsten-3β,16α,17β-triol	25	QF-1	215	0.95/chn	818
			SE-30	225	1.21/chn	
		21py	SE-30	225		337
		43	OV-1	180→	28.40 MU	123
			OV-17	180→	28.80 MU	339

Table 11-4. Androstanes (cont'd.)

Formula	Compound	Method	Stat. Phase	Temp.	Retention Data, Physical Constants	Ref.
$C_{19}H_{30}O_3$	11β-Hydroxyandrosterone (5α-Androstan-3α,11β-diol-17-one)	25	QF-1	215	1.78/chn	818
			SE-30	225	0.70/chn	
			Mass Spec.			
		25	SE-30	219	0.70/chn	409
			XE-60	208	1.54/chn	
		22	XE-60	225	1.790/preg	181
			QF-1	210	1.343/preg	
		43	OV-1	180→	$T_1(3)$ 25.90 MU	339
			OV-17	180→	$T_1(3)$ 29.47 MU	
		44	OV-1	180→	$T_2(3\alpha,11)$ 26.43 MU	339
			OV-17	180→	$T_2(3,11)$ 28.31 MU	
		25	SE-30	219	0.70/chn	410
			XE-60	208	1.54/chn	
		26	STAP	230	0.783/dean	560
		22c	XE-60	195	3.59/chn	46
		22c	NGS	215	5.25/ando	412
			XE-60	215	4.53/ando	
		43 (MO)	OV-1	180→260	$T_1(3)$ 26.67 MU	155, 339
			OV-17		$T_1(3)$ 29.73 MU	
		44 (MO)	OV-1	180→260	$T_2(3,11)$ 26.93 MU	155, 339
			OV-17		$T_2(3,11)$ 28.55 MU	
	11β-Hydroxyetiocholanolone (5β-Androstan-3α,11β-diol-17-one)	25	QF-1	215	2.01/chn	818
			SE-30	225	0.75/chn	
			Mass Spec.			
		25	SE-30	219	0.71/chn	409
			XE-60	208	1.80/chn	
		22z	XE-60	225	3.34/chn	291
		22	XE-60	262	2.57/chn	298
			NGS	231	1.87/chn	
			HiEff	242	2.59/chn	

Table 11-4. Androstanes (cont'd.)

Formula	Compound	Method	Stat. Phase	Temp.	Retention Data, Physical Constants	Ref.
$C_{19}H_{30}O_3$	11β-Hydroxyetiocholanolone (5β-Androstan-3α,11β-diol-17-one)	26	QF-1		2.14/chn	603
			XE-60		2.58/chn	
			DC-200	222	0.66/chn	
		25	SE-30	219	0.71/chn	410
			XE-60	208	1.80/chn	
		26	XE-60		2.48/chn	614
		25	SE-30	220		124
			TLC			
			Mass Spec.			
		22	XE-60	225	2.18/preg	181
			QF-1	210	1.452/preg	
		26	STAP	230	0.938/dean	560
		22c	XE-60	195	4.36/chn	46
		22c	SE-30/NGS	205	1.57/chn	746
		22c	NGS	215	6.90/ando	412
			XE-60	215	5.40/ando	
		21, 22	OV-1	170 or	$T_1(3)$ 26.00 MU	155
			OV-17	200→260	$T_1(3)$ 29.70 MU	
		22, 23	OV-1		$T_2(3,11)$ 26.68 MU	155
			OV-17		$T_2(3,11)$ 28.60 MU	
		36, 43	OV-1	180→260	$T_1(3)$ 26.00 MU	155, 339
			OV-17		$T_1(3)$ 29.70 MU	
		36, 44	OV-1	180→260	$T_2(3,11)$ 26.68 MU	155, 339
			OV-17		$T_2(3,11)$ 28.60 MU	
		36-11	OV-1	170 or 200→260	$T_2(3,11)$ 26.68 MU $T_2(3,11)$ 28.60 MU	155
		36-11	SE-30 Mass Spec. (MO)	190→250	$T_3(3,11,enol)$	263

Table 11-4. Androstanes (cont'd.)

Formula	Compound	Method	Stat. Phase	Temp.	Retention Data, Physical Constants	Ref.
$C_{19}H_{30}O_3$	11β-Hydroxyetiocholanolone (MO) (5β-Androstan-3α,11β-diol-17-one)	43 44	OV-1 OV-17 OV-1 OV-17	180→260	$T_1(3)$ 26.18 MU $T_1(3)$ 29.79 MU $T_2(3,11)$ 27.12 MU $T_2(3,11)$ 28.70 MU	155, 351
$C_{19}H_{32}O$	Androstan-3β-ol	22	SE-30 XE-60 NGS HiEff	260 260 232 238	5α 0.34, 5β 0.31/chn 5α 0.39, 5β 0.32/chn 5α 0.21/chn 5α 0.24/chn	299
	5α-Androstan-3-ol	22c	JXR SE-52	185 200	α 1.12, β 1.44/pga α 1.11, β 1.46/pga	795
	Androstan-17β-ol	22	SE-30 XE-60 NGS HiEff	260 260 232 238	5α 0.33, 5β 0.49/chn 5α 0.38, 5β 0.52/chn 5α 0.20/chn 5α 0.22/chn	299
	5α-Androstan-17β-ol	26	Mass Spec.		m 101-103°	193
$C_{19}H_{32}O_2$	5α-Androstan-3α,17-diol	26	SE-30 NGS	210 210	α 0.480, β 0.481/chn α 0.320, β 0.312/chn α 24.51, β 24.51 SN	622
		25	QF-1 SE-30 Mass Spec.	215 225	α 0.35, β 0.44/chn α 0.36, β 0.48/chn	818
		22	SE-30 XE-60 NGS HiEff	260 260 232 238	β 0.58/chn β 0.49/chn β 0.31/chn β 0.28/chn	299
		22c	SE-30/NGS	205	β 0.47/chn	746
		22c	JXR SE-52	185 200	β 2.97/pga β 2.96/pga	795
	5α-Androstan-3β,17-diol	25	QF-1 SE-30	215 225	α 0.51, β 0.61/chn α 0.53, β 0.61/chn	818
		25	Mass Spec. NGS	225	α 0.43, β 0.52/chn	306

Table 11-4. Androstanes (cont'd.)

Formula	Compound	Method	Stat. Phase	Temp.	Retention Data, Physical Constants	Ref.
$C_{19}H_{32}O_2$	5α-Androstan-3β,17-diol	22	SE-30	260	β 0.69/chn	299
			XE-60	260	β 0.66/chn	
			NGS	232	β 0.44/chn	
			HiEff	238	β 0.42/chn	
		22c	JXR	185	β 3.77/pga	795
			SE-52	200	β 3.90/pga	
		26	SE-30	210	β 0.612/chn, 25.37 SN	622
			NGS	210	β 0.480/chn	
	5β-Androstan-3α,17-diol	22	SE-30	260	β 0.61/chn	299
			XE-60	260	β 0.50/chn	
			NGS	232	β 0.35/chn	
			HiEff	238	β 0.37/chn	
		25	QF-1	215	β 0.47/chn	818
			SE-30	215	β 0.49/chn	
			Mass Spec.			
			NGA	225	α 0.33, β 0.43/chn	306
	5β-Androstan-3β,17-diol	22	SE-30	260	β 0.56/chn	299
			XE-60	260	β 0.51/chn	
			NGS	232	β 0.28/chn	
			HiEff	238	β 0.28/chn	
		25	NGA	225	α 0.24/chn	306
$C_{20}H_{30}O_2$	17α-Ethyl-19-nortestosterone (17α-Ethyl-19-nor-4-androsten-17β-ol-3-one)	25				131
	17α-Methylandrost-4-en-17β-ol-3-one	25			m 104-111°	131
$C_{21}H_{34}O$	4,4-Dimethylandrost-5-en-3β-ol	26	Mass Spec.		m 127-129°	193

TABLE 11-5. PREGNANES

Formula	Compound	Method	Stat. Phase	Temp.	Retention Data, Physical Constants	Ref.
$C_{21}H_{30}O_2$	5,16-Pregnadien-3β-ol-20-one	22c	JXR SE-52	185 200	4.49/pga 5.07/pga	795
$C_{21}H_{30}O_3$	17α-Hydroxyprogesterone (4-Pregnen-17α-ol-3,20-dione)	22py	SE-30 SE-30/XE-60	225 235	0.471/chl 1.178/chl	521
		22py	SE-30 XE-60 SE-30/XE-60	225 225 225	17.4' 27.0' 20.0'	522
	4-Pregnen-11α-ol-3,20-dione	22c	JXR	185	8.59/pga	795
$C_{21}H_{32}O_2$	4-Pregnen-20-ol-3-one	22py	SE-30 XE-60 SE-30/XE-60	225 225 225	α 19.1', β 17.4' α 15.6', β 13.5' α 14.1', β 12.8'	522
		22py	SE-30 SE-30/XE-60	225 235	α 0.500, β 0.471/chl α 0.863, β 0.779/chl	521
		23	SE-30 EGSS-Z		α 1.21, β 1.14/chn α 5.32, β 4.92/chn	798
		22py	QF-1 SE-30	215 225	α 5.33, β 4.85/chn α 1.21, β 1.13/chn	818
	Pregnenolone (5-Pregnen-3β-ol-20-one)	22c, 22py	SE-30 QF-1 NGS XE-60	224 175 197 205	0.78/chn 1.0/chn 2.02/chn 1.59/chn	11
		22c	XE-60	215	3.12/ando	412
		22py	QF-1 SE-30	215 225	1.90/chn 0.78/chn	818
		22py	SE-30 SE-30/XE-60	225 235	0.326/chl 0.425/chl	521
		22c, 26	SE-30 PhSi QF-1 NGS	205 207 198 210	0.77/chn 1.17/chn 1.81/chn 2.08/chn	498, 499

Table 11-5. Pregnanes (cont'd.)

Formula	Compound	Method	Stat. Phase	Temp.	Retention Data, Physical Constants	Ref.
$C_{21}H_{32}O_2$	Pregnenolone (5-Pregnen-3β-ol-20-one)	25	SE-30 / TLC	200→280		126
		22c	JXR / SE-52	185 / 200	4.79/pga / 5.52/pga	795
		22py	SE-30 / XE-60 / SE-30/XE-60	225 / 225 / 225	12.1' / 5.9' / 6.7'	522
	(MO)	43	OV-1 / OV-17	pr / pr	27.59 MU / 29.91 MU	351
	Pregnenolone-4-C^{14}		TLC			841
$C_{21}H_{32}O_3$	5α-Pregnan-3β-ol-11,20-dione	22c	JXR / SE-52	185 / 200	7.21/pga / 8.74/pga	795
	16α-Hydroxypregnenolone (MO) (5-Pregnen-3β,16α-diol-20-one)		SE-30 / Mass Spec.	190→250		263
	17α-Hydroxypregnenolone (5-Pregnen-3β,17α-diol-20-one)	23	SE-30	pr		337
		22py	SE-30 / SE-30/XE-60	225 / 235	0.467/chl / 0.525/chl	521
		22py	SE-30 / XE-60 / SE-30/XE-60	225 / 225 / 225	17.3' / 4.1' / 7.4'	522
	21-Hydroxypregnenolone (20-MO) (5-Pregnen-3β,21-diol-20-one)	22c	XE-60	215	6.40/ando	412
		23	SE-30			337
			SE-30 / Mass Spec.	190→250		263
	5-Pregnen-3β,16α-diol-20-one (20-MO)	25	SE-30 / Mass Spec.	225		123
	5-Pregnen-3β,17α-diol-20-one (20-MO)	25	SE-30 / Mass Spec.	225		123
$C_{21}H_{32}O_4$	5β-Pregnan-3α,17α-diol-11,20-dione	22c	JXR / SE-52	185 / 200	7.74/pga / 9.60/pga	795

Table 11-5. Pregnanes (cont'd.)

Formula	Compound	Method	Stat. Phase	Temp.	Retention Data, Physical Constants	Ref.
C$_{21}$H$_{32}$O$_4$	5α-Pregnan-3β,17α-diol-11,20-dione	22c	JXR	185	10.25/pga	795
C$_{21}$H$_{34}$O	5α-Pregnan-20-one (oxime)	25	SE-30	225	0.62/chn	123
			NGS	210	0.64/chn	
	5-Pregnen-3β-ol	25	Mass Spec.			123
C$_{21}$H$_{34}$O$_2$	5α-Pregnan-3α-ol-20-one	22py	NGA	225	1.18/chn	156
			QF-1	250	1.45/chn	
		26	SE-30	227	0.66/chn	16
			QF-1	185	1.29/chn	
			NGS	207	1.30/chn	
			XE-60	202	1.01/chn	
			Z	187	1.39/chn	
			JXR	200	0.72/chn	
		22py	XE-60	225	1.37/chn	291
	5α-Pregnan-3β-ol-20-one	26	SE-30	205	0.67/chn	498
			PhSi	207	1.55/chn	
			QF-1	195	2.98/chn	
			NGS	210	6.52/chn	
		26	SE-30	227	0.83/chn	16
			QF-1	185	1.50/chn	
			NGS	207	2.06/chn	
			XE-60	202	1.44/chn	
			Z	187	2.07/chn	
			JXR	200	1.02/chn	
			F-60	223	0.89/chn	
		22py	XE-60	225	1.97	291
		26	SE-30	223	0.80/chn	218
			NGS	223	1.81/chn	
			Mass Spec.			
	(MO)	26	SE-30	223	1.06/chn	218
			NGS	223	1.28/chn	
			Mass Spec.			

Table 11-5. Pregnanes (cont'd.)

Formula	Compound	Method	Stat. Phase	Temp.	Retention Data, Physical Constants	Ref.
$C_{21}H_{34}O_2$	5α-Pregnan-20α-ol-3-one	22py	NGA	225	2.70/chn	156
	5α-Pregnan-20β-ol-3-one	26	SE-30	205	0.72/chn	498
			PhSi	207	1.71/chn	
			QF-1	195	3.70/chn	
			NGS	210	7.64/chn	
		22c	JXR	185	5.85/pga	795
			SE-52	200	6.74/pga	
	Pregnanolone	22	XE-60	215	1.57/chn	180
	(5β-Pregnan-3α-ol-20-one)	22c	XE-60		2.52/ando	412
		22	XE-60	225	1.0'	181
			QF-1	210	0.559/test, 1.0'	
		26	DC-200	222	0.79/chn	603
		22	XE-60	262	1.44/chn	298
			NGS	231	1.08/chn	
			HiEff	242	1.38/chn	
		22c, 22py	SE-30	224	0.54/chn	11
			QF-1	175	0.87/chn	
			NGS	197	1.65/chn	
			XE-60	205	1.03/chn	
		22py	XE-60	225	1.55/chn	291
		22py	NGA	225	1.50/chn	156
			QF-1	250	1.45/chn	
		26	SE-30	227	0.67/chn	16
			QF-1	185	1.42/chn	
			NGS	207	1.67/chn	
			XE-60	202	1.13/chn	
			Z	187	1.68/chn	
			JXR	200	0.84/chn	
			F-60	223	0.73/chn	
			Mass Spec.			
		43	OV-1	180→	26.20 MU	339
			OV-17		28.63 MU	

Table 11-5. Pregnanes (cont'd.)

Formula	Compound	Method	Stat. Phase	Temp.	Retention Data, Physical Constants	Ref.
$C_{21}H_{34}O_2$	Pregnanolone (MO)	43	OV-1	180→	27.08 MU	339
			OV-17		29.16 MU	
	5β-Pregnan-3β-ol-20-one	22py	XE-60	225	β 1.38/chn	291
		22c,	SE-30	224	0.63/chn	11
		22py	QF-1	175	0.71/chn	
			NGS	197	1.27/chn	
			XE-60	205	1.34/chn	
		26	SE-30	227	0.65/chn	16
			QF-1	185	1.29/chn	
			NGS	207	1.29/chn	
			XE-60	202	1.03/chn	
			Z	187	1.29/chn	
			JXR	200	0.71/chn	
			F-60	223	0.68/chn	
			Mass Spec.			
	5β-Pregnan-20α-ol-3-one	22py	NGA	225	2.41/chn	156
	17α-Pregnan-3α-ol-20-one	22py	NGS	225	5α 0.87, 5β 1.14/chn	156
	4-Pregnen-3β,20β-diol	25	SE-30	200-280		126
	Pregnenediol (5-Pregnen-3β,20α-diol)	22c	JXR	185	6.86/pga	795
			SE-52	200	7.18/pga	
		22c	NGS	235	1.85/ando	412
			XE-60	215	1.77/ando	
		25	SE-30	225	Mass Spec.	123
		22py	QF-1	215	1.04/chn	818, 732
			SE-30	225	1.14/chn	
			Mass Spec.			
		43	OV-1	180→	28.18 MU	339
			OV-17		29.19 MU	
	5-Pregnen-3β,20β-diol	25	SE-30			124, 841
			TLC			

Table 11-5. Pregnanes (cont'd.)

Formula	Compound	Method	Stat. Phase	Temp.	Retention Data, Physical Constants	Ref.
$C_{21}H_{34}O_2$	5-Pregnen-3β,20β-diol	22py	QF-1	215	0.98/chn	732,
			SE-30	225	1.07/chn	818
			Mass Spec.			
$C_{21}H_{34}O_3$	5α-Pregnan-3α,6α-diol-20-one	22py	NGS	225	1.55/chn	156
	5α-Pregnan-3α,17α-diol-20-one	22py	SE-30	226		624
	5α-Pregnan-3β,17α-diol-20-one	22c	XE-60	215	5.20/ando	412
		22c	JXR	185	7.33/pga	795
			SE-52	200	8.80/pga	
	5α,17α-Pregnen-3α,6α-diol-20-one	22py	NGA	225	1.23/chn	156
	5β-Pregnan-3α,6α-diol-20-one	22py	NGA	225	1.77/chn	156
	5β,17α-Pregnan-3α,6α-diol-20-one	22py	NGA	225	1.30/chn	156
	5-Pregnen-3α,16α,20-triol	22py	SE-30	226	α 1.13, β 1.22/chn	624
	5-Pregnen-3α,17α,20α-triol	22c	NGS	235	3.30/ando	412
			XE-60	215	3.73/ando	
	5-Pregnen-3β,16α,20β-triol	22py	SE-30	226	1.63/chn	624
	5-Pregnen-3β,17α,20α-triol	26	XE-60	225		292
		25	SE-30	219	1.65/chn	410
			XE-60	208	2.31/chn	
		22py	SE-30	226	1.55/chn	624
		44	OV-1	180→	29.66 MU	339
			OV-17		31.08 MU	
$C_{21}H_{34}O_4$	Pregnanetriolone (5β-Pregnan-3α,17α,20α-triol-11-one)	22	XE-60	225	2.715/preg	181
			QF-1	210	2.74/preg	
		22	XE-60		4.24/chn	180
		25	SE-30	210	1.93/chn	409
			XE-60	208	4.24/chn	
		26	DC-200	222	2.00/chn	603
		26	XE-60	230	3.82/chn	614

Table 11-5. Pregnanes (cont'd.)

Formula	Compound	Method	Stat. Phase	Temp.	Retention Data, Physical Constants	Ref.
$C_{21}H_{34}O_4$	Pregnanetriolone (5β-Pregnan-3α,17α,20α-triol-11-one)	44	OV-1 OV-17	180→	30.00 MU 31.75 MU	339
$C_{21}H_{36}O$	5α-Pregnan-3β-ol	22c	SE-52 JXR	200 185	2.72/pga 2.75/pga	795
	5β-Pregnan-3α-ol	22c	SE-52 JXR	200 185	2.24/pga 2.25/pga	795
$C_{21}H_{36}O_2$	20-Epipregnanediol (5β-Pregnan-3α,20β-diol)	22py	NGA	225	0.75/chn	306
			QF-1 NGS	250 225	0.83/chn 0.90/chn	156
			QF-1	250	0.76/chn	157
		43	OV-1 OV-17	180→	27.30 MU 28.05 MU	339
		22c, 22py	SE-30 QF-1 NGS XE-60	224 175 197 205	0.82/chn 0.86/chn 0.74/chn 0.78/chn	11
		26	SE-30 QF-1 NGS XE-60 SE-30	227 185 207 202 225	0.86/chn 0.76/chn 0.74/chn 0.90/chn 0.95/chn	16
			Mass Spec.			
		22py	XE-60	225	0.807/chn	291
		25	SE-30 XE-60	219 208	0.87/chn 0.84/chn	409, 410
		22c	JXR SE-52	185 200	5.84/pga 5.82/pga	795
	5α-Pregnan-3α,20α-diol	22c, 22py	SE-30 OV-1 NGS XE-60	224 175 197 205	0.91/chn 0.95/chn 0.63/chn 0.80/chn	11

Table 11-5. Pregnanes (cont'd.)

Formula	Compound	Method	Stat. Phase	Temp.	Retention Data, Physical Constants	Ref.
$C_{21}H_{36}O_2$	5α-Pregnan-3α,20α-diol	26	SE-30	227	0.90/chn	16
			QF-1	185	0.85/chn	
			NGS	207	0.64/chn	
			XE-60	202	0.81/chn	
			Z	187	0.65/chn	
			JXR	200	0.88/chn	
			F-60	223	0.88/chn	
			QF-1	250	0.79/chn	157
			SE-30	250	0.88/chn	
			NGA	255	0.75/chn	
		22	XE-60	225	0.77/chn	180
		22	XE-60	225	0.463/preg	181
			QF-1	210	0.534/preg	
		22py	XE-60	225	0.780/chn	291
		22c	XE-60	215	1.77/ando	412
	5α-Pregnan-3α,20β-diol	22py	QF-1	250	0.83/chn	156
			NGA	225	0.74/chn	
			QF-1	250	0.78/chn	157
	5α-Pregnan-3β,20α-diol		QF-1	250	1.05/chn	157
		26	SE-30	227	1.13/chn	16
			QF-1	185	1.14/chn	
			NGS	207	0.94/chn	
			XE-60	202	1.10/chn	
			Z	187	0.96/chn	
			JXR	200	1.16/chn	
			F-60	223	1.14/chn	
		22py	XE-60	225	1.075/chn	291
		26	SE-30	205	0.72/chn	498
			PhSi	207	1.60/chn	
			QF-1	195	2.16/chn	
			NGS	210	7.64/chn	

Table 11-5. Pregnanes (cont'd.)

Formula	Compound	Method	Stat. Phase	Temp.	Retention Data, Physical Constants	Ref.
$C_{21}H_{36}O_2$	5α-Pregnan-3β,20α-diol		NGA	225	1.02/chn	306
		22c, 22py	SE-30	224	1.09/chn	11
			OV-1	175	1.16/chn	
			NGS	197	0.95/chn	
			XE-60	205	1.13/chn	
			SE-30	200	7.94/pga	790
			JXR	185	7.34/pga	
	5α-Pregnan-3β,20β-diol	22c, 22py	SE-30	224	1.03/chn	11
			QF-1	175	1.12/chn	
			NGS	197	0.85/chn	
			XE-60	205	1.05/chn	
		26	SE-30	227	1.07/chn	16
			QF-1	185	1.07/chn	
			NGS	207	0.86/chn	
			XE-60	292	1.01/chn	
			Z	187	0.89/chn	
			JXR	200	1.06/chn	
			F-60	223	1.07/chn	
			Mass Spec.			
		22py	QF-1	250	1.00/chn	157
			XE-60	225	1.00/chn	291
			NGA	225	0.93/chn	306
		26	SE-30	205	0.67/chn	498
			PhSi	207	1.44/chn	
			QF-1	195	1.94/chn	
			NGS	210	6.47/chn	
		22c	SE-30	200	8.46/pga	795
			JXR	185	7.24/pga	
	Pregnanediol (5β-Pregnan-3α,20α-diol)	23, 25	SE-30	219	0.96/chn	409, 410
			XE-60	208	0.91/chn	

Table 11-5. Pregnanes (cont'd.)

Formula	Compound	Method	Stat. Phase	Temp.	Retention Data, Physical Constants	Ref.
$C_{21}H_{36}O_2$	Pregnanediol (5β-Pregnan-3α,20α-diol)	22c, 22py	SE-30	224	0.93/chn	11
			QF-1	175	1.00/chn	
			NGS	197	0.74/chn	
			XE-60	205	0.90/chn	
		26	SE-30	227	0.93/chn	16
			QF-1	185	0.90/chn	
			NGS	207	0.74/chn	
			XE-60	202	0.90/chn	
			Z	187	0.78/chn	
			JXR	200	0.94/chn	
			F-60	223	0.92/chn	
		22py	XE-60	225	0.895/chn	291
			SE-30	225	1.02/chn	121
			Mass Spec.			
			QF-1	250	0.82/chn	157
			SE-30	250	0.92/chn	
			NGA	225	0.89/chn	
		22c	XE-60	215	1.53/ando	412
		25	NGS	220	0.75/chn	123
			Mass Spec.			
		22c	JXR	185	6.18/pga	795
			SE-30	200	6.40/pga	
		25	SE-30	220		124
			TLC			
		22	XE-60		0.88/chn	180
		22	XE-60	225	0.529/preg	181
			QF-1	210	0.562/preg	
		22	XE-60	262	0.78/chn	298
			NGS	231	0.70/chn	
			HiEff	242	0.68/chn	
		43	OV-1	180→	27.58 MU	339
			OV-17		28.32 MU	

Table 11-5. Pregnanes (cont'd.)

Formula	Compound	Method	Stat. Phase	Temp.	Retention Data, Physical Constants	Ref.
$C_{21}H_{36}O_2$	Pregnanediol (5β-Pregnan-3α,20α-diol)	25	SE-30	150→300	0.83/chn	372
			Mass Spec.			306
			NGA			
		22c, 26	SE-30	205	0.98/chn	499
			PhSi	207	0.76/chn	
			QF-1	198	0.96/chn	
			NGS	210	0.83/chn	
		26	SE-30/NGS	198	1.89/andn	542
				197	1.81/andn	
		26	STAP	233	0.543/dean	560
		26	XE-60	210	0.88/chn	614
		26	DC-200	222	1.00/chn	603
			HiEff	205	1.53/ando	776
			JXR/HiEff	210	2.94/ando	
		22py	QF-1	215	0.90/chn	818
			SE-30	225	0.96/chn	
		26	CNSi	202	0.93/chn	801
			NGS	212	0.83/chn	
			QF-1	195	0.96/chn	
			SE-30	205	0.98/chn	
$C_{21}H_{36}O_3$	Pregnanetriol (5β-Pregnan-3α,17α,20α-triol)	25	NGS	220	1.75/chn	123
		22c, 22py	Mass Spec.			11
			SE-30	224	1.32/chn	
			QF-1	175	1.68/chn	
			NGS	197	1.88/chn	
			XE-60	205	1.68/chn	
		25	SE-30	219	1.45/chn	409
			XE-60	208	1.88/chn	
		22c	XE-60	215	3.75/ando	412
		44	OV-1	180→	29.05 MU	339
			OV-17		30.14 MU	

Table 11-5. Pregnanes (cont'd.)

Formula	Compound	Method	Stat. Phase	Temp.	Retention Data, Physical Constants	Ref.
$C_{21}H_{36}O_3$	Pregnanetriol (5β-Pregnan-3α,17α,20α-triol)	36-44	OV-1		3,17,20 - 28.00 MU	155
			OV-17		3,17,20 - 28.42 MU	
		43	OV-1		3,20 - 29.05 MU	
			OV-17		3,20 - 30.14 MU	
			Mass Spec.			
		22	XE-60		1.88/chn	180
		22	XE-60	225	1.165/preg	181
			QF-1	210	1.22/preg	
		26	STAP	233	1.16/dean	560
		26	XE-60	230	1.81/chn	614
		26	QF-1		1.94/chn	603
			XE-60	222	1.98/chn	
			DC-200		1.52/chn	
		22py	SE-30	226	1.30/chn	624
		22c	JXR	185	9.64/pga	795
			SE-52	200	10.40/pga	
		25	SE-30	219	2.38/chn	409
			XE-60	208	2.52/chn	
		25	SE-30	220	T_2 only	124, 126
			TLC			
	5β-Pregnan-3α,17α,20β-triol	44-36	Mass Spec.			155
	5β-Pregnan-3α,17α,20-triol	25	SE-30	219	α 1.45, β 1.29/chn	410
			XE-60	208	α 1.88, β 1.77/chn	
$C_{21}H_{36}O_4$	5β-Pregnan-3α,11β,17α,20β-tetrol (T_2-3,20)	25	SE-30	219	2.38/chn	410
			XE-60	208	2.52/chn	
		25	SE-30	200→280		126
			TLC			

TABLE 11-6. CORTICOSTEROIDS

Formula	Compound	Silylation	Method	Stat. Phase	Temp.	Retention Data, Physical Constants	Ref.
$C_{21}H_{26}O_5$	Prednisone (3,20-MO) (1,4-Pregnadien-17α,21-diol-3,11,20)	T_2	26	SE-30	235	3.06/chn	297
$C_{21}H_{28}O_5$	Aldosterone (4-Pregnen-11β,21-diol-3,18,20-trione)	T_2	22py	SE-30 TLC	275	2.33/chn	279
	Cortisone (3,20-MO) (4-Pregnen-17α,21-diol-3,11,20-trione)	T_2 T_2	26 43	SE-30 OV-1 OV-17	235 pr pr	2.59/chn 32.79 MU 37.11, 37.33 MU	297 351
	Prednisolone (3,20-MO) (1,4-Pregnadien-11β,17α,-21-triol-3,20-dione)	T_3	26	SE-30	235	3.04/chn	297
$C_{21}H_{30}O_3$	Deoxycorticosterone (3,20-MO) (4-Pregnen-21-ol-3,20-dione)	T_1	26	SE-30	235	1.80/chn	297
	4-Pregnen-17α-ol-3,20-dione (3,20-MO)	T_1	44py	OV-1 Mass Spec.	222	1.48/chn	809
	5-Pregnen-3β,17α-diol-20-one (20-MO)	T_2	44py	OV-1 Mass Spec.	222	1.30/chn	809
$C_{21}H_{30}O_4$	Corticosterone (3,20-MO) (4-Pregnen-11β,21-diol-3,20-dione)	T_2	26	SE-30	235	2.69/chn	297
	20β-Dihydro-11-dehydrocorticosterone (4-Pregnen-11β,21-diol-3,11-dione)	T_2	22c	SE-30 TLC	275	2.17/chn	279
	17α-Hydroxydeoxycorticosterone (3,20-MO) (4-Pregnen-17α,21-diol-3,20-dione)	T_2 $T_1(21)$ T_2	26 44py	SE-30 OV-1 Mass Spec.	235 222	2.01/chn 3.12/chn 2.39/chn	297 809

Table 11-6. Corticosteroids (cont'd.)

Formula	Compound	Silylation	Method	Stat. Phase	Temp.	Retention Data, Physical Constants	Ref.
$C_{21}H_{30}O_5$	Cortisol (4-Pregnen-11β,17α,21-triol-3,20-dione)	T_1(21)	22c	SE-30 / TLC	275	1.73/chn	279
		T_2 (11,17)(11,21)	22pyc	SE-30 / TLC	275	2.06/chn / 1.90/chn	
		T_2 (11,17)(11,21)	22py	SE-30 / TLC	275	1.97/chn / 1.90/chn	
		T_3	22pyc	SE-30 / TLC	275	2.33/chn	
		T_3	22py	SE-30 / TLC	275	2.38/chn	
	(3,20-MO)		26	SE-30	235	3.03/chn	297
	(3,20-MO)	T_2 (17,21)	43	OV-1 / OV-17		33.74 MU / 38.32, 38.53 MU	351
		T_3	44	OV-1 / OV-17		33.85 MU / 36.81, 37.08 MU	
	20β-Dihydrocortisone (4-Pregnen-17α,20β,21-triol-3,11-dione)	T_2 (20,21)	22c	SE-30 / TLC	275	2.93/chn	279
		T_3	22c	SE-30 / TLC	275	3.55/chn	
$C_{21}H_{32}O_3$	20β-Dihydro-11-deoxycorticosterone (4-Pregnen-20β,21-diol-3-one)	T_2	22c	SE-30 / TLC	275	2.03/chn	279
$C_{21}H_{32}O_4$	4-Pregnen-11β,20β,21-triol-3-one	T_3	22c	SE-30 / TLC	275	3.10/chn	279
	Tetrahydrodehydrocorticosterone (5β-Pregnan-3α,21-diol-11,20-dione)	T_2	43	OV-1 / OV-17	180→	29.88 MU / 32.65 MU	339
	(20-MO)	T_2	24	SE-30	190→250		263
	(MO)	T_2	43	OV-1 / OV-17	180→	29.71 MU / 31.85 MU	339

Table 11-6. Corticosteroids (cont'd.)

Formula	Compound	Silyl-ation	Method	Stat. Phase	Temp.	Retention Data, Physical Constants	Ref.
$C_{21}H_{32}O_4$	Tetrahydrodehydrocortico-sterone (dioxime) (5β-Pregnan-3α,21-diol-11,20-dione)	T_4	22py, 24py	NGS	210		123
$C_{21}H_{32}O_5$	Tetrahydrocortisone (20-MO) (5β-Pregnan-3α,17α,21-triol-11,20-dione)	T_2 (3,21)	36, 43	OV-1, OV-17	170→260, 170→260	31.21 MU, 33.77 MU	155
		T_3	36-11	OV-1, OV-17	170→260, 170→260	29.60 MU, 30.92 MU	
		T_3	44	OV-1, OV-17	170→260, 170→260	29.60 MU, 30.92 MU	
		T_3	24	SE-30	190→250		263
		T_2 (3,21)	43	OV-1, OV-17	180→, 180→	31.21 MU, 33.75 MU	339
	(dioxime)	T_4 (3,21; dioxime)	22py, 24py	NGS	220	5.48/chn	123
$C_{21}H_{34}O_4$	5α-Pregnan-3α,11β,21-triol-20-one	T_2 (3,21)	43	OV-1, OV-17	180→	30.77 MU, 33.82 MU	339
		T_3	44	OV-1, OV-17		30.58 MU, 32.00 MU	
	(MO)	T_3	24	SE-30	190→250		263
	(MO)	T_2 (3,21)	43	OV-1, OV-17	180→	30.45 MU, 32.75 MU	339
		T_3	44	OV-1, OV-17		30.11 MU, 31.08 MU	
	(oxime)	T_3 (3,21, oxime)	22py, 24py	NGS	210		123

Table 11-6. Corticosteroids (cont'd.)

Formula	Compound	Silyl-ation	Method	Stat. Phase	Temp.	Retention Data, Physical Constants	Ref.
$C_{21}H_{34}O_4$	Tetrahydrocorticosterone (5β-Pregnan-3α,11β,21-triol-20-one)	T_2(3,21)	43	OV-1 / OV-17	180→	30.68 MU / 33.74 MU	339
		T_3	44	OV-1 / OV-17		30.59 MU / 32.00 MU	
	(MO)	T_2(3,21)	43	OV-1 / OV-17	180→	30.17 MU / 32.57 MU	339
		T_3	44	OV-1 / OV-17		29.94 MU / 31.02 MU	
	(oxime)	T_3(3,21,oxime)	22py, 24py	NGS	210		123
$C_{21}H_{34}O_5$	α-Cortolone (5β-Pregnan-3α,17α,20α,21-tetrol-11-one)	T_4	22py, 22c	SE-30 / QF-1 / TLC	235 / 220		623
		T_4	43	OV-1 / OV-17	180→	32.07 MU / 33.25 MU	339
	(oxime)	T_4(3,20,21,oxime)	22py, 24py	NGS / Mass Spec.	210		123
	β-Cortolone (5β-Pregnan-3α,17α,20β,21-tetrol-11-one)	T_4	22py, 22c	SE-30 / QF-1 / TLC	235 / 220		623
		T_4	43	OV-1 / OV-17	180→	32.35 MU / 33.79 MU	339
		T_3(3,20,21)	22py, 24py	NGS / Mass Spec.	220	5.84/chn	123
	(oxime)	T_4(3,20,21,oxime)	22py, 24py	NGS / Mass Spec.	210		123

Table 11-6. Corticosteroids (cont'd.)

Formula	Compound	Silylation	Method	Stat. Phase	Temp.	Retention Data, Physical Constants	Ref.
$C_{21}H_{34}O_5$	α-Tetrahydrocortisol (MO) (5α-Pregnan-3α,11β,17α,21-tetrol-20-one)		24	SE-30	190→250	31.96 MU	263
		T_3 (3,17,21)	43	OV-1	180→	34.76 MU	339
				OV-17		31.86 MU	
		T_4	44	OV-1			
				OV-17		33.25 MU	
	β-Tetrahydrocortisol (MO) (5β-Pregnan-3α,11β,17α,21-tetrol-20-one)	T_2 (3,21)	36,43	OV-1	170→260	31.82 MU	155, 351
				OV-17		34.54 MU	
		T_3 (3,11,21)	36	OV-1	170→260	31.79 MU	
				OV-17		33.16 MU	
		T_2 (3,21)	43	OV-1	180→	31.82 MU	339
				OV-17		34.61 MU	
		T_3 (3,11,21)	44	OV-1		31.79 MU	
				OV-17		33.16 MU	
		T_4	44, 36-11	OV-1	170→260	30.23 MU	155
				OV-17		30.52 MU	
			24	SE-30	190→250		263
$C_{21}H_{36}O_5$	α-Cortol (5β-Pregnan-3α,11β,17α,20α,21-pentol)	T_3	43	OV-1	170→260	32.66 MU	155
				OV-17		33.91 MU	
		T_4 (3,11,20,21)	44py	Mass Spec.			
				OV-1		33.07 MU	
				OV-17		33.06 MU	
				Mass Spec.			
		T_3 (3,20,21)	43	OV-1	180→	32.66 MU	339
				OV-17	180→	33.91 MU	
		T_4 (3,11,20,21)	44	OV-1	180→	33.07 MU	
				OV-17	180→	33.06 MU	
		T_4	22c	QF-1	220		
				SE-30	235		
				TLC			
		T_5	22py	QF-1	220	m 158–162°	623
				SE-30	235		
				TLC			

Table 11-6. Corticosteroids (cont'd.)

Formula	Compound	Silyl-ation	Method	Stat. Phase	Temp.	Retention Data, Physical Constants	Ref.
$C_{21}H_{36}O_5$	α-Cortol (5β-Pregnan-3α,11β,17α, 20α,21-pentol)	T_5	44–36py	OV-1		31.22 MU	155
				OV-17		31.43 MU	
				Mass Spec.			
			24	SE-30	190→250		263
	β-Cortol (5β-Pregnan-3α,11β,17α, 20β,21-pentol)	T_3 (3,20,21)	43	OV-1	170→260	32.85 MU	155
				OV-17		34.17 MU	
				Mass Spec.			
		T_4 (3,11,20,21)	44py	OV-1		33.13 MU	
				OV-17		33.24 MU	
				Mass Spec.			
		T_5	44–36py	OV-1		30.79 MU	
				OV-17		30.15 MU	
				Mass Spec.			
		T_3 (3,20,21)	43	OV-1	180→	32.85 MU	339
				OV-17	180→	34.17 MU	
		T_4 (3,11,20,21)	44	OV-1	180→	33.13 MU	
				OV-17	180→	33.24 MU	
		T_4	22c	QF-1	220		623
				SE-30	235		
				TLC			
		T_5	22py	QF-1	220		623
				SE-30	235		
				TLC			
		T_3 (3,20, 21)	22py, 24py	Mass Spec.			123
$C_{23}H_{30}O_6$	Cortisone acetate(3,20-MO) (4-Pregnen-17α-ol-3,11,20 -trione-21-acetate)	T_1	26	SE-30	235	3.26/chn	297
$C_{23}H_{32}O_6$	Cortisol acetate (3,20-MO) (4-Pregnen-11β,17α-diol -3,20-dione-21-acetate)	T_2	26	SE-30	235	3.56/chn	297

TABLE 11-7. GLYCOSIDES AND AGLYCONES

Formula	Compound	Silylation Method	Stat. Phase	Temp.	Retention Data, Physical Constants	Ref.
$C_{23}H_{34}O_4$	Digitoxigenin	26	SE-30	220	37.5'	377
		22py	SE-30	250,285		868
		$T_1(3)$ 25	SE-30	200→260	34.45 MU	515
			OV-17	230→290	39.71 MU	
		T_2 (3,23-enol) 43,44	SE-30	200→260	32.00 MU	
			OV-17	230→290	34.55 MU	
		T_3 (3,14,23-enol) 36-44	SE-30	200→260	32.23 MU	
			OV-17	230→290	32.42 MU	
			Mass Spec.			
$C_{23}H_{34}O_5$	Digoxigenin	26	SE-30	220	47.5'	377
		22py	SE-30	250,285		868
		T_2 (3,12) 25	SE-30	200→260	35.41 MU	515
			OV-17	230→290	38.95 MU	
		T_3 (3,12,23-enol) 43,44	SE-30	200→260	32.64 MU	
			OV-17	230→290	34.22 MU	
		T_4 (3,12,14,23-enol) 36-44	SE-30	200→260	32.83 MU	
			OV-17	230→290	33.20 MU	
			Mass Spec.			
	Gitoxigenin	22py	SE-30	250,285		868
		T_2 (3,16) 25	SE-30	200→260	35.41 MU	515
			OV-17	230→290	39.07 MU	
		T_3 (3,16,23-enol) 43,44	SE-30	200→260	32.93 MU	
			OV-17	230→290	34.47 MU	
		T_4 (3,14,16,23-enol) 36-44	SE-30	200→260	32.85 MU	
			OV-17	230→290	33.23 MU	
			Mass Spec.			
$C_{23}H_{34}O_8$	Ouabagenin	22py	1% SE-30	250		868
			1.6% SE-30	285		
$C_{23}H_{36}O_5$	Dihydrodigoxigenin	T_2 (3,12) 43,44	SE-30	200→260	34.33 MU	515
			OV-17	230→290	37.87 MU	
		T_3 (3,12,14) 36-44	SE-30	200→260	33.84 MU	
			OV-17	230→290	35.33 MU	
			Mass Spec.			

Table 11-7. Glycosides and Aglycones (cont'd.)

Formula	Compound	Silyl-ation	Method	Stat. Phase	Temp.	Retention Data, Physical Constants	Ref.
$C_{24}H_{32}O_4$	Resibufogenin	T_1	26	SE-30	235	2.29/chl	666
$C_{24}H_{34}O_4$	Bufalin		26	SE-30	235	2.73/chl	666
$C_{26}H_{34}O_6$	Cinobufagin	T_1	25	SE-30	235	3.59/chl	666
$C_{26}H_{34}O_7$	Cinobufotalin		26	SE-30	235	5.72/chl	666
$C_{26}H_{36}O_6$	Bufotalin		26	SE-30	235	5.00/chl	666
$C_{26}H_{39}O_8$	5-Androsten-17-one-3β-yl-β-D-glucopyranosiduronic acid methyl ester	T_3	22py	SE-30 NGS	250 240	29.0/andn 11.0/andn	799
$C_{26}H_{41}O_8$	Androstan-17-one-3α-yl-β-D-glucopyranosiduronic acid methyl ester	T_3	22py	SE-30 NGS	250 240	15.8/andn 4.72/andn	799
$C_{29}H_{44}O_8$	Digoxigenin mono-digitoxoside		22py	SE-30	250,285		868
$C_{29}H_{33}O_{12}$	Oubain		22py	SE-30	250,285		868
$C_{35}H_{54}O_{10}$	Digitoxigenin bis-digitoxoside		22py	SE-30	250,285		868
$C_{35}H_{54}O_{11}$	Digoxigenin bis-digitoxoside		22py	SE-30	250,285		868
$C_{41}H_{60}O_{14}$	Digoxin		22py	SE-30	250,285		868
$C_{41}H_{64}O_{13}$	Digitoxin		22py	SE-30	250,285		868
$C_{41}H_{64}O_{14}$	Gitoxin		22py	SE-30	250,285		868

TABLE 11-8. TRITERPENES

Formula	Compound	Method	Stat. Phase	Temp.	Retention Data, Physical Constants	Ref.
$C_{29}H_{50}O$	31-Norcycloartanol					61
$C_{30}H_{48}O_3$	Saikogenin A	25	SE-30	240	6.58/chn	447
	Saikogenin B	25	SE-30	240	4.33/chn	447
	Saikogenin C	25	SE-30	240	5.75/chn	447
	Saikogenin D	25	SE-30	240	7.59/chn	447
$C_{30}H_{50}O$	α-Amyrin	25	CNSi	225	3.77/chn	360
			QF-1	220	3.65/chn	
			NGS	220	3.96/chn	
		25h	XE-60	205→245	m 107-111°	474
			TLC			
			Mass Spec.			
	β-Amyrin	25	CNSi	225	3.34/chn	360
			QF-1	220	3.12/chn	
			NGS	220	3.42/chn	
		25h	Mass Spec.	205→245	m 156.5-159.5°	474
			TLC			
	Butyrospermol	25h	XE-60	205→245		474
			TLC			
			Mass Spec.			
	Cycloartenol	25	XE-60	205→245	20.9'	58
		23c	SE-30	225	4.66/chn	427
			DC-560	225	5.11/chn	
			FS-1265	225	3.78/chn	
			HiEff(S)	225	4.30/chn	
			HiEff(PVP)	225	6.05/chn	
			EGSP-Z	200	5.07/chn	
		25h	XE-60	205→245	m 103-106.5°	474
			TLC			
			Mass Spec.			
	Isozeorinin	25	0.75% SE-30	240	4.1', 6.3', 7.7'	718
			1.5% SE-30	240	13.3', 22.3'	

Table 11-8. Triterpenes (cont'd.)

Formula	Compound	Method	Stat. Phase	Temp.	Retention Data, Physical Constants	Ref.
$C_{30}H_{50}O$	Lupeol	25h	XE-60 TLC Mass Spec.	205→245	m 176.5-178.5°	474
	4α-Methylstigmasta-7,24(28)-dien-3β-ol	25	XE-60	205→245	24.1'	58
	31-Norcyclolaudenol					61
	Taraxasterol	25	CNSi QF-1 NGS	225 220 220	13.0/chn 7.52/chn	360
	Taraxerol	25	CNSi QF-1 NGS	225 220 220	3.15/chn 3.12/chn 3.33/chn	360
	Zeorinin	25	0.75% SE-30 1.5% SE-30	240 240	4.0' 12.9'	718
$C_{30}H_{50}O_2$	Betulin	25	NGS, QF-1 CNSi SE-30	220 225 240	5.36/chn	360
	Zeorinone	25	0.75% SE-30 1.5% SE-30	240 240	4.0', 6.3', 11.8', 12.7', 20.4', 39.5'	718
$C_{30}H_{50}O_3$	Longispinogenin	25	SE-30	240	5.3/chn	360
	Primulagenin	25	SE-30	240	5.27/chn	447
$C_{30}H_{50}O_4$	Sojasapogenol A	25	SE-30	240	6.57/chn	360
$C_{30}H_{52}O$	Cycloartanol	25h	TLC; Mass Spec.			61 474
$C_{30}H_{52}O_2$	Zeorin	25	0.75% SE-30 1.5% SE-30	240 240	6.4', 11.3', 13.5', 22.0', 38.7'	718
$C_{31}H_{50}O_4$	Hederagenin methyl ester	25	SE-30	240	7.37/chn	360
$C_{31}H_{52}O$	Cyclolaudenol	25	XE-60	205→245	22.7'	61
	24-Methylene cycloartanol	25h	XE-60 TLC;Mass Spec.	205→245	m 140-143°	58 474

12

Miscellaneous Compounds

12-1. INORGANIC ACID DERIVATIVES

Sulfinic acids, sulfonic acids, and sulfonamides were readily silylated, although not many examples were found. The silylation of glycerophosphates and phosphoglyceric acids with boiling HMDS–TMCS was assumed to be complete, including the two phosphate sites (301, 302), as similar experiments with phenyl phosphate had given the bis(TMS) ester in 92% yield (301).

12-2. PEROXIDES

Trimethylorganoperoxysilanes, ROOSiMe$_3$, are stable, distillable liquids. They have been prepared from alkyl or aralkylhydroperoxides and TMCS in pyridine (135, 287, 322, 725) or with a silylamine (585). Their Raman and IR spectra are given (725) and their decomposition has been studied (322). They initiate polymerizations (135, 287).

12-3. EPOXIDES

Although epoxy groups do not contain active protons they do react readily with the usual silyl donors and therefore epoxy compounds are included in this review. The derivatives are less volatile than the starting compounds as the reagent adds to the epoxy group, and no GC data have been reported. The preparations were generally made, as with alcohols, by heating the compound with TMCS. The epoxy group is more reactive than the primary hydroxyl group (621).

$$R-CH-CH_2 \ + \ Me_3SiX \rightarrow R-CH-CH_2X \qquad X = Cl, NEt_2$$
$$\underset{O}{\diagdown\diagup} \qquad\qquad\qquad\qquad\qquad \underset{OSiMe_3}{|}$$

The oxide ring opens predominantly at the primary carbon atom under addition of TMCS or silylamines. NMR data (369) and derivative preparation (505) substantiate this cleavage. Early work (38) indicating ring opening at the secondary carbon atom was disproved (505, 621). However, it is reported that butyl glycidyl ether with silyl acetate does cleave at the secondary carbon atom (435).

$$BuOCH_2-CH-CH_2 + CH_3COOTMS \xrightarrow[\text{Et}_3\text{N cat.}]{89\%}$$
$$\diagdown \diagup$$
$$O$$

$$BuOCH_2-CH(OAc)-CH_2OTMS$$

Further, 1,3-epoxypentane was cleaved at C-1 by TMCS but at C-3 by triethylchlorosilane (505). The epoxy groups of several cyclodiene epoxides related to dieldrin were not silylated by HMDS–TMCS (127).

12-4. ENOLS

For the preparation of TMS enol ethers the free carbonyl compound was reacted directly with TMCS in the presence of base, or the enolate has been treated with TMCS in an inert solvent. A rather unusual method employed refluxing TMCS–triethylamine with zinc chloride as catalyst (609). A series of aldehydes and ketones were converted to TMS enol ethers in fair yields by this method. With some enolizable carbonyl groups there has been some question as to whether silylation has produced C-silyl or O-silyl derivatives. These points have been resolved by NMR and IR spectroscopy. West has shown by IR that the silylation products of acetylacetone (853) and of the sodium enolate of ethyl acetoacetate (854) were O-linked. Even methyl cyanoacetate is silylated as an enol—IR shows the product to be free from carbonyl (187).

Krüger and Rochow found that the silylation of the sodium enolate of ethyl acetate gave a 22% yield of the C-silyl product and a 14% yield of the O-silyl compound (445). Results were proved by IR and NMR.

Klebe et al. (422) silylated cyclic β-keto acids with BSA in ether or benzene and obtained in each case the TMS enol ether–TMS ester. Dalgleish et al. (182) chromatographed the products from α-keto acids on F-60. Multiple products were obtained using HMDS–TMCS in pyridine. With BSTFA–TMCS, however, M. G. Horning et al. (347a) obtained single products, which were identified as TMS enol ether-TMS esters by GC–MS. Also, if the α-keto acid was methylated in dimethylformamide then treated with HMDS–pyridine a single peak was obtained for the enol TMS ether methyl ester (182).

Chambaz et al. (155a) studied the enolization of ketosteroids under a range of silylation conditions. The 4-ene-3-one steroids, such as testosterone, enolized most rapidly, and with a powerful silylating reagent such as TSIM–BSA–TMCS the enol ether was the principal product.

Sodium enolate salts were prepared and reacted *in situ* with TMCS. For this purpose the sodium salt of HMDS (445) or anthracene–sodium in tetrahydrofuran has been used. The TMS enol ethers of digitoxigenin, digoxigenin and gitoxigenin (515) are discussed in section 11-11 under steroid glycosides.

12-5. THIOLS

1-Butanethiol did not react with HMDS—TMCS at reflux (452). To prepare the TMS thioether of this and other saturated alkyl thiols it was necessary to treat the sodium or lead thiol salts with TMCS (Methods 15 and 16, respectively). However, allyl TMS thioether was prepared cold from the thiol and HMDS–TMCS (752). Thiolactic acid and some other thiols were silylated with TMCS–triethylamine. Retention volumns of lower alkyl TMS thioethers on Apiezon L are given (592). There was some decomposition on the column. Mass spectral data for the n-butyl and benzyl TMS thioethers are given (712, 194).

12-6. OXIMES

Aldoximes and ketoximes on silylation under mild conditions, as by TMCS in pyridine, gave TMS derivatives in good yields. The products are quite stable to hydrolysis. IR spectra showed the 1636-1640 cm^{-1} C:N bond (198). Ketoacids, whose silyl derivatives give multiple peaks on GC, yield oxime TMS derivatives stable for gas chromatographic analysis (89, 335). Hexose oxime TMS ethers were not well resolved on an EGS column. Further, analysis was complicated by the possible formation of both cyclic and acyclic modifications of the oxime (764).

12-7. PYRIDINES

Silyl esters of nicotinic, picolinic and quinolinic acids when chromatographed on F-60 gave trailing peaks resembling those from TMS amides (182). In the silylation of pyridoxal and pyridoxol, Korytnyk *et al.* (436) found that reaction in dimethylsulfoxide hastened complete ether formation, as evidenced by a single peak. Generally silylation of pyridoxol had given two peaks. Sennello *et al.* (702) were able to completely silylate these compounds as well as pyridoxamine in refluxing HMDS catalysed by a few drops of TMCS. Products were distilled in high yield. Structures were confirmed by elemental analysis and NMR. Richter *et al.* (611) silylated pyridoxol and pyridoxal with N-TMS-acetamide in pyridine and investigated the mass spectra of the derivatives.

12-8. PYRIMIDINES AND PURINES

Silyl derivatives of pyrimidine and purine bases were prepared mainly by treatment with TMCS in triethylamine or by heating with HMDS. Boiling HMDS was usually sufficient but uric acid required treatment at 200° in an autoclave (72). Silylation has also been effected with BSA in acetonitrile at 150° (268). All bases gave single products except cytosine, which gave two peaks on GC. Silylation of cytosine at room temperature gave one product. The purines however require the higher temperature for complete reaction.

The course of silylation is illustrated by guanine. Except for position 9 purine ring nitrogen atoms are not silylated. Amino groups and hydroxyl groups of lactim tautomeric forms react. The structure of these products

has been proved by IR and NMR (551, 671). 2,4-Bis-O-(trimethylsilyl)-uracil has been especially thoroughly documented. The number of silyl groups was indicated by elemental analysis and weight loss on hydrolysis (551). IR showed the absence of C=O and the presence of C=N, C=C, Si–O–C, and SiMe₃ (671). For purine derivatives the absence of the imidazole N-H bond at position 9 was proved by IR (551). Further, these purine TMS compounds are known to react with loss of silyl to yield 9-glycosides (556).

Sasaki and Hashizume (671) silylated pyrimidines and purines with HMDS–TMCS and chromatographed on DC-430, SE-30, and SE-52 with good resolution and quantification. With some other columns there was tailing or missing peaks. Gehrke et al. (268) silylated with BSA and chromatographed the reaction mixture on 4% SE-30 with good separation.

TABLE 12-1. MISCELLANEOUS COMPOUNDS

Inorganic Acid Derivatives

Formula	Compound	Method (Yield %)	B.P./mm; M.P.	n_D^t	Stat. Phase, Temp., Retention Data	Ref.
CH_4SO_4	Methyl sulfuric acid	11	b 201			686
$C_2H_7NO_3S$	Taurine	43d			SE-30, 117°, 5.8' / 128°, 3.3'	147
$C_2H_7O_5P$	Ethylene glycol-1-phosphate	23			DC-430, 160°	302
$C_3H_7NO_4S$	Cysteinesulfinic acid (hydrate)	43d			SE-30, 117°, 5.8' / 128°, 3.5'	147
$C_3H_7NO_5S$	Cysteic acid	43d			SE-30, 117°, 9.8' / 128°, 4.6'	147
$C_3H_7O_7P$	2-Phosphoglyceric acid	23			DC-430, 160°, 190°, 218°	302
$C_3H_7O_7P$	3-Phosphoglyceric acid	23			DC-430, 160°, 190°, 218°	302
$C_3H_9O_6P$	Glycerophosphoric acid	43			OV-17, 170→260°	347
		23			DC-430, 160°, 190°, 218°	302
$C_4H_{11}O_3P$	n-Butylphosphonic acid	11(15%)	b 107-108/5.5	1.4168^{25}		404
$C_6H_7NO_2S$	Benzenesulfonamide	21b(70%) 31b(85%)	m 63			50
$C_6H_7O_4P$	Phenyl phosphate	23(92%)	b 113-134/4	1.4590^{19}	DC-430, 150°, 2.50'	301
$C_7H_8O_3S$	p-Toluenesulfonic acid	24			Mass Spec.	774
$C_{10}H_{13}N_5O_7S$	Adenosine-5'-sulfate	25			SE-30, 249°, 6.2'	295

Peroxides

Formula	Compound	Method (Yield %)	B.P./mm; M.P.	n_D^t	Stat. Phase, Temp., Retention Data	Ref.
$C_4H_{10}O_2$	t-Butyl hydroperoxide	13e				725
		13e(54%)	b 41/41			287
		13z				322

Table 12-1. Miscellaneous Compounds (cont'd.)

Peroxides (cont'd.)

Formula	Compound	Method (Yield %)	B.P./mm; M.P.	n_D^t	Stat. Phase, Temp., Retention Data	Ref.
$C_4H_{10}O_2$	t-Butyl hydroperoxide	13z(80%) 21e	b 79/215	1.3935^{25}		135
		37(20%)				585
$C_5H_{12}O_2$	t-Pentyl hydroperoxide	13z	b 78/95	1.4032^{25}		135
$C_9H_{12}O_2$	α,α-Dimethylbenzyl hydroperoxide	13z(50%)	b 43/0.05	1.4780^{25}		135
$C_{10}H_{12}O_2$	1,2,3,4-Tetrahydro-1-naphthyl hydroperoxide	12e(50%)	b 53/0.01	1.5102^{25}		135
	Epoxides					
C_2H_4O	Ethylene oxide	11e(59%)	b 72-73/3	1.4593^{20}		506
$C_3H_3Cl_3O$	1,2-Epoxy-3,3,3-trichloro-propane	33(87%) 37(89%)	b 103-104/3.2 b 103-104/1			369
C_3H_5ClO	Glycidyl chloride	37(45%)	b 85-87/1	1.4394^{20}		369
		11(62%)	b 105-107/68	1.4226^{20}		505
C_3H_6O	Propylene oxide	11(77%)	b 50-51/30	1.4342^{20}		507
$C_3H_6O_2$	Glycidol	11(83%)	b 82.5-83/13	1.4342^{20}		621
		11t(75%)	b 181.5	1.4424^{20}		432
$C_4H_8O_2$	Glycidyl methyl ether	11(77%)	b 87-88/30	1.4273^{20}		505
$C_5H_{10}O$	1,3-Epoxypentane	11e(81%)	b 69-70/13	1.4283^{20}		286
$C_6H_{10}O$	Cyclohexene oxide	11e(69%)	b 60-62/3	1.4565^{20}		506
$C_6H_{12}O$	1,3-Epoxyhexane	11e(62%)	b 80-81/13	1.4312^{20}		286
$C_7H_{14}O_2$	Butyl glycidyl ether	54(89%)	b 77-81/0.3			435
$C_9H_{10}O_2$	Phenyl 2,3-epoxypropyl ether	11(60%)	b 109-110/1	1.4990^{20}		35

Table 12-1. Miscellaneous Compounds (cont'd.)

Epoxides (cont'd.)

Formula	Compound	Method (Yield %)	B.P./mm; M.P.	n_D^t	Stat. Phase, Temp., Retention Data	Ref.
$C_{12}H_{14}O_4$	Diglycidyl resorcinol ether	11	b 203-205/2	1.4999^{20}		35
	Diglycidyl hydroquinone ether	11	b 265.8/1	1.5260^{20}		35
	Enols					
C_2H_4O	Acetaldehyde	19(32%)	b 74	1.3892^{20}		609
C_3H_6O	Acetone	15e(17%)		1.39332^{26}	Carb, 87°	445
		19(34%)	b 93-94	1.3961^{20}		609
$C_4H_5NO_2$	Methyl cyanoacetate	14b(50%)	b 75-76/0.65	1.4465^{20}		187
C_4H_6O	2-Butene-1-al	19(77%)	b 131	1.4472^{20}		609
C_4H_8O	Butyraldehyde	19(31%) 14b	b 120	1.4061^{20}		609
	Isobutyraldehyde	19(32%)	b 119	1.4070^{20}		609
	Methylethyl ketone	19b(50%)	b 117-118			609
$C_4H_8O_2$	Ethyl acetate	15e(14%)			Carb, 125°	445
$C_5H_6O_5$	α-Ketoglutaric acid	25			10% F-60, 16.36 MU 1% F-60, 16.54 MU	182
$C_5H_8O_2$	Acetylacetone	12b(41%)	b 191-192/735	1.4516^{20}		429
		13p(46%)	b 66-68/4	1.4546^{25}		853
		15e	b 68/9	1.4522^{20}		445
		47b(65%)	b 102-103/35	1.4551^{20}		413, 418
$C_5H_8O_3$	Methyl acetoacetate	15u(62%) 21dpy			10% F-60, 11.26 MU 1% F-60, 11.24 MU	182

Table 12-1. Miscellaneous Compounds (cont'd.)

Enols (cont'd.)

Formula	Compound	Method (Yield %)	B.P./mm; M.P.	n_D^t	Stat. Phase, Temp., Retention Data	Ref.
$C_5H_8O_3$	Methyl α-ketobutyrate	21dpy			10% F-60, 10.58 MU 1% F-60, 10.42 MU	182
$C_5H_{10}O$	3-Methylbutan-2-one	15t(69%)	b 133	1.4112^{20}		99
	3-Pentanone	15t(81%)	b 140	1.4162^{20}		99
$C_6H_8O_5$	Dimethyl oxaloacetate	21dpy			10% F-60, 12.16 MU 1% F-60, 12.24 MU	182
$C_6H_{10}O$	Cyclohexanone	15t(72%)	b 77.5/28	1.4467^{20}		99
		15b(59%)	b 58-58.5/11	1.4452^{20}		445
		19(61%)	b 165	1.4461^{20}		609
	Mesityl oxide	15e(30%)	b 52-53/12	1.4460^{20}		445
		19(73%)	b 62/18	1.4488^{20}		609
	2-Methyl-2-pentenal	19b(48%)	b 66-69/15	1.4588^{20}		609
$C_6H_{10}O_2$	3-Methyl-2,4-pentanedione	15u(16%)	b 89-91/8	1.4563^{25}		853
$C_6H_{10}O_3$	Ethyl acetoacetate	14b(85%)	b 87-88/12	1.4420^{25}		184
		15u(61%)	b 76-78/7	1.4393^{25}		854
	α-Ketoisocaproic acid	15e			NMR	445
	Methyl α-ketoisovalerate	21dpy			10% F-60, 11.36 MU 1% F-60, 11.30 MU	182
$C_6H_{12}O$	3,3-Dimethylbutanone	15t(79%)	b 138	1.4105^{20}		99
$C_7H_{10}O_3$	Tetrahydro-2-ketobenzoic acid	43e				422
$C_7H_{10}O_5$	Dimethyl α-ketoglutarate	21dpy			10% F-60, 14.24 MU 1% F-60, 14.28 MU	182
$C_7H_{12}O$	2-Methyl-2-hexen-5-one	19b(50%)	b 77/14	1.4635^{20}		609

Table 12-1. Miscellaneous Compounds (cont'd.)

Enols (cont'd.)

Formula	Compound	Method (Yield %)	B.P./mm; M.P.	n_D^t	Stat. Phase, Temp., Retention Data	Ref.
$C_7H_{12}O_3$	Methyl α-ketoisocaproate	21py			10% F-60, 11.60 MU 1% F-60, 11.60 MU	182
$C_7H_{12}O_4$	Diethyl malonate	15e				445
$C_7H_{14}O$	4,4-Dimethylpentan-3-one	15t(71%)	b 71/28	1.4297^{20}		99
		15t(28%)	b 87/28	1.4209^{20}		99
C_8H_8O	Acetophenone	14b,43 (38%)	b 93-94/14	1.5008^{20}		444, 445
		15t(77%)	b 111/28	1.5011^{20}		99
$C_8H_{10}O_5$	2-Keto-1,3-cyclohexane-dicarboxylic acid	43e			SiO, 100→300°	422
$C_8H_{12}O_2$	Dimedone	43b,43py	m 56-58		NMR; SiO, 100→300°, 8.6!	422
$C_9H_8O_3$	Phenylpyruvic acid	25			10% F-60, 17.16 MU 1% F-60, 17.12 MU	182
$C_9H_8O_4$	p-Hydroxyphenylpyruvic	25			10% F-60, 20.74 MU 1% F-60, 20.82 MU	182
$C_{10}H_{10}O_3$	Methyl phenylpyruvate	25			10% F-60, DC-560	348
		21py			F-60, 16.00 MU	182
$C_{10}H_{10}O_4$	Methyl p-hydroxyphenyl-pyruvate	21dpy			10% F-60, 19.16 MU 1% F-60, 19.34 MU	182
$C_{10}H_{14}O_5$	Dimethyl 2-keto-1,3-cyclo-hexanedicarboxylate	43e				422
$C_{10}H_{16}O$	3,7-Dimethyl-3,6-octadienal	19b(74%)	b 73-75/0.3	1.4746^{20}		609
$C_{11}H_9NO_3$	Indolepyruvic acid	21dpy			10% F-60, 24.64 MU 1% F-60, 24.52 MU	182
$C_{11}H_{10}O_3$	1,2,3,4-Tetrahydro-2-keto-1-naphthoic acid	43e			SE-30	422

Table 12-1. Miscellaneous Compounds (cont'd.)

Enols (cont'd.)

Formula	Compound	Method (Yield %)	B.P./mm; M.P.	n_D^t	Stat. Phase, Temp., Retention Data	Ref.
$C_{12}H_{11}NO_3$	Methyl indolepyruvate [→T₂ (N, enol)]	21dpy			10% F-60, 23.70 MU 1% F-60, 23.58 MU	182
	[→T₁ (enol)]	21dpy			10% F-60, 22.80 MU 1% F-60, 22.82 MU	182
$C_{13}H_{17}NO$	1-(Phenylacetyl)-piperidide	15b	m 53-56			421
$C_{19}H_{30}O_3$	11β-Hydroxyetiocholanolone	36(11%)			Mass Spec.	155
$C_{25}H_{23}O_4$	Colupulone	21d			Mass Spec.	183
	Thiols					
$C_2H_4O_2S$	Thioglycollic acid	15e	b 73-75.5/30			745
		14b(65%)	b 108/11.5	1.4552^{20}		613
C_2H_6S	Ethanethiol	16(76%)	b 130	1.4512^{20}		2,592
C_3H_6S	2-Propene-1-thiol	23	b 150/740			752
$C_3H_6O_2S$	Methyl thioglycollate	14b(78%)	b 87/10	1.4678^{20}		613
	Thiolactic acid	14b(73%)	b 100/10	1.4515^{20}		613
C_3H_8S	1-Propanethiol	16(92%)	b 151	1.4524^{20}		2,592
		15h				57
	2-Propanethiol	16(73%)	b 142	1.4497^{20}		2,592
$C_4H_{10}S$	1-Butanethiol	15p	b 171-172.5	1.4540^{20}		452
		15h				57
		16(81%)	b 168	1.4550^{20}		2,592
		52(76%)	b 169	1.4553^{20}		3

Table 12-1. Miscellaneous Compounds (cont'd.)

Thiols (cont'd.)

Formula	Compound	Method (Yield %)	B.P./mm; M.P.	n_D^t	Stat. Phase, Temp., Retention Data	Ref.
$C_4H_{10}S$	1-Butanethiol	53(78%)	b 166-169	1.4542^{20}		2
		21			Mass Spec.	712
	2-Methyl-2-propanethiol	15h				57
		16(70%)	b 157	1.4570^{20}		2, 592
C_6H_6S	Benzenethiol	15h	b 72/8			57
C_7H_6OS	Thiobenzoic acid	14j	b 98-99/1	1.5570^{20}		509
C_7H_8S	α-Toluenethiol	15			SF-96, 180°pr, 4.2' Mass Spec.	194
	2-Phenylethanethiol	15			SF-96, 200°pr, 2.0' Mass Spec.	194
$C_8H_{10}OS$	2-Phenoxyethanethiol	43			SE-30, 190°, 5.1' Mass Spec.	195
$C_{12}H_{26}S$	1-Dodecanethiol	15e	b 210-215/0.1 m 20	1.4750^{20}		88, 190

Oximes

Formula	Compound	Method (Yield %)	B.P./mm; M.P.	n_D^t	Stat. Phase, Temp., Retention Data	Ref.
C_2H_5NO	Acetaldoxime	13b(22%)	b 28-30/39	1.4030^{20}		198
$C_3H_5NO_3$	Pyruvic acid oxime	25			SE-52, 90→170°	335
C_3H_7NO	Acetoxime	21(66%)	b 121/757	1.4100^{20}		234
	Propionaldoxime	13b(50%)	b 120-120.5/776	1.4112^{20}		706
		13b(54%)	b 40/28	1.4102^{20}		198
$C_4H_5NO_5$	Oxaloacetic acid oxime	25			SE-52, 90→170°	335

Table 12-1. Miscellaneous Compounds (cont'd.)

Oximes (cont'd.)

Formula	Compound	Method (Yield %)	B.P./mm; M.P.	n_D^t	Stat. Phase, Temp., Retention Data	Ref.
C_4H_9NO	n-Butyraldoxime	13b(61%)	b 39-41/10	1.4160^{20}		198
	Isobutyraldoxime	13b(53%)	b 41.5-42/16	1.4109^{20}		198
$C_4H_{11}NO$	Diethylhydroxylamine	11	b 35/15			831
$C_5H_7NO_5$	α-Ketoglutaric acid oxime	25			SE-52, 90→170°	335
$C_5H_{11}NO$	Diethylketoxime	21(94%)	b 86/100	1.4170^{20}		234
$C_6H_{13}NO_6$	Galactose oxime	25			EGS, 170°, 1.98/gu	764
	Glucose oxime	25			EGS, 170°, 2.16/gu	764
	Gulose oxime	25			EGS, 170°, 2.10/gu	764
C_7H_7NO	Benzaldoxime	13b(53%)	b 81-82/2.5, 87.5-88/5	1.5114^{20}		706
$C_7H_7NO_2$	o-Hydroxybenzaldoxime → T_1 → T_2	13e(14%) (35%)	b 110-111/4 b 128-128.8/4	1.5200^{20} 1.4950^{20}		706
C_8H_9NO	Acetophenone oxime	13b(44%)	b 93-94/4	1.5073^{20}		706
$C_9H_9NO_3$	Phenylpyruvic acid oxime	23			SE-52, 170°, 6.0/naph	89
$C_9H_9NO_4$	p-Hydroxyphenylpyruvic acid oxime	23			SE-52, 170°, 6.0/naph	89
$C_9H_{19}NO$	Diisobutylketoxime	13b(60%)	b 70/4	1.4267^{20}		706

Table 12-1. Miscellaneous Compounds (cont'd.)

Pyridines and Pyrazines

Formula	Compound	Silyl-ation	Method (Yield %)	B.P./mm; M.P.	Stat. Phase, Temp., Retention Data	Ref.
C_5H_5NO	2-Hydroxypyridine	T_1	14u(86%)	b 63/12		81
$C_6H_5NO_2$	Nicotinic acid	T_1	25		10% F-60, 12.96 MU; 1% F-60, 13.52 MU	182
		T_1	43		OV-17, 150°pr	347
	Picolinic acid	T_1	11	b 91/2		699
		T_1	25		10% F-60, 13.30 MU; 1% F-60, 13.58 MU	182
$C_7H_5NO_4$	Quinolinic acid	T_2	25		10% F-60, 17.94 MU; 1% F-60, 18.00 MU	182
$C_8H_6N_2O_2$	2,3-Dihydroxyquinoxaline	T_2	14u(79%)	b 110/0.2; m 92		81
$C_8H_9NO_3$	Pyridoxal	T_2	42py		SE-30, XE-60, C-20M, SiO; Mass Spec.	611
		T_2	22(85%)	b 93-95/0.01	DC-Hi, 200°, 2.5'	702
		T_2	23s,25		SE-30, 115°, 6.8'	436
	(HCl)	T_2	25,43py		SE-52, 165°	563
$C_8H_{10}NO_6P$	Pyridoxal-5-phosphate		23s,25		SE-30, 175°, 6.9'	436
$C_8H_{11}NO_3$	Pyridoxol	T_3	22(97%)	b 95-96/0.01	DC-Hi, 200°, 4.0'	702
			23s,25		SE-30, 115°, 17.0', 9.9'	436
		T_3	25,43py		SE-52, 165°	563
		T_3	42py		SE-30, XE-60, C-20M, SiO; Mass Spec.	611
$C_8H_{12}NO_5P$	4-Deoxypyridoxol-5-phosphate		25		SE-30, 175°, 3.4'	436
$C_8H_{12}NO_6P$	Pyridoxol-5-phosphate		25		SE-30, 175°, 5.0'	436
$C_8H_{12}N_2O_2$	Pyridoxamine	T_3	43py		SE-52, 165°	563

Table 12-1. Miscellaneous Compounds (cont'd.)

Pyridines and Pyrazines (cont'd.)

Formula	Compound	Silyl-ation	Method (Yield %)	B.P.;mm; M.P.	Stat. Phase, Temp., Retention Data	Ref.
$C_8H_{12}N_2O_2$	Pyridoxamine	T_3	22(85%)	b 100-112/0.01	DC-Hi, 200°, 4.5'	702
$C_{11}H_{15}NO_3$	α^4,3-O-Isopropylidene-pyridoxol	T_1	25		SE-30, 115°, 6.9'	436
	α^4,α^5-Isopropylidene-pyridoxol	T_1	25		SE-30, 115°, 9.7'	436

Pyrimidines and Purines

Formula	Compound	Silyl-ation	Method (Yield %)	B.P.;mm; M.P.	Stat. Phase, Temp., Retention Data	Ref.
$C_3H_2BrN_3O_2$	5-Bromo-6-azauracil	T_2	23(100%)	m 50		715
$C_3H_3N_3O_2$	6-Azauracil	T_2	21(90%)	b 142-144/25, m 35		200
$C_4H_2F_3N_3O_2$	5-Trifluoromethyl-6-aza-uracil	T_2	23(100%)			715
$C_4H_3FN_2O_2$	5-Fluorouracil	T_2	21	b 114-116.5/14		327
$C_4H_4O_3$	Barbituric acid	T_3	21			272
$C_4H_4N_2O_2$	Uracil	T_2	14g(72%)	b 116/12, m 31-33		551, 556
		T_2	14g	b 116/12		670
		T_2	21(94%)	b 123/18		872
		T_2	23b,24	b 98-99/9, 81-83/3, m 31.5-33	DC-430, 180°, 0.16/adn	671
			25		DC-430, 140→225°	300
			43n		SE-30, 120°pr	268
$C_4H_5N_3O$	Cytosine	T_2	14(69%)	b 168/30		551, 556
		T_2	21(90%)	m 122-123		872

Table 12-1. Miscellaneous Compounds (cont'd.)

Pyrimidines and Purines

Formula	Compound	Silyl-ation	Method (Yield %)	B.P./mm; M.P.	Stat. Phase, Temp., Retention Data	Ref.
$C_4H_5N_3O$	Cytosine		43n		SE-30, 95→230°, 11.2', 13.5'; 148°, 161°pr	268
			23		DC-430, 180°, 0.28/adn	671
			25		DC-430, 140→255°	300
$C_4H_5N_3O_2$	6-Azathymine	T_2	21(95%)	b 146-147/20		200
$C_4H_6N_4O_2$	4,5-Diaminouracil	T_4	21(90%)	b $105/10^{-4}$; m 60		72
		T_4	24(90%)	b $105/10^{-4}$		77
$C_5H_3F_3N_2O_2$	5-Trifluoromethyluracil	T_2	22			659
$C_5H_4N_4$	Purine		43n		SE-30, 140°pr	268
$C_5H_4N_4O$	Hypoxanthine	T_2	21	b 150-153/2		670
		T_2	21(87%)	b 113-117/0.15, 135-142/0.8 m 71-74		551, 556
			43n		SE-30, 176°	268
			25		DC-430, 140→255°	300
$C_5H_4N_4O_2$	Xanthine	T_3	14(77%)	b 163/1.5 m 87-90		551, 556
			43n		SE-30, 202°	268
			23		DC-430, 180°, 1.94/adn 230°, 1.77/adn	671
			25		DC-430, 140→255°	300
$C_5H_4N_4O_3$	Uric acid	T_4 (N,N,O,O)	21(70%)	b $130/10^{-3}$ m 114		72
			23		DC-430, 230°, 2.05/adn	671

Table 12-1. Miscellaneous Compounds (cont'd.)

Pyrimidines and Purines

Formula	Compound	Silylation	Method (Yield %)	B.P./mm; M.P.	Stat. Phase, Temp., Retention Data	Ref.
$C_5H_5N_5$	Adenine	T_2	14(91%)	b 137/0.8 m 84-87		551, 556
			43n		SE-30, 185°pr	268
			23		DC-430, 180°, 5.45'; 230°, 1.10'	671
			25		DC-430, 140→255°	300
$C_5H_5N_5O$	Guanine	T_3	14(88%)	b 167-168/1	SE-30, 211°pr	551, 556
			43n			268
			23,25		DC-430, 180°, 2.87/adn; 230°, 2.18/adn	671
$C_5H_6N_2O_2$	Thymine	T_2	14b(89%)	b 123-125/13 63-65		551, 556
		T_2	14b	b 124.5/14		670
		T_2	21d(92%)	b 127-130/18 m 72-74		873
			43n		SE-30, 130°pr	268
			25		DC-430, 140→255°	300
$C_5H_7N_3O$	5-Methylcytosine		43n		SE-30, 152°, 165°pr	268
$C_5H_7N_3O_2$	5(Hydroxymethyl)-cytosine	T_3	21(95%)	b 176-180/18		872
$C_5H_9N_5O$	6-Methoxy-2,4,5-triamino-pyrimidine	T_3	14u(78%)	b 111/0.001		81
$C_6H_6N_2O_3S$	S-Acetyl-5-thiouracil	T_2	14b	b 110-111/0.35 m 53-55		49

Table 12-1. Miscellaneous Compounds (cont'd.)

Pyrimidines and Purines

Formula	Compound	Silylation	Method (Yield %)	B.P./mm; M.P.	Stat. Phase, Temp., Retention Data	Ref.
$C_6H_7N_3O_2$	N-Acetylcytosine	T_2	14(71%)	b 137-138/6; m 62-68		551, 556
$C_6H_8N_2O_2$	1,2-Dihydro-4-ethoxy-2-ketopyrimidine	T_2	21(84%)	b 155/3		872
	4-O-Ethyluracil	T_1	14b			670
$C_7H_8N_2O_2$	5-Allyluracil	T_1	21(85%)	b 115-116/17		872
$C_7H_8N_4O_2$	Theophylline	T_2	14g(87%)	b 140-142/12		532
$C_7H_{10}N_2O_2$	4-O-Ethylthymine	T_1	14b	b 125-126; m 53-54		670, 873
$C_7H_{13}N_5O$	6-Isopropyloxy-2,4,5-tri-aminopyrimidine	T_3	21(97%)	b 105/0.001		81
$C_{11}H_{18}N_2O_4$	Hydroxyamobarbital	T_2	14u(82%) 25b		SE-30, 160°	387
$C_{12}H_9N_5O$	N-Benzoyladenine	T_2	14b(75%)	b 177-184/8×10^{-4}		551
$C_{12}H_{10}FN_3O_2$	5-Fluoro-N-4-toluoylcytosine	T_2	21	b 160-183/0.8		327
$C_{12}H_{20}N_2O_5$	Dihydroxysecobarbital	T_2			SE-30, 162°	784

13

Halomethyldimethylsilyl and Dimethylsilyl Derivatives

13-1. HALOMETHYLDIMETHYLSILYL COMPOUNDS

Chloromethyldimethylsilyl (CMDMS) ethers of lower alcohols have been prepared using chloromethyldimethylchlorosilane (CMDMCS) alone (32, 240, 848) or with a base (33, 438). The methods are analogous to those using TMCS. The Si-C dipole (240) and the Lewis basicity (858) of the silyl ethers have been studied. The basicity was reduced in comparison with the analagous TMS compound, as expected.

Many steroid CMDMS ethers have been prepared, mainly by Vanden-Heuvel (798, 800) and Thomas (777, 779, 780) and co-workers. Preparative methods employed (1) chloromethyldimethylsilyldiethylamine and CMDMCS in chloroform at room temperature overnight (Method 34*) or, (2) bis(chloromethyl)tetramethyldisilazane (CMTMDS) and CMDMCS in pyridine (Method 25*). Silylation was complete and the products were stable to TLC conditions (780). Representative steroid derivatives were isolated and found to possess satisfactory elemental analyses (798, 800).

Gas chromatographic properties of the steroids CMDMS ethers are excellent. They are more stable in GC than TMS derivatives (779). They separate well, 17-ketosteroids ethers on 1% XE-60 (780) and bile acid derivatives on SE-30 (800). Retention times are two to three times those of corresponding TMS compounds, but less than for monochloroacetates. On the other hand the CMDMS ethers have less sensitivity than the monochloroacetates to electron capture detectors (779).

The bromomethyldimethylsilyl ethers of 17-ketosteroids and testosterone were also prepared by Thomas and co-workers (206) using as reagent the reaction product (not isolated) of bromomethyldimethylchlorosilane and diethylamine. The steroid ethers have five times the retention times of TMS derivatives on 1% XE-60. Their response to an electron capture detector is greater than for monochloroacetates, approaching that of heptafluoro-

---

*Starred method is analogous to method of same number for TMS reagents.

butyrates. Quantities of testosterone of the order of 0.1 ng can be thus
detected (206, 779, 830). Testosterone iodomethyldimethylsilyl ether can
be detected in amounts less than 0.05 ng by electron capture (779).

CMDMS sugar derivatives were prepared from CMTMDS and CMDMCS
in pyridine or dimethylformamide at room temperature for 30 minutes
(22, 41). The reaction mixtures were chromatographed on OV-1 at 200°
or 220°. When a flame ionization detector is used 1-2 μg each of several
pentoses and hexoses gave good peaks, well separated (41); with an
electron capture detector sensitivity approached the nanogram level.

13-2. DIMETHYLSILYL COMPOUNDS

Dimethylsilyl (DMS) ethers of hydroxy compounds have been prepared
for GC in the search for volatile derivatives. They have been prepared by
reaction of tetramethyldisilazane and dimethylchlorosilane at room temperature in tetrahydrofuran or in pyridine for periods up to three hours
(761, 798, 852). When the reaction mixtures stood overnight artifacts
appeared in the chromatogram (761). The bis(DMS) ether of pregnanediol was isolated and found pure by elemental analysis (798). Mass spectrometry, Lewis basicity, and NMR of methoxydimethylsilane and meth-
oxytrimethylsilane were compared (819).

The retention times of DMS and TMS derivatives were often compared.
On nonselective SE-30 and JXR for large molecules with one hydroxyl
the ratio of DMS to TMS retention was 0.85. With increase in hydroxyls
there was a steady reduction in this ratio: monophenols and dihydroxy
steroids, 0.75; glycols, 0.6; simple sugars, 0.5; and sugar alcohols, 0.4. On
a selective EGSS-Z column DMS and TMS steroid derivatives had about
the same retention. The separation of the aldohexose DMS ethers on polar
EGS and nonpolar SE-30 columns was inferior to that of the corresponding
TMS derivatives (852).

Bis(DMS)acetamide (BDSA), alone or catalysed with dimethylchlorosilane, was used to silylate many lipids for comparison of DMS and TMS
derivatives by TLC (42). Reactions were completed in 60 minutes or less.
BDSA reacted much faster than BSA with monoglycerides and with
dehydroisoandrosterone.

TABLE 13-1. HALOMETHYLDIMETHYLSILYL COMPOUNDS

Bromomethyldimethylsilyl Compounds

Formula	Compound	Method* (Yield %)	Stat. Phase	Temp.	Retention Data, Physical Constants	Ref.
$C_{19}H_{28}O_2$	Dehydroepiandrosterone		XE-60	210	5.80/chn	206
	Epitestosterone	33h	XE-60	210	9.50/chn	206
			JXR	220	1.65/chn	
	Testosterone	33h	XE-60	210	12.10/chn	206
			JXR	220	1.95/chn	
$C_{19}H_{30}O_2$	Etiocholanolone		XE-60	210	4.80/chn	206
	Androsterone		XE-60	210	4.10/chn	206

Chloromethyldimethylsilyl Compounds

Simple O-H and N-H Compounds

Formula	Compound	Method* (Yield %)	Stat. Phase	Temp.	Retention Data, Physical Constants	Ref.
CH_4O	Methanol	18(30%)			b 116.5-117°/750 n_D^{20} 1.4310	33
C_2H_6O	Ethanol	11(42%)			b 132°/741 n_D^{25} 1.4124	240
		11			b 131-132°	858
		11(80%)			b 131-132°/745 n_D^{20} 1.4185	32
		18(79%)			b 131.5°/745 n_D^{20} 1.4185	33
		18(70%)			b 130-132° n_D^{19} 1.4188	438
C_3H_8O	Isopropylalcohol	18			b 144.5°/750 n_D^{20} 1.4192	33

*Method numbers refer to procedures for trimethylsilylation but use corresponding reagents.

Table 13-1. Halomethyldimethylsilyl Compounds (cont'd.)

Simple O-H and N-H Compounds (cont'd.)

Formula	Compound	Method* (Yield %)	Stat. Phase	Temp.	Retention Data, Physical Constants	Ref.
$C_4H_{10}O$	Butanol	18(73%)			b 37-38°/3; n_D^{20} 1.4262	33
$C_4H_{11}N$	Diethylamine	11e(86%)			b 75°/25; n_D^{25} 1.4435	780
$C_5H_{12}O$	3-Methyl-1-butanol	18(64%)			b 38-40°/1; n_D^{20} 1.4270	33
$C_{14}H_{12}O$	4-Hydroxystilbene	23	SE-52	183	5.48'	727
$C_{14}H_{12}O$	2-Hydroxystilbene	23	SE-52	200		727
$C_{14}H_{12}O_2$	4,4'-Dihydroxystilbene	23	SE-52	216	9.77'	727
$C_{15}H_{14}O_2$	4-Hydroxy-3-methoxystilbene	23	SE-52	200		727
Carbohydrates						
$C_5H_{10}O_5$	Ribose	22d,25	OV-1	200	0.161/gu	22
	Xylose	22d,25	OV-1	200	0.168/gu	22
$C_6H_{12}O_6$	Galactose	22d,25	OV-1	200	α 0.581/gu	22
	Glucose	22d,25	OV-1	200	α 15.0'	22
	Mannose	22d,25	OV-1	200	0.355/gu	22
$C_{12}H_{16}O_7$	Arbutin	22d,25	OV-1	200	1.55/gu	22
Steroids						
$C_{19}H_{28}O_2$	Dehydroepiandrosterone		XE-60	210	3.75/chn	206
		33h	XE-60 HiEff/JXR			778
		33c	JXR	215	1.03/chn	780
			XE-60	210	4.35/chn; m 107-108°	

*Method numbers refer to procedures for trimethylsilylation but use corresponding reagents.

Table 13-1. Halomethyldimethylsilyl Compounds (cont'd.)

Steroids (cont'd.)

Formula	Compound	Method* (Yield %)	Stat. Phase	Temp.	Retention Data, Physical Constants	Ref.
$C_{19}H_{28}O_2$	Epitestosterone		XE-60	210	5.62/chn	206
		23t	SE-30	235	1.25/chn	798
			EGSS-Z	205	9.58/chn	
		33c	JXR	215	1.31/chn	780
	Testosterone		XE-60	210	7.03/chn	206
		23t	SE-30	235	1.52/chn	798
			EGSS-Z	205	11.6/chn	
		33c	JXR	215	1.55/chn m 89-90°	780
$C_{19}H_{30}O_2$	Androsterone	33h	XE-60 HiEff/JXR			778
		33c	XE-60	210	3.05/chn	780
			XE-60	210	2.75/chn	206
	Etiocholanolone	33h	XE-60 HiEff/JXR			778
		33c	XE-60	210	3.54/chn	780
			XE-60	210	3.13/chn	206
$C_{21}H_{32}O_2$	4-Pregnen-20-ol-3-one	23t	SE-30	235	α 2.81, β 2.58/chn	798
			EGSS-Z	205	α 23.1, β 20.6/chn	
$C_{21}H_{36}O_2$	Pregnanediol	23t	SE-30	235	4.72/chn	798
			EGSS-Z	205	12.3/chn	
$C_{25}H_{40}O_4$	Methyl 3α-hydroxy-7-ketocholanate	25	SE-30	238	6.78/chn	800
$C_{25}H_{42}O_3$	Methyl 3α-hydroxycholanate	25	SE-30	238	4.43/chn	800
	Methyl 7α-hydroxycholanate	25	SE-30	238	2.99/chn	800

*Method numbers refer to procedures for trimethylsilylation but use corresponding reagents.

Table 13-1. Halomethyldimethylsilyl Compounds (cont'd.)

Steroids (cont'd.)

Formula	Compound	Method* (Yield %)	Stat. Phase	Temp.	Retention Data, Physical Constants	Ref.
$C_{25}H_{42}O_3$	Methyl 7β-hydroxycholanate	25	SE-30	238	3.66/chn	800
	Methyl 12α-hydroxy-cholanate	25	SE-30	238	2.68/chn	800
$C_{25}H_{42}O_4$	Methyl 3α, 6α-dihydroxy-cholanate	25	SE-30	238	11.2/chn	800
	Methyl 3α, 7α-dihydroxy-cholanate	25	SE-30	238	10.4/chn	800
	Methyl 3α, 7β-dihydroxy-cholanate	25	SE-30	238	12.5/chn	800
	Methyl 3α,12α-dihydroxy-cholanate	25	SE-30	238	8.40/chn	800
$C_{25}H_{42}O_5$	Methyl 3α,7α,12α-trihydroxy-cholanate	25	SE-30	238	20.8/chn	800
$C_{27}H_{46}O$	Cholesterol	23t	SE-30 EGSS-Z	235 205	5.33/chn 8.94/chn	798
	Epicholesterol	23t	SE-30 EGSS-Z	235 205	4.03/chn 6.12/chn	798

*Method numbers refer to procedures for trimethylsilylation but use corresponding reagents.

TABLE 13-2. DIMETHYLSILYL COMPOUNDS

Simple O-H and N-H Compounds

Formula	Compound	Method* (Yield %)	Stat. Phase	Temp.	Retention Data, Physical Constants	Ref.
CH_4O	Methanol	52 (97%)	Mass Spec.		m <-134°	819
$C_3H_8O_2$	1,3-Propanediol	25	ApL	120	0.48/btd	761
$C_4H_{10}O_2$	1,4-Butanediol	25	ApL	120	9.0'	761
$C_5H_{12}O_2$	Neopentyl glycol	25	ApL	120	0.63/btd	761
$C_5H_{12}O_2$	1,5-Pentanediol	25	ApL	120	1.95/btd	761
C_6H_6O	Phenol	25	ApL	120	8.5'	761
$C_6H_7O_3$	Phloroglucinol	25	JXR	175	0.317/gu	761
$C_6H_{12}O_6$	Inositol	25	SE-30 / JXR	160 / 175	1.95/srbl / 1.296/gu	761
C_7H_8O	Cresol	25	ApL	120	o 1.73, m 1.85, p 1.98/pol	761
$C_{12}H_{26}O$	Dodecanol	25	ApL	120	0.19/hdl	761
$C_{14}H_{30}O$	Tetradecanol	25	ApL	120	0.43/hdl	761
$C_{16}H_{34}O$	Hexadecanol	25	ApL	120	8.9'	761
$C_{18}H_{38}O$	Octadecanol	25	ApL	120	2.29/hdl	761
$C_{25}H_{36}O_4$	Colupulone	21d / 25	F-60	170	25.0 MU	183

*Method numbers refer to procedures for trimethylsilylation but use corresponding reagents.

Table 13-2. Dimethylsilyl Compounds (con'd.)

Carbohydrates

Formula	Compound	Method* (Yield %)	Stat. Phase	Temp.	Retention Data, Physical Constants	Ref.
$C_5H_{10}O_4$	2-Deoxy-D-ribose	25	JXR	175	0.165/gu	761
$C_5H_{10}O_5$	Arabinose	25	JXR	175	0.281/gu	761
	Xylose	25	JXR	175	0.338/gu	761
$C_5H_{12}O_5$	Arabinitol	25	JXR	175	0.317/gu	761
	Ribitol	25	JXR	175	0.356/gu	761
	Xylitol	25	JXR	175	0.308/gu	761
$C_6H_{12}O_5$	2-Deoxy-D-glucose	25	JXR	175	0.488/gu	761
	Fucose	25	JXR	175	0.314/gu	761
$C_6H_{12}O_6$	Galactose	25	JXR	175	0.690/gu.	761
		25	EGS / SE-30	156 / 160	β 0.97/gud / β 0.92/gud	852
	Glucose	25	EGS / SE-30	156 / 160	α 4.7', β 1.51/gud / α 7.4', β 1.38/gud	852
	Mannose	25	JXR	175	0.548/gu	761
		25	EGS / SE-30	156 / 160	β 1.18/gud / β 0.97/gud	852
$C_6H_{14}O_6$	Dulcitol	25	SE-30	160	1.02/srbl	761
	Mannitol	25	SE-30	160	1.15/srbl	761
	Sorbitol	25	SE-30	160		761

*Method numbers refer to procedures for trimethylsilylation but use corresponding reagents.

Table 13-2. Dimethylsilyl Compounds (cont'd.)

Steroids

Formula	Compound	Method* (Yield %)	Stat. Phase	Temp.	Retention Data, Physical Constants	Ref.
$C_{19}H_{28}O_2$	Epitestosterone	23	SE-30 / EGSS-Z	235 / 205	0.48/chn / 2.17/chn	798
	Testosterone	23	SE-30 / EGSS-Z	235 / 205	0.56/chn / 2.66/chn	798
$C_{27}H_{44}O$	7-Dehydrocholesterol	25	OV-17	254	2.21/chn	761
	Desmosterol	25	OV-17	254	2.28/chn	761
$C_{27}H_{46}O$	Cholesterol	25	OV-17	254	1.89/chn	761
		26	SE-30 / EGSS-Z	235 / 205	2.06/chn / 2.26/chn	798
	Epicholesterol	26	SE-30 / EGSS-Z	235 / 205	1.64/chn / 1.71/chn	798
$C_{21}H_{32}O_2$	4-Pregnen-20-ol-3-one	26	SE-30 / EGSS-Z	235 / 205	α 1.04, β 0.97/chn / α 5.14, β 4.64/chn	798
$C_{21}H_{36}O_2$	Pregnanediol	23	SE-30 / EGSS-Z	235 / 205	0.72/chn / 0.75/chn	798

*Method numbers refer to procedures for trimethylsilylation but use corresponding reagents.

14

Properties of Silylated Compounds

This chapter outlines the properties noted by investigators who have prepared and used silylated organic compounds, sometimes for chemical rather than analytical purposes. No literature search purely for properties was made, hence some significant properties or uses may have been overlooked.

14-1. VOLATILITY

Silylation effects a substantial increase in volatility only for polyhydroxy compounds. The difference in atmospheric boiling points, parent minus derivative, is given in Table 14-1.

Table 14-1. Volatility of Silyl Compounds

Carbon Atoms	n-Primary alcohols	Polymethylene glycols	Aliphatic acids	n-Primary amines
1	−12°		−14	78°
2	−3	−30°	−14	74
3	2	−28*	−19	63
4	5	−32		57
5	9	−35*		
6	14	−15*		
7				40*
8	11			

*Calculated from boiling points at reduced pressure.

As has been observed (452), there is a crossover point in the alcohol series, which may be explained by the strong hydrogen bonding of methyl and ethyl alcohols. The greater differential shown by the glycol derivatives shows the effect of the second hydroxyl group. For glycerine the difference is −60°; for pentaerythritol, −112°, both values based on calculated atmospheric boiling points.

There is no difference in boiling points in the case of phenol. For the cresols and most of the xylenols the difference is small. The dihydric phenols boil 20 to 40° above their derivatives, but the difference between the mono- and di-TMS ethers of each isomer is only a few degrees:

	Monoether	Diether
Pyrocatechol	−20°	−18°
Resorcinol	−37	−42
Hydroquinone	−36	−40

TMS esters of lower aliphatic acids boil slightly lower than the free acids; the difference for benzoic acid is −30°. For amines, where there is less hydrogen bonding, there is a large boiling point elevation, which decreases gradually with increase of chain length.

14-2. HYDROLYSIS AND ALCOHOLYSIS

The ease of hydrolysis of silylated compounds is both an advantage and a disadvantage. It permits the simple recovery of the parent compound, but the extreme sensitivity of some silyl derivatives to moisture creates problems in their preservation and use.

The general condition for hydrolysis of TMS ethers, which are the most stable silyl derivatives, was developed by Martin (511), and consists in simply heating with aqueous alcohol. Sometimes other solvents may be used or acid or base catalysts. Reaction progress can be followed by GC.

The stability of silyl compounds to hydrolysis depends on structure and steric arrangement. As might be expected the order of ease of hydrolysis of the variously linked TMS groups: N-TMS compound > TMS ester > TMS ether is opposite to the ease of formation of these derivatives (section 1-5). Brooks et al. (124) observed the ease of acid-catalysed hydrolysis to be: TMS esters > TMS phenol ethers > TMS alcohol ethers. When tris(TMS)serine, $TMS-OCH_2-CH(NH-TMS)-CO-OTMS$, is treated with wet ether and a catalytic quantity of HCl the N-TMS group is removed; when this product, $TMS-OCH_2-CH(NH_2 \cdot HCl)-CO-OTMS$, is treated with absolute alcohol the ester is converted to the acid (325). When the tetrakis (TMS) tartaric acid derivative is treated with alcohol or exposed to moist air partial hydrolysis is rapid and the first product is the 2,3-$(TMS)_2$ ether of tartaric acid (307). Similarly, 1-[bis(TMS)amino]-2-trimethylsiloxypropane on methanolysis yields 2-trimethylsiloxy-1-propylamine (146). Thio-TMS ethers are more readily hydrolysed than the corresponding TMS ethers (613).

There is some selectivity in the hydrolysis of silyl ethers which may be at least partly steric in nature. Of the four ether linkages in methyl 2,3,4,6-tetra-O-TMS-α-D-glucopyranoside only the C-6, a primary group, is cleaved by methanol at 0° (356). The hydrolysis of t-pentyl TMS ether in boiling aqueous alcohol or pyridine did not proceed unless a trace of HCl was added (241). Boiling aqueous dioxane hydrolysed a long chain primary alkyl TMS ether in a few hours but a t-butyl group in the 1-position hindered the reaction completely (361).

14-3. PEPTIDE SYNTHESIS

This is an example of acylation of TMS compounds, which has been studied by Birkofer and co-workers (71, 82). An N-carbobenzyloxy (Cbz) amino acid or peptide reacts with a silylamino acid silyl ester by way of (1) phosphorus oxychloride in triethylamine, (2) N,N-carbonyldiimidazole, or (3) carboxylic alkoxyformic anhydride (I) from ethyl chloroformate reaction. A new peptide bond is formed and the resulting peptide silyl ester (II) may be hydrolysed to the Cbz-peptide or treated again via (3) to add another amino acid unit. The reaction via (3):

$$CbzNHCHRCOOH + ClCOOEt \rightarrow CbzNHCHRCOOCOEt(I)$$

$$I + TMS-NHCHR'CO-OTMS \rightarrow$$

$$CbzNHCHRCONCHR'CO-OTMS (II) + CO_2 + C_2H_5OTMS$$

Peptides with as many as five units were synthesized in this way with yields of 70-96% per step (82).

14-4. METHYLATION

O-Silylated heterocyclic nitrogen compounds such as TMS derivatives of α-pyridone (81), 2,3-dihydroxyquinoxaline (81) and thymine (873) are methylated with methyl iodide or sulfate, the methyl group attaching to nitrogen.

14-5. GLYCOSIDE SYNTHESIS

This reaction is similar to the methylation reaction just described, except that an acyl sugar halide replaces methyl iodide. The reaction between these sugar halides and silylated pyrimidines has been studied by Nishimura and co-workers (552, 553, 554, 556, 557) and others (49, 327, 532, 659, 872, 874, 875). The preparation of uridine is typical (557):

In the condensation reaction (1), which here is shown as a fusion, the silyl group at the 2-O-position is removed as TMS chloride or bromide and the sugar residue becomes linked at the N-1 position. Wittenburg (872) has also carried out the condensation under milder conditions by (1) fusion at 90-100° under vacuum, or (2) heating in dry solvents such as toluene or dimethylformamide, or (3) at room temperature in a solvent in the presence of mercuric oxide or acetate. Best yields were by (3), and this method is described in detail (659). Aqueous alcohol hydrolyses the remaining TMS ether and the methylate removes the benzoyl groups.

Acetyl, benzoyl and substituted benzoyl derivatives of hexosyl and pentosyl bromides and chlorides were condensed with TMS derivatives of uracil, thymine, N-acetylcytosine, adenine, hypoxanthine and xanthine. Silylated derivatives of 5-acetylmercaptouracil (49), 5-fluorocytosine and 5-fluorouracil (327), 5-allyluracil (532), and 5-trifluorouracil (659) were also condensed. Overall yields were 25-50%, and products were usually anomeric. The anomers were sometimes separated by chromatography or by fractional crystallization. Thorough identification was established by optical rotation, NMR and comparison with known samples (554, 557, 659).

Work with purines, adenine and hypoxanthine, indicated that 9-glycosides were formed from them (553); indeed, adenosine thus obtained failed to depress the melting point of an authentic sample (557). However, xanthine under various mild condensation conditions yielded 3-mono-, 7-mono-, and 3,7-diglycosides. Monosubstitution at position 9 was also indicated (175).

Glycosides also have been prepared from α-pyridone (81), benzotriazole (100), and *as*-triazine (200) via their TMS derivatives.

Following the methods already described for nucleosides, nucleotides have been synthesized from phosphorylated ribosyl or glucosyl bromides (555, 670, 719, 720). For instance, the condensation of bis(TMS)-N-benzoyladenine and 2,3-di-O-benzoyl-5-diphenylphosphoryl-D-ribofuranosyl bromide followed by removal of protecting groups and hydrogenolysis yielded α-adenosine-5'-monophosphate (720).

14-6. ADDITIONS

Secondary N-TMS-amides react with aliphatic and aromatic aldehydes to give N-alkyl-N-α-trimethylsiloxyalkyl (or aryl) amides (67, 192):

$$PhCHO + CH_3CON(CH_3)TMS \rightarrow PhCH(OTMS)N(CH_3)COCH_3$$

When silylamines react with isocyanates there is cleavage of the Si-N bond and N-silylureas are formed (226, 417, 421).

$$C_6H_5NCO + R_2N-TMS \rightarrow R_2N-CO-N(C_6H_5)(TMS)$$

In the addition of primary silylamines (RNH—TMS) two products may be formed, in equilibrium with each other through silyl—proton exchange, as shown by NMR data (421).

$$RNH-CO-NR'(TMS) \leftrightarrows RN(TMS)-CO-NHR'$$

In the addition of HMDS to isocyanates the product has been shown to be the N,N'-bis(TMS)urea (421) rather than the N,N-product, as earlier reported (832). Isothiocyanates and silylamines form analagous products; ureas yield biurets (421).

There is also Si-N cleavage in the addition of silylamines to carbon dioxide (103, 562), carbon disulfide (102), and sulfur trioxide (687).

$$TMS-NEt_2 + CO_2 \rightarrow TMS-O-CO-NEt_2$$

14-7. REARRANGEMENTS

West and co-workers (856, 857) have studied via NMR 1,2 and 1,4 anionic rearrangements in silyl hydrazines and ethylenediamines. In the presence of n-butyllithium bis(TMS) hydrazines form an equilibrium mixture.

$$TMS-NH-N(CH_3)TMS \leftrightarrows (TMS)_2N-NHCH_3$$

The amounts of 1,1- and 1,2-bis(TMS)methylhydrazines at equilibrium are approximately equal. The equilibrium mixture of bis(TMS)phenylhydrazines contains 96% of $(TMS)_2N-NHC_6H_5$.

Rearrangement of ethylenediamine compounds is slow but the reaction goes to completion. N,N-bis(TMS)methylethylenediamine rearranges to the N,N'-bis(TMS) compound; N,N'-bis(TMS)phenylethylenediamine, in the opposite sense, rearranges to the N,N-bis(TMS) derivative. This is analagous to the hydrazine example of the preceding paragraph, where the predominant isomer was also free of silyl on the phenyl-bearing nitrogen.

N-Ethyl-N-TMS-N',N'-ethyleneurea when heated undergoes a 1,3 shift with ring enlargement (679).

$$\text{TMS-N}(C_2H_5)-CO-N\underset{CH_2}{\overset{CH_2}{\diagup\diagdown}} \rightarrow \text{TMS-N}\overset{\overset{O}{\overset{\|}{C}}}{\underset{CH_2-CH_2}{\diagup\diagdown}}NC_2H_5$$

14-8. DISPROPORTIONATION

Fully silylated amino acids (646) and thiol-substituted acids (631) react with the free acid to yield silyl ester derivatives.

$$CH_3-CH(Y-TMS)-CO-OTMS + CH_3CY-COOH \rightarrow$$

$$2CH_3CYCO-OTMS \quad Y = S \text{ or } NH$$

N-TMS-allylamine when refluxed in the presence of ammonium sulfate disproportionates to allylamine and N-allylhexamethyldisilazane (753).

14-9. TRIMETHYLSILYL AS A BLOCKING GROUP

Under anhydrous nonacid conditions the TMS group has been found useful for blocking or protective purposes. This use has been suggested for Friedel-Craft reactions, halogenations and Grignards (657). The TMS group has the advantage of being easily removed under mild conditions.

Phenolic hydroxyl groups have been silylated prior to Grignard reactions involving halide (657) or aldehyde (876) groups on the ring. The final hydrolysis step of the Grignard removed the TMS group also. Hydroxyl groups of benzyl-substituted sugars were silylated before hydrogenolysis of the benzyl. The anomeric hydroxyl group seemed to require this protection (408).

The use of TMS esters in peptide synthesis is illustrated in section 14-5, Thiol and hydroxy groups of amino acids have been protected by formation of TMS ethers (189, 288). Schmidt and co-workers (688, 689) made extensive use of TMS malonate and acetoacetate esters in the synthesis of β-ketoesters and diacyl methanes. They used the lithium compounds of the silyl esters.

The hydrogenolysis of a 3-(N,N-dimethylaminomethyl)-catechol to the corresponding 3-methylcatechol did not proceed until the hydroxyl groups were silylated. It appears that hydrogen bonding prevented the hydrogenolysis of the free catechol (140).

Bibliography

1. Abe, M., M. Niwano, H. Kobuna, and T. Akiguchi, *Bull. Chem. Soc. Japan*, **38**, 2011 (1965); *Chem. Abstr.*, **64**, 3585a (1966).
2. Abel, E. W., *J. Chem. Soc.*, 4406 (1960).
3. Abel, E. W., *J. Chem. Soc.*, 4933 (1961).
4. Abel, E. W., D. A. Armitage, and G. R. Willey, *Trans. Faraday Soc.*, **60**, 1257 (1964).
5. Abel, E. W., R. P. Bush, C. R. Jenkins, and T. Zobel, *Trans. Faraday Soc.*, **60**, 1214 (1964).
6. Abel, E. W., and G. R. Willey, *J. Chem. Soc.*, 1528 (1964).
7. Acree, T. E., R. S. Shallenberger, and L. R. Mattick, *Carbohydrate Res.*, **6**, 498 (1968).
8. Adcock, J. W., and T. J. Betts, *J. Chromatog.*, **34**, 411 (1968).
9. Adlard, E. R., and G. W. Roberts, *J. Inst. Petrol.*, **51**, 376 (1965).
10. Adlercreutz, H., *Acta Med. Scand., Suppl.*, **412**, 123 (1964).
11. Adlercreutz, H., and T. Luukkainen, *Ann. Med. Exp. Biol. Fenniae* (Helsinki), **42**, 161 (1964).
12. Adlercreutz, H., and T. Luukkainen, *Biochim. Biophys. Acta*, **97**, 134 (1965).
13. Adlercreutz, H., and T. Luukkainen, in "Gas Chromatography of Steroids in Biological Fluids", M. B. Lipsett, Ed., Plenum Press, N.Y., 1965, pp 215-228.
14. Adlercreutz, H., and T. Luukkainen, *J. Reprod. Fertility*, **9**, 137 (1965).
15. Adlercreutz, H., and T. Luukkainen in "Research on Steroids", Vol. II, C. Cassano, Ed., Tipografia Poliglotta Vaticana, Rome, 1965, pp 21-5.
16. Adlercreutz, H., T. Luukkainen, and W. Taylor, *Eur. Journ. Steroids*, **1**, 117 (1966).
17. Adlercreutz, H., A. Salokangas, and T. Luukkainen, *Mem. Soc. Endocrinol.*, No. 16, 89 (1967).
18. Akerman, E., *Acta Chem. Scand.*, **10**, 298 (1956).
19. Alexander, N. M., and R. Scheig, *Anal. Biochem.*, **22**, 187 (1968).
20. Alexander, R. J., and J. T. Garbutt, *Anal. Chem.*, **37**, 303 (1965).
21. Allen, A. D., and G. Modena, *J. Chem. Soc.*, 3671 (1957).
22. Al-Shakir, S. H., Ph.D. Thesis, University of Georgia, Athens, Ga., 1967; *Diss. Abstr. B*, **28**, 2892 (1968).
23. Anderson, H. H., *J. Am. Chem. Soc.*, **73**, 5802 (1951).
24. Anderson, H. H., *J. Am. Chem. Soc.*, **74**, 2371 (1952).
25. Anderson, H. H., and H. Fischer, *J. Org. Chem.*, **19**, 1296 (1954).
26. Andreev, D. N., and G. S. Afanaseva, *Zh. Obshch. Khim.*, **36**, 1628 (1966); *J. Gen. Chem.*, **36**, 1629 (1966); *Chem. Abstr.*, **66**, 65562 (1967).
27. Andreev, D. N., B. N. Dolgov, and E. V. Kukharskaya, *Izv. Akad. Nauk SSSR, Otd. Khim. Nauk*, 528 (1955); *Bull. Acad. Sci. USSR, Div. Chem. Sci.*, 465 (1955); *Chem. Abstr.*, **50**, 6298b (1956).
28. Andreev, D. N., and E. V. Kukharskaya, *Zh. Obshch. Khim.*, **30**, 2782 (1960); *J. Gen. Chem.*, **30**, 2763 (1960); *Chem. Abstr.*, **55**, 15332g (1961).
29. Andreev, D. N., and L. L. Shchukovskaya, *Izv. Akad. Nauk SSSR, Otd. Khim. Nauk*, 135 (1953); *Bull. Acad. Sci. USSR, Div. Chem. Sci.*, 121 (1953); *Chem. Abstr.*, **48**, 3244i (1954).
30. Andrianov, K. A., V. V. Astakhin, and B. P. Nikiforov, *Zh. Obshch. Khim.*, **34**, 914 (1964); *J. Gen. Chem.*, **34**, 908 (1964); *Chem. Abstr.*, **60**, 15901g (1964).
31. Andrianov, K. A., and T. N. Ganina, *Zh. Obshch. Khim.*, **29**, 605 ((1959); *J. Gen. Chem.*, **29**, 601 (1959).
32. Andrianov, K. A., and M. A. Golubenko, *Dokl. Akad. Nauk SSSR*, **104**, 725 (1955); *Chem. Abstr.*, **50**, 11233i (1956).

33. Andrianov, K. A., and M. A. Golubenko, *Dokl. Akad. Nauk SSSR*, **112**, 257 (1957); *Proc. Acad. Sci. USSR*, **112**, 25 (1957); *Chem. Abstr.*, **51**, 11987g (1957).
34. Andrianov, K. A., and L. V. Gornets, *Dokl. Akad. Nauk SSSR*, **101**, 259 (1955); *Chem. Abstr.*, **50**, 3216i (1956).
35. Andrianov, K. A., G. A. Kurakov, and L. M. Khananashvili, *Zh. Obshch. Khim*, **33**, 2634 (1963); *J. Gen. Chem.*, **33**, 2567 (1963); *Chem. Abstr.*, **60**, 541c (1964).
36. Andrianov, K. A., A. A. Mamedov, and L. M. Volkova, *Izv. Akad. Nauk SSSR, Ser. Khim.*, 2042 (1966); *Chem. Abstr.*, **66**, 95108 (1967).
37. Andrianov, K. A., V. I. Pakhomov, and N. E. Lapteva, *Izv. Akad. Nauk SSSR, Otd. Khim. Nauk*, 2039 (1962); *Bull. Acad. Sci. USSR, Div. Chem. Sci.*, 1948 (1962); *Chem. Abstr.*, **58**, 9112g (1963).
38. Andrianov, K. A., N. N. Sokolov, E. N. Khrustaleva, and L. N. Yukina, *Izv. Akad. Nauk SSSR, Otd. Khim. Nauk*, 531 (1955); *Bull. Acad. Sci. USSR Div. Chem. Sci.* 469 (1955); *Chem. Abstr.*, **50**, 6302i (1956).
39. Andrianov, K. A., and L. M. Volkova, *Izv. Akad. Nauk SSSR, Otd. Khim. Nauk*, 577 (1957); *Bull. Acad. Sci. USSR, Div. Chem. Sci.*, 591, (1957); *Chem. Abstr.*, **51**, 15398g (1957).
40. Anonymous, *Aerograph Research Notes*, Fall issue (1964).
41. Anonymous, *Gas-Chromatog. Newsletter*, 7, 1 (1966).

42. Anonymous, *Chromatog. Lipids*, 1, 1 (1967).
43. Appel, H. H., C. J. W. Brooks, and M. M. Campbell, *Perfumery Essent. Oil Record*, 58, 776 (1967).
44. Arpin, N., and S. L. Jensen, *Bull. Soc. Chim. Biol.*, 49, 527 (1967).
45. Arpin, N., and S. L. Jensen, *Phytochemistry*, 6, 995 (1967).
46. Bailey, E., in "Gas Chromatography of Steroids in Biological Fluids", M. B. Lipsett, Ed., Plenum Press, N.Y., 1965, pp 57-65.
47. Band, S. J., I. M. T. Davidson, C. A. Lambert, and I. L. Stephenson, *Chem. Commun.*, 723 (1967).
48. Barbato, P. C., *Facts and Methods*, 6, 2 (1965).
49. Bardos, T. J., M. P. Kotick, and C. Szantay, *Tetrahedron Letters*, 1759 (1966).
50. Becke-Goehring, M., and G. Wunsch, *Ann. Chem.*, **618**, 43 (1958).
51. Bedford, G. R., and D. Gardiner, *Chem. Commun.*, 287 (1965).
52. Bell, S., and A. D. Walsh, *Trans. Faraday Soc.*, **62**, 3005 (1966).
53. Benkeser, R. A., and H. R. Krysiak, *J. Am. Chem. Soc.*, 75, 2421 (1953).
54. Bentley, R., and N. Botlock, *Anal. Biochem.*, 20, 312 (1967).
55. Bentley, R., N. C. Saha, and C. C. Sweeley, *Anal. Chem.*, 37, 1118 (1965).
56. Bentley, R., C. C. Sweeley, M. Makita, and W. W. Wells, *Biochem. Biophys. Res. Commun.*, 11, 14 (1963).
57. Berger, A., and J. A. Magnuson, *Anal. Chem.*, 36, 1156 (1964).
58. Bergman, J., B. O. Lindgren, and C. M. Svahn, *Acta Chem. Scand.*, 19, 1661 (1965).
59. Beroza, M., *J. Agr. Food Chem.*, 4, 49 (1956).
60. Berrett, C. R., and C. McNeil, *Clin. Chem.*, 12, 399 (1966).
61. Berti, G., F. Bottari, A. Marsili, I. Morelli, M. Polvani, and A. Mandelbaum, *Tetrahedron Letters*, 125 (1967).
62. Bethge, P. O., C. Holmstrom, and S. Juhlin, *Svensk Papperstid.*, 69, 60 (1966).
63. Betts, T. J., and P. J. Holloway, *J. Pharm. Pharmacol. Suppl.*, 19, 97S (1967).
64. Bidaud, A. F., and P. Dumont, French Patent 950,583 (1949); *Chem. Abstr.*, 45, 5713h (1951).
65. Birkofer, L., Belgian Patent 615,401 (1963); *Chem. Abstr.*, 59, 2826a (1963).

66. Birkofer, L., and D. Brokmeier, *Tetrahedron Letters*, 1325 (1968).
67. Birkofer, L., and H. Dickopp, *Angew. Chem. Intern. Ed. Engl.*, 3, 514 (1964).
68. Birkofer, L., and H. Dickopp, *Tetrohedron Letters*, 4007 (1965).
69. Birkofer, L., and M. Donike, *J. Chromatog.* 26, 270 (1967).
70. Birkofer, L., W. Knipprath, and A. Ritter, *Angew. Chem.*, **70**, 404 (1958).
71. Birkofer, L., W. Konkol, and A. Ritter, *Chem. Ber.*, 94, 1263 (1961).
72. Kirkofer, L., H. P. Kühlthau, and A. Ritter, *Chem. Ber.*, 93, 2810 (1960).
73. Birkofer, L., P. Richter, and A. Ritter, *Chem. Ber.*, 93, 2804 (1960).
74. Birkofer, L., and A. Ritter, *Angew. Chem.*, 68, 461 (1956).

75. Birkofer, L., and A. Ritter, *Ann. Chem.*, **612**, 22 (1958).

76. Birkofer, L., and A. Ritter, *Chem. Ber.*, **93**, 424 (1960).
77. Birkofer, L., and A. Ritter, *Angew. Chem. Intern. Ed. Engl.*, **4**, 417 (1965).
78. Birkofer, L., A. Ritter, and F. Bentz, *Chem. Ber.*, **97**, 2196 (1964).
79. Birkofer, L., A. Ritter, and H. Dickopp, *Chem. Ber.*, **96**, 1473 (1963).
80. Birkofer, L., A. Ritter, and W. Giessler, *Angew. Chem. Intern. Ed. Engl.*, **2**, 96 (1963).
81. Birkofer, L., A. Ritter, and H. P. Kühlthau, *Chem. Ber.*, **97**, 934 (1964).
82. Birkofer, L., A. Ritter, and P. Neuhausen, *Ann. Chem.*, **659**, 190 (1962).
83. Birkofer, L., A. Ritter, and P. Richter, *Angew. Chem. Intern. Ed. Engl.*, **1**, 267 (1962).
84. Birkofer, L., A. Ritter, and P. Richter, *Tetrahedron Letters*, 195 (1962).
85. Birkofer, L., A. Ritter, and P. Richter, *Chem. Ber.*, **96**, 2750 (1963).
86. Birkofer, L., A. Ritter, and J. Schramm, *Chem. Ber.*, **95**, 426 (1962).
87. Bissett, F. H., M. E. Evans, and F. W. Parrish, *Carbohydrate Res.*, **5**, 184 (1967).
88. Blackman, L. C. F., and M. J. S. Dewar, *J. Chem. Soc.*, 169 (1957).
89. Blakley, E. R., *Anal. Biochem.*, **15**, 350 (1966)
90. Bluestein, B. A., (Compagnie Francaise Thomson-Houston), French Patent 1,419,143 (1965); *Chem. Abstr.*, **65**, 10621f (1966).
91. Blum, J., and W. R. Koehler, *J. Gas Chromatog.*, **6**, 120 (1968).
92. Bock, H., and H. Alt, *Chem. Commun.*, 1299 (1967).
93. Boldeback, E. M., and J. F. Klebe, U. S. Patent 3,303,157 (1967); *Chem. Abstr.*, **66**, 96125 (1967).
94. Bollinger, J. N., *Lipids*, **2**, 143 (1967).
95. Bolton, C. H., J. R. Clamp, G. Dawson, and L. Hough, *Carbohydrate Res.*, **1**, 333 (1965).
96. Bolton, C. H., J. R. Clamp, and L. Hough, *Biochem. J.*, **96**, 5C (1965).
97. Bott, B. W., C. Eaborn, and B. M. Rushton, *J. Organometal. Chem.* (Amsterdam), **3**, 455 (1965).
98. Boughton, O. D., R. Bryant, W. J. Ludwig, and D. L. Timma, *J. Pharm. Sci.*, **55**, 951 (1966).
99. Bourhis, R., and E. Frainnet, *Bull. Soc. Chim. France*, 3552 (1967).
100. Bräuniger, H., and A. Koine, *Arch. Pharm.*, **296**, 665 (1963).
101. Breed, L. W., W. J. Haggerty, Jr., J. Harvey, *J. Org. Chem.*, **25**, 1804 (1960).
102. Breederveld, H., *Rec. Trav. Chim.*, **79**, 1126 (1960)
103. Breederveld, H., *Rec. Trav. Chim.*, **81**, 276 (1962).
104. Breederveld, H., C. H. Steuns, and H. I. Waterman, *Rec. Trav. Chim.*, **72**, 706 (1953).
105. Brendel, K., P. H. Gross, and H. K. Zimmerman, *Ann. Chem.*, **691**, 192 (1966).
106. Brieskorn, C. H., and H. Reinartz, *Z. Lebensm. Untersuch. Forsch.*, **135**, 55 (1967).
107. Briggs, T., and S. R. Lipsky, *Biochim. Biophys. Acta.*, **97**, 579 (1965).
108. Brimacombe, J. S., A. B. Foster, E. B. Hancock, W. G. Overend, and M. Stacey, *J. Chem. Soc.*, 201 (1960).
109. British Thomson-Houston Co., Ltd., British Patent 670,476 (1952); *Chem. Abstr.*, **46**, 8894g (1952).
110. Brittain, G. D., L. Schewe, and J. Sullivan, presented at the Fourth Ann. Winter Meeting of the Chicago Gas Chromatography Discussion Group, Chicago, Ill., Jan. 1968.
111. Brobst, K. M., and C. E. Lott, Jr., *Cereal Chem.*, **43**, 35 (1966).
112. Brobst, K. M., and C. E. Lott, Jr., *Am. Soc. Brewing Chem. Proc.*, **71**, (1966).
113. Brochmann-Hanssen, E., and A. B. Svendsen, *J. Pharm. Sci.*, **51**, 938 (1962).
114. Brochmann-Hanssen, E., and A. B. Svendsen, *J. Pharm. Sci.*, **51**, 1095 (1962).
115. Brochmann-Hanssen, E., and A. B. Svendsen, *J. Pharm. Sci.*, **52**, 1134 (1963).
116. Brockway, L. O., and N. R. Davidson, *J. Am. Chem. Soc.*, **63**, 3287 (1941).

117. Brockway, L. O., and H. O. Jenkins, *J. Am. Chem. Soc.*, **58**, 2036 (1936).
119. Brook, A. G., C. Warner, and M. McGriskin, *J. Am. Chem. Soc.*, **81**, 981 (1959).

120. Brooks, C. J. W., *Proc. Soc. Anal. Chem.*, **4**, 113 (1967).
121. Brooks, C. J. W., *Process Biochem.* **2**, 27 (1967), *Chem. Abstr.* **67**, 18153 (1968).
122. Brooks, C. J. W., and J. G. Carrie, *Biochem. J.*, **99**, 47P (1966).

123. Brooks, C. J. W., E. Chambaz, W. L. Gardiner, and E C. Horning, *Excerpta Med. Intern. Congr. Series No. 132,* 366 (1966).
124. Brooks, C. J. W., E. Chambaz, and E. C. Horning, *Anal. Biochem.,* **19,** 234 (1967).
125. Brooks, C. J. W., W. A. Harland, and G. Steel, *Biochim. Biophys. Acta,* **125,** 620 (1966).
126. Brooks, C. J. W., and J. Watson, *J. Chromatog.,* **31,** 396 (1967).
127. Brooks, G. T., and A. Harrison, *Chem. Ind.* (London), 1414 (1966).
128. Brooks, S. C., L. Horn, and J. P. Horwitz, *Biochim. Biophys. Acta,* **104,** 250 (1965).
129. Brooksbank, B. W. L., and D. B. Gower, *Steroids,* 4, 787 (1964).
130. Brower, H. E., J. E. Jeffery, and M. W. Folsom, *Anal. Chem.,* **38,** 362 (1966).
131. Brown, E. A., and I. Laos, U.S. Patent 3,311,644 (1967); *Chem Abstr.,* **67,** 11671 (1967).
132. Brunelle, R. L., R. L. Schoeneman, and G. E. Martin, *J. Assoc. Offic. Anal. Chemists,* **50,** 329 (967).
133. Budzikiewicz, H., C. Djerassi, and D. H. Williams, "Mass Spectrometry of Organic Compounds," Holden-Day, Inc., San Francisco, 1967.
134. Bullock, A. L., V. O. Cirino, and S. P. Rowland, *Can. J. Chem.,* **45,** 255 (1967).
135. Buncel, E., and A. G. Davies, *J. Chem. Soc.,* 1550 (1958).
136. Burkhard, C. A., *J. Org. Chem.,* **15,** 106 (1950).
137. Burkhard, C. A., *J. Org. Chem.,* **22,** 592 (1957).
138. Burkhard, C. A., J. V. Schmitz, and R. E. Burnett, *J. Am. Chem. Soc.,* **75,** 5957 (1953).
139. Bush, R. P., N. C. Lloyd, and C. A. Pearce, *Chem. Commun.,* 1270 (1967).
140. Byck, J. S., and C. R. Dawson, *J. Org. Chem.,* **33,** 2451 (1968).
141. Bygdeman, M., and O. Holmberg, *Acta Chem. Scand.,* **20,** 2308 (1966).
142. Bygdeman, M., and B. Samuelsson, *Clin. Chim. Acta,* **10,** 566 (1964).
143. Byrd, J. D., and J. E. Curry, *Inorg. Chem.,* **5,** 2042 (1966).
144. Byrne, G. A., D. Gardiner, and F. H. Holmes, *J. Appl. Chem.* (London), **16,** 81 (1966).
145. Cabezas, J. A., *Rev. Espan. Fisiol.,* **21,** 125 (1965).
146. Calas, R., N. Duffaut, and J.-P. Picard, *Compt. Rend., Ser. C,* **265,** 516 (1967).
147. Caldwell, K. A., and A. L. Tappel, *J. Chromatog.,* **32,** 635 (1968).
148. Capella, P., and E. C. Horning, *Anal. Chem.,* **38,** 316 (1966).
149. Carnes, W. J., Abstracts, Conference on Anal. Chem. and Appl. Spectroscopy, Pittsburgh, Pa., Feb. 1966, No. 32.
150. Carter, H. E., and R. C. Gaver, *J. Lipid Res.,* 8, 391 (1967).
151. Carter, H. E., R. C. Gaver, and R. K. Yu, *Biochim. Biophys. Res. Commun.,* **22,** 316 (1966).
152. Castillo, J. B., C. J. W. Brooks, and M. M. Campbell, *Tetrahedron Letters,* 3731 (1966).
153. Catroux, G., and H. Blachere, *Compt. Rend., Ser. D.,* **262,** 1345 (1966).
154. Cavell, B. D., J. MacMillan, R. J. Pryce, and A. C. Sheppard, *Phytochemistry,* **6,** 867 (1967).
155. Chambaz, E. M., and E. C. Horning, *Analytical Letters,* 1, 201 (1967).
155a. Chambaz, E. M., G. Maume, B. Maume, and E. C. Horning, *Analytical Letters,* in press. This paper was received too late for tabulation.
156. Chamberlain, J., B. A. Knights, and G. H. Thomas, *J. Endocrinol.,* **26,** 367 (1963).
157. Chamberlain, J., B. A. Knights, and G. H. Thomas, *J. Endocrinol.,* **28,** 235 (1964).
158. Chang, C. D., and H. B. Hass, *J. Org. Chem.,* **23,** 773 (1958).
159. Chapman, J. R., M. Barber, and W. A. Wolstenholme, presented at Conference on Anal. Chem. and Appl. Spectroscopy, Pittsburgh, Pa., March 1967.
160. Cheminat, A., and M. Brini, *Bull. Soc. Chim. France,* 80 (1966).
161. Chipperfield, J. R., and R. H. Prince, *J. Chem. Soc., A,* 3567 (1963).
162. Chizhov, O. S., N. V. Molodtsov, and N. K. Kochetkov, *Carbohydrate Res.,* 4, 273 (1967).
163. Choby, E. G., Jr., and M. B. Neuworth, *J. Org. Chem.,* **31,** 632 (1966).
164. Chvalovsky, V. in "Organosilicon Chemistry," Plenum Press, New York, 1966, pp 231-45.

165. Cifonelli, J. A., P. Rebers, M. B. Perry, and J. K. N. Jones, *Biochemistry*, **5**, 3066 (1966).
166. Clark, I. T., *J. Gas Chromatog.*, **6**, 53 (1968).
167. Claussen, U., W. Borger, and F. Korte, *Ann. Chem.*, **693**, 158 (1966).
168. Clayton, D. W., and M. E. J. MacMillan, Abstracts, Winter Meeting of the American Chemical Society, Phoenix, Ariz., Jan. 1966; personal communication, 1967.
169. Connor, J. A., R. N. Haszeldine, G. J. Leigh, and R. D. Sedgwick, *J. Chem. Soc.*, 768 (1967).
170. Cook, R. L., and A. P. Mills, *J. Phys. Chem.*, **65**, 252 (1961).
171. Cooper, G. D., *J. Org. Chem.*, **26**, 925 (1961).
172. Cooper, G. D., H. S. Blanchard, G. F. Endres, and H. Finkbeiner, *J. Am. Chem. Soc.*, **87**, 3996 (1965).
173. Copenhaver, J. H., *Anal. Biochem.*, **17**, 76 (1966).
174. Cornelius, J., and H. Yang, *J. Gas Chromatog.*, 327 (1967).
175. Covill, M. J., H. G. Garg, and T. L. V. Ulbricht, *Tetrahedron Letters*, 1033 (1968).
176. Cox, R. I., and A. R. Bedford, *Steroids*, **3**, 663 (1964).
177. Creech, B. G., *J. Gas Chromatog.*, **2**, 194 (1964).
178. Currell, B. R., and W. Gerrard, *Chem. Ind.* (London), 1289 (1958).
179. Curtis, M. D., and A. L. Allred, *J. Am. Chem. Soc.*, **87**, 2554 (1965).
180. Curtius, H.-C., *Z. Klin. Chem.*, **4**, 114 (1966).
181. Curtius, H.-C., and M. Müller, *J. Chromatog.*, **39**, 410 (1967).
182. Dalgliesh, C. E., E. C. Horning, M. G. Horning, K. L. Knox, and K. Yarger, *Biochem. J.*, **101**, 792 (1966).
183. Dalgliesh, C. E., A. K. Mills, and S. J. Shaw, *Am. Soc. Brewing Chemists Proc.*, 53 (1967).
184. De Benneville, P. L., U.S. Patent 2,775,605 (1956); *Chem. Abstr.*, **51**, 7401g (1957).
185. De Benneville, P. L., and M. J. Hurwitz, U.S. Patent 2,847,409 (1958); *Chem. Abstr.*, **53**, 12746i (1959).
186. De Benneville, P. L., and M. J. Hurwitz, U.S. Patent 2,876,209 (1959); *Chem. Abstr.*, **53**, 12321 (1959).
187. De Benneville, P. L., M. J. Hurwitz, and L. J. Exner, *J. Org. Chem.*, **24**, 873 (1959).
188. DeJongh, D. C., J. D. Hribar, S. Hanessian, P. W. K. Woo, *J. Am. Chem. Soc.*, **89**, 3364 (1967).
189. Denkewalter, R. G., H. Schwam, R. G. Strachan, T. E. Beesley, D. G. Veber, E. F. Schoenwaldt, H. Barkemeyer, W. J. Paleveda, Jr., T. A. Jacob, and R. Hirschmann, *J. Am. Chem. Soc.*, **88**, 3163 (1966).
190. Dewar, M. J. S., H. Hampson, and L. C. F. Blackman, British Patent 839,352 (1960); *Chem. Abstr.*, **55**, 1445e (1961).
191. Dick, W. E., Jr., B. G. Baker, and J. E. Hodge, *Carbohydrate Res.*, **6**, 52 (1968).
192. Dickopp, H., Ph.D. Thesis, University of Cologne, Germany, 1966.
193. Diekman, J., and C. Djerassi, *J. Org. Chem.*, **32**, 1005 (1967).
194. Diekman, J., J. B. Thomson, and C. Djerassi, *J. Org. Chem.*, **32**, 3904 (1967).
195. Diekman, J., J. B. Thomson, and C. Djerassi, *J. Org. Chem.*, **33**, 2271 (1968).
196. Dittmer, D. C., W. Hertler, and H. Winicov, *J. Am. Chem. Soc.*, **79**, 4431 (1957).
197. Djerassi, C., and C. Fenselau, *J. Am. Chem. Soc.*, **87**, 5747 (1965).
198. Dolgov, B., Z. Sergeeva, N. Zubkova, and M. Voronkov, *Zh. Obshch. Khim.*, **30**, 3347 (1960); *J. Gen. Chem.*, **30**, 3314 (1960); *Chem. Abstr.*, **55**, 19765f (1961).
199. Donato, S. J., *J. Pharm. Sci.*, **54**, 917 (1965).
200. Durr, G. J., J. F. Keiser, and P. A. Ierardi, *J. Heterocyclic Chem.*. **4**, 291 (1967).
201. Dutton, G. G. S., and A. M. Unrau, *Can. J. Chem.*, **42**, 2048 (1964).
202. Dutton, G. G. S., and A. M. Unrau, *Can. J. Chem.*, **43**, 1738 (1965).
203. Dutton, G. G. S., and A. M. Unrau, *Carbohydrate Res.*, **1**, 116 (1965).
204. Dutton, G. G. S., and A. M. Unrau, *J. Chromatog.*, **20**, 78 (1965).

205. Eaborn, C., "Organosilicon Compounds," Butterworths Scientific Publications, London, 1960.
206. Eaborn, C., D. R. M. Walton, and B. S. Thomas, *Chem. Ind.* (London), 827 (1967).
207. Ebsworth, E. A. V., *Chem. Commun.*, 15, 530 (1966).
208. Egan, T. J., and W. W. Wells, *Am. J. Diseases Children*, 111, 400 (1966). Eglinton, see 214.
209. Eneroth, P., B. Gordon, R. Ryhage, and J. Sjövall, *J. Lipid Res.*, 7, 511 (1966).
210. Eneroth, P., B. Gordon, and J. Sjövall, *J. Lipid Res.* 7, 524 (1966).
211. Eneroth, P., K. Hellström, and R. Ryhage, *J. Lipid Res.*, 5, 245 (1964).
212. Eneroth, P., K. Hellström, and R. Ryhage, *Steroids*, 6, 707 (1965).
213. Eneroth, P., and E. Nyström, *Steroids*, 11, 417 (1968).
214. Eglinton, G., and D. H. Hunneman, *Phytochemistry*, 7, 313 (1968).
215. Etienne, M. Y., *Compt. Rend.*, 235, 966 (1952).
216. Ettre, L. S., and A. Zlatkis (Eds.), "The Practice of Gas Chromatography," Interscience Publishers, New York, 1967.
217. Fahmy, M. A. H., R. L. Metcalf, T. R. Fukuto, and D. J. Hennessy, *J. Agr. Food Chem.*, 14, 79 (1966).
218. Fales, H. M., and T. Luukkainen, *Anal. Chem.*, 37, 955 (1965).
219. Faucett, W., B. O. Musser, and L. P. Cawley, Abstracts, 19th Annual Meeting, American Association of Clinical Chemists, Phila., Pa., Aug. 1967, *Clinical Chemistry*, 13, 707 (1967).
220. Ferrier, R. J., *Tetrahedron*, 18, 1149 (1962).
221. Ferrier, R. J., and M. F. Singleton, *Tetrahedron*, 18, 1143 (1962).
222. Fessenden, R. J., and M. D. Coon, *J. Org. Chem.*, 29, 1607 (1964).
223. Fessenden, R. J., and D. F. Crowe, *J. Org. Chem.*, 25, 598 (1960).
224. Fessenden, R. J., and D. F. Crowe, *J. Org. Chem.*, 26, 4638 (1961).
225. Finch, R. C., and H. W. Post, *J. Org. Chem.*, 24, 969 (1959)
226. Fink, W., *Chem. Ber.*, 97, 1433 (1964).
227. Fioriti, J. A., and R. J. Sims, *J. Am. Oil Chemists' Soc.*, 44, 221 (1967).
228. Fishbein, L., and W. L. Zielinski, Jr., *J. Chromatog.*, 20, 9 ((1965).
229. Fishbein, L., W. L. Zielinski, Jr., *J. Chromatog.*, 28, 418 (1967).
230. Fishbein, L., W. L. Zielinski, Jr., and R. O. Thomas, *Nature*, 212, 180 (1966).
231. Fishbein, L., W. L. Zielinski, Jr., and R. O. Thomas, *J. Chromatog.*, 30, 596 (1967).
232. Flint, D. R., T.-C. Lee, and C. G. Huggins, *Federation Proc.*, 24, No. 2, Pt. 1, 662 (1965).
233. Flint, D., T.-C. Lee, and C. G. Huggins, *J. Am. Oil Chemists' Soc.*, 42, 1001 (1965).
234. Frainnet, E., and F. Duboudin, *Compt. Rend. Ser. C*, 262, 1693 (1966).
235. France, J. T., N. L. McNiven, and R. I. Dorfman, *Acta Endocrinol. Suppl.*, 90, 71 (1964).
236. France, J. T., R. Rivera, N. L. McNiven, and R. I. Dorfman, *Steroids*, 5, 687 (1965).
237. Freedman, B., *J. Am. Oil Chemists' Soc.*, 44, 113 (1967).
238. Freedman, R. W., and G. O. Charlier, *Anal. Chem.*, 36, 1880 (1964).
239. Freedman, R. W., and P. P. Croitoru, *Anal. Chem.*, 36, 1389 (1964).
240. Freiser, H., M. V. Eagle, and J. Speier, *J. Am. Chem. Soc.*, 75, 2824 (1953).
241. Friedman, S., and M. L. Kaufman, *Anal. Chem.*, 38, 144 (1966).
242. Friedman, S., M. L. Kaufman, B. D. Blaustein, R. E. Dean, and I. Wender, *Tetrahedron*, 21, 485 (1965).
243. Friedman, S., M. L. Kaufman, W. A. Steiner, and I. Wender, *Fuel*, 40, 33 (1961).
244. Friedman, S., M. L. Kaufman, and I. Wender, *J. Org. Chem.*, 27, 664 (1962).
245. Friedman, S., W. A. Steiner, R. Raymond, and I. Wender, Abstracts of the 132nd National Meeting of the American Chemical Society, Sept 1957, No. 16, p 6K.
246. Friedman, S., C. Zahn, M. L. Kaufman, and I. Wender, U.S. Bureau of Mines Bulletin 609, U.S. Government Printing Office, Washington, D.C., 1963.
247. Frisch, K. C., U.S. Patent 2,711,417 (1955).
248. Frisch, K. C., and P. D. Shroff, *J. Am. Chem. Soc.*, 75, 1249 (1953).
249. Frisch, K. C., and M. Wolf, *J. Org. Chem.*, 18, 657 (1953).

250. Frye, C. L., U.S. Patent 2,814,572 (1957); *Chem. Abstr.*, **52**, 5450c (1958).
251. Frye, C. L., *J. Am. Chem. Soc.*, **86**, 3170 (1964).
252. Frye, C. L., G. E. Vogel, and J. A. Hall, *J. Am Chem. Soc*, **83**, 996 (1961).
253. Fumagalli, R., P. Capella, and W. J. A. VandenHeuvel, *Anal. Biochem.*, **10**, 377 (1965).
254. Fumagalli, R., R. Niemiro, and R. Paoletti, *J. Am. Oil Chemists' Soc.*, **42**, 1018 (1965).
255. Furuya, T., *J. Chromatog.*, **18**, 152 (1965).
256. Furuya, T., *J. Chromatog.*, **19**, 607 (1965).
257. Furuya, T., and H. Kojima, *J. Chromatog.*, **29**, 382 (1967).
258. Furuya, T., S. Shibata, and H. Iizuka, *J. Chromatog.*, **21**, 116 (1966).
259. Futterweit, W., G. L. Siegel, R. Freeman, S. I. Griboff, M. Drosdowsky, N. Gibree, R. I. Dorfman, and L. J. Soffer in "Gas Chromatography of Steroids in Biological Fluids," M. B. Lipsett, Ed., Plenum Press, N.Y., 1965, pp 19-22.

260. Gaffield, W., A. C. Waiss, Jr., and J. Corse, *J. Chem. Soc., C,* 1885 (1966).
261. Gardiner, D., *Carbohydrate Res.*, **2**, 234 (1966).
262. Gardiner, D., *J. Chem. Soc.*, 1473 (1966).
263. Gardiner, W. L., C. J. W. Brooks, E. C. Horning, and R. M. Hill, *Biochim. Biophys. Acta,* **130**, 278 (1966).
264. Gardiner, W. L., and E. C. Horning, *Biochim. Biophys. Acta,* **115**, 524 (1966).
265. Gaudiano, G., P. Bravo, and A. Quilico, *Tetrahedron Letters,* 3567 (1966).
266. Gaver, R. C., and C. C. Sweeley, *J. Am. Oil Chemists' Soc.*, **42**, 294 (1965).
267. Gaver, R. C., and C. C. Sweeley, *J. Am. Chem. Soc.*, **88**, 3643 (1966)
268. Gehrke, C. W., D. L. Stalling, and C. D. Ruyle, *Biochem Biophys. Res. Commun.,* **28**, 869 (1967).
269. Gerrard, W., and K. D. Kilburn, *J. Chem. Soc.*, 1536 (1956).
270. Gerrard, W., and P. Tolcher, *J. Chem. Soc.*, 3640 (1954).
271. Geyer, H. U., *Die Stärke,* **17**, 307 (1965).
272. Giessler, W., Ph.D. Thesis, University of Cologne, Germany (1963).
273. Gilman, H., and G. E. Dunn, *Chem. Rev.*, **52**, 77 (1953).
274. Glassner, S., H. N. Graham, A. R. Pierce, and H. Madlin, Abstracts, 153rd National Meeting of American Chemical Society, Miami Beach, Fla., April 1967, No. B6.
275. Glaudemans, C. P. J., and H. G. Fletcher, Jr., *J. Am. Chem. Soc.*, **87**, 2456 (1965).
276. Golding, B. T., R. W. Rickards, and M. Barber, *Tetrahedron Letters,* 2615 (1964).
277. Golding, B., R. Rickards, W. E. Meyer, J. B. Patrick and M. Barber, *Tetrahedron Letters,* 3551 (1966).
278. Golodnikov, G. V., B. N. Dolgov, and V. F. Sedova, *Zh. Obshch. Khim.*, **30**, 3352 (1960); *J. Gen. Chem.*, **30**, 3319 (1960); *Chem. Abstr.*, **55**, 19844f (1961).
279. Gottfried, H., in "Gas Chromatography of Steroids in Biological Fluids," M. B. Lipsett, Ed., Plenum Press, N.Y., 1965, pp 89-100.
280. Goubeau, J., E. Heubach, D. Paulin, and I. Widmaier, *Z. Anorg. Allgem. Chem.*, **300**, 194 (1959).
281. Grant, D. W., and G. A. Vaughan, *Gas Chromatog., Intern. Symp.,* **4**, 305 (1962).
282. Grisebach, H., and U. Döbereiner, *Z. Naturforsch,* **21**, 429 (1966).
283. Grubb, W. T., *J. Am. Chem. Soc.*, **76**, 3408 (1954).
284. Grundy, S. M., E. H. Ahrens, Jr., and T. A. Miettinen, *J Lipid Res.*, **6**, 397 (1965).
285. Gustafsson, B. E., J. A. Gustafsson, and J. Sjövall, *Acta Chem. Scand.*, **20**, 1827 (1966).
286. Gverdtsiteli, I. M., R. Y. Papava, and E. S. Gelashvili, *Zh. Obshch. Khim.*, **36**, 112 (1966); *J. Gen. Chem.*, **36**, 115 (1966); *Chem. Abstr.*, **64**, 14207f (1966).

287. Hahn, W., and L. Metzinger, *Makromol. Chem.*, **21**, 113 (1956).
288. Halpern, B., and J. W. Westley, *Tetrahedron Letters,* 2283 (1966).
289. Halpern, Y, Y. Houminer, and S. Patai, *Analyst*, **92**, 714 (1967).
290. Hamilton, R. J., W. J. A. VandenHeuvel, and E. C. Horning, *Biochim. Biophys. Acta,* **70**, 679 (1963).
291. Hammond, K. B., and H. Leach, *Clin. Chim. Acta,* **12**, 363 (1965).

292. Hammond, K. B., and H. Leach, *Clin. Chim. Acta*, **14**, 569 (1966).
293. Hammond, K. B., and H. Leach, *Clin. Chim. Acta*, **15**, 145 (1967).
294. Hanaineh, L., and C. J. W. Brooks, *Biochem. J.*, **92**, 9P (1964).
295. Hancock, R. L., *J. Gas Chromatog.*, 4, 363 (1966).
296. Hancock, R. L., and D. L. Coleman, *Anal. Biochem.*, **10**, 365 (1965).
297. Hara, S., T. Watabe, and Y. Ike, *Chem. Pharm. Bull.* (Tokyo), **14**, 1311 (1966).
298. Hartman, I. S., and H. H. Wotiz, *Steroids*, 1, 33 (1963).
299. Hartman, I. S., and H. H. Wotiz, *Biochim. Biophys. Acta*, **90**, 334 (1964).
300. Hashizume, T., S. Higa, Y. Sasaki, H. Yamazaki, H. Iwamura, and H. Matsuda, *Agr. Biol. Chem.* (Tokyo), **30**, 319 (1966).
301. Hashizume, T., and Y. Sasaki, *Anal. Biochem.*, **15**, 199 (1966).
302. Hashizume, T., and Y. Sasaki, *Anal. Biochem.*, **15**, 346 (1966).
303. Hashizume, T., T. Yamagami, and Y. Sasaki, *Agr. Biol. Chem.* (Tokyo), **31**, 324 (1967).
304. Heaysman, L. T., E. A. Walker, and D. T. Lewis, *Analyst*, **92**, 450 (1967).
305. Hedgley, E. J., and W. G. Overend, *Chem. Ind.* (London), 378 (1960).
306. Heitzman, R. J., and G. H. Thomas, *J. Endocrinol.*, **33**, 455 (1965).
307. Henglein, F. A., G. Abelsnes, H. Heneka, K. Lienhard, P. Nakhre, and K. Scheinost, *Makromol. Chem.*, **24**, 1 (1957).
308. Henglein, F. A., and H. Gräser, *Makromol. Chem.*, **26**, 236 (1958).
309. Henglein, F. A., and W. Knoch, *Makromol. Chem.* **28**, 10 (1958).
310. Henglein, F. A., and B. Kösters, *Chem. Ber.*, **92**, 1638 (1959).
311. Henglein, F. A., and J. Krämer, *Chem. Ber.*, **92**, 2585 (1959).
312. Henglein, F. A., and K. Lienhard, *Makromol. Chem.*, **32**, 218 (1959).
313. Henglein, F. A., and N. Niebergall, *Chemiker-Ztg.*, **80**, 611 (1956).
314. Henglein, F. A., and K. Scheinost, *Makromol. Chem.*, **21**, 59 (1956).
315. Henneberg, G., Ph.D. Thesis, University of Rostock, Germany, 1966.
316. Hertzberg, S., and S. L. Jensen, *Acta Chem. Scand.*, **21**, 15 (1967).
317. Hertzberg, S., and S. L. Jensen, *Phytochemistry*, **6**, 1119 (1967).
318. Herz, J. E., and E. Gonzalez, *J. Chromatog.*, **34**, 251 (1968).
319. Hess, G. G., F. W. Lampe, and L. H. Sommer, *J. Am. Chem. Soc.*, **87**, 5327 (1965).
320. Heyns, K., and H. Scharmann, *Chem. Ber.*, **99**, 3461 (1966).
321. Heyns, W., A. Hendrikx, and P. De Moor, *Ann. Endrocrinol.* (Paris), **26**, 168 (1965).
322. Hiatt, R. R., *Can. J. Chem.*, **42**, 985 (1964).
323. Hils, J., V. Hagen, H. Ludwig, and K. Rühlmann, *Chem. Ber.*, **99**, 776 (1966).
324. Hils, J., C. Michael, and K. Rühlmann, *Makromol. Chem.*, **103**, 257 (1967).
325. Hils, J., and K. Rühlmann, *Chem. Ber.*, **100**, 1638 (1967).
326. Ho, C.-H., and S.-L. Liu, *J. Chinese Chem. Soc.* (Taiwan), **10**, 66 (1963).
327. Hoffman-La Roche & Co., A.-G., Netherlands Patent 6,610,360 (1967); *Chem. Abstr.*, **67**, 91093 (1967).
328. Höfler, F., and U. Wannagat, *Monatsh. Chem.*, **97**, 1598 (1966).
329. Hofmann, A. F., and E. H. Mosbach, *J. Biol. Chem.*, **239**, 2813 (1964).
330. Hogben, M. G., A. J. Oliver, and W. A. G. Graham, *Chem. Commun.*, 1183 (1967).
331. Hogenkamp, H. P. C., *Carbohydrate Res.*, **3**, 239 (1966).
332. Holmstedt, B., W. J. A. VandenHeuvel, W. L. Gardiner, and E. C. Horning, *Anal. Biochem.*, **8**, 151 (1964).
333. Hörhammer, L., H. Wagner, L. Rosprim, T. Mabry, and H. Rösler, *Tetrahedron Letters*, 1707 (1965).
334. Horii, Z., M. Makita, I. Takeda, Y. Tamura, and Y. Ohnishi, *Chem. Pharm. Bull.* (Tokyo), **13**, 636 (1965).
335. Horii, Z., M. Makita, and Y. Tamura, *Chem. Ind.* (London), **34**, 1494 (1965).
336. Horning, E. C., presented at the Conference on Anal. Chem. and Applied Spectroscopy, Pittsburgh, Pa., March 1967, No. 123.
336a. Horning, E. C., Baylor University, personal communication.
337. Horning, E. C., C. J. W. Brooks, L. Johnson, and W. L. Gardiner, *Separation Science*, 1, 555 (1966); *Chem. Abstr.*, **66**, 62230 (1967).
338. Horning, E. C., and W. Gardiner in "Research on Steroids," Vol. II, C. Cassano, Ed., Tipografia Poliglotta Vaticana, Rome, 1965, pp 121-146.

339. Horning, E. C., M. G. Horning, N. Ikekawa, E. M. Chambaz, P. I. Jaakonmaki, and C. J. W. Brooks, *J. Gas Chromatog.*, **5**, 283 (1967).
340. Horning, E. C., M. G. Horning, W. J. A. VandenHeuvel, K. L. Knox, B. Holmstedt, and C. J. W. Brooks, *Anal. Chem.*, **36**, 1546 (1964)
341. Horning, E. C., T. Luukkainen, E. O. A. Haahti, B. G. Creech, and W. J. A. VandenHeuvel, *Recent Progr. Hormone Res.*, **19**, 57 (1963).
342. Horning, E. C., K. C. Maddock, K. V. Anthony, and W. J. A. VandenHeuvel, *Anal. Chem.*, **35**, 526 (1963).
343. Horning, E. C., E. A. Moscatelli, and C. C. Sweeley, *Chem. Ind.* (London), 751 (1959).
344. Horning, E. C., and W. J. A. VandenHeuvel in "New Biochemical Separations," L. J. Morris and A. T. James, Eds., Van Nostrand, London, 1964, p 25.
345. Horning, E. C., and W. J. A. Vandenheuvel in "Advances in Chromatography," Vol. 1, A. Zlatkis, Ed., Preston Technical Abstracts Co., Evanston, Ill., 1966, pp 153-198.
346. Horning, E. C., W. J. A. VandenHeuvel, and B. G. Creech in "Methods of Biochemical Analysis," Vol. 11, D. Glick, Ed., Interscience Publishers, New York, 1963, pp 69-147.
347. Horning, M. G., E. A. Boucher, and A. M. Moss, *J. Gas Chromatog.*, **5**, 297 (1967), and as presented at the Fourth International Symposium on Advances in Gas Chromatography, New York, Apr 1967.
347a. Horning, M. G., E. A. Boucher, A. M. Moss, and E. C. Horning, *Analytical Letters*, in press. This paper was received too late for tabulation.
348. Horning, M. G., K. L. Knox, C. E. Dalgliesh, and E. C. Horning, *Anal. Biochem.*, **17**, 244 (1966).
349. Horning, M. G., A. M. Moss, E. A. Boucher, and E. C. Horning, *Analytical Letters*, **1**, 311 (1968).
350. Horning, M. G., A. M. Moss, and E. C. Horning, *Biochim. Biophys. Acta*, **148**, 597 (1967).
351. Horning, M. G., A. M. Moss, and E. C. Horning, *Anal. Biochem.*, **22**, 284 (1968).
352. Horowitz, M. I., and M. R. Delman, *J. Chromatog.*, **21**, 300 (1966).
353. Horton, D., and J. S. Jewell, *Carbohydrate Res.*, **5**, 149 (1967).
354. Hulyalkar, R. K., J. K. N. Jones, and M. B. Perry, *Can. J. Chem.*, **43**, 2085 (1965).
355. Hulyalkar, R. K., and M. B. Perry, *Can. J. Chem.*, **43**, 3241 (1965).
356. Hurst, D. T., and A. G. McInnes, *Can. J. Chem.*, **43**, 2004 (1965).
357. Hurst, M. W., C. G. Huggins, and J. G. Hamilton, presented at the 58th Annual Meeting of the Americal Oil Chemists Society, New Orleans, La., May 1967, No. 92.
358. Hurwitz, M. J., and P. De Benneville, U.S. Patent 2,876,234 (1959); *Chem. Abstr.*, **53**, 12238d (1959).
359. Ikekawa, N., O. Hoshino, R. Watanuki, H. Orimo, T. Fujita, and M. Yoshikawa, *Anal. Biochem.*, **17**, 16 (1966).
360. Ikekawa, N., S. Natori, H. Itokawa, S. Tobinaga, and M. Matsui, *Chem. Pharm. Bull.* (Tokyo), **13**, 316 (1965).
361. Illuminati, G., and F. Tarli, *Ric. Sci., Rend. Sez. A*, **3**, 329 (1963); *Chem. Abstr.*, **59**, 10105c (1963).
362. Imanari, T., and Z. Tamura, *Chem. Pharm. Bull.* (Tokyo), **15**, 1677 (1967).
363. Institute of Organic Chemistry, Siberian Dept., Academy of Sciences, U.S.S.R., French Patent 1,439,588 (1966); *Chem. Abstr.*, **66**, 18763 (1967).
364. Iritani, N., and W. W. Wells, *J. Lipid Res.*, **7**, 372 (1966).
365. Ishikawa, S., and G. Katsui, *J. Vitaminol.* (Kyoto), **12**, 106 (1966).
366. Ishizuka, I., N. Ueta, and T. Yamakawa, *Japan J. Exp. Med.*, **36**, 73 (1966).
367. Ismail, R. M., *Naturforsch.*, **18b**, 582 (1963).
368. Ismail, R. M., German Patent 1,182,232 (1964); *Chem. Abstr.*, **62**, 7797b (1965).

369. Itoh, K., S. Sakai, and Y. Ishii, *J. Org. Chem.*, **32**, 2210 (1967).
370. Ivin, S. Z., V. K. Promonenkov, and G. V. Konopatova, *Zh. Obshch. Khim.*, **37**, 1681 (1967); *Chem. Abstr.*, **68**, 39699 (1968).
371. Jaakonmaki, P. I., K. L. Knox, E. C. Horning, and M. G. Horning, *European J. Pharmacol.*, **1**, 63 (1967).

372. Jaakonmaki, P. I., K. A. Yarger, and E. C. Horning, *Biochim. Biophys. Acta*, 137, 216 (1967).
373. Jack, J., (Imperial Chemical Industries Ltd.), British Patent 857,153 (1960); *Chem. Abstr.*, 55, 18684i (1961).
374. Jacovic, M., *Z. Anorg. Allgem. Chem.*, 288, 324 (1956).
375. Jaffé, H. H., *J. Phys. Chem.*, 58, 185 (1954).
376. Jarvie, A. W., and D. Lewis, *J. Chem. Soc.*, 1073 (1963).
377. Jelliffe, R. W., and D. H. Blankenhorn, *J. Chromatog.*, 12, 268 (1963).
378. Johnson, C. B., and R. T. Holman, *Lipids*, 1, 371 (1966).
379. Johnson, W. K., and K. A. Pollart, *J. Org. Chem.*, 26, 4092 (1961).
380. Jones, H. G., D. M. Smith and M. Sahasrabudhe, *J. Assoc. Offic. Anal. Chemists*, 49, 1183 (1966).
381. Jones, P. H., and R. E. Erb, *J. Dairy Sci.*, 50, 772 (1967).
381a. Jones, T. C., and I. Schmeltz, *Tobacco Sci.*, 166, 20 (1968).
382. Jungmann, R. A., E. Calvary, and J. S. Schweppe, *J. Clin. Endocrinol. Metab.*, 27, 355 (1967).
383. Kadunce, R. E., *J. Chromatog.*, 30, 204 (1967).
384. Kagan, J., *Phytochemistry*, 6, 317 (1967).
385. Kagan, J., and T. J. Mabry, *Anal. Chem.*, 37, 288 (1965).
386. Kamenskii, I. V., I. K. Sanin, and V. V. Korshak, *Plasticheskie Massy*, No. 3, 8 (1962); *Chem. Abstr.*, 59, 654g (1963).
387. Kamm, J. J., and E. J. Van Loon, *Clin. Chem.*, 12, 789 (1966).
388. Kantor, S. W., *J. Am. Chem. Soc.*, 75, 2712 (1953).
389. Karabatsos, G. J., J. L. Fry, and S. Meyerson, *Tetrahedron Letters*, 3735 (1967).
390. Karabatsos, G. J., N. Hsi, and S. Meyerson, *J. Am. Chem. Soc.*, 88, 5649 (1966).
391. Karabatsos, G. J., R. A. Mount, D. O. Rickter, and S. Meyerson, *J. Am. Chem. Soc.*, 88, 5651 (1966).
392. Karabatsos, G. J., C. E. Orzech, Jr., and S. Meyerson, *J. Am. Chem. Soc.*, 87, 4394 (1965).
393. Kärkkäinen, J. E., E. O. Haahti, and A. A. Lehtonen, *Anal. Chem.*, 38, 1316 (1966).
394. Kärkkäinen, J., A. Lehtonen, and T. Nikkari, *J. Chromatog.*, 20, 457 (1965).
395. Karlsen, J., and A. B. Svendsen, *Medd. Norsk. Farm. Selskap.*, 27, 91 (1965).
396. Karlsson, K.-A., *Acta Chem. Scand.*, 19, 2425 (1965).
397. Karlsson, K.-A., *Acta Chem. Scand.*, 20, 2884 (1966).
398. Karlsson, K.-A., and G. A. L. Holm, *Acta Chem. Scand.*, 19, 2423 (1965).
399. Kaufman, M. L., S. Friedman, and I. Wender, *Anal. Chem.*, 39, 1011 (1967).
400. Kaufmann, K.-D., U. Mann, and K. Rühlmann, *Z. Chem.*, 5, 188 (1965).
401. Kawai, S., T. Nagatsu, T. Imanari, and Z. Tamura, *Chem. Pharm. Bull.* (Tokyo), 14, 618 (1966).
402. Kawai, S., and Z. Tamura, *Chem. Pharm. Bull.* (Tokyo), 15, 1493 (1967); *J. Chromatog.*, 25, 471 (1966).
403. Kawanami, J., *J. Biochem.* (Japan), 62, 105 (1967).
404. Keeber, W. H., and H. W. Post, *J. Org. Chem.*, 21, 509 (1956).
405. Keith, E. S., and J. J. Powers, *J. Food Sci.*, 31, 971 (1966)
406. Kelly, M., and S. L. Jensen, *Acta Chem. Scand.*, 21, 2578 (1967).
407. Kerr, R. W., and K. C. Hobbs, *Ind. Eng. Chem.*, 45, 2542 (1953).
408. Kim, S. M., R. Bentley, and C. C. Sweeley, *Carbohydrate Res.*, 5, 373 (1967).
409. Kinoshita, K., K. Isurugi, Y. Kumamoto, and H. Takayasu, *J. Clin. Endocrinol. Metab.*, 26, 1219 (1966).
410. Kinoshita, K., K. Isurugi, Y. Matsumoto, and H. Takayasu, *Steroids*, 11, 1 (1968).
411. Kirschner, M. A., and M. B. Lipsett, *J. Clin. Endocrinol. Metab.*, 23, 255 (1963).
412. Kirschner, M. A., and M. B. Lipsett, *Steroids*, 3, 277 (1964).
413. Klebe, J. F., *J. Am. Chem. Soc.*, 86, 3399 (1964).
414. Klebe, J. F., *J. Polymer Sci.*, 2, 1079 (1964).
415. Klebe, J. F., *J. Polymer Sci.*, 2, 2673 (1964).
416. Klebe, J. F., U.S. Patent 3,172,874 (1965).

417. Klebe, J. F., French Patent 1,434,770 (Compagnie Française Thomson-Houston); *Chem. Abstr.*, **65**, 20163f (1966).
418. Klebe, J. F., French Patent 1,442,585 (1966) (Compagnie Française Thomson-Houston); *Chem. Abstr.*, **66**, 85854s (1967).
419. Klebe, J. F., presented at Symposium on Silicon-Nitrogen Chemistry, University of Wisconsin, Madison, Wisconsin, April 1968.
420. Klebe, J. F., and J. B. Bush, Jr., presented at the International Symposium on Organosilicon Chemistry, Prague 1965.
421. Klebe, J. F., J. B. Bush, Jr. and J. E. Lyons, *J. Am. Chem. Soc.*, **86**, 4400 (1964).
422. Klebe, J. F., H. Finkbeiner, and D. M. White, *J. Am. Chem. Soc.*, **88**, 3390 (1966).
423. Knaak, J. B., J. M. Eldridge, and L. J. Sullivan, *Agr. Food Chem.*, **15**, 605 (1967).
424. Knights, B. A., *J. Gas Chromatog.*, **2**, 160 (1964).
425. Knights, B. A., *J. Gas Chromatog.*, **2**, 338 (1964).
426. Knights, B. A., *J. Gas Chromatog.*, **5**, 273 (1967).
427. Knights, B. A., *Mem. Soc. Endocrinol.*, No. 16, 211 (1967).
428. Knights, B. A., and W. Laurie, *Phytochemistry*, **6**, 407 (1967).
429. Knoth, W. H., Ph.D. Thesis, Pennsylvania State University, 1954.
430. Kobata, A., and S. Ziro, *Biochim. Biophys. Acta*, **107**, 405 (1965).
431. Kohama, S., and S. Fukukawa, *Nippon Kagaku Zasshi*, **81**, 170 (1960); *Chem. Abstr.*, **56**, 496e (1962).
432. Kohama, S., and S. Fukukawa, *Nippon Kagaku Zasshi*, **81**, 472 (1960); *Chem. Abstr.*, **56**, 497b (1962).
433. Kohlschütter, H. W., and G. Jaekel, *Z. Anorg. Allgem. Chem.*, **271**, 185 (1953).
434. Kolb, B., *Appl. Gas Chromatog. Bull.*, No. 5E (1963), Bodenseewerk Perkin-Elmer & Co.
435. Körner, G., German Patent 1,234,719 (1967); *Chem. Abstr.*, **67**, 22005 (1967).
436. Korytnyk, W., G. Fricke, and B. Paul, *Anal. Biochem.*, **17**, 66 (1966).
437. Kreshkov, A. P., V. A. Drozdov, and S. Kubiak, *Zh. Obshch. Khim.*, **31**, 3099 (1961); *Chem. Abstr.*, **56**, 13617d (1962).
438. Kreshkov, A. P., and D. A. Karoteev, *Zh. Prikl. Khim.*, **33**, 413 (1960); *J. Appl. Chem.*, **33**, 408 (1960); *Chem. Abstr.*, **54**, 11977a (1960).
439. Kreshkov, A. P., L. V. Myshlyaeva, and L. M. Khananashvili, *Zh. Obshch. Khim.*, **28**, 2112 (1958); *J. Gen. Chem.*, **28**, 2150 (1958); *Chem. Abstr.*, **53**, 2074g (1959).
440. Kresze, G., K. Bederke, and F. Schäuffelhut, *Z. Anal. Chem.*, **209**, 329 (1965).
441. Kresze, G., and J. Firl, *Tetrahedron Letters*, 1163 (1965).
442. Kresze, G., and F. Schäuffelhut, *Z. Anal. Chem.*, **229**, 401 (1967).
443. Kriegsmann, H., in "Organosilicon Chemistry," Plenum Press, New York 1966, pp 206-8.
444. Krüger, C. R., and E. G. Rochow, *Angew. Chem. Intern. Ed. Engl.*, **2**, 617 (1963).
445. Krüger, C. R., and E. G. Rochow, *J. Organometal. Chem.* (Amsterdam), **1**, 476 (1964).
446. Krüger, C. R., E. G. Rochow, and U. Wannagat, *Chem. Ber.*, **96**, 2138 (1963).
447. Kubota, T., and F. Tonami, *Tetrahedron*, **23**, 3353 (1967).
448. Kuksis, A., in "Methods of Biochemical Analysis," Vol. 14, D. Glick, Ed., Interscience Publishers, N.Y., 1966, pp 325-73.
449. Kumada, M., in "Organosilicon Chemistry," Plenum Press, New York, 1966, pp 184-6.
450. Kurlansik, L., C. Damon, and E. F. Salim, *J. Pharm. Sci.*, **56**, 1158 (1967).
451. Lach, J. L., and J. S. Sawardeker, *J. Pharm. Sci.*, **54**, 424 (1965).
452. Langer, S. H., S. Connell, and I. Wender, *J. Org. Chem.*, **23**, 50 (1958).

453. Langer, S. H., R. A. Friedel, I. Wender, and A. G. Sharkey, Jr., *Anal. Chem.*, **30**, 1353 (1958).

454. Langer, S. H., P. Pantages, *Nature*, **191**, 141 (1961).
455. Langer, S. H., P. Pantages, and I. Wender, *Chem. Ind.* (London), 1664 (1958).
456. Lau, H. L., *J. Gas Chromatog.*, **4**, 136 (1966).
457. Lee, Y. C., and C. E. Ballou, *J. Biol. Chem.*, **239**, 3602 (1964).
458. Lee, Y. C., and C. E. Ballou, *Biochemistry*, **4**, 257 (1965).

459. Lee, Y. C., and C. E. Ballou, *Biochemistry*, 4, 1395 (1965).
460. Lee, Y. C., and C. E. Ballou, *J. Chromatog.*, 18, 147 (1965).
461. Leemans, F. A. J. M., and J. A. McCloskey, *J. Am. Oil Chemists' Soc.*, 44, 11 (1967).
462. Lehmann, J., *Angew, Chem. Intern. Ed. Engl.*, 4, 874 (1965).
463. Lehmann, J., *Carbohydrate Res.*, 2, 1 (1966).
464. Lehnert, G., W. Mücke, and H. Valentin, *Endokrinologie*, 46, 241 (1964).
465. Lehrfeld, J., *J. Chromatog.*, 32, 685 (1968).
466. Lehtonen, A. A., J. K. Kärkkäinen, and E. O. Haahti, *Acta Chem. Scand.*, 20, 1456 (1966).
467. Lehtonen, A. A., J. K. Kärkkäinen, and E. O. Haahti, *Anal. Biochem.*, 16, 526 (1966).
468. Lehtonen, A. A., J. K. Kärkkäinen, and E. O. Haahti, *J. Chromatog.*, 24, 179 (1966).
469. Leibman, K. C., and E. Ortiz, *J. Chromatog.*, 32, 757 (1968).
470. Lemieux, R. U., and S. W. Gunner, *Can. J. Chem.*, 46, 397 (1968).
471. Lewis, B., and F. Stewart, *S. African J. Lab. Clin. Med.*, 8, 160 (1962).
472. Licht, K., and H. Kriegsmann, *Z. Chem.*, 5, 462 (1965).
473. Limburg, W. W., and H. Post, *Rec. Trav. Chim.*, 81, 430 (1962).
474. Lindgren, B. O., and C. M. Svahn, *Acta Chem. Scand.*, 20, 1763 (1966).
475. Lindstedt, S., *Clin. Chim. Acta.*, 9, 309 (1964).
476. Liu, S.-L., *J. Chinese Chem. Soc.* (Taiwan), 9, 273 (1962).
477. Liu, S.-L., and C.-H. Ho, *J. Chinese Chem. Soc.* (Taiwan), 6, 137 (1960).
478. Liu, S.-L., and C.-H. Ho, *J. Chinese Chem. Soc.* (Taiwan), 8, 380 (1962).
479. Liu, S.-L., and T.-F. Lin, *J. Chinese Chem. Soc.* (Taiwan), 13, 166 (1966).
480. Liu, S.-L., and B.-H. Rei, *J. Chinese Chem. Soc.*, (Taiwan), 8, 237 (1961).
481. Liu, S.-L., and B.-H. Rei, *J. Chinese Chem. Soc.* (Taiwan), 8, 384 (1961).
482. Liu, S.-L., and T. Wang, *J. Chinese Chem. Soc.* (Taiwan), 10, 166 (1963).
483. Liu, S.-L., and I.-Y. Wei, *J. Chinese Chem. Soc.* (Taiwan), 13, 172 (1966).
484. Liu, S.-L., and M.-F. Yahg, *J. Chinese Chem. Soc.* (Taiwan), 11, 202 (1964).
484a. Livingston, R. L., and L. O. Brockway, *J. Am. Chem. Soc.*, 68, 719 (1946).
485. Lloyd, K. O., S. Beychok, and E. A. Kabat, *Biochemistry*, 6, 1448 (1967).
486. Lloyd, K. O., E. A. Kabat, E. J. Layug, and F. Gruezo, *Biochemistry*, 5, 1489 (1966).
487. Loeb, H. G., V. J. Jahnsen, and H. Goldenberg, *Scientific Sessions*, 13, 705 (1967).
488. Loewus, F., *Carbohydrate Res.*, 3, 130 (1966).
489. Lott, C. E., Jr., and K. M. Brobst, *Anal. Chem.*, 38, 1767 (1966).
490. Lott, C. E., Jr., K. M. Brobst, and E. E. Fisher, Abstracts, 154th National Meeting of the American Chemical Society, Chicago, Ill Sept 1967, No. E-39.
491. Ludlow, C. J., T. M. Harris, and F. T. Wolf, *Phytochemistry*, 5, 251 (1966).
492. Ludwig, G., and F. Korte, *Life Sciences*, 4, 2027 (1965).
493. Lukevits, E. Ya., Yu. P. Romadan, and S. A. Hillers, *Latvijas PSR Zinatnu Akad. Vestis*, 59 (1961); *Chem. Abstr.*, 57, 12525h (1962).
494. Lukevits, E. Ya., Yu. P. Romadan, S. A. Hillers, and M. G. Voronkov, *Dokl. Akad. Nauk SSSR*, 145, 806 (1963); *Proc. Acad. Sci. USSR*, 145, 668 (1963); *Chem. Abstr.*, 58, 1485e (1963).
495. Luukkainen, T., and H. Adlercreutz, *Biochim. Biophys. Acta*, 70, 700 (1963).
496. Luukkainen, T., and H. Adlercreutz, *Biochim. Biophys. Acta*, 107, 579 (1965).
497. Luukkainen, T., and H. Adlercreutz in "Research on Steroids," Vol. II, C. Cassano, Ed., Tipografia Poliglotta Vaticana, Rome, 1965, pp 165-166.
498. Luukkainen, T., W. J. A. VandenHeuvel, E. A. O. Haahti, and E. C. Horning, *Biochim, Biophys. Acta*, 52, 599 (1961).
499. Luukkainen, T., W. J. A. VandenHeuvel, and E. C. Horning, *Biochim. Biophys. Acta*, 62, 153 (1962).
500. Mabry, T. J., J. Kagan, and H. Rösler, The University of Texas Publication, No. 6418 (1964).
501. Mabry, T. J., J. Kagan, and H. Rösler, *Phytochemistry*, 4, 177 (1965).
502. Mabry, T. J., J. Kagan, and H. Rösler, *Phytochemistry*, 4, 487 (1965).
503. MacMillan, J., R. J. Pryce, G. Eglinton, and A. McCormick, *Tetrahedron Letters*, 2241 (1967).
504. Makita, M., and W. W. Wells, *Anal. Biochem.*, 5, 523 (1963).

505. Malinovskii, M. S., and M. K. Romantsevich, *Zh. Obshch. Khim.*, **27**, 1680 (1957); *J. Gen. Chem.*, **27**, 1749 (1957); *Chem. Abstr.*, **52**, 3669d (1958).
506. Malinovskii, M. S., and M. K. Romantsevich, *Zh. Obshch. Khim.*, **27**, 1873 (1957); *J. Gen. Chem.*, **27**, 1935 (1958); *Chem. Abstr.*, **52**, 4471i (1958).
507. Malinovskii, M. S., and M. K. Romantsevich, *Zh. Obshch. Khim.*, **29**, 888 (1959); *J. Gen. Chem.*, **29**, 871 (1959); *Chem. Abstr.*, **54**, 1374a (1960).
508. Marinelli, L., and D. Whitney, *J. Inst. Brewing*, **72**, 252 (1966).
509. Martel, B., and N. Duffaut, *Compt. Rend., Ser. C*, **263**, 74 (1966).
510. Martin, G. E., and J. S. Swinehart, *Anal. Chem.*, **38**, 1789 (1966).
511. Martin, R. W., *J. Am. Chem. Soc.*, **74**, 3024 (1952).
512. Martin, R. W., U.S. Patent 2,804,480 (1957); *Chem. Abstr.*, **52**, 2071h (1958).
513. Mason, P. S., and E. D. Smith, *J. Gas Chromatog.*, **4**, 398 (1966).
514. Masuhara, E., K. Kojima, and N. Tarumi, *Shika Zairo Kenkyusjo, Hokoku*, **18** (1954); *Chem. Abstr.*, **52**, 1671d (1958).
515. Maume, B., W. E. Wilson, and E. C. Horning, *Anal. Letters*, **1**, 401 (1968).
516. McBride, J. J., Jr., and H. C. Beachell, *J. Am. Chem. Soc.*, **70**, 2532 (1948).
517. McCloskey, J. A., R. N. Stillwell, and A. M. Lawson, *Anal. Chem.*, **40**, 233 (1968).
518. McCormick, A., and S. L. Jensen, *Acta Chem. Scand.*, **20**, 1989 (1966).
519. McInnes, A. G., *Can. J. Chem.*, **43**, 1998 (1965).
520. McKerns, K. W., and E. Nordstrand, *Biochim. Biophys. Acta*, **82**, 198 (1964).
521. McKerns, K. W., and E. Nordstrand, *Biochim. Biophys. Acta*, **104**, 237 (1965).
522. McKerns, K. W., and E. Nordstrand in "Gas Chromatography of Steroids in Biological Fluids," M. B. Lipsett, Ed., Plenum Press, N.Y., 1965, pp 255-261.
523. McKillican, M. E., *J. Am. Oil Chemists' Soc.*, **41**, 554 (1964).
524. Mehrotra, R. C., *Pure Appl. Chem.*, **13**, 111 (1966).
525. Mehrotra, R. C., and B. C. Pant, *J. Indian Chem. Soc.*, **40**, 623 (1963).
526. Miettinen, T. A., *Acta Chem. Scand.*, **21**, 286 (1967).
527. Miettinen, T. A., E. H. Ahrens, Jr., and S. M. Grundy, *J. Lipid Res.*, **6**, 411 (1965).
528. Mironov, V. F., and N. G. Maksimova, *Izv. Akad. Nauk SSSR, Otd. Khim. Nauk*, 2059 (1960); *Bull. Acad. Sci. USSR, Chem. Sci. Sect.*, 1911 (1960); *Chem. Abstr.*, **55**, 14297b (1961).
529. Mizuno, Y., N. Ikekawa, T. Itoh, and K. Saito, *J. Org. Chem.*, **30**, 4066 (1965).
530. Mjörne, O., *Kem. Tidskr.*, **62**, 120 (1950).
531. Montalvo, R., and O. H. Wheeler, *Can. J. Chem.*, **44**, 100 (1966).
532. Montgomery, J. A., and K. Hewson, *J. Heterocyclic Chem.*, **2**, 313 (1965).
533. Morris, L. J., *Biochem. Biophys. Res. Commun.*, **20**, 340 (1965).
534. Morrison, I. M., and M. B. Perry, *Can. J. Biochem.*, **44**, 1115 (1966).
535. Morrison, I. M., R. Young, M. B. Perry, and G. A. Adams, *Can. J. Chem.*, **45**, 1987 (1967).

536. Nagy, S., Ph.D. Thesis, Rutgers University, New Brunswick, N.J., 1965.
537. Nair, P. P., *Advan. Lipid Res.*, **4**, 227 (1966).
538. Nair, P. P., C. Bucana, S. deLeon, and D. A. Turner, *Anal. Chem.*, **37**, 631 (1965).
539. Nair, P. P., and S. de Leon, *Prog. Biochem. Pharm.*, **3**, 498 (1967).
540. Nair, P. P., and J. Machiz, *Biochim. Biophys. Acta*, **144**, 446 (1967).
541. Nair, P. P., I. J. Sarlos, and J. Machiz, *Arch. Biochem. Biophys.*, **114**, 488 (1966).
542. Nair, P. P., I. J. Sarlos, D. Solomon, D. A. Turner, *Anal. Biochem.*, **7**, 96 (1964).
543. Nair, P. P., and D. A. Turner, *Federation Proc. 22, No. 2, Pt. 1*, 198 (1963).
544. Nakayama, F., *J. Lab. Clin. Med.*, **69**, 594 (1967).
545. Nakhapetyan, L. A., and G. V. Varvanina, *Zh. Obshch. Khim.*, **37**, 395 (1967); *Chem. Abstr.*, **67**, 54376 (1967).
546. Nambara, T., T. Kudo, and H. Ikeda, *J. Chromatog.*, **34**, 526 (1968).
547. Narumi, K., and T. Tsumita, *J. Biol. Chem.*, **240**, 2271 (1965).
548. Nelson, P. F., and J. G. Smith, *Tappi*, **49**, 215 (1966).
549. Neville, R. G., *J. Org. Chem.*, **25**, 1063 (1960).
550. Newell, J. A., M. E. Mason, and R. S. Matlock, *J. Agr. Food Chem.*, **15**, 767 (1967).
551. Nishimura, T., and I. Iwai, *Chem. Pharm. Bull.* (Tokyo), **12**, 352 (1964).

552. Nishimura, T., and I. Iwai, *Chem. Pharm. Bull.* (Tokyo), **12**, 357 (1964).
553. Nishimura, T., and B. Shimizu, *Agr. Biol. Chem.*, **28**, 224 (1964).
554. Nishimura, T., and B. Shimizu, *Chem. Pharm. Bull.* (Tokyo), **13**, 803 (1965).
555. Nishimura, T., and B. Shimizu, and M. Futai, *Biochim. Biophys. Acta*, **129**, 654 (1966).
556. Nishimura, T., B. Shimizu, and I. Iwai, *Chem. Pharm. Bull.* (Tokyo), **11**, 1470 (1963).
557. Nishimura, T., B. Shimizu, and I. Iwai, *Chem. Pharm. Bull.* (Tokyo), **12**, 1471 (1964).
558. Noller, C. R., "Chemistry of Organic Compounds," 3rd Ed., W. B. Saunders Company, Philadelphia, Pa., 1965, p 670.
559. Nony, C. R., T. E. Shook, J. J. Berky, and B. M. McClure, presented at the Southwest Regional Meeting of the American Chemical Society, Little Rock, Arkansas, Dec. 1967.
560. Oaks, D. M., E. J. Bonelli, and K. P. Dimick, *J. Gas Chromatog.*, **3**, 353 (1965).
561. Oates, M. D. G., and J. Schrager, *J. Chromatog.*, **28**, 232 (1967).
562. Oertel, G., H. Malz, and H. Holtschmidt, *Chem. Ber.*, **97**, 891 (1964).
563. Ohnishi, Y., Z. Horii, and M. Makita, *J. Pharm. Soc.* (Japan), **87**, 747 (1967).
564. Okishio, T., P. P. Nair, and M. Gordon, *Biochem. J.*, **102**, 654 (1967).
565. Ottenstein, D. M., *J. Gas Chromatog.*, **1**, 11 (1963).
566. Oydvin, K., *Medd. Norsk Farm. Selskap*, **28**, 116 (1966).

567. Panicucci, F., and G. Taponeco, *Boll. Soc. Ital. Biol. Sper.*, **41**, 874 (1965).
568. Paoletti, R., R. Fumagalli, E. Grossi, and P. Paoletti, *J. Am. Oil Chemists' Soc.*, **42**, 400 (1965).
569. Paris, R., and M. Paris, *Compt. Rend.* **263**, 792 (1966).
570. Parrish, F. W., and E. T. Reese, *Carbohydrate Res.*, **3**, 424 (1967).
571. Pasarela, N. R., R. E. Tondreau, W. R. Bohn, and G. O. Gale, *J. Agr. Food Chem.*, **15**, 920 (1967).
572. Pauling, L., "The Nature of the Chemical Bond", 2nd. Ed., Cornell University Press, Ithaca, N.Y., 1948.
573. Penick, R. J., and R. H. McClurer, *Biochim. Biophys. Acta*, **116**, 288 (1966).
574. Percival, E., *Carbohydrate, Res.*, **4**, 441 (1967).
575. Perrine, T. D., C. P. J. Glaudemans, R. K. Ness, J. Kyle, and H. G. Fletcher, Jr., *J. Org. Chem.*, **32**, 664 (1967).
576. Perry, M. B., *Can. J. Biochem.*, **42**, 451 (1964).
577. Perry, M. B., *Can. J. Chem.*, **45**, 1295 (1967).
578. Perry, M. B., and G. A. Adams, *Biochem. Biophys. Res. Commun.*, **26**, 417 (1967).
579. Perry, M. B., and R. K. Hulyalkar, *Can. J. Biochem.*, **43**, 573 (1965).
580. Petersson, G., H. Riedl, and O. Samuelson, *Svensk Papperstid.*, **70**, 371 (1967).
581. Petersson, G., O. Samuelson, K. Anjou, and E. Sydow, *Acta Chem. Scand.*, **21**, 1251 (1967).
582. Petrov, A. D., V. F. Mironov, and V. G. Glukhovtsev, *Izv. Akad. Nauk SSSR, Otd. Khim. Nauk*, 461 (1956); *Bull. Acad. Sci. SSSR, Chem. Sci. Sect.*, 451 (1956); *Chem. Abstr.*, **50**, 16663f (1956).
583. Pfleiderer, W., R. Lohrmann, F. Reisser, and D. Söll, Pteridine Chem., Proc. Intern. Symp., 3rd. Stuttgart 1962 (Pub. 1964); *Chem. Abstr.*, **62**, 9224c (1965).
584. Pike, R. A., and R. L. Schank, *J. Org. Chem.*, **27**, 2190 (1962).
585. Pike, R. A., L. H. Shaffer, *Chem. Ind.* (London), 1294 (1957).
586. Pike, R. M., *J. Org. Chem.*, **26**, 232 (1961).
587. Pike, R. M., and S. J. Weaver, *Rec. Trav. Chim.*, **86**, 606 (1967).
588. Pisano, J. J., presented at Symposium on Theory and Application of Gas Chromatography in Industry and Medicine, Philadelphia, Pa., Dec 1966.
589. Pitt, C., presented at the Symposium of Silicon-Nitrogen Chemistry, Madison, Wisconsin, Apr 1968.
590. Pivovarov, I. G. A., *Lab. Delo*, **11**, 656 (1966); *Chem. Abstr.*, **66**, 26307 (1967).
591. Plimmer, J. R., N. Pravdic, and H. G. Fletcher, Jr., *J. Org. Chem.*, **32**, 1982 (1967).
592. Pollard, F. H., G. Nickless, and P. C. Uden, *J. Chromatog.*, **11**, 312 (1963).

593. Popovic, M., *Biochim. Biophys. Acta*, 125, 178 (1966).
594. Pravdic, N., T. D. Inch, and H. G. Fletcher, Jr., *J. Org. Chem.*, 32, 1815 (1967).
595. Prey, V., and K.-H. Gump, *Ann. Chem.*, 682, 228 (1965); *Chem. Abstr.*, 62, 16353e (1965).
596. Prey, V., and N. Kubadinow, *Ann. Chem.*, 701, 40 (1967).
597. Pump, J., and E. G. Rochow, *Chem. Ber.*, 97, 627 (1964).
598. Pump, J., and U. Wannagat, *Monatsh. Chem.*, 93, 352 (1962).
599. Radhakrishnamurthy, B., E. R. Dalferes, Jr., and G. S. Berenson, *Anal. Biochem.*, 17, 545 (1966).
600. Radhakrishnamurthy, B., E. R. Dalferes, Jr., and G. S. Berenson, Abstracts, Seventh Intern. Congr. Biochem., Tokyo, in press.
601. Radosavljevic, S. D., M. S. Jacovic, and M. D. Dragojevic, *Glasnik Khem. Drushtva, Beograd*, 20, 273 (1955); *Chem. Abstr.*, 52, 16260e (1958).
602. Raju, P. K., and C. M. Cater, *J. Am. Oil Chemists' Soc.*, 44, 465 (1967).
603. Raman, P. B., R. Avramov, N. L. McNiven, and R. I. Dorfman, *Steroids*, 6, 177 (1965).
604. Ramnäs, O., and O. Samuelson, *Carbohydrate Res.*, 6, 355 (1968).
605. Raunhardt, O., H. W. H. Schmidt, and H. Neukom, *Helv. Chim. Acta*, 50, 1267 (1967).
606. Ray, B. R., and M. Wilcox, *J. Chromatog.*, 30, 428 (1967).
607. Reisser, F., and W. Pfleiderer, *Chem. Ber.*, 99, 547 (1966); *Chem. Abstr.*, 64, 11300g (1966).
608. Resnick, G. L., D. Corbin, and D. H. Sandberg, *Anal. Chem.*, 38, 582 (1966).
609. Rhone-Poulenc, S. A., Belgian Patent 670,769 (1966); *Chem. Abstr.*, 65, 5487d (1966).
610. Richey, J. M., H. G. Richey, Jr., and R. Schraer, *Anal. Biochem.*, 9, 272 (1964).
611. Richter, W., M. Vecchi, W. Vetter, and W. Walther, *Helv. Chim. Acta*, 50, 364 (1967).
612. Riggs, N. V., and F. M. Strong, *Anal. Biochem.*, 19, 351 (1967).
613. Rimpler, M., *Chem. Ber.*, 99, 1523 (1966).
614. Rivera, R., R. I. Dorfman, and E. Forchielli, *Acta Endocrinol.*, 54, 37 (1967).
615. Roberts, E. J., and S. P. Rowland, *Can. J. Chem.*, 45, 261 (1967).
616. Roberts, R. M., R. H. Shah, and F. Loewus, *Plant Physiol.*, 42, 659 (1967).
617. Roberts, R. N., in "Lipid Chromatographic Analysis," Vol. 1, G. V. Marinetti, Ed., Dekker, New York, 1967, pp 447-63.
618. Roberts, R. N., J. A. Johnston, and B. W. Fuhr, *Anal. Biochem.*, 10, 282 (1965).
619. Rochow, E. G., "Introduction to the Chemistry of the Silicones," 2nd ed., Wiley, New York, 1951, pp 18-28.
620. Rohrschneider, L., *J. Chromatog.*, 22, 6 (1966).
621. Romantsevich, M. K., and M. S. Malinovskii, *Zh. Obshch. Khim.*, 30, 232 (1960); *J. Gen. Chem. USSR*, 30, 249 (1960); *Chem. Abstr.*, 54, 22347g (1960).
622. Rongone, E. L., *Steroids*, 7, 489 (1966).
623. Rosenfeld, R. S., *Steroids*, 4, 147 (1964).
624. Rosenfeld, R. S., in "Gas Chromatography of Steroids in Biological Fluids," M. B. Lipsett, Ed., Plenum Press, New York, 1965, pp 127-133.
625. Rösler, H., T. J. Mabry, M. F. Cranmer, and J. Kagan, *J. Org. Chem.*, 30, 4346 (1965).
626. Rösler, H., T. J. Mabry, and J. Kagan, *Chem. Ber.*, 98, 2193 (1965).
627. Rösler, H., U. Rösler, T. J. Mabry, and J. Kagan, *Phytochemistry*, 5, 189 (1966).
628. Rosowsky, A., A. C. Crocker, D. H. Trites, and E. J. Modest, *Biochim. Biophys. Acta*, 98, 617 (1965).
629. Roversi, G., and A. Ferrari, *J. Chromatog.*, 24, 407 (1966).
630. Rowland, M., and S. Riegelman, *Anal. Biochem.*, 20, 463 (1967).
631. Rowland, M., and S. Riegelman, *J. Pharm. Sci.*, 56, 717 (1967).
632. Rowland, S. P., A. L. Bullock, V. O. Cirino, E. J. Roberts, D. E. Hoiness, C. P. Wade, M. A. F. Brannan, H. J. Janssen, and P. F. Pittman, *Textile Res. J.*, 37, 1020 (1967).

633. Rowland, S. P., A. L. Bullock, V. O. Cirino, and C. P. Wade, *Can. J. Chem.*, **46**, 451 (1968).
634. Rowland, S. P., V. O. Cirino, and A. L. Bullock, *Can. J. Chem.*, **44**, 1051 (1966).
635. Roy, N., and T. E. Timell, *Carbohydrate Res.*, **6**, 482 (1968).
636. Rozanski, A., *Anal. Chem.*, **38**, 36 (1966).
637. Ruchelman, M. W., and V. W. Cole, *Clin. Chem.*, **12**, 771 (1966).
638. Rudman, R., W. C. Hamilton, S. Novick, and T. D. Goldfarb, *J. Am. Chem. Soc.*, **89**, 5157 (1967).
639. Rühlmann, K., *Angew. Chem.*, **71**, 650 (1959).
640. Rühlmann, K., *J. Prakt. Chem.*, **4**, 86 (1959); *Chem. Abstr.*, **54**, 4439d (1960).
641. Rühlmann, K., *J. Prakt. Chem.*, **9**, 315 (1959).
642. Rühlmann, K., *Chem. Ber.*, **94**, 1876 (1961).
643. Rühlmann, K., *J. Prakt. Chem.*, **16**, 172 (1962).
644. Rühlmann, K., and W. Giesecke, *Angew. Chem.*, **73**, 113 (1961).
645. Rühlmann, K., and J. Hils, *Ann. Chem.*, **683**, 211 (1965).
646. Rühlmann, K., J. Hils, and H.-J. Graubaum, *J. Prakt. Chem.*, **32**, 37 (1966).
647. Rühlmann, K., K.-D. Kaufmann, and U. Mann, *Z. Chem.*, **5**, 107 (1965).
648. Rühlmann, K., and U. Kaufmann, *Ann. Chem.*, **656**, 22 (1962).
649. Rühlmann, K., K. Liebsch, and C. Michael, *J. Prakt. Chem.*, **32**, 225 (1966).
650. Rühlmann, K., and G. Michael, *Z. Naturforsch.*, **15b**, 811 (1960).
651. Rühlmann, K., and G. Michael, in "Gas-Chromatographie 1963," Akademie-Verlag, Berlin, 1964, 221-9.
652. Rühlmann, K., and G. Michael, *Bull. Soc. Chim. Biol.*, **47**, 1467 (1965).
653. Rühlmann, K., and G. Michael, in "Gas-Chromatographie 1965," Akademie-Verlag, Berlin 1966, pp 245-256.
654. Rühlmann, K., and B. Rupprich, *Ann. Chem.*, **686**, 226 (1965).
655. Rühlmann, K., H. Simon, and M. Becker, *Chem. Ber.*, **99**, 780 (1966).
656. Rumsby, M. G., *J. Chromatog.*, **34**, 461 (1968).
657. Runge, F., and H. Herbst, *Angew. Chem.*, **68**, 618 (1956).
658. Rushton, B. M., *J. Org. Chem.*, **30**, 3988 (1965).
659. Ryan, K. J., E. M. Acton, and L. Goodman, *J. Org. Chem.*, **31**, 1181 (1966).
660. Ryan, K. J., H. Arzoumanian, E. M. Acton, and L Goodman, *J. Am. Chem. Soc.*, **86**, 2497 (1964).
661. Ryhage, R., *Anal. Chem.*, **36**, 759 (1964); *Arkiv Kemi*, **26**, 305 (1967).
662. Sahasrabudhe, M. R., *J. Am. Oil Chemists' Soc.*, **44**, 376 (1967).
663. Sahasrabudhe, M. R., and J. J. Legari, *J. Am. Oil Chemists' Soc.*, **44**, 379 (1967).
664. Saito, A., and D. R. Idler, *Can. J. Biochem.*, **44**, 1195 (1966).
665. Saito, A., and D. R. Idler, *Proc. Can. Fed. Biol. Soc.*, **10**, 92 (1967)
666. Sakurai, K., E. Yoshii, and K. Kubo, *J. Pharm. Soc.* (Japan), **84**, 1166 (1964).
667. Sandberg, D. H., N. Ahmad, W. W. Cleveland, and K. Savard, *Steroids*, **4**, 557 (1964).
668. Sandberg, D. H., J. Sjövall, K. Sjövall, and D. A. Turner, *J. Lipid Res.*, **6**, 182 (1965).
669. Sandberg, D. H., N. Ahmad, M. Zachmann, and W. W. Cleveland, *Steroids*, **6**, 777 (1965).
670. Sankyo Co., Ltd., Netherlands Patent Appl. 6,510,323 (1966); *Chem. Abstr.*, **65**, 10652f (1966).
671. Sasaki, Y., and T. Hashizume, *Anal. Biochem.*, **16**, 1 (1966).
672. Sato, A., K. Kitao, and M. Senda, *Wood Res.* (Kyoto), No. 34, 94 (1965); *Chem. Abstr.*, **65**, 2457h (1966).
673. Sato, A., M. Senda, T. Kakutani, Y. Watanabe, and K. Kitao, *Wood Res.* (Kyoto), No. 39, 13 (1966).
674. Sato, A., and E. von Rudloff, *Can. J. Chem.*, **42**, 635 (1964).
675. Sauer, R. O., *J. Am. Chem. Soc.*, **66**, 1707 (1944).
676. Sauer, R. O., and R. H. Hasek, *J. Am. Chem. Soc*, **68**, 241 (1946)
677. Sawardeker, J. S., and J. H. Sloneker, *Anal. Chem.*, **37**, 945 (1965).
678. Sawardeker, J. S., J. H. Sloneker, and R. J. Dimler, *J. Chromatog.*, **20**, 260 (1965).
679. Scherer, O. J., and M. Schmidt, *Chem. Ber.*, **98**, 2243 (1965).
680. Schindler, A. E., and W. L. Herrmann, *Am. J. Obstet. Gynecol.*, **95**, 301 (1966).

681. Schindler, A. E., and W. L. Herrmann, *Gynaecologia*, **161**, 446 (1966).
682. Schindler, A. E., M. C. Lindberg, and W. L. Herrmann in "Gas Chromatography of Steroids in Biological Fluids," M. B. Lipsett, Ed., Plenum Press, New York, 1965, pp 237-241.
683. Schindler, A. E., V. Ratanasopa, and W. L. Herrmann, *Clin. Chem.*, **13**, 186 (1967).
684. Schindler, A. E., V. Ratanasopa, T. Y. Lee, and W. L. Herrmann, *Gynaecologia*, **164**, 55 (1967).
685. Schmidt, H. W. H., *Tetrahedron Letters*, 235 (1967).
686. Schmidt, M., and H. Schmidbaur, *Angew. Chem.*, **70**, 469 (1958); *Chem. Abstr.*, **52**, 19644i (1958).
687. Schmidt, M., and H. Schmidbaur, *Angew. Chem.*, **70**, 657 (1958).
688. Schmidt, U., and M. Schwochau, *Monatsh. Chem.*, **98**, 1492 (1967).
689. Schmidt, U., and M. Schwochau, *Tetrahedron Letters*, 875 (1967).
690. Schoenfield, L. J., and J. Sjövall, *Acta Chem. Scand.*, **20**, 1297 (1966).
691. Scholler, R., and L. Dehennin, in "Chromatography and Methods of Immediate Separation," Vol. 1, G. Parissakis, Ed., Union of the Greek Chemists, Athens, 1966, pp 213-26.
692. Schott, G., and G. Henneberg, *Z. Anorg. Allgem. Chem.*, **323**, 228 (1963).
693. Schott, G., and G. Henneberg, *Z. Chem.*, **7**, 21 (1967).
694. Schuyten, H. A., J. W. Weaver, and J. O. Reid, *J. Am. Chem. Soc.*, **69**, 2110 (1947).
695. Schuyten, H. A., J. W. Weaver, J. D. Reid, and J. F. Jurgens, *J. Am. Chem. Soc.*, **70**, 1919 (1948).
696. Schwartz, N. N., E. O'Brien, S. Karlan, and M. M. Fein, *Inorg. Chem.*, **4**, 661 (1965).
697. Schwarz, R., E. Baronetzky, and K. Schoeller, *Angew. Chem.*, **68**, 335 (1956).
698. Schwarz, R., and K. Schoeller, *Beitr. Silikose-Forsch, Sonderband 2*, 271 (1956); *Chem. Abstr.*, **53**, 1162e (1959).
699. Searle, G. H., and C. J. Wilkins, *J. Chem. Soc.*, 3897 (1961).
700. Seikel, M. K., *Tetrahedron Letters*, 1105 (1965).
701. Sen, N. P., and P. L. McGeer, *Biochem. Biophys. Res. Commun.*, **13**, 390 (1963).
702. Sennello, L. T., F. A. Kummerow, and C. J. Argoudelis, *J. Heterocyclic Chem.*, **4**, 295 (1967).
703. Sephton, H. H., *J. Org. Chem.*, **29**, 3415 (1964).
704. Sephton, H. H., and N. K. Richtmyer, *Carbohydrate Res.*, **2**, 289 (1966).
705. Sergeeva, Z. I., B. N. Dolgov, and D. D. Tsitovich, *Khim. i Prakt. Primenenie Kremneorg. Soedinenii, Trudy Konf., Leningrad*, No. 1, 235 (1958); *Chem. Abstr.*, **53**, 11199b (1959).
706. Sergeeva, Z. I., Z. M. Matveeva, and M. G. Voronkov, *Zh. Obshch. Khim.*, **31**, 2017 (1961); *J. Gen. Chem.*, **31**, 1886 (1961); *Chem. Abstr.*, **55**, 27176g (1961).
707. Seyferth, D., G. Singh, and R. Suzuki, *Pure Appl. Chem.*, **13**, 159 ((1966).
708. Seyferth, D., and L. G. Vaughan, *J. Am. Chem. Soc.*, **86**, 883 (1964).
709. Shahrokhi, F., and C. W. Gehrke, Abstracts, 154th National Meeting of the American Chemical Society, Chicago, Sept 1967, No. C-158.
710. Shallenberger, R. S., and T. E. Acree, *Carbohydrate Res.*, **1**, 495 (1966).
711. Sharkey, A. G., Jr., "Encyclopedia of Spectroscopy," Clark, Ed., Reinhold Publishing Corp., New York, 1960, pp 607-13.
712. Sharkey, A. G., Jr., R. A. Friedel, and S. H. Langer, *Anal. Chem.*, **29**, 770 (1957).
713. Sharkey, A. G., Jr., G. Wood, J. L. Shultz, I. Wender, and R. A. Friedel, *Fuel*, **38**, 315 (1959).
714. Shaw, P. D., *Anal. Chem.*, **35**, 1580 (1963).
715. Shen, T. Y., W. V. Ruyle, and R. L. Bugianesi, *J. Heterocyclic Chem.*, **2**, 495 (1965).
716. Sheriha, G. M., G. R. Waller, T. Chan, and A. D. Tillman, *Lipids*, **3**, 72 (1968).
717. Sherman, W. R., and M. A. Stewart, *Biochem. Biophys. Res. Commun*, **22**, 492 (1966).
718. Shibata, S., T. Furuya, and H. Iizuka, *Chem. Pharm. Bull.* (Tokyo), **13**, 1254 (1965).

719. Shimizu, B., M. Asai, and T. Nishimura, *Chem. Pharm. Bull.* (Tokyo), **13**, 230 (1965).
720. Shimizu, B., T. Nishimura, and M. Ikehara, *Agr. Biol. Chem.* (Tokyo), **31**, 637 (1967).
721. Shostakovskii, M. F., A. S. Atavin, V. M. Nikitin, B. A. Trofimov, V. V. Keiko, and V. I. Lavrov, *Izv. Akad. Nauk SSSR, Ser. Khim.*, **11**, 2049 (1967); *Chem. Abstr.*, **64**, 8226d (1966).
722. Shum. L.-H., Ph.D. Thesis, Harvard University, 1966; *Diss. Abstr.*, **27**, 1800B (1966).
723. Shyluk, J. P., C. Youngs, and O. L. Gamborg, *J. Chromatog*, **26**, 268 (1967).
724. Siddiqui, B., and R. H. McCluer, *J. Lipid Res.*, **9**, 366 (1968).
725. Simon, A., and H. Arnold, *J. Prakt. Chem.*, **8**, 241 (1959).
726. Simon, G., and G. Rouser, *Lipids*, **2**, 55 (1967).
727. Sinsheimer, J. E., and R. V. Smith, *J. Pharm. Sci.*, **56**, 1280 (1967).
728. Sjöström, E., P. Haglund, and J. Janson, *Acta Chem. Scand.*, **20**, 1718 (1966).
729. Sjövall, J., in "Biomedical Applications of Gas Chromatography", H. A. Szymanski, Ed., Plenum Press, New York, 1964, pp 151-67.
730. Sjövall, J., and R. Vihko, *Steroids*, **6**, 597 (1965).
731. Sjövall, J., and R. Vihko, Proc. 2nd Intern. Cong. Hormonal Steroids, Milan, May 1966, *Excerpta Medica Foundation, Intern. Cong. Ser.*, No. 132, 210 (1967).
732. Sjövall, J., and R. Vihko, *Steroids*, **7**, 447 (1966).
733. Sjövall, K., J. Sjövall, K. Maddock, and E. C. Horning, *Anal. Biochem.*, **14**, 337 (1966).
734. Slanski, J. M., and R. J. Moshy, *J. Chromatog.*, **35**, 94 (1968).
735. Sloneker, J. H., and J. S. Sawardeker, Abstracts, Winter Meeting of the American Chemical Society, Phoenix, Ariz., Jan. 1966, No. 23C.
736. Slover, H. T., L. M. Shelley, and T. L. Burks, *J. Am. Oil Chemists' Soc.*, **44**, 161 (1967).
737. Smirnyagin, V., C. T. Bishop, and F. P. Cooper, *Can. J. Chem.*, **43**, 3109 (1965).
738. Smith, B., *Doktorsavhandl. Chalmers Tek. Högskola*, No. 6, (1951); *Chem. Abstr.*, **49**, 909g (1955).
739. Smith, B., and O. Carlsson, *Acta Chem. Scand.*, **17**, 455 (1963).
740. Smith, B., and L. Tullberg, *Acta Chem. Scand.*, **19**, 605 (1965).
741. Smith, B., and L. Tullberg, Dept. Technical and Analytical Chemistry, Lund Institute of Technology, Lund, Sweden, personal communication, 1967.
742. Smith, E. D., P. S. Mason, and W. O. Walker, presented at the Regional Meeting of the American Chemical Society, Memphis, Tenn., Dec 1965.
743. Smith, E. D., and H. Sheppard, Jr., *Nature*, **208**, 878 (1965).
744. Smith, M. E., R. Fumagalli, and R. Paoletti, *Life Sciences*, **6**, 1085 (1967).
745. Societe Monsavon-l'Oreal, British Patent 827,419 (1960); *Chem. Abstr.*, **54**, 19494g (1960).
746. Solomon, D., D. Strummer, and P. P. Nair, *Am. J. Clin. Pathol.*, **48**, 295 (1967).
747. Sommer, L. H., "Stereochemistry, Mechanism and Silicon," McGraw Hill, New York, 1965.
748. Sommer, L. H., J. D. Citron, and C. L. Frye, *J. Am. Chem. Soc.*, **86**, 5684 (1964).
749. Speier, J. L., *J. Am. Chem. Soc.*, **74**, 1003 (1952).
750. Speier, J. L., U.S. Patent 2,584,752 (1953); *Chem. Abstr.*, **46**, 9126h (1952).
751. Speier, J. L., U.S. Patent 2,626,272 (1953); *Chem. Abstr.*, **48**, 1418f (1954).
752. Speier, J. L., U.S. Patent 2,746,956 (1956); *Chem. Abstr.*, **51**, 1246g (1957).
753. Speier, J. L., R. Zimmerman, and J. Webster, *J. Am. Chem. Soc.*, **78**, 2278 (1956).
754. Sprung, M. M., and L. S. Nelson, *J. Org. Chem.*, **20**, 1750 (1955).
755. Still, G. G., *Science*, **159**, 992 (1968).
756. Stinson, E. E., C. J. Dooley, J. M. Purcell, and J. S. Ard, *J. Agr. Food Chem.*, **15**, 394 (1967).
757. Stone, F. G. A., and D. Seyferth, *J. Inorg. Nuclear Chem.*, **1**, 112 (1955).
758. Suchanec, R. R., *Anal. Chem.*, **37**, 1361 (1965).

759. Suffis, R., T. J. Sullivan, and W. S. Henderson, *J. Soc. Cosmetic Chemists*, **16**, 783 (1965).
760. Sullivan, J., Pierce Chemical Co., Rockford, Ill., unpublished work.
761. Supina, W. R., R. F. Kruppa, and R. Henley, *J. Am. Oil Chemists' Soc.*, **44**, 74 (1967).
762. Swain, C. G., R. M. Esteve, Jr., and R. H. Jones, *J. Am. Chem. Soc.*, **71**, 965 (1949).
763. Sweeley, C. C., Michigan State University, Lansing, Mich., personal communication, 1968.
764. Sweeley, C. C., R. Bentley, M. Makita, and W. W. Wells, *J. Am. Chem. Soc.*, **85**, 2497 (1963).
765. Sweeley, C. C., and T.-C. L. Chang, *Anal. Chem.*, **33**, 1860 (1961).
766. Sweeley, C. C., W. H. Elliott, I. Fries, and R. Ryhage, *Anal. Chem.*, **38**, 1549 (1966).
767. Sweeley, C. C., and D. Vance in "Lipid Chromatographic Analysis", G. Marinetti, Ed., Dekker, New York, 1967, pp 465-495.
768. Sweeley, C. C., and B. Walker, *Anal. Chem.*, **36**, 1461 (1964).
769. Takiguchi, T., M. Abe, H. Kobuna, and K. Kurosaki, *Kogyo Kagaku Zasshi*, **68**, 1276 (1965); *Chem. Abstr.*, **63**, 14894f (1965).
770. Tallent, W. H., and R. Kleiman, *J. Lipid Res.*, **9**, 146 (1968).
771. Tallent, W. H., R. Kleiman, and D. G. Cope, *J. Lipid Res.*, **7**, 531 (1966).
772. Talmage, J. M., and M. H. Penner, *J. Pharm. Sci.*, **56**, 657 (1967).
773. Tamura, Z., and T. Imanari, *Chem. Pharm. Bull.* (Tokyo), **12**, 1386 (1964).
774. Teeter, R. M., presented at the Tenth Annual Conference on Mass Spectrometry and Allied Topics, New Orleans, La., June 1962.
775. Ternay, A. L., Jr., and D. W. Chasar, *J. Org. Chem.*, **33**, 2237 (1968).
776. Thomas, B. S., in "Gas Chromatography of Steroids in Biological Fluids", M. B. Lipsett, Ed., Plenum Press, New York, 1965, pp 1-9.
777. Thomas, B. S., C. Eaborn, and D. R. M. Walton, *Chem. Commun.*, **13**, 408 (1966).
778. Thomas, B. S., and D. R. M. Walton, *J. Endocrinol*, **37**, xxvii (1967).
779. Thomas, B. S., and D. R. M. Walton, presented at an Informal Symposium, Inst. Petroleum Gas Chromatography Gas Discussion Group, London, Apr 1967.
780. Thomas, B. S., and D. R. M. Walton, *Mem. Soc. Endocrinol.*, No. 16, 199 (1967).
781. Thorpe, S. R., and C. C. Sweeley, *Biochemistry*, **6**, 887 (1967).
782. Thysen, B., W. H. Elliott, and P. A. Katzman, *Steroids*, **11**, 73 (1968).
783. Timell, T. E., and M. Zinbo, *Tappi*, **50**, 195 (1967).
784. Toki, S., and E. W. Maynert, *Federation Proc.*, **25**, No. 2, Pt. 1, 531 (1966).
785. Törnquist, J., *Acta Chem. Scand.*, **21**, 2095 (1967).
786. Traynham, J. G., and J. Schneller, *J. Am. Chem. Soc.*, **87**, 2398 (1965).
787. Traynham, J. G., and M. T. Yang, *J. Am. Chem. Soc*, **87**, 2394 (1965).
788. Tschesche, R., F. Inchaurrondo, and G. Wulff, *Ann. Chem.*, **680**, 107 (1964).
789. Tschesche, R., W. Schmidt, and G. Wulff, *Z. Naturforsch.*, **20**, 708 (1965)
Tschesche, R., F.-J. Kämmerer, and G. Wulff, *Z. Naturforsch.*, **21**, 596 (1966)
Tschesche, R., and W. Schmidt, *Z. Naturforsch.*, **21**, 896 (1966)
Tschesche, R., R. Kottler, and G. Wulff, *Ann. Chem.*, **699**, 212 (1966).
790. Uno, T., and H. Okuda, *Yakugaku Zasshi*, **86**, 1148 (1966); Abstract No. 686313, Preston Technical Abstracts Co., Evanston, Ill.
791. Valade, J., *Bull. Soc. Chim. France*, 238 (1957).
792. Vance, D. E., and C. C. Sweeley, *J. Lipid Res.*, **8**, 621 (1967).
793. Vandenheuvel, F. A., Canada Dept. of Agriculture, Ottawa, personal communication, 1968.
794. Vandenheuvel, F. A., R. Fumagalli, R. Paoletti, and P. Paoletti, *Life Sciences*, **6**, 439 (1967).
795. Vandenheuvel, F. A., G. J. Hinderks, J. C. Nixon, and W. G. Layng, *J. Am. Oil. Chemists' Soc.*, **42**, 283 (1965).
796. VandenHeuvel, W. J. A., presented at Eastern Analytical Symposium and Instrument Exhibit, New York, Nov 1966.
797. VandenHeuvel, W. J. A., *J. Chromatog.*, **25**, 29 (1966).
798. VandenHeuvel, W. J. A., *J. Chromatog.*, **27**, 85 (1967).
799. VandenHeuvel, W. J. A., *J. Chromatog.*, **28**, 406 (1967).

800. VandenHeuvel, W. J. A., and K. L. K. Braly, *J. Chromatog.*, **31**, 9 (1967).
801. VandenHeuvel, W. J. A., B. G. Creech, and E. C. Horning, *Anal. Biochem.*, **4**, 191 (1962).
802. VandenHeuvel, W. J. A., W. L. Gardiner, and E. C. Horning, *Anal Chem.*, **36**, 1550 (1964).
803. VandenHeuvel, W. J. A., W. L. Gardiner, and E. C. Horning, *J. Chromatog.*, **19**, 263 (1965).
804. VandenHeuvel, W. J. A., W. Gardiner, and E. C. Horning, *J. Chromatog.*, **26**, 387 (1967).
805. VandenHeuvel, W. J. A., and E. C. Horning, *Biochem. Biophys. Res. Commun.*, **3**, 356 (1960).
806. VandenHeuvel, W. J. A., and E. C. Horning, *Biochim. Biophys. Acta*, **64**, 416 (1962).
807. VandenHeuvel, W. J. A., and E. C. Horning in "Biomedical Applications of Gas Chromatography," H. A. Szymanski, Ed., Plenum Press, New York, 1964, pp 89-150.
808. VandenHeuvel, W. J. A., and E. C. Horning, *Mem. Soc. Endocrinol.*, No. 16, 39 (1967).
809. VandenHeuvel, W. J. A., J. L. Patterson, and K. L. K. Braly, *Biochim, Biophys. Acta*, **144**, 691 (1967).
810. VandenHeuvel, W. J. A., C. C. Sweeley, and E. C. Horning, *J. Am. Chem. Soc.*, **82**, 3481 (1960).
811. Vaver, V. A., A. N. Ushakov, and L. D. Bergel'son, *Izv. Akad. Nauk SSSR, Ser. Khim.*, 1187 (1967); *Chem. Abstr.*, **67**, 105837 (1967).
812. Vecchi, M., and K. Kaiser, *J. Chromatog.*, **26**, 22 (1967).
813. Vecchi, M., W. Vetter, S. F. Jermstad, and G. W. Schutt, *Helv. Chim. Acta*, **50**, 1243 (1967).
814. Venkateswaran, P. S., and T. Bardos, *J. Org. Chem.*, **32**, 1256 (1967).
815. Vessman, J., and G. Ahlen, *Acta Pharm. Seucica*, **1**, 209 (1964).
816. Vestergaard, P., and E. Raabo, *J. Gas Chromatog.*, **4**, 422 (1966).
817. Vestergaard, P., E. Raabo, and S. Vedso, *Clin. Chim. Acta*, **14**, 540 (1966).
818. Vihko, R., *Acta Endocrinol., Suppl.*, **109**, 67 pp (1966).
819. Viswanathan, N., and C. H. Van Dyke, *J. Chem. Soc., A*, 487 (1968).
820. Vollmer, K.-O., and H. Grisebach, *Z. Naturforsch.*, **21**, 435 (1966).
821. Voronkov, M. G., "Organosilicon Chemistry," Plenum Press, New York, 1966, pp 35-59.
822. Voronkov, M. G., L. I. Libert, and E. Ya. Lukevits, *Zh. Obshch. Khim.*, **37**, 1673 (1967).
823. Voronkov, M. G., and Z. I. Shabarova, *Zh. Obshch. Khim.*, **29**, 1528 (1959); *J. Gen. Chem.*, **29**, 1501 (1959); *Chem. Abstr.*, **54**, 8601c (1960).
824. Voronkov, M. G., and Z. I. Shabarova, *Zh. Obshch. Khim.*, **30**, 1955 (1960); *Chem. Abstr.*, **55**, 6424c (1961).
825. Waiss, A. C., Jr., J. A. Kuhnle, J. J. Windle, and A. K. Wiersema, *Tetrahedron Letters*, 6251 (1966).
826. Waiss, A. C., Jr., R. E. Lundin, and D. J. Stern, *Tetrahedron Letters*, 513 (1964).
827. Walker, H. G., Jr., *Intern. Sugar J.*, **67**, 237 (1965).
828. Walle, T., G. Schill, and J. Vessman, *Acta Pharm. Suecica*, **3**, 167 (1966); *Chem. Abstr.*, **65**, 6997b (1966).
829. Wallwitz, U., H. Schmidt, and W. Gosda, *J. Prakt. Chem.* **32**, 274 (1966).
830. Walton, D. R. M., C. Eaborn, and B. S. Thomas, *Chem. Ind.* (London), in press.
831. Wannagat, U., *Angew. Chem. Intern. Ed. Engl.*, **5**, 614 (1966).
832. Wannagat, U., H. Bürger, C. Krüger, and J. Pump, *Z. Anorg. Allgem. Chem.*, **321**, 208 (1963).
833. Wannagat, U., and F. Höfler, *Monatsh. Chem.*, **97**, 976 (1966).
834. Wannagat, U., and C. Krüger, *Monatsh. Chem.*, **94**, 63 (1963).
835. Wannagat, U., C. Krüger, and H. Niederprüm, *Z. Anorg. Allgem Chem.*, **314**, 80 (1962); *Chem. Abstr.*, **57**, 2244c (1962).
836. Wannagat, U., and W. Liehr, *Z. Anorg. Allgem. Chem.*, **299**, 341 (1959).
837. Wannagat, U., and H. Niederprüm, *Angew. Chem.*, **71**, 574 (1959).
838. Wannagat, U., and H. Niederprüm, *Z. Anorg. Allgem. Chem.*, **310**, 32 (1961).

839. Wannagat, U., R. Schwarz, H. Voss, and K. G. Knauff, *Z. Anorg. Allgem. Chem.*, **277**, 73 (1954).
840. Watson, J. T., and K. Biemann, *Anal. Chem.*, **36**, 1135 (1964); *Anal. Chem.*, **37**, 844 (1965).
841. Watson, J., and C. J. W. Brooks, *Biochem. J.*, **104**, 3P (1967).
842. Watts, R., and R. Dils, *Nature*, **212**, 458 (1966).
843. Weisz, L., and Z. Havas, *Acta Univ. Szeged., Acta Phys. Chem.*, **10**, 105 (1964); *Chem. Abstr.*, **62**, 6535b (1965).
844. Wellburn, A. R., and F. W. Hemming, *J. Chromatog.*, **23**, 51 (1966).
845. Wells, H. J., and W. W. Wells, *Biochemistry*, **6**, 1168 (1967).
846. Wells, W. W., T. Chin, and B. Weber, *Clin. Chim. Acta*, **10**, 352 (1964).
847. Wells, W. W., T. Katagi, R. Bentley, and C. C. Sweeley, *Biochim. Biophys. Acta*, **82**, 408 (1964).
848. Wells, W. W., and M. Makita, *Anal. Biochem.*, **4**, 204 (1962).
849. Wells, W. W., T. A. Pittman, and T. J. Egan, *J. Biol. Chem.*, **239**, 3192 (1964).
850. Wells, W. W., T. A. Pittman, and H. J. Wells, *Anal. Biochem.*, **10**, 450 (1965).
851. Wells, W. W., T. A. Pittman, H. J. Wells, and T. J. Egan, *J. Biol. Chem.*, **240**, 1002 (1965).
852. Wells, W. W., C. C. Sweeley, and R. Bentley in "Biomedical Applications of Gas Chromatography", H. A. Szymanski, Ed., Plenum Press, New York, 1964, pp 199-200.
853. West, R., *J. Am. Chem. Soc.*, **80**, 3246 (1958).
854. West, R., *J. Org. Chem.*, **23**, 1552 (1958).
855. West, R., and R. H. Baney, *J. Am. Chem. Soc.*, **81**, 6145 (1959).
856. West, R., M. Ishikawa, and R. E. Bailey, *J. Am. Chem. Soc.*, **89**, 4068 (1967).
857. West, R., M. Ishikawa, and S. Murai, *J. Am. Chem. Soc.*, **90**, 727 (1968).
858. West, R., L. S. Whatley, and K. J. Lake, *J. Am. Chem. Soc.*, **83**, 761 (1961).
859. Wetter, W., M. Vecchi, H. Kutmann, R. Rüegg, W. Walther, and P. Meyer, *Helv. Chim. Acta*, **50**, 1866 (1967).
860. Weygand, F., A. Prox, E. C. Jorgensen, R. Axén, and P. Kirchner, *Z. Naturforsch.*, 18b, 93 (1963).
861. White, D. M., U.S. Patent 3,367,978 (1968); *Chem. Abstr.*, **68**, 68698 (1968).
862. Wiley, R. C., M. Tavakoli, and M. D. Moore, *Proc. Am. Soc. Hort. Sci.*, **89**, 34 (1966); *Chem. Abstr.*, **66**, 82974 (1967).
863. Williams, C. M., *Anal. Biochem.*, **11**, 224 (1965).
864. Williams, C. M., and M. Greer, *Clin. Chim. Acta*, **11**, 495 (1965).
865. Williams, C. M., and C. C. Sweeley in "Biomedical Applications of Gas Chromatography," H. A. Szymanski, Ed., Plenum Press, New York, 1964, pp 225-65.
866. Williams, L. D., and R. R. Allen, *J. Am. Oil Chemists' Soc.*, **44**, 436 (1967).
867. Wilson, J. L., Ph.D. Thesis, University of Oklahoma, Tulsa, 1967; *Diss. Abstr. B*, 2314 (1967).
868. Wilson, W. E., S. A. Johnson, W. H. Perkins, and J. E. Ripley, *Anal. Chem.*, **39**, 40 (1967).
869. Wisniewski, J. V., *Facts and Methods Sci. Res.*, **7**, 4 (1966); *Chem. Abstr.*, **68**, 111195 (1968).
870. Wisniewski, J. V., and A. J. Testa, *Facts and Methods Sci. Res.*, **6**, 11 (1965).
871. Witsch, H.-G., Doctor's Thesis, Technischen Hochschule, Karlsruhe, 1961.
872. Wittenburg, E., *Z. Chem.*, **4**, 303 (1964).
873. Wittenburg, E., *Chem. Ber.*, **99**, 2380 (1966).
874. Wittenburg, E., *Z. Chem.*, **7**, 13 (1967).
875. Wittenburg, E., *Chem. Ber.*, **101**, 1095 (1968).
876. Wolf, E., and M. Hoffman, *Z. Chem.*, **4**, 30 (1964).
877. Wood, R., *J. Gas Chromatog.*, **6**, 94 (1968).
878. Wood, R., E. L. Bever, and F. Snyder, *Lipids*, **1**, 399 (1966).
879. Wood, R. D., P. K. Raju, and R. Reiser, *J. Am. Oil Chemists' Soc.*, **42**, 81 (1965).
880. Wood, R. D., P. K. Raju, and R. Reiser, *J. Am. Oil Chemists' Soc.*, **42**, 161 (1965).
881. Wood, R., and F. Snyder, *Lipids*, **1**, 62 (1966).
882. Wood, R., and F. Snyder, *Lipids*, **2**, 161 (1967).
883. Wotiz, H. H., and S. C. Chattoraj in "Gas Chromatography of Steroids in Biological Fluids", M. B. Lipsett, Ed., Plenum Press, New York, 1965, pp 195-214.

884. Wotiz, H. H., and S. J. Clark, "Gas Chromatography in the Analysis of Steroid Hormones," Plenum Press, New York, 1966.
885. Wyatt, C. J., R. L. Pereira, and E. A. Day, *Lipids*, **2**, 208 (1967).
886. Yamakawa, T., S. Nishimura, and M. Kamimura, *Japan J. Exp. Med.*, **35**, 201 (1965).
887. Yamakawa, T., and N. Ueta, *Japan J. Exp, Med.*, **34**, 37 (1964).
888. Yamakawa, T., and N. Ueta, *Japan J. Exp. Med.*, **34**, 361 (1964).
889. Yamakawa, T., N. Ueta, and I. Ishizuka, *Japan J. Exp. Med.*, **34**, 231 (1964).
890. Yamamoto, M., S. Iguchi, and T. Aoyama, *Chem. Pharm. Bull.* (Tokyo), **15**, 123 (1967).
890a. Yoder, C. H., and J. J. Zuckerman, Abstracts, 152nd National Meeting, American Chemical Society, New York, Sept. 1966, No. O-166.
891. Yoshitoshi, Y., T. Oda, H. Fukushima, S. Saito, and E. Nakamura, *Seikagaku*, **38**, 185 (1966); Abstract No. 67-4780 (1967), Preston Technical Abstracts Co., Evanston, Ill.
892. Zahn, C., A. G. Sharkey, Jr., and I. Wender, Report No. 5976, U.S. Dept. of the Interior, Bureau of Mines, 33 pp (1962).
893. Zielinski, W. L., Jr., and L. Fishbein, *J. Chromatog.*, **20**, 140 (1965).
894. Zielinski, W. L., Jr., and L. Fishbein, *Anal. Chem.*, **38**, 41 (1966).
895. Zielinski, W. L., Jr., and L. Fishbein, *J. Chromatog.*, **25**, 475 (1966).
896. Zinkel, D. F., M. B. Lathrop, and L. C. Zank, *J. Gas Chromatog.*, **6**, 158 (1968).
897. Zuckerman, J., presented at the Symposium on Silicon-Nitrogen Chemistry, Madison, Wisconsin, April 1968.
898. Zumwalt, R. W., D. L. Stalling, and C. W. Gehrke, Abstracts, 154th National Meeting of the American Chemical Society, Chicago, Sept. 1967, No. C-159; D. L. Stalling, C. W. Gehrke, and R. W. Zumwalt, *Biochem. Biophys. Res. Commun.*, **31**, 616 (1968). The published paper was received too late for tabulation.

Glossary

1. GENERAL ABBREVIATIONS

Ac	Acetyl
ASB	Acetone Schiff base
BDSA	Bis(dimethylsilyl)acetamide
b, bp	Boiling point
BSA	N,O-Bis(trimethylsilyl)acetamide
BSTFA	Bis(trimethylsilyl)trifluoroacetamide
Bu	Butyl
CBz	Carbobenzoxy
CMDMCS	Chloromethyldimethylchlorosilane
CMDMS	Chloromethyldimethylsilyl
CMTMDS	Bis(chloromethyl)tetramethyldisilazane
DMF	Dimethylformamide
DMS	Dimethylsilyl
DMSO	Dimethylsulfoxide
DNP	2,4-Dinitrophenyl
Et	Ethyl
fur	Furanose
GC	Gas chromatography
GC–MS	Gas chromatography–mass spectrometry
HCl	Hydrochloride
HFB	Heptafluorobutyryl
HMDS	Hexamethyldisilazane
m, mp	Melting point
Me	Methyl
MO	Methoxime $(=NOCH_3)$
MSA	N-Trimethylsilylacetamide
Ph	Phenyl
pyr	Pyranose
T	Trimethylsilyl
TFA	Trifluoroacetyl
THF	Tetrahydrofuran
TLC	Thin layer chromatography
TMCS	Trimethylchlorosilane
TMS	Trimethylsilyl
TMSDEA	N-Trimethylsilyl-diethylethylamine
TSIM	N-Trimethylsilyl-imidazole

2. TABLE NOTATION

Formula. Molecular formulas list C, H, then other element symbols in alphabetical order. The formula is for the parent compound; hence does not include indicated derivatives such as salts, methoximes, Schiff bases, etc.

Compound. Listing is alphabetical under the molecular formula. Derivatives are indicated in parentheses. Metal salts are not thus indicated if they are implied by Methods 15 (sodium salts) and 16 (salts other than sodium).

Silylation. The number of trimethylsilyl groups introduced is a subscript to the letter 'T', with location, if known, indicated in parentheses where there is more than one possibility. Proof is good in cases of elemental, IR, NMR, or mass spectral analysis of the derivative. The behavior of the silylated compound on gas chromatography furnishes additional evidence: whether there is one peak or several and whether the chromatogram changes with time after adding reagents to the sample. The reagent used, the kind of proton-active groups available, and the yield are also helpful information.

Method numbers refer to the procedures described in Chapter 1. Small letters following the number indicate additional solvent(s). Hyphenated numbers designate two methods, used successively on the same sample.

Gas Chromatography. Stationary phases are abbreviated and shown in a separate list following this section. Percentage of loading is given where results were obtained at more than one level. Biphases or mixed phases are indicated by a slant mark. Substantial use of mass spectrometry, TLC, or NMR is also indicated under the Stationary Phase heading.

Under column temperature programming is designated by an arrow or 'pr'. The former shows the program range; the latter the temperature of elution when programming, usually not faster than a few degrees per minute. Other temperatures are isothermal.

Most of the retention times for gas chromatography are reported relative to standards, whose abbreviations (2-4 small letters) are listed in this glossary. Those standards capable of silylation are assumed to be silylated along with the sample, before injection into the chromatograph. Where no standard is used the retention time is given in minutes.

3. SILYLATION METHODS

This classification is the same as given in Chapter 1. The method number may be combined with a letter or letters indicating additional solvent(s).

10. Trimethylchlorosilane-based methods
  11. Trimethylchlorosilane (TMCS) alone; HCl is boiled off
  12. Ammonia is passed in
  13. Pyridine as acid acceptor
  14. Triethylamine (TEA) as acid acceptor
  15. Sodium salt of starting compound
  16. Salt other than sodium; *e.g.* Li, Sr
  17. Formamide, pyridine, hexane
  18. Base other than pyridine or TEA as acid acceptor
  19. TEA, ZnCl$_2$ catalyst

20. Hexamethyldisilazane-based methods
  21. Hexamethyldisilazane (HMDS) alone; elimination of NH$_3$
  22. TMCS, 10% or less of HMDS taken, by volume
  23. TMCS, more than 10% of HMDS taken
  24. Acid catalyst (not TMCS)
  25. TMCS, pyridine
  26. TMCS, THF

30. Silylamine methods
  31. TMS-methylamine
  32. TMS-aniline
  33. TMS-diethylamine (TMSDEA)
  34. TMS-diethylamine, acid catalyst
  35. TMS-n(or t)-butylamine
  36. TMS-imidazole (TSIM)
  37. Miscellaneous silylamines

40. Silylamide methods
  41. TMS-formamide
  42. TMS-acetamide (MSA)

43. N,O-Bis(TMS)acetamide (BSA)
44. BSA-TMCS
45. N-TMS-N-methylacetamide
46. N,O-Bis(TMS)trifluoroacetamide (BSTFA)
47. TMS-diphenylurea
48. Miscellaneous silylamides

50. Miscellaneous methods
51. Hexamethyldisiloxane
52. Hexamethyldisilthiane
53. Alkylthiotrimethylsilane
54. TMS acetate

Solvents used:

a. Acetone
b. Benzene
c. Chloroform
d. Dimethylformamide (DMF)
e. Ether
f. Formamide
g. Dioxane
h. Hexane
j. Cyclohexane
k. Ethyl acetate

m. Methylene chloride
n. Acetonitrile
p. Petroleum ether
py. Pyridine
r. Carbon disulfide
s. Dimethylsulfoxide (DMSO)
t. Tetrahydrofuran (THF)
u. Toluene
x. Xylene
z. Miscellaneous

4. STATIONARY PHASES

Abbr.	Commercial or Chemical Name
ApK	Apiezon K
ApL	Apiezon L
ApM	Apiezon M
ApN	Apiezon N
BDS	Butanediol succinate polymer
Castor	Castorwax
Carb	Carbowax, type undesignated
C 1540	Carbowax 1540
C 20M	Carbowax 20M
C 6000	Carbowax 6000
CHDMS	Cyclohexanedimethanol succinate polymer
CNSi	Methyl-β-cyanoethylsiloxane polymer (General Electric)
DBTCP	Di-n-butyltetrachlorophthalate
DC 200	Methyl silicone
DC 430	Silicone rubber
DC 550	Methyl silicone, about 25% phenyl groups (Dow Corning)
DC 560	Methyl silicone, probably about 5% phenyl groups (Dow Corning)
DC 710	Methyl silicone, about 50% phenyl groups (Dow Corning)
DDS	Decanediol succinate polymer
DEGS	Diethyleneglycol succinate polymer
DLP	Dilauryl phthalate
DNP	Dinonylphthalate
DOP	Dioctyl phthalate
DOSb	Dioctyl sebacate
ECNSS	ECNSS-M, approx. 30% cyanoethylmethyl silicone in EGS
EG 400	Polyethyleneglycol 400
EGA	Ethyleneglycol adipate polymer
EGS	Ethyleneglycol succinate polymer
EGSS-X	Approx. 5% methylsilicone in EGS
EGSS-Y	Approx. 30% methyl silicone in EGS
EGSS-Z	Methylphenylsilicone in EGS

EGSP-Z	Approx. 30% silicone in EGS
Emb	Embaphase
Ester	Polyester, undesignated
F-60	Methyl-p-chlorophenylsilicone (Dow Corning)
F-60-Z	7% Methyl-p-chlorophenylsilicone/1% EGSS-Z
Flex	Flexol 8N8, 2,2'(2-ethylhexamido)-diethyl-di(2-ethylhexoate)
FS 1265	Fluoroalkyl silicone
GE-96	Silicone
GESF-96	Methyl silicone (General Electric)
HiEff	Hi-Eff-8B, cyclohexanedimethanol succinate (Applied Science Labs.)
HTC	Hexatriacontane
JXR	Methylsilicone (Applied Science Labs.)
Lan	Lanolin
MeSiO	Methyl silicone
MS 550	Silicone oil
MS 2211	Silicone gum
NGA	Neopentylglycol adipate polymer
NGS	Neopentylglycol succinate polymer
NGSb	Neopentylglycol sebacate polymer
NP-10	Polymeric plasticiser (Eastman)
OS-138	Polyphenylether
OV-1	Methyl silicone
OV-17	Methyl silicone, 50% phenyl groups
OV-22	Methyl silicone, 65% phenyl groups
PDDS	Polydecane-1,10-diol succinate
PhSi	Phenylmethylsiloxane polymer
PhSiO	Phenyl silicone
PGA	Polyethylene glycol adipate
PPE	Polyphenol ether
PPG	Polypropylene glycol
PTC	Pentatriacontane
PVP	Polyvinylpyrrolidinone
QF-1	Methyl silicone, probably 50% trifluoropropyl groups (Dow Corning)
SE-30	Methylsiloxane polymer
SE-52	Methyl silicone, about 5% phenyl groups (General Electric)
SE-949	Cyanoethylmethylsilicone (General Electric)
SF-96	Methyl silicone (General Electric)
SiO	Silicone, type undesignated
SKT-V or SKT	Silicone
Squal	Squalene
STAP	A modified Carbowax
TCP	Tri-o-cresyl phosphate
TTP	Tritolyl phosphate
TXP	Tri-2,4-xylenyl phosphate
Ucon	Ucon LB 550X
UCW-09	Applied Science Labs.
Vers	Versamide
XE-60	Methyl silicone, 25% cyanoethyl groups (General Electric)
XE-61	Phenyl methyl silicone
XF-1105	Methyl silicone, 5% cyanoethyl groups (General Electric)
XF-1112	Nitrile-silicone gum (General Electric)
XF-1150	Methyl silicone, 50% cyanoethyl groups (General Electric)
XPO4	Xylenyl phosphate
Z	Methyl siloxane—ethyleneglycol succinate copolymer

5. RELATIVE RETENTION STANDARDS

Abbr. Compound

aarl	Penta-O-acetyl-L-arabinitol
adgl	2-Acetamido-2-deoxyglucitol
adn	Adenine
adns	Adenosine
agup	1,6-Anhydro-β-D-glucopyranose
ahsp	N-Acetyl-C_{18}-dihydrosphingosine
ala	Alanine
andn	Androsterone
ando	5α-Androstane-17-one
andr	Andrenosterone
anth	Anthracene
apgn	Apeginidin chloride
arbn	Arbutin
arl	Arabitol
arlt	Arabinono-1,4-lactone
btd	1,4-Butanediol
cal	Chimyl alcohol
camp	Camphorol
cat	Catechin
cbdl	Cannabidiol
chl	Cholesterol
chn	Cholestane
cina	Cinnamic acid
cmpl	Campesterol
dcap	Chloramphenicol
dean	Dehydroepiandrosterone
dmgu	6-O-(2-Diethylaminoethyl)-glucose
dpm	Diphenylmethane
eic	n-Eicosane
epin	Epinephrine
eryl	Erythritol
estl	17β-Estradiol
estn	Estrone
ga	α-D-Galactose
gall	Gallic acid
gcl	Guaiacol
gent	Gentisic acid
gl	Glucitol
gu	α-D-Glucose
β-gu	β-D-Glucose
gum	β-D-Glucosamine
gun	Glucono-1,4-lactone
gyp	Glyceryl monopalmitate
hdcn	Hexadecane
hdl	Hexadecanol
hsph	C_{18}-Dihydrosphingosine
indl	5-Indanol
ippc	Isopropyl N-phenylcarbamate
malv	Malvidin chloride
man	D-Mannose
marp	Methyl α-arabinopyranoside

mcap	Monochloro analog of chloramphenicol
mcho	Methyl cholanate
mdch	Methyl deoxycholate
mddc	Methyl dodecanoate
mdgu	2-Amino-2-deoxyglucose
mdpa	Methyl 3,4-dimethoxyphenylacetate
mesl	3-O-Methyl-17α-estradiol
mgaf	Methyl β-D-galactofuranoside
mgap	Methyl α-D-galactopyranoside
mguf	Methyl β-D-glucofuranoside
mgup	Methyl α-D-glucopyranoside
mhip	Methyl hippurate
min	*myo*-Inositol
miss	*myo*-Inosose-2
mkdc	Methyl 7-ketodeoxycholate
mlgs	Malvidin 3-monoglucoside
mmgu	Methyl 2,3,4,6-tetra-O-methyl-α-glucoside
mmy	Methyl myristate
moba	4-Methoxybenzoic acid
moty	3-Methoxytyramine
mpam	Methyl palmitate
mpg	Methyl phenylglucopyranosiduronate
mpmg	Methyl phenyl-2,3,4-tri-O-methyl-glucopyranosiduronate
mqin	4-Methylquinaldine
mseg	6-O-Methylsulfonyl-D-glucose
mst	Methyl stearate
MU	Methylene Unit
mxyp	Methyl α-D-xylopyranoside
naph	Naphthalene
octd	Octadecane
octs	Octacosane
perl	Pentaerythritol
pga	5α-Pregnane
pgun	6-Phosphogluconolactone
phba	p-Hydroxybenzoic acid
pin	Pinosylvin monomethyl ether
pip	Piperonal
pipl	Piperonol
pot	Phenol
preg	Pregnanolone
pts	p-Toluenesulfonamide
rb	D-Ribose
sin	*scyllo*-Inositol
SN	Steroid Number
sph	C_{18}-Sphingosine
srbl	Sorbitol
suc	Sucrose
test	*cis*-Testosterone
toca	α-Tocopherol acetate
tocl	Tocol
van	Vanillin
vana	Vanillic acid
xy	β-Xylose
xyp	Tri-2,4-xylenylphosphate

6. SILYLATION REAGENTS

Compound	Molecular Weight	B.P./mm or M.P.	n_D^t	d_4^t
N,O-Bis(trimethylsilyl)-acetamide (BSA)	203.4	b 67.5/30	1.4180[20]	0.832[21]
Bis(trimethylsilyl)-trifluoroacetamide	257.4	b 45-50/14	1.3810[27]	0.970[20]
Hexamethyldisilazane (HMDS)	161.4	b 125-216	1.4080[20]	0.7742[20]
Hexamethyldisiloxane	162.4	b 100	1.3773[20]	0.7637[20]
N-Methyl-N-trimethylsilyl-acetamide	145.3	b 154 b 57/14	1.4392[20]	0.9009[20]
Trimethylchlorosilane (TMCS)	108.7	b 57	1.3885[20]	0.8580[20]
N-Trimethylsilyl-acetamide	131.3	m 52-54 b 185-186 b 84/13		
N-Trimethylsilyl-t-butylamine	147.2	b 118-119	1.4060[25]	
N-Trimethylsilyl-diethylamine (TMSDEA)	145.3	b 126 b 33/26	1.4109[20]	0.7627[20]
N-Trimethylsilyl-imidazole (TSIM)	140.3	b 91/12	1.4754[20]	0.949[24]
N-Trimethylsilyl-N,N'-diphenylurea	284.4	m 67-69		

Index

This subject index is for the descriptive sections only. Compounds are listed only if information is given additional to that in the numbered tables. References to gas chromatography (GC) of separate classes of compounds are not indexed as this subject is discussed where pertinent throughout the book. The combining form, -TMS, indicates a silylated derivative, regardless of number or location of TMS groups.